METHODS AND MATERIALS
FOR TEACHING
THE BIOLOGICAL SCIENCES

(*Courtesy of The Ohio Forestry Association.*)

METHODS AND MATERIALS FOR TEACHING THE BIOLOGICAL SCIENCES

A Text and Source Book for Teachers

in Training and in Service

DAVID F. MILLER

*Professor of Zoology and
Chairman of the Department
of Zoology and Entomology
The Ohio State University*

GLENN W. BLAYDES

*Professor of Botany
The Ohio State University*

Second Edition

McGRAW-HILL BOOK COMPANY, INC.

New York   Toronto   London   1962

METHODS AND MATERIALS
FOR TEACHING THE BIOLOGICAL SCIENCES

41989

-·«{ Preface }»·-

Educational theory and basic educational processes may be taught with little regard to subject-matter areas, but they are not of much direct help to the teacher in the classroom, where subject matter and its related materials are of prime importance.

This book was originally prepared as a direct response to the many questions and problems of teachers of biological subjects who were already in service as well as those still in training.

In offering this second edition we have maintained the style and much of the material found to be most useful by students and teachers who have used the book as a text and as a handbook of information. We have added many new projects and suggestions, especially in conservation, ecology, radiobiology, and chromatography.

Since the first edition there has been an awakening in the field of teaching, especially in science, and a consequent upgrading of content and methods. This is good in most respects, but there are some outstanding examples of cases where advance has gone so far that interest was diminished, rather than heightened, because the general student lacked sufficient prerequisites. Outstandingly apt students should have special attention and opportunity; it is not necessary that all participate on the same level.

Division into Parts One and Two has been retained. Part One lends itself to thought-provoking reading and to special-methods classwork, while Part Two gives hundreds of suggestions for useful materials and how to use them in the classroom and laboratory. The past success of this arrangement leads us to believe that it accomplishes our four principal objectives: (1) To encourage the teachers of biological subjects to abandon the all-too-common method of teaching from the textbook with little use of materials. (2) To assist the teacher in locating, securing, or culturing living and interesting materials at little expense. (3) To suggest how these materials may be used in classroom demonstrations and student projects, as well as how simple, homemade, and inexpensive apparatus and devices may solve the persistent problem of lack of equipment or funds. (4) To foster, through suggestion, the use of the problem and project method in order to give to the student not merely biological information but also practice in using this information in the understanding of principles and the application of these principles to his daily life.

v

The bibliography is completely new and, though not intended to be exhaustive, should furnish stimulating and helpful reading. Most of the journal references are to articles written by teachers from their own experiences. It is our sincerest hope that the new edition will be as helpful to future teachers as its predecessor has been to those of the past.

Many of the suggestions offered in this book are original with the authors, but much of the material has been drawn from such a variety of sources that complete acknowledgment is impossible. However, the authors wish to express their appreciation especially to the following persons who, by their counsel, suggestions, and criticisms, have aided materially in the preparation of the manuscript: Dr. J. W. A. Burley, Dr. W. W. Charters, Dr. Edgar Dale, Dr. R. H. Davidson, Dr. F. W. Fisk, Dr. R. O. Freeland, Dr. J. G. Haub, Dr. C. S. Johnson, Mrs. Mildred Knopf, Dr. J. N. Knull, Dr. B. S. Meyer, Dr. W. C. Myser, Dr. H. C. Sampson, Dr. L. H. Snyder, Dr. C. E. Taft, Dr. L. H. Tiffany, and Dr. R. W. Tyler.

David F. Miller
Glenn W. Blaydes

Contents

---⊰ Do You Really Want to Teach School? ⊱---

Before going any further, answer that question honestly. If you do not feel a thrill of anticipation at the thought of being a teacher, don't teach. You will save yourself and many youngsters a lot of grief. But if you want to teach, there is no higher or more satisfying profession. Don't let your need for a job or the public's need for teachers induce you to seek a teaching position if you don't like it. Some jobs you might be justified in accepting temporarily out of a sense of duty or because of the personal necessity for being employed—but not teaching.

The teacher who does not like teaching soon comes to dislike the subject matter and the students as well and is, in turn, disliked by them. A good teacher approaches the classroom with eagerness for the adventure, leaves with a feeling of satisfaction for what has been accomplished, and looks forward with determination to remedy any failures. Most of your waking hours will be spent at your job. What could be worse than spending them at tasks which you dislike? What could be finer than spending them on a job that you love?

It is the purpose of this book to make the teaching of biology pleasant as well as effective.

The New AIBS Biological Science Film Series

A contemporary high school biology course, upgraded and updated for modern teaching needs and sponsored by the American Institute of Biological Sciences. The series consists of 120 half-hour sound motion pictures (available in black and white or in color) in 10 major areas of the course with 12 films in each area. The 10 major areas covered are as follows:

Part I   Cell Biology

Part II   Microbiology

Part III   Multicellular Plants

Part IV   The Multicellular Animal

Part V   Reproduction, Growth, and Development

Part VI   Genetics

Part VII   Plant Diversity

Part VIII   Animal Diversity

Part IX   Ecology

Part X   Life, Time, and Change

Write to McGRAW-HILL TEXT-FILMS for detailed information.

⸻⸼ Part One ⸽⸻

CLASSROOM METHODS FOR
TEACHING BIOLOGICAL PRINCIPLES

CHAPTER 1

⋯⊰ Education Is for the Future ⊱⋯

The future progress of man rests upon his ability to apply the achievements of science. This being the case, it is of utmost importance that our youth be thoroughly schooled in the principles of science so that they may properly understand and contribute to this progress. In these future ventures a leading part will be played by our teachers of science. For this reason the teacher of the life sciences should have a clear understanding of the basis for his profession and a command of the facts of science as well as the ability to encourage and inspire the students who study under his direction.

Primitive man needed to know two things well if he were to survive. He had to be able to hunt successfully in order to provide food, and he had to be able successfully to defend himself and his family from enemies. In these respects he did not differ from many other animals. He was concerned with self-preservation and the preservation of his species. These fundamental needs are the basis for all education. Man has become so much of a social animal and his activities have grown so specialized that they obscure the fact that after all they are modern man's ways of maintaining himself and his species. However, modern man, in addition to these activities for primitive needs, has developed mental needs that lie almost completely outside the realm of lower animals. These are due to the human capacity of thought. As a result we have the fine arts, music, literature, philosophy, religion, science, and entertainment as major activities of his intellectual life. With the advance of modern science and invention the struggle for food and protection has been reduced to a much smaller proportion of his endeavors, with the result that there has arisen an increased demand for something else to satisfy the growing amount of time which he has for intellectual life. This rapid advance in his mechanical occupations has made it easy to produce more food than can be consumed and more of the other necessities than can be used, and yet large numbers go unfed and unclothed while others seek to find ways of using the unoccupied portion of their time. It is this leisure time which has brought about the tremendous growth of professional entertainment and made of it one of the leading industries of modern times. Yet the primary concern of the greater portion of human beings is, and will continue to be for a long time to come, involved with those activities which have to do with his more physical needs, though it is impossible to separate them entirely from the needs of his intellect.

The education of primitive man was as simple as the unsocialized life in which he lived, while the education of modern man must be of a degree of complexity commensurate with the high specialization of the society in which he lives. In our effort to elevate the entire social level and to improve the standing and opportunities of each individual we have instituted a system of public education which has become mass education. The education of special groups or of a few individuals was relatively simple, but the education of an entire oncoming generation so that each individual might take his place in so complex a society has presented problems of surprising magnitude. The children of today will become the adults of tomorrow, and with them will evolve the needs of their social order and the problems arising out of the progress of their times.

Education, then, must seek to permit the individual to develop to the fullest his capacities for adjustment to continuous change in order that he may meet the problems of his day and solve them successfully when they arise. He must be free and unhampered yet steady and reliable, capable of cooperating for mutual good but capable of clear, independent thinking unswayed by propaganda and emotionalism. To do this education needs individualization and liberation.

Society as an Ecological Situation. We need to visualize society as an ecological situation, the vital factors of which are biological entities. When the biologist views his environment, his long study has taught him that, if a region is elevated, has sandy alkaline soil, little rainfall, deep drainage, persistent winds, low latitude, and is far removed from large bodies of water, the area is likely to be at least semidesert. He knows that the ability of a species of animal to maintain itself successfully in any given region depends upon not one but a multitude of factors. Some of these factors are environmental; others are inherent in the organism itself. Of the first class, some are physical, others are biological. Soil, water, wind, sunlight, extremes of temperature, oxygen, pollution, barriers, friends, enemies, predators, parasites, population pressures, migrations, and a multitude of other factors confront each individual with problems arising not only out of each of these factors but out of a myriad of combinations of them. In addition, there are the inherent factors of the organism itself. Its morphological and physiological peculiarities, its fluctuations, mutations, and stability all aid in determining its chances for survival both as individuals and as a species. The ecologist has recognized this to the extent that under limited and well-controlled conditions he has experimentally demonstrated his ability to predict mathematically the future progress of some groups.

Man is a species of animal. Structurally and physiologically he is akin to the rest of his kingdom. He is confronted with the same problems of maintaining himself individually and collectively. Friendly neighbors and enemies, mild and rigorous climate, abundance of food and starvation, health and disease, problems of the pioneer living in a wilderness and problems of the masses living in the slums of cities, how do they differ from those of other organisms whatever and wherever they happen to be? Since man is an animal, his society is an ecological situation. His problems are fundamentally the problems of living organisms everywhere. He is subject to the same laws and forces as any other organism, and if his problems are open to solution they are subject to investigation by the same rigorous, unemotional method that science applies to other natural phenomena. The human method of attacking these problems is intellectual. Man tries to anticipate, to analyze, and to understand the cause-and-effect relationships that exist. In his more advanced studies he inquires, observes, and experiments. He becomes scientific. To train individuals to do this effectively is one of the chief problems of education.

Many of the great world problems of today are ecological problems. Our inability to solve them arises out of our emotional attitudes which thrust aside our intelligent, rational thinking. Millions go to bed hungry each night. It has always been so. In pity we offer them a share of our abundance, and the best we have offered as a solution to their ills is an attempt to teach them how to grow more food. But with more food their overcrowded lands only increase in population and their hunger continues to grow. Will we ever teach them the true causes of their predicament and allow them and ourselves to control populations to whatever size can be properly provided for? If we do not, the whole world will become as they are. The two principal objections raised emotionally against population control are religious dogma and the statement that control would be expensive. Wars, starvation, disease, and pestilence are expensive too, but we indulge in them continually.

The biotic elements of a society are its individuals. What the society is depends largely upon the individuals that compose it. What the individual is depends upon the interaction between his almost infinitely complex genetic elements and the equally intricate factors of their environment. Any sexually produced offspring is by virtue of the random assortment of its genes both similar to and yet different from the organisms which produce it. In education these fundamental similarities have frequently been overemphasized while the import of the essential differences has been overlooked. Mass education has flourished on the foundation of similarities, while too little attention has been paid to individual differences in needs, abilities, interests, and methods of learning.

We shall not claim that there is nothing common to the masses of students that are educable nor that there is no value in the effort to establish an educational system on such a basis. Literacy, which is so often pointed to as an index of a nation's progress, can be raised by such a method. The value of regimentation to a society depends, obviously, upon what level of society or what ideals are taken as the standards. If these standards are of such a nature as to be of value to a very large percentage of that society, the merit of the educational method is correspondingly high. At best, however, such methods are based upon the assumption of more uniformity within a range of society than actually exists and make but scant provision for the individual variations within, above, and below the assumed standards.

The Effects of Indoctrination. Reading, writing, and arithmetic in their simplest forms constitute a universal language or means of communication without a knowledge of which an individual is sorely at a loss in any society even if of a very primitive type. Words, letters, and numbers are symbols designed to convey to others the ideas and concepts of the user. There is no reason why the letters *m*, *a*, and *n* combined into *man* should always mean a male individual of the genus *Homo*, nor why 1 and 2 equal 3. They just do by common agreement and usage. They become axiomatic. In other words, they need and admit of no proof or explanation. Since the use of these symbols becomes practically imperative whenever even a very small number of human beings come into contact with each other, they become increasingly important with a more complex society even in their much more complicated forms. To be able to use and understand them, therefore, is an unquestionable necessity.

Some other types of learning may stand in much the same fundamental relationship to man. These are the understandings that have to do with the general well-being and survival of himself and his species. An individual living entirely alone must be able to distinguish between those things in his environment which are suitable as food and those which are not. An infant may watch the goldfish swimming under 2 ft. of water in the garden pool, but if he attempts to do the same the result may be fatal. If a very young child playing near the edge of a high cliff is attracted by a passing butterfly, he may attempt to follow it beyond the brink, but with very different and dire results. There are fundamental effects of mass and space relationships and the effects of the operation of gravity that he must know if he is to survive. He must know these effects and how to avoid them even though he has no understanding of why they operate as they do. The infant must know that attempts at breathing water are to be avoided, even though he fails to understand why the fish can do it and he cannot.

Fortunately the nervous system and muscles are so arranged that a great proportion of our acts of unfavorable behavior bring about reflexes, movements, and sensations which are negative and save us from our ignorance, but there are many which do not, and the exceedingly complex character of our social life and of modern civilizations has enormously increased their number. Many of the very fundamental learnings are accomplished so early in life that they are well established before the child starts school. Some of these need to be augmented or modified, and this becomes one of the early duties of the school. There are some fundamental learnings about health and disease and personal and social welfare which need to be acquired early in life that are of such nearly universal usage as to justify dogmatic teachings if they are based upon results of research and upon cause-and-effect relationships too involved for the youthful mind to comprehend.

It is not of such fundamental things that we speak when we complain against indoctrination as one of the sins of mass education. It is the fact that, while the method is useful in some ways, it soon becomes so fixed in the minds of the teacher and learner alike that it dominates all educational procedure and all "thinking." Our citizens go about using such authorities as "my father always said" and "I see in the paper," making decisions and ordering the activities of their daily lives upon the basis of habits formed throughout their early years, of accepting as fact the dictum of others without ever questioning its validity or the adequacy of what may seem to be proof. We "educate" our youth to fall ready prey to the social, political, commercial, and religious propaganda with which their lives are beset.

We criticize indoctrination not because it can never play a useful part in education but because of the bad effects it has upon the mental habits of the child and because, when the child has become docile through the practice of these habits, the teacher finds it much the easiest way of "covering ground" in his subject. Therefore the way to correct the ill effects is to change the method early in the child's life. The earlier it is done, the greater the benefits derived from it. For example, a child of seven years may be taught to place a handkerchief over his nose and mouth when sneezing or coughing and not to place soiled fingers or pencils in his mouth or nose. There is no denying that these habits would work to his good. But the same child could as readily be taught to carry a charm about his neck or a rabbit's foot in his pocket. Now if the teacher should prepare several sterile agar plates or potato slants and permit the student to cough into one, scratch another with a pencil, allow a drop of water which was thoroughly boiled to run over a dirty finger and on to a third plate, while to a fourth is added a drop of the boiled water alone, in a day or two there would be well-developed colonies of bacteria in all except the last plate. This would not make clear to him how these organisms by their metabolism destroy tissues and pour poisons into the body causing pain and disturbing normal functions, but it would be a beginning toward establishing the idea of evidence and proof and toward creating an attitude of the "feeling of need" for understanding.

Individual Variation and Intelligence Levels. We speak confidently of normal and of average individuals. What is an average individual? How far may one vary from the average and still be normal? Of course, no such individual as the "normal" person really exists. The term is one coined to express in words a set standard arrived at statistically. As used by most teachers, it has a vagueness of meaning that can hardly be described. It may be based upon tests for intelligence or aptitude, but to establish fixed standards for these latter terms is extremely difficult. If the children in a certain school, representing a given community, are tested, they may establish their own norms. Their percentiles may be distributed on a normal curve. However, we note when this curve is compared with curves established in other communities that a "superior" individual in one group would classify as an "average" individual in another group. If a large number of groups is included in a curve, it may be made to cover a state or nation. But does the position of an individual on a curve for an entire nation indicate with much accuracy his chances for success or the degree of normality for the region or community in which he may live? To what extent have his environmental influences or his physical and physiological peculiarities been instrumental in establishing his position? Are the standards assumed in the test equally valid for each group tested? As the area tested is enlarged and the variety of individuals increased, the efficacy of the standards is correspondingly weakened.

From such normal curves there is ordinarily selected a middle division comprising approximately one-half of the total number of individuals tested. This establishes the normal group. On either side of this group lies approximately one-fourth. The members of these extremes may be considered as supernormal and subnormal. Together they constitute the other 50 per cent of those tested. By what right can the middle division of 50 per cent claim 90 per cent of the time and effort of our educational endeavors? A very widespread attitude of our educators is that the supernormal group is composed of near geniuses who will get along without the teacher's attention, or in spite of it, while the lower fourth are mostly "dumbbells" who couldn't profit from education anyway; so the only ones really needing attention are the middle group.

Recognizing this fallacy has led some to contend that the upper quarter is the only place to spend educational effort since these persons are most able to profit from advantages given and the return to society is greatest from this group. In general there is much truth in this point of view, and one of the most valid criticisms against our standardized education has been the lack of attention devoted to the superior student. But when special attention has been given to such a group, it has usually taken the form of crowding more of the same mental pabulum down their intellectual throats in a relatively shorter interval of time. If the kind of effort required of the student is not different, if the same educational ideals are maintained, if no consideration for individual growth is recognized and the selected group does merely the same routine class procedure in less time or more of it in the same time, then the effort put forth in their behalf is wasted. There must be ample opportunity afforded for individual development and growth and for guidance and encouragement in the pursuit of interest and aptitudes. If any of these students are really superior in any marked degree, they deserve the opportunity of gaining whatever is profitable from the routined classwork in as short a time as possible plus the opportunity of personal development in those ways which will enable them to reach such planes of accomplishment and peculiar social adjustments as will make for their own personal happiness and for the greatest social good. If any individual deviates radically from the standards established for the so-called average group, his greatest worth to himself and society must be looked for within this margin of deviation and the proper development of those qualities that characterize him as being different should be given free chance for maturing. To subdue these qualities and to endeavor to compel him to become as near "normal" as possible is contrary to the biological character of his differences and as unreasonable as it is futile.

The group comprising the lower fourth, according to a "normal distribution," is one which is even more difficult to consider in such an educational plan as is in vogue in most of our public schools. Some have felt that it deserves the greatest amount of attention since many of its members are less capable of progressing independently and need more directing and assistance in order to meet or approach the standards of speed and perfection set for the "normal group." All this, of course, is based upon the assumption that the ideals set for and by the middle group are those which are in some unexplained manner the standards which most nearly meet the needs of the individual and offer most to the progress of society.

Any normal distribution is based upon individual differences. To group the individuals into three or more divisions lessens the degree of variation in any one division and permits of more uniformity of treatment than if the entire group is considered. Still there is greater difference between the individuals of the upper end of the middle group compared with individuals of the lower end of the middle group than between those in the lower end of the middle group and those in the upper end of the lower group. Further subdivision of groups tends to render any subdivision more homogeneous than the whole for the factors measured and increases the value of uniform treatment.

In the supposedly lower levels are also some individuals who may have mental or physical peculiarities, but who, on the mere basis of mental capability, do not belong in this classification. Take for example the student whose hearing or sight is deficient to the extent that he does not see or hear clearly such things as orders or directions, especially when given from the front of a classroom. His reaction is almost certain to be that of waiting to see what someone nearby does and to follow his example. This is not dishonesty. Suppose that the example followed is in error. So is the follower. Suppose that the example followed is very slow. The follower is of necessity slower. The results obtained by the handicapped individual are more of a measure of his affliction than a measure of his abilities. If such a condition continues for long, it produces two kinds of results. First, the student frequently does poorly and his relative standing with his classmates is low, from which he comes to be looked upon by the teacher and classmates as incapable, causing him to lose confidence in his own ability. Second, he acquires a series of habits of following instead of forging ahead and of depending upon others instead of upon his own ingenuity. The feeling of inferiority and the habits of following destroy his self-confidence and self-respect, and he is likely to continue as an "inferior" individual. His classification is fundamentally wrong, but he tends to remain where he is placed and is accepted and treated on this level. As time goes on and habits become more fixed, he tends to grow into rather than out of his classification. If his physical handicaps are later discovered and steps taken to remedy them, it does not follow that he will immediately assume a position commensurate with his native abilities, for he has established habits of behavior and emotion as well as attitudes which operate strongly to keep him upon the level to which he has become accustomed. Nor is this confined to the classroom. It is manifest in his play, where he will no longer engage in sports in which he cannot excel and in which he is constantly demonstrating his "inferiority." It spreads to his home and other social relations in like manner. It takes a period of retraining for establishing new attitudes based upon a feeling of confidence and a demonstration of the rediscovery of his latent abilities.

True it is that the percentage of such handicapped individuals in a group of "inferiors" is small, but it shows, nevertheless, the inadequacy of such measurements when their use is made general and when mass education makes difficult the amount of individual attention that each student deserves. This is no plea for the mentally incapable nor an attempt to emotionalize in their behalf, but is intended to call attention to a grievous error that so often arises out of a misapplication of group standards devoid of individualization.

Regardless of the degree of ability or lack of ability possessed by an individual, each child in school, each man and woman, needs to discover whatever abilities he or she may possess and to have the opportunity to develop and use those abilities for personal and social good. He needs the feeling of self-confidence and security which comes with accomplishment. He must know that he can contribute something to a program and that there is an appreciation of his contribution, however small. Without this feeling emotional states are engendered that unfit him for desirable development and for fulfilling his proper place in life.

Freedom of Choice and Individual Development. Complete individualization for mass education is physically impossible and economically and socially unsound. What, then, can be done to permit each individual to attain the highest level of which he is capable and to acquire from society and to return to society the most that he can?

Society is evolving or is in a state of constant flux. Can we by teaching the rapidly accumulating store of factual knowledge continue to equip each youth with all necessary knowledge for his years of life? Learning has long since passed such bounds. Can we by intensively specializing produce an assortment of specialists who will be able to coordinate their activities into a unified program of efficiency and happiness? This has been done with considerable success but has many fallacies as well as limitations. Too high a degree of specialization usually results in lack of understanding and sympathy and makes for disrespect and unhappiness. Furthermore, some fields of specialization offer opportunities whereby those individuals may take advantage of the rest. This is difficult to eliminate, but specialization alone rather aggravates than alleviates the difficulty. What procedure, then, offers some means of fitting the individual best to adjust himself to the changing needs of an evolving society? What procedure will yield most to the largest number in a society that is committed to the ideal of mass education and yet is sincere in its commitment to the rewards of individual endeavor and enterprise?

A program should allow for individual differences and make possible individual growth and development with free choice and specialization. But freedom of choice and individual growth are factors which in themselves call for a type of educational procedure that has not been frequently met with in our public program. It is something that calls for keen understanding and skillful administration on the part of teachers in our new era of education.

These trends should begin early in the child's education. Concepts of what constitutes proof, validity, adequacy, and cause and effect are capable of simplification and reduction to any level of teaching and need not be confined to high school and college. They should be made available to the child from the very first and continued throughout his schooling. Even in our day the percentage of children who continue in school through college is small, and the so-called man on the street is the one who most of all needs to be able to see his way clearly, to do all the thinking possible for himself, and to protect himself from his modern enemies, the dispensers of propaganda. This must be accomplished if the ideals of true democracy are to be preserved successfully. The methods of science need not be confined to the supposed subject matter of science—they apply everywhere. The teachers of science, however, stand at a unique point of vantage for beginning the transition away from traditional education toward scientific thinking as a primary aim and educational objective.

Science and scientific thinking have been the key to modern progress in all lines of human endeavor. Science still will be the key to our progress in future generations, but out of it there will arise a new philosophy which will itself be scientific. A new education is imperative, and the new education must be scientific. This does not mean that it must merely impart the new discoveries of science; it means that education itself must become scientific. We shall demand a new and scientific psychology to supplant the introspective, emotional, and prejudicial methods of earlier efforts. This is already well under way. We shall know more of the genetics of human beings as well as of plants and guinea pigs and domestic stock. We shall understand the principles and possibilities of eugenics as well as of environment and social organization. We shall know more of physiological processes and more of the value of foods, chemicals, drugs, and internal secretions as they apply to and modify our understanding of students, of fellow members of society, and of educational methods. We shall substitute understanding for mere learning, proof for indoctrination, and reasoning for dogma and emotionalism.

PROBLEMS

1. Prepare for presentation and class discussion a group of fundamental understandings from biology which you consider that a child should learn during the first 10 years in school.

2. Make a collection of common beliefs which are unscientific and which cannot be proved. Estimate how many of these are of a biological character and might be corrected by the proper training in biology in early years of school.

3. Explain what is meant by indoctrination in education and give several illustrations.

4. What is meant by I.Q.? Show how it is obtained. How may it be of special value to the teacher?

5. What is meant by a normal distribution? How is it shown graphically? Explain median and mean. How are these useful in testing and grading?

6. Look up the following article, prepare a resumé and discuss its contents in the light of man's educational needs: Julian Huxley, "World Population," *Scientific American,* vol. 194, no. 3, March, 1956.

CHAPTER 2

⊶⊰ The Objectives of Teaching ⊱⊷

The objectives of good teaching in biological subjects are essentially the objectives of the teaching of all subject matter. These objectives have been stated by various writers in many different terms. Some prefer to divide them into numerous statements, others to condense them. In general it seems most fitting here that we condense, at least at first. We believe that practically all objectives, regardless of their number, may be grouped into four categories. These, stated in general terms, furnish the background of our educational philosophy as applied to biology teaching. First among these objectives is *the acquisition of information*. This implies primarily the exercise of memory. Facts are derived from whatever sources available such as reading, lectures, and observation. It implies little more than the ability of retention and recall. Second, *the development of methods of thinking*. This necessitates the acquisition of information since facts are the materials without which reflective thinking cannot be accomplished. However, it is vastly different from the learning of facts. The learning of facts gives knowledge, but the practice of reflective thinking gives understanding. Third, *the induction and application of principles*. With the accumulation of a store of factual knowledge in a field of learning and with the development of the ability to think clearly and scientifically with this store, one goes far beyond the plane of recall, makes generalizations, and should be able to apply these to new situations. Fourth, *the formation of attitudes*. The individual who has learned sufficient facts, learned to handle these facts in scientific thinking, and developed the ability to generalize with his thinking to the extent that he makes constant use of these accomplishments in meeting the personal and social problems of his daily life must have established attitudes of inestimable value to successful living. These statements are in themselves so general as to lack clarity, and for this reason each will be discussed more fully, with illustrations. How they may be made to function in direct relation to biology teaching will appear at appropriate places throughout the discussions.

The Acquisition of Information. This was at one time the very essence of education. It still is in all too many instances. To have a tremendous grasp of facts was and still is looked upon as an indication of great learning. How often does the physician, the lawyer, the professor, weave a spell of awe over the layman by his easy flow of technical terminology or his reiteration of professionally well-known facts? The student who remembers best the most sentences from his text or repeats the most statements made by the teacher is likely to be declared the smartest or best in his class.

12

The old-fashioned deacon who could quote the largest number of Bible verses was looked upon by the congregation as "well learned in scripture." The boy who knew what events took place upon the longest list of dates was an outstanding history scholar, and the little girl who spelled down everyone else at the bee was one of the smartest girls in school. Did the deacon understand the full meaning of his verses, and were they exemplified by his daily living? Did the agonized deaths of thousands of young men upon the field of battle hundreds of years ago do anything really to benefit mankind? Were the events which brought about their sacrifice avoidable or justified? Did the course of civilization following the signing of a document affect in any way the status of political and social well-being of people today? Is there anything in the knowledge of dates and events that can aid the present generation in solving more surely the problems with which it is confronted? Did the little spelling champion know the meaning of the words she spelled so glibly? Were they a part of her vocabulary? Did she speak more clearly or more intelligently or more beautifully? Did the things she read have more meaning because of her spelling ability?

Too often the answers to these questions were given scant consideration, for was not each a champion in his field like the athlete who made the most touchdowns or ran the fastest mile or swam the swiftest course? Was not the learning an end in itself? Some may well contend that such was true in the past but that education has long since passed such a stage. Frequent visits into classrooms and repeated examination of textbooks disclose the fact that there is still a wide gap between the ideals of educational theory and the practical execution of these ideals in the school. Professional educators have been known to condemn as stupid the teachers who are unable to put into operation the philosophy which they so freely declaim, while the teachers in turn brand as "impractical theory" this same philosophy.

Despite all criticism the acquisition of information must remain a primary aim of all education. There is no denying that knowledge of facts is the foundation of understanding, the material with which habits of thinking and attitude are built, the substances from which principles are induced. That which is untenable, therefore, is the allowing of this objective to be the dominant, almost the sole objective.

Granting, then, that the student must learn facts but not merely for facts' sake alone, what must be done with this information? If the facts are learned in an encyclopedic fashion, it matters little what facts are learned. The student sometimes embarrasses the teacher with the question "Why must I study this subject?" or "Is it important to remember these particular facts?" This situation points to the necessity for the proper objectives and to the Spencerian query "What knowledge is of most worth?" That knowledge is of most worth which will function in the most significant manner in rendering the student individually and socially efficient. This necessitates a choice of knowledge and the ability to distinguish between fact and mere information.

Scientific Method of Thinking. A phrase that has become widely used in education is that teaching should follow "the scientific method." Many, however, do not fully realize the significance of this expression at least to the point where it can be successfully applied to a method of teaching. The attempt to apply the scientific method to education involves a number of steps. One must first decide what elements of the scientific method can be made of specific pedagogic value. After this has been done, it is necessary to modify the curriculum so as to permit the free application of these elements in the attack upon subject matter. The scientific method involves:

1. The appreciation of the existence of a problem and a desire to solve it
2. The accumulation of facts and data which are pertinent to the problem
3. The formation of hypotheses as partial explanations, their testing, and their acceptance or rejection
4. Logical interpretation of data with an unwillingness to accept as proved any conclusion not supported by adequate valid evidence

The use of these steps means that the individual first recognizes the existence of a problem to be solved and sets about to solve it. He next establishes all available facts concerning the problem, which involves the accumulation of data. On the basis of these facts he constructs hypotheses which are logical explanations of the parts of the original problem. These hypotheses he must clearly recognize as tentative and must not confuse them with proved conclusions. He then tests his hypotheses by experimentation and further accumulation of evidence to establish their degree of adequacy. If a given hypothesis is supported by sufficient evidence, it may be accepted as a conclusion and as a step in the solution of the problem.

What constitutes validity is also an important point in scientific procedure. Any number of analogies is not proof, though frequently believed to be so. Experimentation with repetitions and control are often essential. The problem should be analyzed by breaking it down into its parts for the sake of simplicity. The final step is a synthesis and integration of these parts into a whole. The student must at all times distinguish clearly between those points which are definitely proved, those which are definitely disproved, and those which are neither proved nor disproved. This latter consideration is so frequently overlooked.

To be of true worth educationally the frequent use of the scientific method must produce in the mind of the student an attitude toward all problems of life which demands that claims be proved, that facts take precedence over prejudices and desires, and that such sources as "they say" and "I see by the paper" cease to be regarded as sufficiently authoritative. In short, the fruits of scientific method are scientific thinking and attitudes in the processes of daily life.

Perhaps the most universal exhortation of teachers to students has always been, "Now think!" Check any conversation you may chance to overhear, and notice how many sentences begin with "I think." What does one really do when he says he thinks? The teacher usually means "recall" for she is probably asking the student to repeat what was included in an assignment. What the adult usually means by "I think" is "I feel," for what he is doing is emotionalizing and taking stock of his prejudices to determine his attitude. Scientific thinking is the antithesis of this.

All the foregoing may be technical and abstract. What the teacher wants is a concrete example of how such a method may be made to apply to the teaching of subject matter. There is no need for any one procedure to be called *the* scientific method. Any method which embodies all the above-mentioned elements is bound to be scientific. However, for purposes of illustration we offer the following outline and explanation presented according to one use of the scientific method.

A skillful teacher once prepared a demonstration for use in his biology class. It consisted of a 5-gal. bottle, or carboy, slightly more than half full of water. In the bottom was 2 in. of sand in which were anchored a few aquatic plants. Floating in the water was a small amount of a filamentous alga. On the sides of the bottle were several small water snails, and swimming about among the plants was a small goldfish. A cork had been pressed tightly into the neck and covered with a heavy layer of melted paraffin. Such an aquarium is most generally known as a "microcosm."

This microcosm was placed in the schoolroom without comment. It aroused much interest and discussion among the members of the class. Some of the students approached the teacher with questions. These the teacher did not answer but at the same time further stirred their curiosity by a few questions of his own, taking great care not to stifle any enthusiasm. Soon the entire class was examining the demonstration and waxing argumentative with questions and solutions. Some were laying wagers as to whether the fish would still be alive on the following day.

The teacher made note of most of their questions but answered none. The news spread and other students came in between class periods to see the curiosity. Two days passed before the teacher decided that the interest had reached its peak and that further delay would be ill advised. One student, assuming somewhat the role of class spokesman, almost demanded, "When are you going to tell us how that fish can live sealed up in a bottle?" The teacher surveyed the class and noted the almost universal expression of interrogation on their faces.

"I have written down most of your questions during the past two days," he replied, "and I find that you have asked nearly all the most important and most interesting questions about life and living things. It might take some time to get the answers to all of them, but there are a number of extremely interesting experiments which we might perform to prove and test our solutions and I'd be glad to help if enough of you want to work on them." There were ample signs of approval, but for psychological reasons a vote was taken and the class voted overwhelmingly in favor of undertaking the project. Two boys refused to vote since they had decided before they entered the class that they were not going to like biology anyhow. We shall see what happened to them later.

The teacher now consulted his list of questions and wrote a number of them on a part of the blackboard where they could be left for some time. Some of the questions were: How long can the fish live sealed in the bottle? How does the fish get more air over a period of time? Why doesn't the fish starve? Does the fish eat the snails? What happens to all the carbon dioxide which the animals produce? Do plants need air to keep alive? Will the water become foul if not changed? Is air necessary for water forms of life, or do they just breathe water? These and other questions made up the list.

For the teacher this point marked the end of the first problem-setting period. That the students had recognized the existence of a problem, or problems, was self-evident, and that they were ready and willing to proceed toward a solution was obvious. This, therefore, marks our first step in the use of the scientific method applied to a teaching situation.

When asked which question they wished to answer first the class, with a view toward finality, immediately chose, "How can the fish live sealed in the bottle?" This, of course, had the substance of all the other questions in it and was a fortunate choice pedagogically. The teacher countered by asking what a fish did to maintain itself when not sealed in a bottle. The suggestions offered by the class, which were in reality an analysis of the problem, included such statements as that it breathed, ate food, got rid of wastes, avoided enemies, and avoided very unfavorable conditions of its environment. As each suggestion was made it was either accepted or rejected by the class and, if accepted, carefully recorded by the teacher, who then proposed that they decide what would be necessary for the organisms if they were to maintain themselves indefinitely in a sealed bottle. This was an easy step, and the students saw that if all the conditions of life which they had proposed were satisfactorily met in a bottle the fish might be expected to live. The students then went to some of their more specific questions such as, "How can the fish continue to breathe?" and "What happens to all the carbon dioxide produced?" Several students wanted to propose answers as to how these were accomplished. Some of the proposals went unquestioned, while others were vigorously opposed. These proposals were finally written down on paper and collected by the teacher who had several students group them according to the problems which they purported to solve. This was the next step in the scientific method, that of proposing hypotheses.

Up to this point there had been developed a common interest in a general problem. It was now deemed advisable to break up the work into parts which would provide for individual differences both in interests and abilities and allow for a cooperative contracting and socialization. Following their own interests, they chose to work in one of several fields, as with problems concerned with breathing and respiration, or problems concerned with pollution, or problems concerned with foods and feeding, and so on. It might be stated here that in large classes and for a teacher having four or five classes it might become a necessity to limit the work to one general problem at a time.

Using the statements (hypotheses) suggested by the members of the class, the teacher prepared lists which were duplicated and a copy was given to each student working in that particular area. For the sake of brevity we include here but one list as an example. It should be stated that slight alteration of wording was made by the teacher in a few of the statements to ensure clarity of meaning.

The Maintenance of a Fish in a Microcosm

Breathing and Respiration

1. The fish will soon use all the available oxygen and then die.
2. The fish will continue to live indefinitely.

3. Fish breathe water and do not need a renewed oxygen supply.

4. Only air-breathing animals use oxygen.

5. Plants produce oxygen in order that the fish may have a constant supply.

6. There is a very slow passage of air through the glass of the bottle which is sufficient to replace that used by the fish.

7. Minerals in the sand dissolve in the water, giving off oxygen to the air and water.

8. Bacteria on the plants and in the water produce oxygen sufficient for the fish.

9. Plants use carbon which they obtain from the carbon dioxide, leaving free oxygen.

10. Sunlight acting on water forms oxygen.

11. Water is H_2O, and a fish can get the oxygen from the water.

On the tenth day the fish was dead, and the following hypotheses were added:

12. There was enough oxygen to last the fish for 10 days only.

13. There was plenty of oxygen but the fish died from other causes.

Other similar lists were made up for the other topics, and a copy of all the statements made was given to each student for study with the directions that he consider each statement on its merit and then mark it by placing one of the following letters before the number: P = proved, D = disproved, or N = neither proved nor disproved for the time being. The lists were given to the students to be studied and worked over, and a general class or group discussion followed in which an individual read a statement and told whether he had marked it P, D, or N and gave his reasons for so doing.

At first there was some reticence at contradiction, and the teacher found it necessary to supply a pertinent question here and there, but soon it was necessary to guard against overenthusiasm in support of one's answer. The students, however, quickly learned to respect the decisions of each other but to demand proof instead of opinion, hearsay, or prejudice. Most important of all, perhaps, was the acquiring of the attitude that, without definite proof one way or the other, a statement was not necessarily true nor was it necessarily untrue and that the fact that one could not disprove a statement did not of necessity mean that it was true.

Statement 1 was soon disposed of with a D since on the day of the discussion the fish had already lived 8 days. Of course the word "soon" had to be defined. Statement 2 was marked N with the necessity for further observation. Statement 3 was marked N after considerable argument, and two boys elected to devise a demonstration which would disprove the statement.

This was done in the following manner: Three pint and three quart fruit jars with self-sealing lids were procured and 1 pt. of water was added to each jar. In the water of each jar were placed two small goldfish. The jars were then all sealed tightly and set on a table. This was done early in the morning, and by 3 p.m. the pint jars contained four dead fish and two which were apparently nearly suffocated. The three quart jars, with an atmosphere of 1 pt. of air above water, contained six fish which seemed to be in a normal condition. Two of these quart jars were kept closed and the third was opened, and all were left until the following day. At that time all the fish in the closed jars were dead while those in the one which had been left open were alive. The class accepted this experiment as sufficient evidence that air is a vital factor in respiration of fish and that fish do not breathe water alone.

The group also decided to mark statement 4 with an *N* pending the outcome of the experiment for statement 3, since this same experiment might be sufficient to decide statement 4 as well as statement 3. Statement 5 was made to serve as an illustration of bad thinking. The first part of the statement was checked by a student testing for oxygen release from a piece of elodea in a test tube of water inverted in a glass of water and placed in direct sunlight for several hours. This was repeated for several kinds of plants and accepted as adequate proof that many aquatic plants release oxygen. Some discussion ensued before a student pointed out that since the plants released oxygen in sunlight regardless of the presence or absence of the animals, it was not justifiable to attribute purpose to natural phenomena and to say that the plants gave oxygen so that the fish might have a constant supply. Another student went still further and showed experimentally that plants did not release oxygen in the dark even when the animals were present; so the class decided that the purposive part of the statement must be marked *D*.

The remaining statements were each attacked in turn and ultimately disposed of. In some cases references to literature and scientific papers were made and specialists were consulted, but as far as possible they resorted to their own firsthand experimentation and observation. In every case each student kept an account of all tests and experiments done and the results obtained. At the end a summary and conclusion were agreed upon. Thus the group had tested and accepted or rejected each hypothesis proposed. In the experimentation they devised methods and simple apparatus and collected and interpreted data. Whether information, analogies, and facts which were offered in the testing of hypotheses were sufficiently pertinent to be considered valid evidence was a question that had to be decided frequently. Reliability of sources was often questioned, and the members of the groups became extremely cautious in the carrying out of experiments and in the accuracy of their statements. The other major problems of foods and pollution were handled in like manner and the results made available to all. Thus much of the subject matter usually included in a general biology course was covered. Information was gained in a very convincing manner without the sheer necessity of memorization. Many generalizations were made from the conclusions drawn, and constant drill in a scientific method of thinking was provided. Interest was seldom lacking, and the continuous use of the scientific method produced an attitude which had far-reaching effects upon the daily life of the student.

The two boys who had decided before entering the class that they would not like biology saw a way out one day when some crayfish were needed, and they offered to go to the creek and fetch them. They returned even earlier than they had expected and brought four crayfish, a frog, and one hellgrammite, or dobson-fly larva. Evidently an argument had arisen over the latter as to whether it was rightly called a hellgrammite and as to whether it was the larva of an insect or a centipede. One boy decided to go to a bait store for proof, and the other wanted to see if it could live without oxygen. The net result was that their attempt to get out of the classwork was the thing which brought them unwittingly into it.

The Induction and Application of Principles. Without a knowledge of facts in sufficient numbers there can be no generalizations of an intelligent character. One might memorize generalizations made by another, but one cannot have an understanding of them and one cannot make these generalizations oneself without a sufficient knowledge of the component elements, scientific facts.

Nor is the mere acquisition of these factual elements alone a guarantee that generalizations can be drawn from them. Much training in thought processes is essential to, though perhaps no guarantee of, the satisfactory induction of such generalizations as might be looked upon as principles. *Principles are scientific truths of wide application.* How wide the application has to be before it becomes a principle is a matter to be arbitrarily defined and is a difficult thing to do since there are of necessity all intergrades from simple isolated facts to universal generalizations. For example, one might, after study, decide that a certain species of insect produced specialized cells which after fusion produce a new individual like the original ones. This is primarily fact. One might, after study of many other species of insects, decide that each of these species produces new individuals in a similar fashion. This would be little more than enlarging the scope of factual knowledge in this field. But if one were to continue the study to include many species of both the plant and animal kingdoms and to decide that most plants and animals produce specialized cells (germ cells) that unite in the production of new individuals, it becomes a generalization which might be looked upon as the principle of sexual reproduction. One might go further, as Weismann did, and say that individuals produce germ cells which are living parts of the body and which continue the stream of life from generation to generation in an unbroken chain while the somatic cells, or body cells, die, and thus he would state what is known as the principle of the continuity of the germ plasm.

The question may then be asked, "What has the induction of generalizations and principles, as used by great scientists in advanced research, to do with the teaching of elementary science?" The answer is "Much." It is a matter of observation as well as a matter of actual measurement that there is but relatively slight retention of factual learning and of the meaning of words but that there is a very considerable retention of knowledge of generalizations and of the ability to apply these generalizations to concrete examples. Furthermore, the methods of great scientists in research are a valuable goal of practical importance to the layman in establishing his thinking procedure and his attitudes toward the intelligent fulfillment of his position in a highly propagandized society.

For example, it may be important to the student in his personal and his social behavior to realize thoroughly that common colds are produced by bacteria or viruses that are distributed from infected to noninfected individuals and that getting one's feet wet or sitting in a draft will not produce the condition if the causative organisms are not present. An intelligent application of the principle of cause of infection by contamination is worth infinitely more than the memorization of the name of a particular organism that causes a particular disease.

That the common housefly may spread typhoid germs may be a biological fact sufficient to justify a swat-the-fly campaign, but it sinks into insignificance when the student is made thoroughly conscious of the fact that for every thousand flies swatted many millions are breeding in manure piles, privy vaults, and garbage cans, and that one case of improper sewage disposal or inadequate filtration of a water supply will offset a thousandfold the possible good from a whole summer of swatting the fly.

The biology of the classroom begins really to function in the student's life when he is first able to generalize effectively on the basis of learned facts and to apply these generalizations to the conduct of his daily activities. This he will do only when practice and understanding have produced in him an attitude that is thoroughly scientific, causing him to think clearly, to see cause-and-effect relationships and to demand reasonable proof for the statements, claims, and attitudes of others.

Attitudes. Just as the ability to think and, in so doing, to use the scientific method depends upon a knowledge of facts with which the thinking is done and just as the drawing of inferences, the making of generalizations, and the induction and application of principles depend largely upon the ability to think logically and scientifically, so the formation of attitudes is the result of the correlation of all these.

An attitude is a condition of mind involving imagination and emotional states which are the result of previous experiences. Attitudes condition behavior, establishing patterns of conduct. Attitudes are ethics. Thus education for attitudes becomes of paramount importance. We must not, however, overlook the indisputable fact that each individual has a genetic composition that, for him, is unalterable. Like seeds they may be exposed to variations of soil, sunlight, and moisture that may greatly modify the appearance, structure, and usefulness of the growing plant, but only within the limits which were predetermined at the time of fertilization. So the students whose lives we attempt to modify are capable of modification only within well-defined limits. The genetic compositions of the members of a class are all different, and to expose them all to similar experiences and expect identical results is fruitless. Recognizing, then, that all persons will not profit equally by their participation in similar experiences, we may yet find that there are sufficient fundamental similarities among normal individuals to make education for attitudes a successful venture.

Some such objectives as are indicated by the expression "education for social efficiency" have long been a part of the philosophies of professional educators. Emphasis has been placed in varying degrees upon the importance of society as the unit. In so many instances the importance of the individual as an independent entity has been lost from sight. Society has been looked upon as a more or less fixed organic whole, possessing unaltering, almost unalterable, qualities and characteristics. Into its intricate pattern the individual must be made to fit. Mass education with its highly formalized curricula is well suited to this philosophy. Religions in nearly all forms greatly encourage the error by their emphasis upon the unalterable and permanent character of their doctrines. They depend upon deity for the authority so necessary to their precepts, and since deity cannot be wrong it cannot change.

There must be some stability in any successful social order, but fixity should not be mistaken for stability. *One must not fail to recognize that a society is but a group of individuals each of which contributes in some measure, however small, to the characteristics of that society.* Then if those individuals are not even genetically alike, if the social composition changes, if immigration and emigration are going on, if through its own activities and through the activities inherent in the rest of nature the environment is constantly varying, how can one rightfully look upon any social order except in the light of an evolution and constant change? Education, therefore, based upon the tenet of fixation and upon the immutability of ideals can produce little more than stagnation and ultimate degeneration.

The present age is an age of science. Science is progressive. Progress means change. Science touches the life of every individual in society at every turn. Fields that are not scientific and fields that are deliberately unscientific are endeavoring to capitalize on the prestige of science and use clever, and sometimes not so clever, pseudoscientific language, imitations, and arguments. How, then, can the layman who is not a scientist recognize true worth or meaning in the kaleidoscopic offerings of an over-propagandized social life?

Ordinarily we create the conditions to which our students react during the few hours while they are within the walls of our classrooms. But to what are they reacting during the much greater part of their lives while not in school? What are we giving them that will be of value in meeting the challenges of their environments during that time? On the way home from school the adolescent girl, who has recently become sensitive to what can be accomplished by feminine charm, stops to look at a display in the drugstore window. An exceedingly attractive picture of a well-known actress occupies the place of prominence. With the picture is written a statement that she uses a particular brand of cosmetic or toilet preparation, and it bears her signature. The clever advertising manager has appended a statement of his own to the effect that the beauty and charm of many actresses are the result of using his company's product. Thus, a direct appeal is made to one of the most powerful instincts of young womanhood.

A young boy arrives at home after school, turns on the radio or television to listen to a wild story of the exciting adventures of an imaginary character of his own age. While his imagination is still tingling with admiration for the exploits of the fictitious hero, the announcer reads an exhortation to the nation's youth to drink a certain preparation three times per day if they would become like the hero in every respect. Young people open the pages of the daily newspapers and popular magazines and are regularly greeted with pictures of a nationally known athlete or famous coach, giving the impression that he is smoking a particular brand of cigarette or eating a dish of some brand of food. The picture is accompanied by a meaningless but misleading signed statement presuming to show that this food builds strong bodies and should be eaten by young boys.

Many of the headlines and half the editorials in newspapers are designed deliberately to fashion the attitudes and build up the prejudices of the readers. Regular campaigns for raising funds for this and that are so conducted as to play upon the emotions, with little or no regard for proved facts. Individuals, political parties, business concerns, and the governments of states and nation make use of the method. Hate, fear, greed, love, admiration, sex, all the emotions are being constantly assaulted from all sides. How shall the growing children of today find their way through this intricate maze? Science is freely parasitized. Each advertisement and speech quotes freely such phrases of science as most nearly suit its needs. There are always such statements as "science has proved," or "a great scientist has discovered," or "Dr. So and So says," and there is the ever-present picture of the bewhiskered gentleman in a white coat peering through a microscope at some mystery too obscure to understand, but impressive enough to convince the lay mind of the virtues of the advertised product.

What shall be done? Articles have been written and books published to expose the perfidy of the modern propagandist. To create a widespread attitude of skepticism is not sufficient. Attitudes, however, if combined with habits of thinking may do more than anything else to help the citizen of tomorrow steer a safe and sane course through the problems that confront him and the society in which he lives. He spends most of his life making decisions. From the time he decides what kind of tooth paste he should use on his teeth in the morning until he decides which make of mattress he should sleep on at night, he is confronted with the necessity for choosing. Not everything that confronts him is false. He is not always being led or coerced. His problem, then, is to be able to select and decide correctly.

If there is any one thing that the study of science should do for the student it is to produce a scientific attitude toward all problems that arise in his daily life. Facts, if not used, may be forgotten, but the establishment of an attitude which impels an individual to look at each problematic situation in an analytical fashion, to attack it in a scientific manner, to demand proof in the form of adequate facts results in a habit of thinking which can and will be used regularly by the individual in making the innumerable adjustments that are necessitated by a constantly changing society.

Some Desirable Understandings Derived from the Study of Biology. The understandings might be summarized in the following statements:

1. The only known source of life is from living substance.
2. The unit of living substance is the cell.
3. The basic process in the formation of living substance is photosynthesis.
4. Life processes are chemical reactions involving interchanges of materials and energy.
5. Life processes are essentially the same regardless of the organism in which they occur.
6. Diseases and disorders are the result of interference by factors which affect these processes.
7. Vitamins, enzymes, and endocrines are regulators of these processes.
8. Immunization and correction of diseases and disorders often may be obtained through the proper use of antitoxins, vaccines, drugs, and foods.
9. Much of the commercial advertising of foods, antiseptics, drugs, vitamins,

and other preparations is not supported by scientific data and is often deliberately false, misleading, and sometimes detrimental.

10. Sufficient familiarity with facts combined with scientific thinking is a safeguard against such imposition and is useful in solving everyday problems.

11. Reasonable understanding of natural phenomena is a source of satisfaction and a means of fuller living.

12. The most fundamental industries of man are based directly upon plant and animal life.

13. Living things have descended through time with wide variation in form of expression.

14. Variation in the expression of life through time is a function of the genetic composition of the individual and the environment in which it develops.

15. Improvement of domestic animals and cultivated plants can be brought about most rapidly and most efficiently through the understanding and application of the principles and laws of genetics.

16. These same principles and laws are applicable to man.

17. Social problems are essentially biological problems and should be solved as such without resorting to emotionalism.

18. Science is ready to modify its generalizations in the light of new evidences.

PROBLEMS

1. Prepare a brief but careful explanation of the following terms as they apply to scientific thinking: hypothesis, validity, adequacy, conclusion.

2. Using the illustration given in this chapter, or any similar examples, prepare a short plan for a unit in biology with the subject matter arranged according to a scientific approach.

3. Work out a set of about 10 biological principles which you think should be understood by the members of a class in general biology by the time the course is completed.

4. What are some of the attitudes that you would hope to develop in the students in a class of high school biology which should have some social value in their everyday life? Connect these attitudes with certain parts of the subject matter and certain methods which you think should help to produce them.

REFERENCES

1. Burnett, R. W.: "The Science Teacher and His Objectives," *Teachers Coll. Record*, 45:241–251, January, 1944.

2. Cole, C. C., Jr.: "Encouraging Scientific Talent," College Entrance Examination Board, 1956. 425 W. 117th St., New York 27, N.Y.

3. Commission on the Secondary School Curriculum of the Progressive Education Association: *Science in General Education: A Progress Report*, New York, 1937. A particularly progressive treatment on the relation of science to life. Especially Parts I and II.

4. Conant, J. B.: *Science and Common Sense*, Yale University Press, New Haven, Conn., 1951.

5. Cunningham, H. A.: "Objectives in High School Biology," *School Sci. and Math.*, 35:462–467, 606–612, 1935.

6. Curtis, F. D.: "Teaching Scientific Methods," *School Sci. and Math.*, 34:816–819, 1934.

7. Dewey, John: "The Supreme Intellectual Obligation," *Sci. Educ.*, 18:1–4, 1934.

8. Dressel, P. L., and Mayhew, L. B.: *Science Reasoning and Understanding,* William C. Brown Company, Dubuque, Iowa, 1954.

9. Huxley, Julian: "World Population," *Sci. American,* vol. 194, no. 3, March, 1956. Documented discussion by an authority.

10. Lassen, H. C.: "The Scientific Method in Use," *School Sci. and Math.,* vol. 50, no. 7, October, 1950.

11. Massachusetts Institute of Technology: *Educational Opportunities* and other well written pamphlets designed to stimulate interest in scientific careers. Director of Admissions, Massachusetts Institute of Technology, 69 Massachusetts Ave., Cambridge 39, Mass.

12. McKibben, M. J.: "Analysis of Principles and Activities of Importance for General Biology Courses in High Schools," *Sci. Educ.,* **39**:187–196, April, 1955.

13. Meglitsch, P. A., and J. P. Wessel: *Introduction to Biological Principles,* Burgess Publishing Company, Minneapolis, 1948.

14. Miller, D. F.: "Biology for Survival," *Am. Biol. Teacher,* **12**:7–12, January, 1950.

15. Miller, J. V.: "Objectives and Grades in Biology," *Am. Biol. Teacher,* **12**:99–102, May, 1950.

16. Nixon, A. F.: *Teaching Biology for Appreciation,* Chapman & Grimes, Inc., Boston, 1950. Aims and objectives. Bibliography.

17. Obourn, E. S., and G. C. Montgomery: "Procedures for Developing the Elements of Problem Solving," *Sci. Educ.,* **25**:72–80, February, 1941.

18. Powers, S. R.: *The Objectives of Science Teaching,* National Society for the Study of Education, Thirty-first Year Book, part I, chap. IV, 1932.

19. Stevens, N. E.: "Objectives in Biological Courses," *School Sci. and Math.,* **46**:551–559, June, 1946.

20. Washton, N. S.: "Syllabus in Biology for General Education," *Sci. Educ.,* **35**:84–92, March, 1951.

21. Woodworth, R. H.: "Biology Is More Than Principles," *J. Gen. Educ.,* **2**:199–203, April, 1948. Aims and objectives.

CHAPTER 3

Should a Course Conform to a Type

The teacher who is about to start upon his career may expect his supervisor to tell him just what items of subject matter he should include in his course, the proper sequence, and how it should be taught. What he seeks, however, is seldom given. He is disappointed. All through his education he has been taught to rely upon the authority of books, the authority of teachers. Sometimes he has been told bluntly that he is either right or wrong. Now he seeks assurance in that authority, and it fails him. Perhaps the student is not yet aware of the fact that there is no such thing as *one correct course* which should be given under *all* circumstances.

No matter how thoroughly a teacher is grounded in subject matter, he is well aware of the feeling of insecurity that attends his first attempts at presenting a course to his classes. Time and repetition should dispel this sense of insecurity. Sometimes this is done so thoroughly that the teacher loses sight of the fact that with the beginning of each new term the work is just as unfamiliar to the student as it was the first time it was taught and that the student continues to experience the feeling of insecurity incident to treading upon new ground. Teachers who at first are greatly concerned about the choice and amount of subject matter and about methods of presentation may lose this concern and become completely satisfied with their choices and their technics. This is one of the surest signs of "growing old" professionally. It has little to do with years of age, for as we look about we see teachers who are actually old in years but who have kept mentally young. They have not settled down to a thoroughly routined procedure in their teaching but have retained much of the buoyancy and sensitivity that was inherent in those early years of their experience when they were prompted by this feeling of insecurity to be on the lookout for new ideas, new methods, and new applications of the subject matter which they taught.

A discussion of methodology, because of the scope of the subject, might involve a large number of topics. In this chapter, however, we shall limit it to the following problems:

1. The amount of subject matter to be covered in a course
2. The kind of subject matter to be covered in a course
   a. Factors determining the kind of subject matter
   b. Factors complicating the choice of subject matter
3. The tabulation of courses according to fundamental types

THE AMOUNT OF SUBJECT MATTER

The Text as a Criterion. How should the teacher determine the amount of subject matter to be included in a course? Experienced teachers seem frequently to have settled this question or to have had it settled for them. Such criteria as the content of the textbook, the experience of the student, and the student's needs are used. The most widely used criterion for making the decision seems to be the size of the text selected. It is a general rule that the course consists of the subject matter included in the book and that it is the business of the teacher to crowd that amount of subject matter into the semester or year, as the case may be, if the content is large, and to stretch that amount out over the same time, if the content is small. Under the most favorable circumstances this is a poor method.

The publishers, and sometimes the writers, of texts imply that they have prepared an ideal course of study which is complete in their book. One expects salesmen to use this argument, and by it school boards and administrators are sometimes misled into thinking that a particular book or set of books will standardize the work in a highly desirable fashion. But this standardization of the work of a course from school to school or even from class to class is one of the undesirable outgrowths of mass education. It is highly improbable that any school system of appreciable size will have such uniformity in student make-up that one course is equally good for all. Yet the larger the school system, the more likely it is to adopt a standard text or course of study. The students in a single school building may be sectioned upon various bases. Sometimes it is done upon the results of intelligence ratings, sometimes upon the results of grades made in previous, and often different, courses, sometimes upon the curriculum groupings such as college preparatory, manual arts, or fine arts. Sometimes a section is rated as "fast" or "slow" which is usually understood to reflect in some degree relative intelligence.

Student Needs. In large school systems where there is a wide variation in the population of its several communities, it is quite possible that a member of a "fast" section in one community might actually rank lower than some member of a "slow" section in another community. It is inconceivable, then, that a standardized course or uniform treatment of a subject can provide equally or even passably well for the needs of all students. How much subject matter should be covered by any class is a problem that should be decided by the composition of that class. The solution should vary widely between different schools in a single system and between different classes in a single school. As a matter of fact it may, and probably should, vary considerably between different students in a single class. In general it may be said that how much a student does is of less importance than what he does and how he does it. If this is true, it then becomes of primary importance that the teacher, especially the beginning teacher, first determine what should be taught in the course, allowing the amount to be decided later.

THE KIND OF SUBJECT MATTER

Factors Determining the Kind of Subject Matter. In the consideration of this problem there arise such questions as the location of the school, the make-up of the community, the intelligence of the individuals, their interests and ability to profit from various types of experiences, and the possibilities of their future. It may be impossible for a new teacher entering a strange community to know all these things at the start, but to learn them at the earliest moment becomes one of the teacher's first duties. If a class consists of students whose interests, inherent abilities, and social-economic status all combine to cause them to profit most from training in manual and household arts, and whose abilities or economic status necessitate their leaving school at the end of the junior or senior high school period, it is best that they gain from their high school science a knowledge of and correct attitude toward those phases of biology which will better enable them to maintain their personal health and social well-being. A consciousness of infections and communicable diseases, epidemics and their causes and control, an interest in personal and community betterment, some knowledge of heredity and, as far as possible, a tendency to do as much thinking as he is capable of doing for himself are ideals worthy of incorporating in the course for these students. For some students it may be necessary and desirable to concentrate exclusively upon such phases of the course. To memorize the classification of the echinoderms or the nomenclature of the Compositae may seem learned at the time but such knowledge is soon deservedly forgotten.

If, on the other hand, the composition of the class is such that their genetic, social, and economic inheritance assures them of obtaining a college education or its equivalent, the "what" of the subject matter may well be altered. They will profit by and be interested in the more purely personal and social phases of the work, but much of this they will already have learned or come to accept as matter of fact because of home training or influences. These experiences plus native abilities may make it possible to add numerous topics to the content of their course, and some students may profitably learn how a starfish uses its tube feet or why a tomato is a berry and not a vegetable. The somewhat more technical phases of their science, methods of experimentation, and more emphases upon problem solving and scientific thinking are definitely a part of the course for those students.

It may very well happen that your class is composed of a mixture of types of students. The problem is then not different from either of the above situations but is a combination of them, for again the question of what to include in the course is answered by a consideration of the composition of the class. Therefore, in a mixed class there exists the necessity for a variable program which is sufficiently flexible to meet the needs of its members, and there is neither demand nor excuse for having all members do the same kind or amount of subject matter under such circumstances. All the above considerations will have to conform to the length of class periods, number of periods per week, and whether the course extends over a semester or a year.[1]

A few other factors may arise to complicate the problem of preparing a course. Any one of these may or may not exist in a given locality but should not be overlooked if present.

Location of the School. Schools located in rural districts or in small towns have at their disposal large parts of the outdoors from which a great quantity of materials may be obtained. (See especially Chaps. 7 and 12.) There should be no necessity for calling this to the attention of the teacher; yet it is one of the foremost criticisms of biology teaching that little use is made of materials which lie within easy reach of some school buildings, while the teachers complain about lack of funds for purchasing more. This may be laid at the doors of our colleges and teacher-training institutions where the students often see only preserved materials, museum specimens, charts and models, and a few living forms purchased from a supply company. If, by contrast, the building is located well within a large city, these natural sources become less accessible, but there are often museums, zoological and botanical gardens, packing plants, large markets, and manufacturing establishments making many uses of plant and animal materials. Thus, the location of the school may radically influence your selection of subject matter, but it need seldom be a serious handicap. As a matter of fact, the available materials are probably the ones best suited to your pupils' needs.

Administrative Limitations. The amount of administrative control over classroom work varies from none to complete control. In some schools the teacher is entirely free to choose, plan, and execute the course as may seem fit. In others there is a general plan or outline of the subjects to be taught, and it is expected that the teacher will follow it. In some large schools there are department heads who may even have unit or lesson outlines which are given to each teacher. In some places there are subject supervisors who govern the work throughout the school system. Where such supervision does not exist, the teachers of similar classes are expected to cooperate in the formulation of a course. This is intended to provide more uniformity. It means a certain amount of give and take, and for an inexperienced or incoming teacher it may mean more take than give. Do not expect to revolutionize immediately the teaching under any such conditions, but work gradually step by step in instituting changes or new ideas. Also remember that, if your experience is small, their decisions may be more practicable than yours. Under such conditions you will generally find sufficient opportunity for working out your own ideas so that it will be unnecessary to sacrifice your individuality or progressive points of view. Unless there is direct interference, and this is rare, a reasonable amount of administrative guidance is likely to be a distinct advantage at first. Once you have shown the ability to plan and carry out the work efficiently, the administration is almost certain to prefer to devote its attention to other matters.

Selecting Topics. With the above guiding considerations definitely in mind, the teacher may proceed to the selection of topics which are to be the sub-

[1] See Chap. 6 for sample of a questionnaire which may be used in obtaining valuable information concerning the social background of your class as an aid to determining the probable needs of the class members.

stance of the course. If he has been properly prepared as a student, he should have ample background in his field for the choosing of these topics. A number of good texts written for the level of the classes to be taught can be of some assistance in making the selection. In no sense should the course be limited by such tables of contents, although there probably will be more topics than can be included since textbooks have a way of embodying more subject matter than one course is likely to cover. Nor should they unduly influence the method of presentation which you employ. Keeping well in mind the needs of the class as determined from a firsthand study, decide first of all upon the general objectives. These will serve as a guide in the choice of topics, sequence, and manner of treatment.

The general procedure of preparing a course can be summed up in the following steps:

1. Study your class composition to determine its success, progress, and intelligence ratings. These should be a matter of school record in the office.

2. Get as accurate a picture as possible of the social-economic make-up of your class. If this has not been done, it will be necessary to obtain the information from a questionnaire given to each student. (First consult your principal.)

3. Using the first two steps as guides, prepare your objectives in fairly definite form.

4. Select subject matter that is best suited to the accomplishment of these objectives especially as regards their utility to the student.

5. Prepare a condensed and later a detailed outline of the course based upon a time-budget distribution. Detailed lesson planning can come later and may best be worked out as the course progresses.

The Pretest. As early as possible, preferably at the very beginning of the term, it is desirable to prepare a very general test covering such subject matter as you feel is likely to be known already to the students in your class. To this add adequate samples of the subject matter which you intend to cover in your course. Use a strictly objective type of test for two reasons. First, the test will be lengthy for the student to take and, second, it needs to be scored as soon as possible for your own guidance. By summarizing the parts of the test you will have a cross section of what your classes already have as background for your course. This will serve as a further guide to you in selecting topics and in deciding upon the kind and amount of emphasis to be placed upon various parts. It will also help in a way with any individualization of your work. (See Chap. 6, Evaluation.)

Pupil Interests. Such information as can be obtained concerning the pupils of a class in regard to their home and community life, economic status, probable future interests and activities, and their native abilities furnishes a relatively sound basis for determining the content, methods, and emphasis of a course. In addition to this, attempts have been made to establish specific interests of students in types of subject matter by means of questionnaires giving their likes and dislikes after they have had certain courses. This information may be of value to a teacher as an after check since it will throw some light upon what parts of the course as given have been of most interest to those students. Studies of this kind, however, made by others upon limited groups of students are of doubtful value. They will indicate what interests and appeals have been made to *those* students by use of the subjects included in *that* course with such methods as were employed by *those* teachers. The amount of emphasis placed upon heredity and the technics employed by one teacher make it a first or second choice with her students, but for similar reasons another group prefers a study of flowers or microorganisms, etc. Hence, it is obvious that such data are of value in determining what results have been obtained rather than as a guide to what should be taught. It probably is true that certain topics make more of a natural appeal to large numbers of students than do others, but the way that they have been approached and the methods pursued have more to do with the student's final estimate than do their intrinsic values.

There are undoubtedly certain fundamental interests of boys and girls in early puberty, such as their interests in sex, social relations, life achievements, the novel and spectacular in nature (witness the believe-it-or-not cartoons) and physical accomplishments (as in athletics), which if worked out in sufficient detail and properly catalogued and studied might furnish sound bases for guidance in determining the contents and treatment of courses. Unfortunately little has been done concerning this problem, but it holds many possibilities for future investigations.

The fields of biology, botany, physiology, and zoology are all of sufficient scope that the selection of topics becomes a matter of choosing and eliminating. Once this has been done, there arise the problems of sequence and emphasis.

Sequence. The traditional manner of arranging the subject matter of a text or of a course in the phylogenetic sequence has been so widely adopted that it still persists even in courses of the junior high school level. This logical arrangement appeals to the mind of the taxonomist and evolutionist and can be used with some advantage in more highly specialized courses. For the more elementary classes and for courses designed for students, very few of whom are likely to specialize in the field, there are other arrangements that might be used to better advantage. One author states that he has arranged the sequence in his text to conform to the materials available at different seasons of the school year. This might be a factor worthy of considering in many localities. It should be evident from preceding discussions that no one set of topics could possibly be suited to the needs of all courses in any field but should vary for many reasons. Likewise it should be equally apparent that no one sequence of topics could be suited to all courses in the same subject. As a matter of fact the point of starting and subsequent order of arrangement could in most cases follow any one of a number of patterns. As examples of this consider the following illustrations:

1. Let us suppose that you are teaching a class in physiology, or that part of biology which deals largely with the structure and function of the human body. Most textbooks on the subject would begin with the gross anatomy of the body, with the names of the systems and the organs, and end with the functions. This development would accomplish the results so far as the learning of facts is concerned but is likely to be introduced with a rather lengthy period of arid memorizing. Which topic comes first and which second is of relatively little importance. Let us assume that you plan to start your course

with the study of circulation. Most courses do not do this. You may say, "But the class is not yet ready for circulation." Consider, however, the following sequence: You may safely assume that the members of your class already know that there are such things as blood, blood vessels, and a heart. They know that the heart beats and pumps the liquid blood through the vessels. They all have seen blood, but they most probably have not seen it actually circulate.

You prepare one or more demonstrations such as placing the fin of a fish, tail of a tadpole, or web of a frog's foot beneath the microscope (see Chap. 18, Circulation). Each student is now able to see the smaller arteries, veins, and capillaries and to see that what he has always thought of as a deep red fluid has much more of the appearance of a great mass of tiny golden disks which go tumbling through small tubes. He now has a new concept of the nature of blood and blood flow. His interest and curiosity are aroused, and a follow-up discussion by the class introduces the study of blood. This requires the preparation of blood smears from the specimen and from some member of the class for comparison (see Chap. 18). A drop of Wright's stain discloses types of blood cells, and the more detailed study of blood functions and composition is well motivated. After a few class periods there will be felt the need for a new "lift" or motivation. You may be ready to introduce the study of the heart, its functions, and structure. Now suppose that you present a demonstration of the beating heart of a frog. No class will fail to thrill at the sight of a throbbing heart. A little guidance during the observation period will bring out the auricular and ventricular contractions. The problem of how the blood flows always in one direction calls for a knowledge of the internal heart structures. This can be done from material obtained from slaughterhouses or butcher shops. Individual or small-group participation or the small-group demonstration method can be used. A study of drug effects and blood and heart hygiene can be covered and definite application to personal welfare introduced since heart failure is considered to be first in the list of causes of man's death.

The relation of circulation and parts of the circulatory system to all other structures of the body can be demonstrated in a specimen such as a frog or small mammal. The relation to the digestive tract explains absorption of food, that to the lungs explains absorption and disposal of oxygen and carbon dioxide, that to the kidneys explains the relation it bears to excretion, that to muscles relates it to behavior, etc., each being a point of departure for introducing a study of any of the other body functions and their structures. It requires but little imagination to understand how a sequence of topics may begin with such a project as circulation and yet follow a perfectly psychological and coherent arrangement though such may not be widely used in books or courses of study.

2. Let us now consider another illustration of sequence that starts from an entirely different point of view. You might choose to introduce your course from a study of the behavior of organisms and how they respond to stimulating factors of their environment. This may not be an unwise choice although in most texts it would be one of the last items instead of the first. In Chap. 21 you will find numerous suggestions and descriptions of problems

and demonstrations that will be found suited to arouse a keen interest in a group of students. From Chap. 21 you may select a series of experiments which show that such an animal as a toad or frog will respond with mechanical precision to such stimulations as you choose. These responses bring out the fact that sense organs (receptors) exist at various points on the animal's body. From this general observation follows a more detailed study of the sense organs, and a few further demonstrations which the student may perform upon himself (see Chap. 21) definitely relate the subject to his own person. But a study of responses implies a direct relation between sense organs and organs of movement. Hence the need for a study of the elements of the nervous system. The nerve structures, brain, and impulses are then covered because of this feeling of need.

Generalizing upon this study of the responses of organisms may well lead to the topic of the relations of organisms to their environment (elementary ecology) and to a consideration of dominant influences which govern man's social organization and behavior. Or from the study of the relation of the nervous system to muscles in simple responses might come the study of muscles and their function. The functioning of muscles requires the transformation of energy, as respiration. The transformation of energy implies a source of this energy as foods, which leads most naturally into the study of digestion and the digestive system. On the other hand, it also implies the production of waste products, which suggests the studies of breathing and excretion. Without carrying the illustration into more detail, it must be obvious that it is equally possible to begin a course, or any of its major units, from any one of a number of different points and to pursue a sequence of items in such a fashion as to produce a psychologically well-coordinated course of study.

TYPES OF COURSES

So much, then, for the problem of materials and the general sequence. A matter of much greater importance is that of the choice of the type of course into which the factual matter is to be arranged. This is important because upon this decision rests the fulfillment of one of the major objectives of biology teaching, the induction and application of principles. Attempts at classifying courses in the natural sciences are indeed difficult since there has been presented so many courses differing from each other in what sometimes amounts to but minor details. For our purposes of discussion, however, we shall use three general groupings into which most courses might fall, although in many instances there has been a combination which would place some courses in more than one of these categories.

The Morphological, or Types, Courses. In courses of this grouping we find that subject matter centered around the study of types of plants and animals usually is arranged in phylogenetic sequence. Type forms are studied in detail as illustrations of the major groups. An understanding of morphology and taxonomy is the primary aim of these courses. Such courses are typical of work done in colleges and very often in high schools when botany and zoology are offered as separate subjects. A variation of this is the case of a so-called biology course which consists of one semester of botany and one semester of zoology. There is but little to recommend in such an arrangement for the general student. It is somewhat of a relic of the early days when the elementary courses in any field were designed as if all students who took them intended to become specialists in the field. We cannot afford to forget, however, that in all probability less than 3 per cent of students taking the secondary school course may ever go into more advanced studies in that field.

The Civic and Economic Courses. These purported to be of such a character as to fit the individual for better fulfilling his place in the state. They were the outgrowth of the movement which is characterized by "education for citizenship." The theoretical ideal was that of making each individual a better citizen. The idea spread from other fields into biology, especially in the high schools. Textbooks began appearing under titles of civic biologies. In some cases these were but little more than the same older courses dressed in new clothing. It was a vogue, and authors rewrote their texts and re-named them to keep them on the market. Much good came from this change in emphasis, however. It thoroughly broke the domination of the morphological course plan as applied to secondary school biology. Later books sought definitely, and with varying degrees of success, to produce courses that offered distinct advantages to the great proportion of our public school students who received no further training in the field. In fact it opened up to study the whole problem of kinds of courses and has made possible greater flexibility and freedom in the selection and formation of types of courses suitable to the group of students for which they may be designed.

The Principles Courses. Closely allied to courses based upon citizenship were those which were dedicated to the social improvement and personal well-being of the student. The manner in which courses were constructed, when so designed, did not follow any set formula. They did emphasize such points as

1. Man's place in the biological world
2. The relation of microorganisms to personal and public health
3. The relation of the physical environment to man's well-being
4. What man can do about the community, etc.

These topics were sometimes a little overstressed, but they injected new life of a practical character into what had often been a cold, formalized science course. The most recent tendencies seem to involve some return toward the treatment of biology as a field of science rather than as sociology but without losing the social significance which this subject above all others should rightfully involve. The point of view is that of basing the study upon fundamental principles of biology. This is a very plausible procedure if properly executed. It involves a number of desirable elements that were inherent in other types but permits of a somewhat different treatment. These elements conform directly to our accepted objectives as stated in Chap. 2.

1. It necessitates the teaching of biological knowledge as scientific facts and thus retains the desirable feature of the earlier kinds of courses.
2. It necessitates the utilization of this factual knowledge in inducing generalizations which are formulated as principles.

3. It necessitates the application of these principles when they are used in problem solving. When these problems are made of personal and social significance, the method retains those desirable characteristics found in more recent courses.

4. When facts are made to have fuller meaning through generalization, when generalizations are made to live through application to life problems, and when their meaning and utility are combined with habits of thinking, they are bound to produce attitudes in the learner which should definitely function in his adjustments to the needs of his life.

Thus, the true principles course endeavors to accomplish these ideals. It is not so much a new type of course as it is an organization which emphasizes the objectives in a different manner.

PROBLEMS

1. Examine one or more high school texts in the biological subjects (biology, botany, physiology, or zoology), noting the subject matter that is covered. Disregarding the arrangement in the texts, prepare, in brief outline only, a course for a class of students who will not have an opportunity of attending college, who will have to become self-supporting upon graduation from high school, and whose outlook for the future is urban or metropolitan.

2. Following the same procedure as in Problem 1, prepare the outline of a course for a class that is made up almost exclusively of students who will attend college or other special school, that will not have to be self-supporting for at least four years after graduation from high school, and that probably will be urban in make-up and outlook.

3. Prepare, as in Problems 1 and 2, a course in outline for a class of students of rather uniform abilities, half of whom will have the opportunity of attending college or special school, the other half of whom will not be pressed to self-support immediately after graduation from high school and for whom the community life and future are largely rural and village.

4. Examine a text on high school biology and make a copy of its table of contents. Assume that this represents the author's suggestion for a course of study. Note the sequence of topics and determine from the preface what the author's reasons are for this sequence. Then, using the same topics, arrange them in one or more different sequences which in your opinion might result in a psychologically coherent course. (Consult pages 30 to 32 of this chapter for a discussion of the problem of sequence.) Present your new arrangement in class for discussion, giving your reasons for your arrangement.

5. Consult the prefaces of at least three texts on high school biology and note the type of course which the authors have had in mind according to their own statements. They may not give it a special name such as "types course" or "principles course," but you are to determine what type it is. This may involve studying the table of contents and some of the chapters. What are the author's reasons for his choice of type of course?

6. Consult the prefaces of at least three texts on high school biology and note what the authors have to say about the desired objectives of the biology course. Compare the different points of view and discuss them before the methods class.

REFERENCES

1. Brown, M. G.: "Fitting a Program of Biology into a Community Centered School," *Am. Biol. Teacher,* **13**:87–90, April, 1951.

2. Burton, W. H.: *The Guidance of Learning Activities,* Appleton-Century-Crofts, Inc., New York, 1952.

3. Hauber, U. A.: "High School Biology Course," *Natl. Catholic Educ. Assoc. Bull.,* **49**:22–29, 1952–53.

4. Herzog, E. G., and P. B. Sheatsley: "Science Education as the Scientists See It," *The Educational Forum,* vol. 12, no. 4, May, 1948.

5. Hoff, A. G.: *Secondary-school Science Teaching,* McGraw-Hill Book Company, Inc., New York, 1947.

6. Lowry, N. L.: "Biology and Physical Science for Ninth and Tenth Grade Students," *Sci. Educ.,* **35**:71–73, March, 1951.

7. Miller, J. V.: "Teacher-Pupil Planning for Biology," *Am. Biol. Teacher,* **12**:51–54, March, 1950.

8. Miller, M. A.: "General Education Type of Biology Course," *Am. Biol. Teacher,* **15**:51–53, February, 1953.

9. National Education Association, Teachers Association Department: *Science Teaching Ideas:* II, 1955. 1201 16th St., N.W., Washington 6, D.C. -

10. National Education Association, Science Teachers Association Department: *Science Courses of Study,* 1955. 1201 16th St., N.W., Washington 6, D.C.

11. National Education Association, Science Teachers Association Department: *Abstracts of Science Teaching Ideas,* 1955. 1201 16th St., N.W., Washington 6, D.C.

12. Odell, C. W.: "An Annotated Bibliography Dealing with the Classification and Instruction of Pupils to Provide for Individual Differences," *Univ. Illinois Bull.* 16, 1923.

13. Schneck, J. W.: "Practical Value of Certain Topics in a Course of Biology," *School Sci. and Math.,* **46**:318–322, April, 1946.

14. Vinal, W. G.: "What Kind of Biological Education," *Am. Biol. Teacher,* **18**:102–103, February, 1956.

15. Wells, H.: *Elementary Science Education,* McGraw-Hill Book Company, Inc., New York, 1951.

CHAPTER 4

❧ Methods of Presentation ❧

Whatever the formally designated course may be, it is an expression of some very general underlying philosophy. Some specific philosophical background is a necessity for intelligent teaching, but the mere reiteration of this or that type of course by name gives of itself little guarantee of the results to be accomplished. The methods employed in its presentation are of much importance to the success of the type of course. These, too, have been classified under commonly accepted names such as:

1. The textbook-recitation method
2. The laboratory method
3. The demonstration-discussion method
4. The problem-project method

These four groups include the elements of nearly all other methods which are, in most cases, modifications or combinations of them.

We must not lose sight of the fact that the mere name of a method tells little concerning the value or success of the teaching procedure in any particular class. Two teachers may use the laboratory method and one do an excellent job of teaching while the other fails miserably. Too many factors enter into all good teaching for one to be able to classify them under a given method. Of first rank among these other factors are the teacher's personality, method of approach, means of motivation, choice of materials, etc., some of which will be given more consideration later.

The Textbook-Recitation Method. Before the days of easy printing, teaching was done by use of a few manuscripts and from the teacher's store of knowledge which was passed out by lecturing and questioning. In colleges and universities the lecture is still the accepted means of imparting information. Though this is sometimes practiced in secondary schools, it has been supplanted to a very large degree by the assignment of readings in the textbook which are then called for in a subsequent period of questioning called the recitation. So widely was this followed that it became accepted as *the* method of teaching. In spite of the broadside of criticism which has been leveled at it in recent years, it still persists as the most widely used procedure in secondary schools. To read literature upon any subject and to be able to answer questions upon that subject are commendable. The error comes from making this process the entire or at least the major method. It has elicited a strong following especially with inexperienced teachers because it is an easy way to teach, gives a superficial showing of scholarly attainment, makes it possible to cover large amounts of subject matter in a relatively short period of time, gives the teacher less to do in planning and preparing, and offers a feeling of security by a reliance upon the supposed authority of the author.

It is one of the easiest methods to follow because the author has arranged the subject matter in chapters and paragraphs which are in most cases logical and which may be apportioned out as assignments to be memorized and recited upon. There is need for very little planning on the part of the teacher if the method is not varied. Such things as examples, illustrations, and experiments are worked out and explained so that even the demonstrations may be discussed from diagrams, pictures, and verbal descriptions instead of being performed in class.

It makes a superficial show of scholarship since youthful minds seem to be able to retain verbal impressions for sufficient lengths of time to permit successful recitation. This is true even when the real meaning of the words is obscure to the student. His ability to quote at length from printed pages is sometimes unintentionally misleading as to the exact amount of understanding which he possesses. While the quoting of authorities is a valuable asset, it has lost much of its prestige as a measure of true learning.

The textbook-recitation method also encourages the student to rely upon one authority, and since ordinarily there is little questioning of this authority the student fails to develop a critically analytical attitude toward his learning. He misses the training which he should get in problem solving since the problems are usually solved by the text. When so-called problems or questions are appended to the chapters of the texts, they most generally can be answered by turning back to the pages of that chapter. Such questions are useful only as after checks to test memory when they are interrogations for which a declarative counterpart has been given in the text. If principles are embodied in the text, they usually appear as definitions and often appear first, the explanations or basis being given afterward. The student is given no occasion for formulating his own generalizations.

The feeling of security that comes from this method may be of value to a beginning teacher in helping to establish a necessary confidence, but when indulged in too freely it destroys the self-reliance of both teacher and student. The results of this training in overdependence upon authority is so apparent in beginning college students that attempts at having them solve problems and depend upon their own conclusions are disconcerting to students and instructors alike. They will refuse to believe their own observations or experimental results unless these are substantiated in a text. A very striking and amusing illustration of this took place in a university class when a student took issue with his professor upon some point which had been made in his lecture. The student's reason for differing with the professor was the feeling that he had somewhere read a statement to the contrary. The professor suggested that the student look up his point and bring in the references. Next day the student appeared, book in hand. He admitted frankly that he had been mistaken, since he had found the reference in a book from the medical library. The professor, glancing at the book, inquired who the authority was. The student had not thought of this until now. Imagine his embarrassment when he saw that the title page bore the name of the professor whose oral declarations he had been disputing. The written word, however, he was willing to accept without question, even without caring who wrote it. The blame for this slavish attitude toward books rests upon ourselves as teachers who are not permitting our students to do their own thinking even in the sciences, and the results show that we are allowing attitudes to form and crystallize in the student's mind which are a handicap to his meeting and solving the problems of his life. It is little wonder that the masses are propaganda ridden.

The Laboratory Method. This expression as a method is not definable in a few words. It is used in most cases to mean that each student or pair of students is provided with specimens, or a work guide, and some sort of equipment for making dissections or studying materials by classification or otherwise. In some schools a double class period is provided twice a week for this kind of study while single periods for recitation are used on the other three days. Most teachers look upon the provision of laboratory work as a great advantage. Perhaps this is because there is more likely to be a greater amount of physical equipment for classes that have a laboratory than for those which are arranged to meet one period per day. There are distinct advantages inherent in the laboratory method even when applied to single periods and in rooms not designed primarily as laboratories. Some of the methods and provisions of the laboratory are useful tools of science in any event.

1. It usually implies learning by doing.
2. The student handles materials.
3. He learns to follow directions carefully.
4. He performs experiments, records observations and results, summarizes data, and draws conclusions.
5. He learns to handle apparatus and does much thinking for himself, if the course is properly developed.

On the other hand, its objectionable features, especially in general biology, are somewhat as follows:

1. It is more expensive if separate equipment is provided.
2. It is difficult to schedule if double periods are provided.
3. It is much more wasteful of time because students are unskilled workers.
4. There is some evidence that students of the junior high school age learn more readily from demonstrations than by doing.
5. There is no guarantee that the student will learn to solve problems or think scientifically in the laboratory any more than in another class.
6. Skill in the usual technic of the laboratory is of questionable value as objectives for the great majority of students who will have little use for them later.

Whether the advantages outweigh the disadvantages is still a highly debatable question. The fact is that for the more elementary sciences, such as general science and biology, the laboratory has been mostly abandoned, while for botany, zoology, and physiology it has been mostly retained. There is a difference between the use of a formal laboratory period as a method and the use of certain laboratory methods in connection with problems, projects, and demonstrations. When used in this latter sense, it is of recognized value and should never be dispensed with.

The Demonstration-Discussion Method. The demonstration method of teaching is self-explanatory. It is designed for two purposes. First, to provide a means of making clear certain parts of the subject matter by objectifying it, somewhat after the fashion of the laboratory, and second, to do the above with as much economy as possible. It can be used in a great number of ways. As a method it was designed originally to take the place of the laboratory method by having the equipment and materials centered on the instructor's desk where all work of a laboratory character was performed while the class observed from their seats. The use of the demonstration is an old device, but its adoption as the principal technic for elementary science is much more recent. Like all other methods, it has its advantages and disadvantages. Among its advantages we may note the following:

1. It is about the least expensive method of utilizing laboratory activities.
2. It is timesaving.
3. All students see the same operation and technic.
4. It is more efficient since the teacher is, supposedly, more competent than most students.
5. The teacher explains each step, thus ensuring that each pupil sees and interprets all the work in the same manner.

Likewise the method, as usually employed, has its disadvantages. Some of these disadvantages have been considered sufficient to bar its continuance, but it is a widely used method nevertheless.

1. It may deprive the student of many of the advantages of the laboratory method, such as handling of the materials and apparatus and the making of his own interpretations.
2. It assumes that all students see and hear all parts of demonstrations equally well, but this does not necessarily follow.
3. It is subject to misuse in two important ways. The teacher may slight the work at times because of uncertainty due to lack of familiarity, and the teacher tends to exclude student activity.

In general the demonstration method when combined with a well-directed discussion is a rather successful teaching technic. It can be modified by allowing limited student participation and by problem solving at times. It fits well the regular method of uniform class procedure for all students but does not permit of very wide individualization. If widely individualized and modified, it approaches a method usually called the problem, or project, method.

The Problem-Project Method. The word "project" has been so widely and diversely employed in education that its meaning has grown correspondingly vague. Like the word "unit," it has been applied to almost any sort of division of subject matter without regard to its organization or treatment. A project is really an extended problem or series of related problems that are the outgrowth of the student's own interests and endeavors at problem solving. For example, let us suppose that during a study of heredity a student discovers that albino corn seedlings have some green spots developing upon the white blades. His interest is aroused, and examining them more carefully he discovers that these spots can be rubbed off but will return in a few days. He uses a microscope and finds them to be a growth of mold. Recalling a similar growth in the tumbler which he used in watering the plants, he seeks for a method which would prevent the mold from attacking the plants. This leads to a study of sterile technics and a study of fungi and the plant diseases caused by them. The original problems of rearing albino and green corn seedlings for heredity initiates a series of problems resulting in a project for this student on molds and plant diseases.

Some rather strong opposition has been raised against the use of the problem and project methods of teaching, much of which is based upon valid grounds.

1. This is the most difficult method for the teacher, requiring more planning and more effort of execution.

2. If properly operated it calls for somewhat more materials and equipment than the strictly demonstration method.

3. The amount of time consumed by the projects may be so great as to make it impossible to cover a wide variety of topics, thus resulting in an incomplete course.

4. It may result in a lack of proper coordination of subject matter when individualized, since students may be working upon problems or projects which may be parts of the general subject, but each student may miss the relationship between all the parts.

5. Difficulties of the method increase in proportion to the number of students in large classes and in proportion to the number of classes per day which the teacher must have.

In spite of these objections it offers advantages not inherent in most other methods. Many of its advantages consist in overcoming its disadvantages, and those who use it are notably in favor of the method whenever it is possible to use it. They point to the following merits:

1. Though it is the most difficult method for the teacher, requiring more effort and planning, the lack of this effort is one of the reasons for much of the mediocre teaching that is done. The results of the method, when it is properly executed, more than compensate for the extra work that is required.

2. The necessity for more materials and equipment is generally an excuse rather than a reason for not using the method. The problems and experiments can be so devised that they will require nothing that cannot be had at little or no expense. The providing of these materials might well become a part of the student's responsibility. Part Two of this book, especially Chaps. 12 and 13, are designed to assist the teacher in meeting these problems.

3. As to economy of time, there is much doubt as to whether time well spent upon less subject matter might not be worth more to the student than the same time spent in hurrying over more subject matter.

4. The lack of coordination which sometimes is the result of individual work is little more than the result of poor planning and lax execution upon the part of the teacher.

5. In no other method is there equal provision for those essential factors demanded by our objectives. The solving of problems is essential to the training in scientific thinking and the following of projects is a vital part of the production of those attitudes which should be the outgrowth of science teaching. Proper planning will provide for group or even class participation as a means of diminishing the problem of numbers of students and numbers of classes that must be taught and will still make possible a sufficient amount of independent work to provide for the necessary individualization.

No one method should exclude the valuable elements of other methods. The teacher should always plan the procedure in such a fashion as to embody those technics which are best suited to the accomplishment of the objectives for that phase of the course. The problem-project method permits of the utilization of most of the better features of other methods besides adding those vital factors of problem solving plus student interest. It matters little whether separate laboratory periods are provided or whether classwork is limited to single periods. If time, equipment, and numbers of students and classes permit, a larger amount of individual or small group work may be undertaken profitably. If larger numbers must limit the amount of individual work, this fact does not limit the method. Each demonstration may become a problem, and the major subject units might well be handled as a class project, in which case the smaller problems are merely steps in its completion. The examples given in Chap. 2 furnish a satisfactory illustration of how this method may be used both as a class project and for individual problems.

DEMONSTRATIONS AS PROBLEMS

There are teachers of science who prefer to have their students memorize statements from assigned pages in a book or answer a list of questions based upon the text rather than have them see or give demonstrations, solve problems, or work out projects. It is so much easier to look at a poor illustration in a book than to look for materials to objectify the facts. It is so much easier to have a student memorize a definition than to train him to use learned facts in such a manner as to be able to derive his own definition or to induce a principle and use it in problem-solving. In questioning it is easier to say "Where is this?" "What was that?" or "Define the following" than to present a problematic situation the solving of which demands a knowledge of the facts plus their intelligent application and their arrangement in cause-and-effect relationship.

Many widely used textbooks are written as compendiums of biological information rather than as educational instruments. This is very well if the book does not determine the method of procedure but is merely a source book. For example, let us suppose that we turn to the chapter in such a book dealing with the cellular structure of organisms. In most instances one finds that the first paragraph deals with a definition of a cell and a statement of the cell theory. Facts establishing the proof of these statements follow, and the discussion finally ends with suggested demonstrations and review questions. How often does the teacher, following the authority of the text or precedent of past experience, require the student to remember the substance of the book in its original sequence and test for and measure the "learning" on this basis? If the function of the teacher and text is to impart information only, this is at least tolerable. But if education is more than this memorizing, then the method becomes little less than vicious. Questions, especially problematic questions, belong at the beginning of a study. The student should be made to feel that there is an interesting problem ahead, the solving of which is a fascinating procedure as well as a worthy accomplishment.

Demonstrations should not be passive illustrations like still pictures in a book to be viewed as evidence of the written statements but should be living problems, the understanding and solving of which will demand the acquisition of certain facts, the discovery of causes and effects, and the induction and application of principles. Demonstrations are most frequently given to a class as an illustration of something already learned. This may be a legitimate usage, but it is one of the less important. A demonstration should do much more than this. It should appear to the student as a challenge to his skill in the use of what he may have learned already or as a stimulus in his search for new knowledge. It should give meaning to the effort that he is to put forth, causing him to feel that he is working for the solution of something that he may achieve. This is important, especially with young students. Thus the study of the cellular structure of organisms should begin with demonstrations or examinations of materials from various sources followed by readings and discussions until the student from his own experimentation and study is able to formulate for himself a statement of the "cell theory" and to describe clearly in his own words the chief characteristics of cells. The student should not be robbed of the privilege of discovering for himself these very fundamental concepts of biology. A definition memorized from a book may sound as good as, or better than, one which he may create for himself and may count as high or higher on a testing sheet, but there is a difference in the meaning, a difference in appreciation, and a difference in training values which usually remain unmeasured in our evaluation programs.

For the purpose of showing the use of demonstrations as problems instead of as illustrations, let us suppose that a class is studying the basic functional phenomena of living things. Eventually something is to be learned of the manner in which organisms meet the problems of their relation to their environment. The traditional procedure would be to state that some of these basic functions are movement, digestion, photosynthesis, respiration, reproduction, and so on, and to have the student learn many facts concerning each of these. He might be supplied with a few illustrations to assist in visualizing the facts. To summarize the ecological relationships, a balanced aquarium might be presented at the end. In short, it would amount to learning what plants and animals do and how they get along in relation to their environment.

Now let us consider how the same subjects might be covered and the same facts learned from the standpoint of solving problems and reasoning with the facts. The teacher begins with the assembling of an aquarium. A small fish is placed in a glass jar of water on the teacher's desk, or on each student desk if possible. Nothing but fish and water are in the jar. What problems are presented by such a situation? The class can suggest most of them. Some will insist upon food for the fish. Others will suggest changing the water frequently. A discussion of this will bring out facts showing that lack of oxygen may be of more immediate importance than lack of food and that wastes will accumulate which must be disposed of. Ways of solving each of these problems of the fish will necessitate a knowledge of the structures involved in the functions. To these will be added the questions of quantities, supplies, and demands. If a so-called balance is reached in the aquarium, the addition of a few more fish upsets it, renewing all the previous problems plus the possibilities of reproduction and cannibalism.

When teachers say that the average student will not see all such problems or appreciate them, it is usually because the student has not been given the opportunity to look for problems of his own accord. As a test of this point, a ninth-grade student who had not had a course in biology and very little science of any kind was asked the following question: Suppose that you captured a live toad and that you wished to keep it alive for some time. What problems would you have to solve in order to make a satisfactory home for your toad? Taking a sheet of paper from his notebook, the boy sat down and wrote the following:

Problems for Keeping One Toad

1. What kind and amount of food does a toad eat?
2. What kind of climate does a toad live in?
3. What kind of soil does a toad live on?
4. How much water should be kept with a toad?
5. Should a toad be kept in the light or in the dark?
6. What material should a toad cage be made of?
7. Should the water be fresh or stagnant?
8. How much space should be allowed for one toad?

When the problem was changed from keeping one toad to keeping several toads, he immediately saw that all the above questions would have to be reconsidered, and a few questions caused him to note that reproduction might follow if there were several toads of opposite sexes. Without being asked to do so, he added the diagram of the cage he would make.

If there are added to any such experiment other animals and plants, new problems arise immediately such as scavenging, preying, and possibly parasitism. A complex society arises, and each individual must make many more adjustments than in the earlier and simpler type of society. There are many questions concerning ecology and conservation to learn about. Man's own social problems can readily be shown to consist of some of these general and fundamental biological problems of nature. Thus the aquarium or vivarium ceases to be merely an ornament for the classroom or an illustration of facts learned from a text and becomes a ready source of vital problems of all forms of life, including those which the student must himself encounter.

PROBLEMS

1. Choose a chapter from a high school biology and outline it briefly. For each part of the outline show how you would pursue it in class if you were using a method adapted to student laboratory work. Plan your work with Problems 2 and 3 so that the same chapter will be used in each problem.

2. Choose a chapter (same chapter as used in Problem 1) from a high school biology and outline it briefly. Show how you would teach it in a class if your method were designed primarily to follow the demonstration-discussion method.

3. Choose a chapter (same chapter as used in Problems 1 and 2) from a high school biology. Show how you would teach this chapter in a high school class if your method is primarily problem-project.

4. An understanding of the physical phenomenon of diffusion is fundamental throughout biology. Assume that you are presenting a unit on this subject to a high school class. Outline your procedure in such a way as to present the basic factual information followed by demonstrations which illustrate these facts. Then make another outline covering the same ground by presenting the demonstrations as problems from the solution of which the class will acquire the needed facts and principles. In Chap. 17 you will find ample suggestions for demonstrating diffusion which may be used in your outline. If time is permitted in your methods class, present your key demonstration along with your discussion.

5. Make a list of the topics that you might expect to include in a study of circulation for a high school class in physiology or biology and arrange these in such a manner as to give all the desired factual information. Include such demonstrations as you might select to illustrate these facts. Now show how you would modify your presentation if your aim was to use the demonstrations as problems instead of illustrations (see Chap. 18).

6. Following the directions in Problem 5, select the topic "photosynthesis" (see Chap. 15).

7. Following the directions in Problem 5, select the topic "reproduction in seed plants" (see Chap. 22).

8. Following the directions in Problem 5, select the topic "foods and digestion" (see Chap. 16).

REFERENCES

1. Anderson, K. E., et al.: "Pilot Study of Various Methods of Teaching Biology," *Sci. Educ.*, **35**:295–298, December, 1951.

2. Bayles, E. E.: *Theory and Practice of Teaching*, Harper & Brothers, New York, 1950.

3. Curtis, F. D.: *A Second Digest of Investigations in the Teaching of Science,* P. Blakiston's Sons & Company, Philadelphia, 1931.

4. Dewey, Evelyn: *The Dalton Laboratory Plan*, E. P. Dutton & Co., Inc., New York, 1922.

5. Dewey, J.: "Method in Science Teaching," *Sci. Educ.*, **29**:119–123, April–May, 1945.

6. Dixon, C. L.: "Biology—A Laboratory Science," *Ohio School*, **22**:210, May, 1944.

7. Eavey, C. B.: *Art of Effective Teaching*, Zondervan Publishing House, Grand Rapids, Mich., 1953.

8. Highet, G. A.: *Art of Teaching*, Alfred A. Knopf, Inc., New York, 1950. Teaching methods for professional teachers.

9. Lyman, R. L.: "Individualization in the Isaac E. Young Junior High School, New Rochelle, N.Y.," *School Rev.*, **39**:257–271, 1931.

10. McEwan, B. A.: "Let's Put Life into Life Science," *Am. Biol. Teacher,* **12**:156–158, November, 1950.

11. Packard, C. E.: "What Biological Facts Interest High School Sophomores," *Am. Biol. Teacher*, vol. 9, no. 2, November, 1946.

12. Reid, C.: "Instructional Materials and Problem-centered Teaching," *Teachers Coll. Record,* vol. 52, no. 1, October, 1950.

13. Simmons, R. H.: "Vitalizing Biology with a Live Animal Project," *Am. Biol. Teacher*, **17**:262–265, December, 1955.

14. Stafford, W. A.: "Textbook versus Supplemental Material in Teaching Biology," *School Sci. and Math.*, **52**:737–742, December, 1952.

15. Weaver, R. L.: "Improvement of Biology Teaching," *School Sci. and Math.*, **56**:257–263, April, 1956.

16. Wheeler, R. E.: "Living Biology," *Sci. Teacher,* **24**:62–66, March, 1957.

CHAPTER 5

⋯◦⊰ Make a Teaching Plan ⊱◦⋯

One of the most important factors of good teaching, and it is especially important for the beginner, is careful planning. After the more general planning of the course, as discussed in Chaps. 3 and 4, the teacher is confronted with the necessity of planning the lessons. The term "lesson" has a variety of meanings. To many teachers and students it suggests the work to be covered in a single day or class period. To others it means the amount of work assigned at one time and may include several periods. Again it may be used as synonymous with the "unit" of subject matter. In general it denotes a unified amount of material somewhat less extensive than that included in the Morrison unit. It is always advisable that the course be laid out in considerable detail. This in no wise implies that such a plan be adhered to rigidly nor that there is not left ample room for student choice, individual differences, and spontaneity. It does imply that the planner has made proper preparation in deciding upon objectives, choosing topics, and devising methods and materials for the term's work, and it tends to prevent what otherwise so often happens, the aimless wandering through unrelated topics and problems. When this wandering has occurred with no plan in the mind of either the teacher or student, attempts at coordination are often futile. Some of the reactions against formalized class procedure have had such dire results. In these cases the student may acquire considerable information and gain practice in problem solving, but lack the ability to coordinate and make generalizations by virtue of the isolated character of the learned facts. Teachers with large experience and natural versatility may deviate more freely from a formal plan, but the beginner had best plan diligently and depend upon changing the plan whenever advisable rather than upon improvising as the work proceeds.

SHOULD THE PLAN BE MADE BY DAYS?

Should the plan be a daily plan, a topic plan, or a unit plan? In so far as the divisions of the course are concerned it makes but little difference, but in its development and in the point of view that it gives the planner it may be important. The primary question is: Where should the plan begin? If the course has been determined as to content and sequence, it should be relatively easy to divide this entire course into its major areas of investigation for the students. Each of these major areas should have its special objectives and should bear its peculiar relationship to each of the other areas. Likewise it will be composed of a group of smaller divisions of subject matter which are intimately interrelated. Each of these smaller divisions will also have its component parts, such as projects, problems, or major questions, the completion of which is an important step or contribution to the understanding of the division to which it belongs.

The extent to which a plan is subdivided depends upon the individual making the plan, the amount of subject matter which it includes, and the methods to be employed in its administration. In all cases there is a time allotment which has to be reckoned with. Each part of a plan has to be looked at from the point of view of the time necessary for its proper development and the time available because of the limitations of the schedule. Whether the organization of the plan is eventually in the form of days is a matter of individual choice, but in any event some attention must be paid to the actual number of days in order that demonstrations, experiments, reports, and the materials which they require may be provided when needed and properly used. To begin a complete plan by producing a large number of daily plans and later attempting to weave these together into a course would, in most cases, be an undesirable method. It would not permit of a correct balance or of a sufficiently coordinated overview in the teacher's mind. To plan by starting with the idea of the whole and work backward into the subdivisions is generally a better method. It is difficult to understand how one could correctly evaluate each of the 180 daily parts of a 9-month plan until he had viewed it in its entirety.

The parts of a plan for a course bear the same relationship to each other as do the items of a well-formed outline. This should make it possible to arrange it in the form of an outline. Teachers often do this and stop there, calling the outline a "plan." It should be obvious, however, that an outline is not a plan unless it includes the objectives, materials, methods, and devices employed in finishing the classroom procedure. To have all these thought out beforehand and provided for is the most valuable part of planning. It is not unusual for a teacher to come to a point in an outline which involves the use of young plants or microorganisms and then to realize that it takes 8 days to grow the seedlings and 2 weeks to develop a hay infusion. Hence a plan should not be merely a list of topics to be covered but should include the objectives, mode of attack, materials and time of preparation, demonstrations, problems, key questions, and evaluation technics that are to be employed. All these must be considered in relation to the entire course and in relation to the time available.

TYPES OF PLANS

If your plan has in it all the above elements, the particular form into which it is arranged should be a matter of convenience. Some persons find it easier to visualize their plan if it is laid out in parallel columns or blocked off with lines. One teacher using such a method prepared a plan like the one given below. She entered her classroom one morning with a small bundle which appeared to be her lunch. This she laid upon her table and began untying it. From the package she took a ham sandwich, a small bottle of milk, a small jar of preserves, an apple, a bottle of vinegar, some cheese, and a cake of baker's yeast. Assuming an attitude of being unaware of the attention of the class, she slowly examined each article as it was removed from the package, even looking inside the sandwich so as to expose the ham. Lying upon her table was the following plan.

Unit III. Ecology: The Relationship of Organisms to Their Environment

Part IV. Microorganisms in Industry, Health, and Disease

Objectives. (1) A contribution to the understanding of the principle of ecology. (2) An understanding of the culture and control of microorganisms. (3) An appreciation of the problems arising out of the relations between microorganisms and man's own health and activities.

A. Subject matter	B. Materials	C. Methods
1. Introduction by questions and discussion from the materials and from the experiences of the class.	1. Lunch brought by teacher: ham sandwich, milk, apple, preserves, vinegar, yeast.	1. Act of eating and questions.
2. The spoiling of foods: Souring of milk. Spoiling of meat, fruits, vegetables. Molding of bread.	2. Same as for 1.	2. Discussion in preparation for the experiments.
3. Methods of preservation: Refrigeration. Cooking and canning. Drying and chemicals. Antibiotics.	3. Cafeteria refrigerator. Self-sealing jars. Benzoate of soda, sugar, salt, vinegar. Aureomycin, Terramycin, streptomycin.	3. Presentation as problems on ways of preserving. Student experimentation for class discussion later.
4. Food and beverage making: Bread making. Sauerkraut making. Vinegar, malt beer, and root beer making.	4. Yeast, sauerkraut, cheese, vinegar, glass tubing, rubber tubing, test tubes or bottles, sugar or fruit juice, limewater.	4. Student experimentation, class discussion, teacher demonstration. Isolation of some microorganisms. Assignment of reports for 6.
5. Discussion and microscope work with the microorganisms involved in preceding experiments.	5. Microscopes, cultures made in previous experiments. Simple microtechnic apparatus.	5. Class group and individual work.
6. Diseases: Pimples, boils, athlete's foot, colds, "flu," tuberculosis, pox, typhoid, diphtheria, hydrophobia, etc. Epidemics.	6. Pictures, special microscope slides, specimens, lantern.	6. Cultures in broth, agar, and potato of organisms from pimples, infections, nose, mouth, etc., for later examination. Special reports.
7. Causes of diseases: Bacteria, molds, protozoa, viruses.	7. Cultures of bacteria, molds, and protozoa made by class and specially prepared slides.	7. Demonstrations, examination of cultures, and individual and class discussion.
8. Preventions and cures: Sterilization, drugs, vac-	8. Cultures of bacteria made in class. Com-	8. Preparation of tests of antiseptics on cultures.

A. SUBJECT MATTER	B. MATERIALS	C. METHODS
cines, toxins and anti-toxins, quarantine and isolation. Elimination of sources and carriers. Immunity and resistance. Study of types of communities and neighborhoods.	mon antiseptics: Lister-ine, Pepsodent antisep-tic, bichloride of mer-cury, iodine, Lysol, phenol, antibiotics. Vac-cine tubes. Mosquitoes, flies, bed-bugs, ticks.	Reports of observa-tions, trips, and read-ings.

D. GROUP AND INDIVIDUAL PROBLEMS AND PROJECTS.

1. Fermentation and its products, a summary.
2. Life-history study of a mold culture with the preservation of spores for future cultures.
3. Special methods of preparing culture media.
4. Visits to type neighborhoods, garbage- and sewage-disposal plants, waterworks, packing house, cold-storage plant. Special group reports on each.
5. Lives of several great scientists working in the field.
6. Special display of posters, booklets, clippings of advertisements of antiseptics, cures and treatments of infections and germ diseases.

E. EVALUATION OF THE ENTIRE STUDY MADE IN PART IV.

1. Critical oral discussion of some of the reports made in class, especially the posters and booklets. (Grades given by teacher after class dismissal.) Two days.
2. Rapid factual quiz by teacher. Spelling-bee type.
3. Grading of most of the special reports.
4. Objective test on meaning of terms, recall of facts, ability to apply generalizations, problem solving.

This teacher felt that she should have her students devote approximately 15 class periods to the above amount of work. One can see that it would be difficult to cover the amount adequately in less time. It is a good, compact, rather complete plan which, because of its arrangement, can be followed easily by the teacher. It contains most of the criteria for a good plan listed above: objectives, mode of attack, materials, problems and demonstrations, and evaluation. Its condensed character, however, prevents a very complete presentation of its mode of attack and the details of its special methods which the teacher must have held in mind. One may note that it is essentially an outline and might be so written instead of in parallel columns. The outstanding feature of merit of this type of plan is that it relates, side by side, the subject matter with its own materials and something of the methods employed.

THE PSYCHOLOGICAL APPROACH

Many successful teachers, even though they have not analyzed their technics critically, are careful about the way in which they introduce each unit of subject matter and how each part is followed through. This is generally spoken of as the "approach." As students we all have experienced the situation where two instructors taught two different parts of the same course and we found that one part was interesting and stimulating while the other was not. In some cases the personality of the instructor was a dominant factor, but many times we probably remarked that it was the teacher's ability to get the subject across to us. This is the student's way of expressing approach. One teacher may do it with comparative ease while another may labor to do it passably well. In any case it should be given very careful attention and should constitute a definite part of the planning. In dealing with younger students particularly, and in fields where the subject content is new to the student, as in introductory courses, care should be exercised to make use of a psychological approach as far as possible. A logical approach may appeal to the teacher, but it is essential that this be translated psychologically for the student. Take for example the following illustration:

A student teacher in general biology was confronted with difficulties of organization and method. The teacher whose class he was teaching followed the text and workbook closely. The subject matter to be covered included the gross structures of plants such as roots, stems, leaves, flowers, the parts of flowers, seeds, and fruits. It was to be covered in the order given. The customary procedure with the class had been the assignment of the text followed the next day by oral questions upon the assignment and the answering of questions and labeling of diagrams in the workbook. Previous results seemed to show that the method obtained little response and aroused little interest on the part of the class. The student teacher realized that the approach of the text was purely a logical one and that past bad habits of attack would result in the pupils learning the names of the parts of a plant and the various parts of flowers, seeds, and fruits because they must be able to repeat them or to label diagrams with them. Many of these would be promptly forgotten. To avoid this the following steps were decided upon: First, he would not mention the text or workbook for the time being, but he would see that the same subject matter was covered by the class. Second, freed from this source of information, he would introduce living plant materials and make each student an investigator for himself. Third, he would start with some of the more obvious observations on these plants, and he would let the direction of the study follow psychologically in the direction which the class found necessary. A problematic question on his part now and then should add stimulus when needed.

The plan worked out much as he had formulated it. Instead of being given as assignment to be read in the text, each student was given a living bean plant and a living corn seedling. With these plants before him, he wrote down all that he knew about them. Such things as roots, stem, and leaves were already known, but there were structures for which his vocabulary was inadequate, such as seed coats, cotyledons, hypocotyl, and root hairs. Here was a distinct need for new terms and for the amount of reading that was necessary to provide this knowledge. A comparison between bean and corn plants brought out the likenesses and differences in leaf, stem, and root, which lead to an understanding of the monocotyledonous and dicotyledonous groups. These comparisons were traced backward into the embryo and seed which developed into a study of germination and food storage. Seeds suggested fruits and the origin of seeds and fruits from flowers. Whence followed a study of flower parts and types and of pollination. With the answering of each question a new problem was born, demanding further study for its solution. Each contained within itself the reason for further study by observation, experimentation, or reference to authorities. The acquisition of new knowledge was not only a necessity but a source of inspiration as well.

The order from plants to germination, from germination to seeds and fruits, from seeds and fruits to flower structures, and from flower structures to pollination seems to run in an illogical direction. Nevertheless it was entirely psychological. The reversal from the natural order did not confuse the student; he learned more facts, he made an interesting investigation, and above all he experienced a degree of understanding that was not possible by the previous method. The interest and response in the class were very gratifying to the student teacher.

A MODIFIED TEXTBOOK PLAN

After a little experience it should be possible for a teacher to plan a course that makes use of a textbook and library reference materials in such a manner that they become useful adjuncts but do not determine the content and mode of attack of the course. This is the most valuable use of textbooks. They should be used freely by the pupils but mostly as references. However, the beginning teacher often feels that a close reliance upon a text is the best method of establishing self-confidence and of ensuring a full-rounded content. The result is a text-dominated course. Once established, it is easier to repeat it than to modify it. Some textbooks are prepared especially to assist such teachers in following the book without becoming too formal. To this end many of these books have included such devices as previews, self-testing and re-testing and demonstrations and experiments. This has helped some teachers in getting away from the routined recitation method, but even such books cannot hope to suit a very wide range of conditions, and the teacher will find it desirable to develop his own methods. Again, such books are not always the ones selected as texts.

A Study of the Animal Groups

Part VI. The Mammals

Primary Objectives. (1) To gain a true concept of the nature of this group of animals and how it is related to the rest of the animal kingdom. (2) To appreciate the importance of this group of animals to man.

OUTLINE OF THE TEXT	METHOD TO BE FOLLOWED IN CLASS
	I. Introduction to the Unit.
	A. No previous reading or assignment.
	B. Presentation and examination of all demonstration material.
	C. Students trace many of the materials to their origin in mammals.

A Study of the Animal Groups (continued)

Par...... What a Mammal Is:
Covering of hair.
Mammary glands.
Diaphragm.
Warm blooded.

II. *D*. What are some of the peculiarities of the mammals from which these products came? List on board.
E. Which of these characteristics are found in no other vertebrates?
F. Are there other characters that make the mammals different from other vertebrates?
G. Special reference: Newman, "Vertebrate Zoology."

Par...... Mammals as Beasts of Burden:
Horse.
Ox.
Elephant.
Camel.
Llama.
Reindeer.
Dog.

III. Mammals as Beasts of Burden.
A. A cooperative project with fine arts, manual arts, social science, geography.
1. Man as the original "beast of burden."
2. Types of animals commonly used as beasts of burden, each studied and presented separately by class members.
3. Special demonstration of the exhibits prepared to accompany the studies.

Par...... Mammals as Sources of Food:
Hoofed mammals: cattle, pigs, sheep.
Others: bear, rabbit, seal, walrus, opossum.

IV. Mammals as Sources of Food:
A. Primitive hunting as an occupation. Report, demonstrations, talk by teacher.
B. Game animals. Modern hunting as sport.
C. Production, marketing, consumption of common domestic food mammals.
1. Trip to packing house, butcher, etc.

Par...... Mammals as Sources of Clothing:
Wool.
Leather.
Fur.

V. Mammals as Sources of Clothing:
A. How the pioneers used wool, skins, and fur.
B. Problem on the production of woolen products and their consumption.
C. Problem on the manufacture of leather.
D. Problem on the fur industry.

Par...... Mammals as Sources of Other Valuable Commercial Products:
Ivory, bone, glue, buttons, ornaments.

VI. Mammals as Sources of Other Valuable Commercial Products:
A. Project: The by-products of a dead horse. Written, oral, demonstrations.
B. Similar projects as suggested by class.

A Study of the Animal Groups (continued)

Par...... Mammals Injurious to Man:

Rats, mice: disease carriers.

Cats, as destroyers of birds.

Rabbits, as destroyers of farm products.

Lions, tigers, bears, wolves, as direct enemies of man.

Par...... The Highest Order of Mammals, Primates.

VII. Mammals Injurious to Man:
  A. Rat plagues and methods of control.
  B. Diseases transmitted by rodents:
    1. Plague. 2. Fever. 3. Tularemia.
  C. Rabbit plagues and control.
  D. Beebe (Jungle Books).
    Bonsel, "An Indian Journey." (Book Reviews)

VIII. The Highest Order of Mammals, Primates:
  A. Common mammal bones from different orders to bring out principles of classification. Class discussion.
  B. Primate characteristics; claws, hoof, nails, etc.
  C. Relation of man to other primates.
  D. Special study of mammalian reproduction.
    Sex and human reproduction.

IX. Review and Summary Worked Together:
  A. An outline of the study of mammals constructed in class by the students (teacher directed).
  B. Final outline mimeographed and given to each student.
  C. Extensive set of review questions suggested by class members used for study and discussion.

Review questions from the end of the text chapter.

X. Evaluation:
  A. Each student will work upon some problem, project, or special report.
  B. Each student held responsible for the contributions of every other student.
  C. An objective test, final.

If at the start the teacher does not feel like setting out boldly in his departure from the text, let him at least make a plan which is somewhat of a compromise, allowing him to inject methods and ideas of his own. One teacher using this method developed the plan shown on pages 50 and 52 which paralleled the outline of a chapter in the textbook but added a number of departures from the text and allowed much more class freedom than could have been had from formal assignment and recitation.

A TEXT-FREE PLAN

The above plan gave this teacher a much needed start in the process of breaking away from the strict adherence to a textbook as a determiner of the course. It will be seen that it offered a number of opportunities for bringing in outside materials, for securing individual and group endeavors at special problems, and for greatly intensifying the interest and activity of the class. The teacher himself profited immeasurably in his technic and sense of independence, as will be seen from what followed. One year later this same teacher prepared a revision of his plan which freed him and his class almost entirely from the text and resulted in a vastly improved method. Each step in the new procedure was represented by a key question which, in most cases, was of a rather general and problematic nature. The manner in which the plan was arranged permitted its adjustment to a variable time scale. It was designed for a class in general biology of tenth-grade level and average abilities. The study came late in the course and had been preceded by the study of other groups of vertebrates such as fish, amphibia, reptiles, and birds. His plan for this new attack is represented in the outline which follows.

A Study of the Animal Groups

Part VI. The Mammals

Objectives. (1) To make the student aware of the great variety of ways in which mammals are directly related to man in his health and everyday life. (2) To demonstrate the many ways in which mammals are of importance to man in his industries and activities. (3) To increase the student's store of factual knowledge concerning this group. (4) To produce, through logical thinking and study, attitudes which will be the outgrowth of the first three objectives.

Procedure. The approach is to be largely psychological; hence, the first few questions are in the nature of recall and review of personal experiences in order to begin with what the student already knows. The later questions and statements require study, the making of collections, displays or demonstrations, or individual and class projects.

1. What are the names of the animal groups that we have studied so far? (A list of these as given by the class is made on the blackboard by the teacher.)

2. How many of you have kept as pets some animals that are members of these groups? (Fish, turtle, frogs, birds are possibilities. These are to be recorded on blackboard. Discussion.)

3. What other kind of pets have you had that cannot be classified in any of these groups? (Cats, dogs, rabbits, guinea pigs, mice, squirrels, ponies, goats, lambs, etc. These should be made into a separate list for reference. Very unusual ones in Questions 2 or 3 may be the subject of reports or story telling at the time or later on.)

4. If the pets listed in Question 3 do not belong to any of the groups of animals studied so far, what kind of animals are they? (The name "mammal" may or may not be used here. The important thing is that the class recognize that this is a distinct group.)

5. What other common animals are members of this group? (This will bring out most of the domestic mammals and many wild ones.)

6. Besides being pets, in what other ways are these animals useful to man? (A large list of these uses will probably appear and should be grouped under such headings as foods, clothing, workers, by-products.)

7. Assignment. Each student is to make an inventory of his own home and prepare a list of all materials that he can find that are of mammal origin. (Next class period is oral. List made on blackboard. Samples of these materials brought by class for an exhibit.)

8. The display and discussion will consume at least one full period. The materials are to be correlated with the particular animal or part of the animal from which it comes.

9. Teacher to furnish a few very unusual samples to stimulate interest. (Glue, ivory, fertilizer, chick food with bone or blood meal.)

10. What other mammals besides those already mentioned could be used as sources of these products? (Milk products, for example, may be obtained from goats, sheep, mares, llamas, reindeer, etc., as well as from cows. This study should be complete.)

11. Could any other animal, besides mammals, supply such products as hair, wool, fur, bristles, milk products, horn and hoof products? (The answer being "no" emphasizes these as mammalian characteristics.)

12. Could any other animal, besides mammals, supply any other of the products mentioned? (Meat, leather, bone products, blood products, etc., could be obtained from many vertebrates other than mammals. These relate the mammals to all vertebrates completing the idea of their classification.)

13. In what other ways are the mammals different from other vertebrates and in what other ways are they similar? (Any amount of enlargement can be made upon the idea of classification.)

14. Have you ever reared more than one generation of your pets? If so, how are the young produced? (By hatching and by being born. This introduces the study of reproduction, the peculiarities of mammalian reproduction, and human reproduction.)

Suggestions for Enlargement

1. Reports upon several major industries based upon mammals and their products.
2. Natural history, distribution, and food habits of unusual forms.
3. Origin and evolution of mammals, as horse, elephant, etc.
4. Original stories about mammals, by students. (Cooperation with English.)
5. Demonstration of living small mammals for observation and discussion.
6. Stuffing of skins or preparation of skeletons.
7. Combinations with fine arts for drawings, paintings, and models of mammals.
8. Special trips to packing houses, dairies, zoos, or museums.

Readings. Special assignments and chosen library references.

We have noted that the first paragraph of the text gave the student the outstanding peculiarities of mammals. If the teaching were to do no more than to impart factual information, this would be very well, but if it is to allow the student to discover through his study *what* a mammal is, then he should be able at the end of his study to formulate his own definition. The text continues with facts about the uses of mammals and their products and ends with a list of review questions, all of which, when followed logically, leaves the student with little choice other than to learn the book statements for the sake of reciting them later if the occasion arises. In the later plan the teacher utilized the fact that the part on mammals comes late in the course, after the study of the other groups of vertebrates, by using a review to introduce the new topic. Thus, the whole class has freshly in mind the recently studied groups of vertebrates, and these are listed on the blackboard for all to see. The question about common pets that are members of these groups is asked which relates the subject to the experiences of the class.

Fish, birds, tadpoles, frogs, toads, and snakes are interesting pets but are not mammals. In the next key question the teacher introduces the new group of animals by tying it into the old. "What pets have you had which could not be placed in any of these groups?" Dogs, cats, rabbits, mice, etc., are listed separately. They are different. The term "mammal" might be introduced but its meaning is not yet apparent. The question "What other well-known animals belong to the same group as this last list of pets?" enlarges the scope.

The next question, "How are some of these animals of use to man other than as pets?" is intended to introduce one of the main objectives, that of the relation of mammals to man. Their knowledge on this point is classified by placing the information under separate heads, such as food, workers, by-products, etc. This separation is made definitely useful later. Note that up to this point there has been no assignment for reading and the whole procedure has been one of drawing upon the student's knowledge and experiences and of organizing these for further use. Here the first assignment is made which stimulates the class to further individual participation. Each pupil makes an inventory of his home and brings to class a list and some samples of many materials of mammal origin. After the lists and display are classified as to milk and milk products, products of hair and wool, products of horn and hoof, the next question is brought forth: "What other mammals besides those mentioned could furnish these same products?" The answers to this are of such a character as greatly to enlarge the factual knowledge of the class as well as to stimulate interest. It should be followed closely by the question, "What other animals besides mammals could furnish these products?" This is a very important question pedagogically since the student draws fully upon his past knowledge as well as upon what he recently has learned about mammals. Since no animals except mammals could furnish these products, the student has derived the chief characteristics of the mammalian group without being told that they are such, as is done in the very first paragraph of the text.

When he has answered the next question, "What other animals could furnish such products as meat, bone products, leather, blood products, etc.?" he has arrived at the rest of the information that is necessary to complete his understanding of classification. The last two questions had led the student to see that mammals differ from all other vertebrates in a few very fundamental respects and that they are much like other vertebrates in many other respects. This is the essence of taxonomy. It is decidedly better for him to have deduced it for himself than to have been told the facts at the beginning. And there has been no tedious memorizing of a scheme of classification for the mere sake of knowing it. A study of reproduction of mammals could logically follow if it is not placed elsewhere.

In this approach it may be seen that each step leads to the next by arousing a question or a feeling of need to go farther. The desired facts are all covered, the interest is maintained, reading is done as an incidental part of a particular problem and for that problem, and there is every opportunity for variety of learning, individual and group participation, and a considerable amount of coordination and deductive and inductive thinking are required.

THE ASSIGNMENT

In the early American public school the teacher was a taskmaster. His principal duty was to set tasks for the students and then to see that they were done. These tasks were the assignments. Later the assignment was retained but consisted largely of solving problems and reading in textbooks. These older notions of the assignment are slowly passing away, and the modern assignment has become a part of the motivation of the classwork.

Many writers have strenuously opposed the misuses of the assignment as it is often practiced. First among these is the assigning of pages from the text to be read and remembered for the recitation. It is so easy for the teacher to make such an assignment in less than a minute. If done at the end of the class period, it is likely to be neglected until the bell has sounded for dismissal. The student's attention is lax at this time, there is confusion and noise, and books are being closed and put away. The feeling of responsibility has faded. Under such conditions the teacher attempts to command attention by speaking loudly and hurriedly, which is more likely to augment the confusion than to dispel it. The alternative that suggests itself is to make the assignment a definitely planned part of the day's program and possibly give it a place at the beginning of the period. This has an obvious advantage but also has the disadvantage of formalizing the assignment and of causing it to be out of place psychologically. The position of the assignment has been juggled about in a rather vain effort to establish a proper fixed place for it. There were, and still are, those who strongly urge that at least half of each class period be devoted to the assignment and the other half to supervised study or recitation. Without entering into further discussion as to the merits of these suggestions, it will be seen that they are based upon a formalized type of class procedure. As long as the assignment is a matter of problems, pages in the text or special report, it may be done in this formalized manner. As to where they occur and when they are given, there need be no set rule. Let them be clear, definite, and within the abilities of the students.

The newer practices of teaching by large subject-matter units has done much to minimize the daily assignment and calls for a large previewing of the unit and for the combining of the general assignment with the introduction. This was most successfully carried out by one student teacher who exhibited unusual skill for one without experience. He would end one unit of subject matter with a quick summarizing review of all the principal points. He would then continue without interruption into the main topics of the next unit, contributing some points of special interest and propounding problems and questions which attracted the attention and aroused the curiosity of the class but which they were, for the most part, unable to solve. When the interest was sufficiently aroused, this teacher would announce that all these interests and many more would be satisfied by the work which would be undertaken during the next week or so of school. Thus his initial assignment was a period of stimulation and problem setting. Subsequently many individual assignments were necessary, but these were given as needed.

In lesson plans such as that on mammals given above, there are no very special assignments called for until several days after the study has been initiated. There arise throughout this part of the unit numerous places where problems, experiments, demonstrations, and readings call for special assignment or, one might almost say, assign themselves. This is the ideal type of assignment when the student feels the necessity for doing some part of the work for a definite reason. To solve this problem he must actually choose an assignment himself, sometimes with the help and encouragement of the teacher. In Chap. 2 is an illustration of how a biology teacher assigned a large unit of work by merely placing a microcosm in the classroom and allowing the problems and questions which it elicited to constitute the groundwork of the study which followed. In these cases the assignment and the motivation are self-initiated and self-sustained, and the teacher becomes a counselor, guide, and source of inspiration instead of a taskmaster.

When high school students are habituated to the use of a single text and not accustomed to the use of a number of reference sources, they are unable to take an assignment that is not specific down to the exact pages and to work it out. This results in many college freshmen being lost when it comes to their doing reference work of a general character. They seem to be unaware of the fact that books generally have an index or in some cases a good table of contents. They should be trained to do reference work from a number of sources and to interpret the meaning of words and their synonyms. They learn this quickly when it is demanded, but they also quickly become accustomed to looking for specified pages when this is done for them, and they will look no further. There is no reason why high school and college students should not be able to do a good job of reference work for themselves, and to do this for them at all times is a sure means of handicapping them for later work which they should be able to do readily for themselves. Some assignments may require this definite form of page reference, but a properly trained student will be able to do it for himself when the occasion demands.

PROBLEMS

1. The preparation of a biology course (a class project). This project is designed to include an entire methods class or at least 10 members, if the class is large. It should not be started until the subjects of *objectives, organization of courses,* and *planning* have been thoroughly covered. *Testing* may be taken up while the project is under way. In colleges where but one semester (or quarter) is devoted to methods in biology, the project should be started not later than the middle of the term. The following steps explain the plan:
   a. Preliminary assignment. Each member of the class is to examine several biology texts and then prepare a list of the subject matter which he thinks should be included in a course of this level.
   b. First class discussion. The entire class agrees jointly upon a list of topics and their sequence.
   c. Project assignment. Each student (or two or more working together) should be responsible for preparing a detailed plan for the teaching of one of these subject-matter units. The plans should be fairly uniform, indicating clearly (1) the details of subject matter, (2) special assignments, (3) materials, (4) demonstrations, (5) problems and projects, and, finally (6) a self-test and a teacher's test.

d. Second class discussion. Each completed teaching plan should be presented in class for final suggestions and revised accordingly.

e. Final product. It should be placed upon sheets of uniform size, bound in a temporary binder, and kept in the library for all to examine. If facilities are available it could be mimeographed or hectographed and each member of the class given a copy.

2. Prepare an explanation of what is meant by a Morrison unit. Illustrate your explanation by selecting subject matter from a botany or zoology text and constructing it into an outline of such a unit. Present this to the methods class for discussion.

3. Using the first plan outlined in this chapter as a model, select a different topic and construct a detailed plan giving all the plan elements suggested, estimating the time that it should consume when used.

4. In Part Two, Chap. 11, is a suggestion for studying the life of a limited area of land. Take the suggestions given in the project and build a plan for teaching it. In doing this select an area near your school and map it for your plan.

5. In Part Two, Chap. 15, you will find an abundance of material for teaching the subject of photosynthesis. Make a detailed plan for teaching photosynthesis to an eleventh-grade class of botany. Choose several pertinent demonstrations, prepare them and present them together with your plan to the class in methods for their criticisms and discussion.

6. Take the topic "The transpiration of water in plants" (see Chap. 20) and develop a plan for teaching it in such a manner that the procedure is strongly psychological. Present your plan for class discussion, emphasizing its psychological aspects.

7. Take from a secondary school text in some biological subject any chapter which seems to you to be written in the logical style. Outline the chapter. Now prepare an outline of the same topics arranged psychologically.

8. Using the ideas of a modified text plan as given in this chapter, take a chapter from a biology textbook and work out a plan for teaching the same chapter with considerable modification, as was done in the example given.

9. Choose a unit of subject matter and prepare a method of assigning it to a biology class. Present your method for class discussion.

REFERENCES

1. Brandwein, P. F.: "Reorganizing Biology to Meet the Needs and Interests of Youth," *Sci. Teacher,* **13**:59–61, December, 1946; and **14**:22–23, February, 1947.

2. Cantor, N.: *Teaching-learning Process,* The Dryden Press, Inc., New York, 1953.

3. Curtis, F. D.: "Some Practical Suggestions for the Teaching of Biology," *School Sci. and Math.,* **51**:95–104, February, 1951.

4. Hollenbeck, E. I.: "Ecology at the Beginning of a High School Biology Course," *Am. Biol. Teacher,* **18**:156–158, April, 1956.

5. Hollenbeck, E. I., and E. N. Stevenson: *Selected Procedures in Teaching Biology,* Oregon State College, Corvallis, Ore., 1950.

6. Miller, J. V.: "Teacher-Pupil Planning for Biology," *Am. Biol. Teacher,* **12**:51–54, March, 1950.

7. Monroe, W. S.: "The Planning of Teaching," *Educ. Research Circ.* 31, *Bull.* 17, vol. 22, 1943.

8. Morrison, H. C.: *The Practice of Teaching in the Secondary School,* University of Chicago Press, Chicago, 1926.

9. Mort, P. R., and W. S. Vincent: *Modern Educational Practice: A Handbook for Teachers,* McGraw-Hill Book Company, Inc., New York, 1950.

10. Wells, H.: *Elementary Science Education,* McGraw-Hill Book Company, Inc., New York, 1951. Over-all approach; philosophy, methods of procedure, and suggested subject content.

CHAPTER 6

⸘ The Program Should Be Evaluated ⸘

While everyone who has gone to school is familiar with the words "test" and "examination," it is hoped that the term "evaluation" will carry a significance which will not become synonymous with these better known words. To test or examine means to try the student in order to discover to what extent he may have attained the standards set for him in the mind of his teacher. Evaluation is intended to do a great deal more than this. An evaluation program, which should be a part of all teaching procedures, will do three things in particular: (1) It will measure in every sense that tests and examinations are supposed to measure. (2) It will motivate, guide, and inspire the student in the pursuit of his studies. (3) It will teach him by disclosing to him his strength and weakness, by indicating clearly his degree of progress, by showing him where emphasis needs to be placed, by training him in ways of obtaining more knowledge, and by giving him practice in its application to life situations.

The making up and grading of the ordinary test, in the form of a list of questions, is relatively simple, but the establishing of an evaluation program is decidedly more complex. While at the start it is more difficult for the uninitiated, the results are proportionately significant and well worth the additional effort. We are at present in the early stages of what amounts to an educational revolution, and it behooves every beginning teacher as well as those of experience to keep in touch with all progress in this direction, not because it is another newfangled idea, but because evaluation represents a scientific approach to an analysis of much that is fundamental in the newer education. It is the purpose of this chapter to discuss and illustrate some of the simpler technics which are being employed by experts in this field.

THE BASIS OF EVALUATION

Objectives. Regardless of the subject-matter field, the evaluation program should be based upon the objectives set up for the course. In Chap. 2 we stated and discussed the following four major objectives for the teaching of biological subjects:

1. The acquisition of information
2. The development of methods of thinking
3. The induction and application of principles
4. The formation of attitudes

If these are valid primary objectives for the teaching of biological subjects, they consequently must be a valid basis for an evaluation program. Such a program would assist in accomplishing the objectives as well as measure the degree of attainment. (1) In other words, this program would provide tests and instruments for measuring the kind, amount, and duration of retention of the factual information as acquired by the students. This is an ancient objective in education and well known to all. (2) The development of reflective or scientific thinking is much newer and, although recognized by some for a long time, little has been done about it in teaching and still less in testing. Therefore, our evaluation program should offer a means of guiding and developing this extremely important quality in the student. It should furnish him with problems to solve and a way of discovering for himself how well he is able to think scientifically and what progress he is making over a period of time. This information is as important to the student as to the teacher. (3) As a result of his ability in reflective thinking, he should be able to induce generalizations and to make application of these not only to similar scientific problems but to the problems of his everyday life. If the student is to achieve success along this line, he should know his mistakes and how to correct them. If the teacher is to assist him, the teacher also needs to know these abilities and shortcomings in order to be able to visualize his needs and his degree of progress. The evaluation program should be a means of assisting both in accomplishing these ends. (4) Over a period of time, as from the beginning of a semester to its close or from the opening of a school year to the end of that year, the student will progress in his factual knowledge, in his ability to think scientifically, and in his ability to generalize and to apply principles. It should follow as a result of all these that his attitude toward the problems of life as well as toward those set up in his field of science should be modified and in some instances completely altered. This certainly is one of the most desirable outcomes of science in education. To be able to measure this progress of the student is, therefore, an important function of evaluation.

TYPES OF EXAMINATIONS IN COMMON USE

In the effort to measure the learning of students, many devices have been employed. The most ancient of these devices is the *question*, either oral or written. Its use is almost universal. Most attempts at modification of the method have centered around the modification of the type of question, standardization of the question lists, and objectifying the question form. Teachers seldom go beyond these, although sometimes, especially in the sciences, "practical" examinations are given in which the questions are used in connection with materials and apparatus, or manipulation tests are given where the student's mechanical skill is supposedly tested.

The Essay Type. Since the oldest objective of most schooling is the memorization of factual information, the testing consists of little more than a list of representative questions covering the facts of the subject matter in the field. This places a premium upon recall, and if the time intervals between learning and testing are long, it places a premium upon retention as well. Various kinds of questions are used for different reasons. The old stand-by is the essay or discussion examination in which the pupil writes freely in his own words the answers to specific interrogations. This form of examination has some virtues not found in most of the more modern forms. It permits, in fact requires, that the student express his ideas verbally and thus do his own recall and his own exposition. In many of the more modern test types these valuable qualities are missing and must be attained by other means. Oral questioning tests a different mode of expression but is open to the other criticisms that may be applied to the essay type.

So-called thought questions may be employed in the essay-type examination in an effort to test the thinking or reasoning powers of the student. In these it is always a source of difficulty to say how much of the deficiency of a poorly written answer is due to lack of learning of the facts, how much to lack of retention in time, and how much to inability to reason correctly with known facts. Hence the teacher does not know quite what he has measured nor how to go about the correction of the weakness. Suppose that the grader decides that a student deserves but half credit on his discussion of the process of photosynthesis. To what was the deficiency due? Was it lack of previous background which hampered his understanding? Was it poor memory of classwork or assignment? Was it inability to apply generalizations to new situations? The inadequacy of such questions for making definite measurements is apparent. A second objection to the essay examination is the extent to which its scoring must be subjective. By way of illustration let us suppose that the teacher asks for the same discussion of photosynthesis. The question is general, and the answers are as varied as the number of individuals in the class. Then it becomes the teacher's duty to decide upon the relative degree of correctness of the thirty or so answers. Anyone who has attempted this is well aware of the sense of inadequacy of his judgment. The first answer read must be weighed against the teacher's own standard of excellence, but after eight or ten such answers have been read, one is almost sure to compare the answers with each other instead of with the original standard. When different teachers grade the same questions, great differences in values are sometimes assigned to them. Even the same teacher will assign different values to the same answers if considerable time elapses between gradings. Also the student's answer is often vague and its true meaning elusive. Words and phrases are employed which seem to imply that the writer had the correct answer in mind though it is not clearly expressed. The teacher must decide if this is right or wrong. This is what is meant by the subjective character of such grading. A third objection to essay answers is the amount of time required for the scoring. Using the same question on photosynthesis, it is evident that any answer that does justice to the question in even an elementary way must be a lengthy one. Ten such answers would entail a large amount of writing by the pupils and much reading time by the teacher. The objection, however, is of little pedagogical importance.

Objective Types. To avoid the indefiniteness of measurement and the effects of the personal equation inherent in the essay type of examinations, there has been devised the objective (new type) examination, the various forms of which are well known to the teacher. There are such forms as true-false, multiple choice, matching, and completion. (1) The simplest and by far the most widely used form of objective test is the *true-false*. In it the examiner gives statements which the students check as being either true or false. This requires no weighing of answers since they are either right or wrong. Hence, the subjective or personal factor is eliminated from the grading but, of course, the establishing of the grading key is largely subjective. This ensures exact uniformity of scoring. The objection that a student can guess and make a grade of 50 per cent on this type of examination is eliminated by grading the number right minus the number wrong, thus placing a penalty upon guessing. It tests the recognition of correctness but allows no opportunity for student expression and calls for very little memory, thus being too limited to be used extensively as an instrument of evaluation. (2) A modified form of this objective test is that known as the *multiple choice,* in which the question is asked, or problem stated, and a number of answers are given with it. Some of these answers are correct, and some are incorrect. If the number of choices approximates as many right as wrong, the score is found by subtracting wrong from right as in the case of the true-false type above. Samples of this kind of questions are given later in this chapter. (3) *Matching* is another type of objective test that is widely used. It takes various forms. In some cases a list of words may be given together with a list of definitions. The student's part is to match the words with the correct definitions. In other cases diagrams are given together with a list of numbered terms to be used as labels. The problem for the student is to match the guide lines of the drawing with the numbers of the correct labels. These questions test the correctness of the student's recognition but do not require much recall and very little application unless the recall involves a series of steps and is not direct. For example, the statement is made, "The energy used in writing this examination is indirectly dependent upon photosynthesis." The student is to mark it as being true or false. Provided that this application has not been made previously during the study of these processes, the student must recall the storage of energy from light by the plant in producing sugar from which animals obtain the energy again through oxidation. (4) *Completion* tests are also widely used and may be made reasonably objective if care is used to avoid ambiguity and vagueness of meaning. The completion test consists of a statement of fact, with one or more words missing from the statement. Blanks are left where the student fills in the missing words. There are two sources of weakness in the construction of these tests that are not easy to overcome. First, the statement designed by the teacher often may be completed in a logical fashion by the use of one of a number of different terms. If the student guesses the word which the teacher had in mind, he scores correctly on the key, but if he chooses a different but perfectly relevant word, he is incorrect. When this ambiguity occurs in a test, the grader should, of course, give credit for any of the correct answers. The following is a sample of such an item:

In sexually reproducing animals new individuals arise from ....

The teacher may expect the blank to be filled in with "fertilized eggs," but the student may use "germ cells" or "gonads" and be perfectly correct. The second type of weakness comes from vagueness due to the frequency of the blanks. The following sample illustrates the point:

> The blood from all over the body is carried through two large .... called .... into the .... The contraction of the .... drives blood through the .... valve into the .... Contraction of the .... drives blood through the .... valve into the .... which carries blood to the ....

In all the above types of objective tests, true-false, multiple choice, matching, or completion, two facts stand out. (1) The subjective element involving the grader's judgment is largely eliminated. (2) Recognition is tested which may be by memory of previously learned facts or by the judgment of the student, but whether it is memory or judgment is not always apparent.

Other Subjective Types. There are types of evaluation that are of value to the teacher which may best be obtained in *questionnaire* form. An example of such a questionnaire which furnishes information concerning the social and economic status of the student is given later in this chapter. Such qualities as attitudes may also be indicated on questionnaire blanks. Where attitudes are to be deduced, it is best not to have the student aware of the fact that attitudes are being expressed in order to avoid his stating what he thinks the teacher wants rather than what he actually holds and practices. Neither should he be reproved for the expression of an attitude which the teacher believes to be unsound. It is the teacher's business to demonstrate scientifically the reasons which show why an attitude is unsound so that the student may choose the better. A change of attitude cannot be forced, and attempts at doing so are most likely to defeat their own end.

Sometimes questionnaires are standardized and, to some extent, objectified. In doing this, the usual method followed is to ask a question and propose two or more answers, one of which is to be checked. This may prove satisfactory for certain purposes, but too often the true answer cannot be given in such simple fashion. If one is checked, however, the teacher may draw invalid conclusions as a result. To illustrate this point, suppose that a questionnaire contains such an item as the following:

> Check one:
>   I prefer: 1. A quiet evening reading by the fireside.
>   2. An evening at the motion pictures.

It may be quite possible that one may be fond of both uses of leisure time and would check one or the other depending upon attendant circumstances. On a cold rainy evening it would be difficult to entice one away from a bowl of popcorn and a good book before an open fire; on a bright crisp evening with nothing special to read, a walk or ride with a friend to a motion picture might prove much more inviting. So to avoid this dilemma the responses should be so arranged as to permit the clarification of points of this kind; otherwise their value is greatly impaired, since this type of differentiation is one of the most desired revelations which a questionnaire may furnish.

Observational (anecdotal) *records* are merely a set of notations which the teacher makes upon the student. They may contain any sort of statement whatever, such as notations concerning the student's health, a record of an interview with the student, a notation to the effect that a student once made a strong declaration of intention to succeed in a certain life work, or a series of observations made at intervals showing the progress of some student in his ability to think scientifically. These are purely subjective but are valuable in making an analysis of the student's personal characteristics. Such anecdotal records may offer a means of accumulating types of information about a student which are not obtainable otherwise. In guidance and other personal dealings, they are indispensable. Teachers sometimes try to retain such information in their minds, but unless the number of students is small and the pupil-teacher relationship long this is ill-advised. It makes a lot of difference in the teacher's ability to deal wisely with the student to know that a boy does excellently in school in spite of the fact that he must go a long way home after school and spend the rest of the afternoon doing chores on the farm, or to know that a timid seemingly unsocial girl was a semi-invalid for three or four years of her childhood. Observational records, well kept, may be a valuable part of evaluation.

The *student's record* of his own activities is another form of anecdotal record that may prove valuable. It may consist of an account of his activities outside school for a given period of time. It might be a record of his procedures in carrying out an individual project or his share of a group project. In the latter case each member of the group should keep such a record so that all of them may be summarized as a complete account of the project. It could consist of the records of field trips or the log of a journey or summer vacation. It may deal with matters connected with the subject matter directly or with widely diverse subjects, and it still will be of service especially in those phases of evaluation involving self-analysis and teacher-pupil relationships.

STARTING AN EVALUATION PROGRAM

To the teacher who is unaccustomed to anything more than the giving of ordinary examinations, the idea of setting up an evaluation program looms as a gigantic task. This is probably because he visualizes the complete program in a finished form and notes the diversity of its elements. But it is generally best to go slowly in establishing a program and allow it to accumulate during a year or more of preparation. It is, furthermore, both advisable and advantageous to work in cooperation with one or more fellow teachers and possibly with the administration. Even if this is not possible, the teacher will find that one or two years of individual effort upon first one and then another of the various steps will net a large gain which is entirely lost if nothing is attempted. Another encouraging factor is that in the program suggested below many steps require but little work on the teacher's part and less class time than is at first evident.

Each teacher may decide for himself which features of evaluation are of most immediate advantage to the needs peculiar to his situation, but the following list is suggested as representing a balance of essentials which would make a good program as it stands.

1. Previous records, including past achievement and intelligence ratings
2. Socioeconomic rating of each student
3. Pretesting and retesting
4. Self-testing and self-analysis
5. Progress rating and analysis by:
   a. Self-testing versus teacher testing
   b. Individual rating checked against class rating

Let us now take each of the phases of evaluation separately and in more detail.

1. *Past Achievement and Intelligence Records.* The teacher should not start the term with a new class without obtaining these two important records for each student. All schools may not have intelligence test records, but the past achievement is a matter of school records and is perhaps more important for the teacher's use. There are school principals and superintendents who disapprove of giving such information to teachers on the ground that it may prejudice the teacher against or in favor of the student. Sometimes it may happen that if a student has accumulated a high past record he finds it possible to do a certain amount of living on his past record, and if he has accumulated a poor record he is expected to do poorly. However, if he has accumulated a good record, it probably was the result of continued good work and he is not likely to drift long upon reputation unless the high quality is maintained. Moreover, this attitude on the part of the administrator is hardly complimentary to his choice of teachers if he cannot depend upon their not being so easily prejudiced. But, granting that such a condition may arise occasionally, it remains a fact that the benefits derived from the teacher's having such records are of such value as to outweigh overwhelmingly a possible misuse of the information. Such records help the teacher in understanding the students in the class and encourage him to see each individual apart from the class. While one student may be naturally slow and another fast, there are many who do generally well in sciences and less well in languages, etc. Perhaps the records and attitudes of individual students have been as much the result of interests and teaching methods as of abilities. Certainly to have the information of past achievement is a valuable tool in the teacher's hands for dealing intelligently with the class if it is borne in mind that each pupil is to stand on the record of his new achievement unbiased by the old.

2. *Socioeconomic Rating.* No other information is of more value to the teacher in dealing intelligently with pupils than that which may be derived from the record of the social and economic status of the members of the class. The ordinary competitive examinations of the schoolroom may measure a great deal more than they are designed to do. Take the case of two students who have achieved mediocre standing as measured by the results of school tests. Both these students show above average upon intelligence records. Consulting their socioeconomic records may disclose that one is the oldest of seven children in a family where the father works for rather low wages and is unemployed part of the year. The boy has a paper route and must attend a market stand three evenings each week. These outside duties require a great amount of his time and energy, and six smaller brothers and sisters with the

limited economic standing of the family are not conducive to high-grade homework. This knowledge serves the teacher well in dealing with the student. It does not mean pitying the boy and granting high grades for poor work. It means understanding his problems and doing all that is possible to adjust his school time to the best advantage. The case of the second student shows that he is an only child who has money to spend which he does not earn by his own efforts. His parents have a good income, and he is permitted to use his leisure time as he sees fit. Because of this he has acquired outside social interests and activities which have required as much of his time and energy as has the work done by the other student. This is not a case for drastic penalties but calls for intelligent maneuvers and a cooperative understanding with the parents.

Many other important points of information such as health, home and family conditions, and social activities may be obtained from the socio-economic questionnaire, a sample of which is given below. Such a blank should be made up by the teacher (when not done by the school) and modified best to suit his own purposes. Great care must be exercised to ensure against creating a feeling on the part of parents that too much of a personal inquiry is being made. Most persons resent this and will not cooperate. For example, the occupation of the father and whether any other member of the family is employed will tell accurately enough what the income of the family is without asking for it in figures. This questionnaire is very valuable but takes almost no class time since it may be passed out to the pupils, filled out at home, and returned later, or with mature students may be done in class in a very few minutes.

It will be noted that the first two steps of our evaluation program have been of such a character as to require but little teacher and student time or effort and yet offer great advantages for the teacher who wishes to understand the problems of the individual student.

3. *Pretesting and Retesting.* In the third division of the evaluation program the teacher is confronted with the problem of building a test which is very general and inclusive and which is varied in the things which it will measure. This takes time and careful preparation. It has to be prepared before the beginning of the school term since the pretest, as the term implies, must be given at the beginning of the study. The pretest must include questions that will measure the objectives of the course. For example, (*a*) there must be questions that call for factual knowledge of sufficient scope to furnish adequate samples of all the term's work. (*b*) There must be problem questions to test the student's ability to think scientifically. (*c*) There must be questions that will call for inferring generalizations and applying generalizations to new situations. (*d*) There should be questions which will give the student the opportunity for expression of attitudes of various kinds. The first object of the pretest is to give the teacher a cross-sectional view of the background and standing of the class in the subject-matter field included in the course which they are just entering. It furthermore gives the teacher a picture of the position of each individual in regard to the same points. It shows what parts of the course are already fairly well known to the class, what parts are entirely new, and where emphasis needs to be placed. Its results are a guide to assist

QUESTIONNAIRE

For Determining Social, Economic, and Guidance Problems *

Name .... Address ....
Name of parents or guardian ....
Your age ...... Where born .... Are both parents living?........
No. of older brothers ..... Younger ..... No. older sisters ..... Younger .....
Occupation of father .... Where employed ....
Other members of the family working .... Occupation ....
No. of automobiles in family .... Kind ....
Do you have use of a car for your own affairs? .... About how much money do
you have to spend for yourself per month? .... Do you work for any of the
money you get? .... Doing what? .... Do you have a
regular allowance? .... How many radios in your home? .... Hifi? ....
Television set? .... Makes? ....
Have you one for yourself alone? .... Which? ....
What are your three favorite radio programs? ....
.... Television programs? ....
Do you have a room that is yours alone? .... Do you have regular duties
to do about your home? .... What are they? ....
What is your favorite form of entertainment? ....
Have you a hobby? .... What is it? ....
How have you spent the last two summer vacations? ....
....
What study do you like best? .... Least? ....
Have you traveled? .... Where? .... When? ....
Do you play a musical instrument? .... What? .... Sing? ....
Do you do any kind of art? .... What? ....
What work do you think you would like to do when through school? ....
Do you expect to go to school after high school? .... Where? ....
Will you have to earn part of your expense if you go? .... How much? ....
Give the names of the clubs, societies, or organizations of which you are a member
....
In general do you think that your health has been poor ... Fair ..... good .....
Check any of the following which you have had:
Whooping cough .... Measles .... Chicken pox ....
Mumps .... Scarlet fever .... Typhoid fever ....
Diphtheria .... Poliomyelitis .... Tonsils removed ....
Adenoids removed .... Appendix removed .... Teeth removed,
number .... Frequent headaches .... Frequent nausea ....
Serious accident (describe) ....
....
....
Mental test score .... Reading test score .... Achievement test
score ....
Additional information from conferences, etc.

*This questionnaire is intended as a sample and should be modified to suit the purposes of your own classes.

the teacher and the class in charting their course for the semester or year. But there is a second vital use for the pretest. It should be repeated, without alteration, as a final examination, or retest, at the close of the term. The scores made upon each part of the retest are then recorded opposite the corresponding scores made upon those parts at the time when it was given as a pretest. The differences in the scores represent to some extent the degree to which the student may have profited in that respect by having taken the course. For example, if a student scored low on knowledge of facts on the pretest but high upon the retest, the difference in the scores is an index to his acquisition in this phase of the course. However, if a student scores high upon any or all parts of the retest and reference to the pretest shows that the score was high at that time also, the net gain was small. If a student's score is but slightly above average on the retest but very low on the pretest, then the net gain was large. Thus, pretesting and retesting offer some means of indicating progress from beginning to end. While this may appear as a rather large amount of work, the teacher should not lose sight of the fact that it would be necessary under any method to make out a comprehensive final examination and that the pretest is nothing more than having such a final examination prepared ahead of time so that it may be given twice. This will mean no extra amount of work except in scoring, but if the questions are mostly of the objective type the scoring is quite simple. Extra class time of one or more periods is required at the beginning of the term for pretesting.

4. *Self-testing and Self-analysis.* We now come to that part of the evaluation program which will yield the largest returns to the student. The idea of self-testing has become rather widespread, and some form of it has been included in a few texts and workbooks. In most of these books it amounts to little more than a short set of review questions upon factual content of the course. Such questions are of some assistance to the pupil in testing his memory, but they usually test little else. The self-test should be as comprehensive in scope as the teacher's test. It is no adequate test for the student if he is able to remember facts recently read but is given no occasion to apply these facts or reason with them before the final teacher's test. The self-test must measure all that the teacher's test measures. It must be sufficiently comprehensive, diversified, and diagnostic: comprehensive to ensure its reliability, diversified to ensure adequacy, and diagnostic to ensure the benefits derived from a measurement of various types of learning. For each self-test a correct score or key must be given so that the student may keep a record of his self-test in each type of learning. A form should be used to make it easy for the student to record the results of each learning skill separately so that he may make comparisons from one test to the next in order to discover wherein his strength or weakness lies and whether he is improving as time passes. In other words, each part of the test should measure the student's progress toward one, and only one, of the objectives. If it is not diagnostic, it cannot do this. If it is diagnostic the student may very readily analyze his own degree of success, and he will take special interest in doing so. Such a record and analysis give the student a sense of personal responsibility for his success and give him and his teacher a common basis for discovering and working out his problems. This has a marked and highly desirable psychological effect upon

the student. He feels that the test is an instrument by which he may improve his own standing and measure his abilities rather than a one-sided contest between himself and the teacher in which the teacher makes all the rules and is out to get him. The golfer likes to play his game even when he must play alone because he is trying to better his own score and there is no serious penalty when he fails to do so. If he does not succeed, he may try again. The student may acquire the same attitude toward his self-tests. In conducting a self-testing program the class average should be made known so that the student may play against par. He should also know the high and low scores of the class in order to place himself in relation to his classmates and thus engage in a harmless sort of competition. The self-tests should be sufficiently similar to the teacher tests (never the same) so that success in self-tests will generally be reflected in success with the teacher tests. This rewards serious effort. A careful self-testing and self-analyzing program is one of the strongest forms of motivation and one of the surest teaching devices when properly administered. In proportion to the time consumed it offers larger returns than do many other teaching methods.

5. *Progress Rating and Analysis.* The teacher will expect to give tests at certain intervals. The results of these tests should furnish the major basis for rating the progress the student is making in his work. As has been said before, these tests should resemble the self-tests in style and content covered. They are to be used by the teacher in analyzing the student's difficulties and may be checked against the self-tests in this respect. Hence, the teacher tests must be diagnostic to be very useful. Therefore, it is necessary to learn to construct tests which will be diagnostic. The beginner may find the building of such a set of questions to be rather more difficult and time-consuming than the compiling of a list of questions which is not diagnostic. For example, from the ordinary set of essay questions it is not possible to analyze the student's difficulties. But if the types of questions are so designed that they will test memory apart from other things, test ability to apply principles or distinguish cause from effect aside from memory of facts, then the examination becomes diagnostic. From such an examination the teacher and student may make an analysis of the progress and type of learning.

The results of the teacher test should be given to the student in the form of the score made upon each type of question so that the student may keep a record of his standing. As in the case of the self-tests, he must have the high, low, and average class scores on each part so that he may place himself in relation to other students and appreciate his weaknesses. Checking himself against the other members of his class gives his standing. When this is repeated with each test, it gives his progress. His standing at the close of a semester or year is some measure of his achievement.

DIAGNOSTIC QUESTIONS AND COMPLETE MEASUREMENT

Validity. When a test has been constructed and given, its results should measure something. If the teacher has decided that the test should measure certain types of learning such as memory of facts, scientific thinking, and ability to apply principles, then the test must contain questions that are designed to measure these qualities. If questions of each type are included the test becomes valid in its measuring capacities, but if the questions are all of one kind the measurement is not valid. By kind of question is not meant the form or structure of the question. Many teachers make this grave error. Tests made out by them, tests sold in printed form, tests in texts and especially in workbooks sometimes show a great variety of forms of questions, but seldom do they measure more than memory of facts. The mere fact that a test consists of true-false, completion, matching, and essay types of questions does not mean that it measures more than one type of learning. The following example should make this meaning clear. Suppose that after completing a study of digestion the teacher asks the following question:

Explain the digestion of different foods as they pass through the digestive tract.

This amounts to an essay-type question and tests the student's memory of facts covered in his previous work. If the question is written as true-false it might appear as:

......Proteins are digested in the mouth.
......Ptyalin aids in the digestion of starch.

Or the question may be put in the form of incomplete statements, as

In the mouth starches are changed to .... when mixed with the enzyme ....

This shows how changing the form of the question does *not* change the type of learning which it measures.

On the other hand, let us suppose that the class has just studied the following facts:

1. Foods are digested in the presence of enzymes.
2. Many undigested foods will not diffuse through membranes.
3. Digested foods will diffuse through membranes.
4. Blood carries food to all parts of the body.
5. Food diffuses from the blood into cells.

After this study the teacher asks,

Why is food digested while in the digestive tract?
    a. So that it will diffuse through the walls of the digestive tract.
    b. So that the cells of the body may be nourished.
    c. To furnish energy to the body.
    d. Because it is mixed with enzymes.

If the student checks *d* as the answer, he is correct, but if he checks *a*, *b*, or *c*, he is incorrect. The question asks for *cause* of digestion. *d* is the cause, *a*, *b*, and *c* are *results*. Therefore, assuming that the answer has not been taught directly, such a question tests the ability of the student to think scientifically by distinguishing between cause and effect. From this it may be seen that the same factual learning may be used as a test of memory or as a test of thinking.

After the student has acquired a fund of information and certain broader generalizations or principles, the teacher wishes to test the ability of the student to apply these principles to new situations. Therefore, it is necessary to put questions into a form which will make this measurement possible. We shall assume that in addition to the information given in the preceding illustration on digestion the student also knows what the end products of digestion are for the three classes of foods, carbohydrates, proteins, and fats. The teacher then constructs a question of the following character:

A man in a hospital has had a serious operation on the digestive tract, making it impossible for him to eat food for many weeks. The doctors decide to give him food by injection directly into the veins. Which of the following should they do?

    a. They should inject liquid glucose into the veins.
    b. They should inject liquid protein into the veins.
    c. They should inject liquid fats into the veins.
    d. They should inject a balanced mixture of carbohydrates, proteins, and fats.
    e. They should inject a natural whole food such as milk.
    f. They should inject a mixture of starch and water.

If the student knows the end products of digestion, if he knows the principle of diffusion, if he knows the principles of enzyme activity, he should be able to apply these here and, hence, will check *a* as the only correct answer. But the teacher may go further if he chooses and add the following to the foregoing question:

In the following list of statements check those which apply directly to your thinking in answering the preceding question, and which give the reasons for your answer.

    a. The body will not grow without protein in the diet.
    b. A balanced diet would be more beneficial than either a protein diet or carbohydrate diet alone.
    c. Protein and starch are unable to diffuse from the digestive tract into the circulatory system.
    d. Glucose is a single sugar and will diffuse into the tissues from the blood.
    e. A natural food such as milk would be easily digested and furnish all food elements.
    f. Food must be diffusible before entering the blood stream if it is to be beneficial to the body.
    g. Nondiffusible substances would be of no value injected as food.
    h. If liquid food is injected directly into the blood stream, it need not be digested since it will not have to diffuse through the membranes of the digestive tract.
    i. Any foreign substance injected directly into the blood would prove fatal.
    j. Glucose alone would sustain the body functions for a long time.
    k. Since individual cells may contain enzymes, the undigested foods will be digested after they get into tissue cells.

If *d, f, g,* and *j* are checked, they indicate a logical series of steps in thinking, and when rearranged in the order of *f, g, d,* and *j* they will read as follows:

Food must be diffusible before entering the blood stream if it is to be beneficial to the body.
Nondiffusible substances would be of no value injected as foods.
Glucose is a single sugar and will diffuse into the tissues from the blood.
Glucose alone would sustain the body functions for a long time.

If the statement "Therefore use glucose" is added after each of these, it makes sense. If it is added after any of the other statements, it does not make sense.

Such a check list goes a step beyond the thinking and indicates how the thinking is done. The correct steps are so disarranged and intermingled with other statements, some of which are true and some not, that they could not be the means of discovering the correct answer if the student does not know sufficient facts and principles and how to apply them.

Reliability. In addition to being valid, that is, testing for such types of learning as are purported to be taught, a test also must be reliable. As stated above under Validity, such types of questions must be used as will measure the qualities desired, but that alone is not sufficient. Enough material must be included to make the test reliable. This is made simple by using the following illustration: Suppose that you spend five class periods upon a unit of subject matter. You prepare an information test that includes all the facts studied and amounts to 100 questions. It is completely reliable if it covers all the learning properly. But you may find after giving it that you can make a random sampling of 50 questions out of the 100 and get about as accurate a measure as with 100. Then it is apparent that the test could be cut to 50 questions and still be a reliable measure of this kind of learning. If, however, but two or three questions were asked, it would probably be found that they represent too small a sample to offer a reliable measure.

In order to ensure the reliability and comparability of tests, attempts have been made to standardize some of them upon the basis of results obtained from giving them to large numbers of students. Some of these are obtainable in printed form. Few of them, however, are very diagnostic, and the validity is further hampered at times by teleological answers and other questionable characteristics of the answer keys. In most respects teachers will do quite as well to construct their own tests. If this is done by groups working as committees, the work is simplified and the construction is not so difficult for any one. It also makes for better examinations by unifying the objectives and enlarging the scope of measurement.

SCORING AND RECORDING

If measuring the effectiveness of teaching by student progress through the semester or year is a desirable objective, it is then essential that the measuring standards be uniform and accumulative. This may be accomplished by constructing tests each time from types of questions that are predominantly objective in order to secure uniformity. Such questions usually may be scored by assigning equivalent values to comparable parts. That is, each correct answer checked in a true-false question may be assigned an arbitrary value of one or two points. With this as a standard other types of answers are assigned values of comparable worth. In constructing another examination later, the same method of scoring and same score values must be used. For example, it would be wrong to assign the value of *one* to each part of a true-false test at one time and on a second similar test to assign a value of two or three points to such answers since progress is to be measured by accumulating the scores upon a record sheet (sample below). If uniform, comparable values are not used for any reason on the different examinations, it will be necessary to translate the scores into standard values in order that a test of 10 questions may not receive an importance equal to a similar test of 20 or 30 questions. This is one of the errors of much of the grading by percentage. The teacher gives a short examination of 10 questions, and a student is given a score of 80 per cent. Later another test is given covering twice as much material and twice as long and important. Upon this test the same student scores 60 per cent. If these scores are averaged, the standing is 70 per cent. But if the second examination was twice as large and important, the score should have been double that assigned to it on a percentage basis.

STUDENT'S RECORD SHEET

		My Record	Class Record
	Pretest		
	Retest		
Unit I	Self-test		
Date	Teacher test		
Unit 2	Self-test		
Date	Teacher test		
Unit 3	Self-test		
Date	Teacher test		
Unit 4	Self-test		
Date	Teacher test		
Unit 5	Self-test		
Date	Teacher test		
Unit 6	Self-test		
Date	Teacher test		
Unit 7	Self-test		
Date	Teacher test		
Parts of examination		My Record columns: 1 Information, 2 Sci. thinking, 3 Principles, 4, 5, 6 Drawings, 7 Reports, Totals	Class Record columns (each low/av./high): 1 Information, 2 Sci. thinking, 3 Principles, 4, 5, 6 Drawings, 7 Reports, Totals

It is much simpler to do as suggested above and grade all tests by assigning arbitrary, uniform score values to each part of an answer and by recording the results upon a score blank from which the student's standing may be obtained at any moment by totaling the scores.

Diagnostic testing is a new, growing, and important feature of modern education, and the progressive teacher cannot afford to overlook it. There are many angles beyond what it is possible to discuss here. Those interested will find greater details and much help from some of the references at the end of this chapter.

PROBLEMS

1. Make out a list of 10 biology questions which might be answered readily with essay-type answers. (*a*) Convert the first five of these into true-false questions. (*b*) Convert the next five into multiple-choice questions. (*c*) Select any two of your questions and make them into a form which requires the application of some general principle. (*d*) Add to your list at least two different types of questions which will serve as tests of attitudes. Discuss the different types of questions before the methods class, showing how you went about preparing them.

2. Take any chapter from a textbook on biology and make a test to cover it with all the questions of the essay type. Write out an analysis of your examination to show to what extent it is valid and to what extent it is reliable, showing what might be done to improve it.

3. Take any chapter from a textbook on biology and make a test to cover it with all the questions of the true-false type. Write out an analysis of your examination to show to what extent it is valid and to what extent it is reliable, showing what might be done to improve it.

4. Take any chapter from a textbook on biology and make a test to cover it with all the questions of the completion type. Write out an analysis of your examination to show to what extent it is valid and to what extent it is reliable, showing what might be done to improve it.

5. Take any chapter from a textbook on biology and make a test to cover it with all the questions of the multiple-choice type. Write out an analysis of your examination to show to what extent it is valid and to what extent it is reliable, showing what might be done to improve it.

6. Take any chapter from a textbook on biology and make a test to cover it with all the questions of the scientific-thinking and problem-solving type. Write out an analysis of your examination to show to what extent it is valid and to what extent it is reliable, showing what might be done to improve it.

7. Take any chapter from a textbook on biology and make a test to cover it with all the questions of the application-of-principles-to-new-situations type. Write out an analysis of your examination to show to what extent it is valid and to what extent it is reliable, showing what might be done to improve it.

8. List a number of attitudes that you might wish a student to develop through the study of biology. Make out a list of questions in answer to which the student must express his "attitude" on the subject. Let the methods class discuss to what extent the questions may fail to be a measure of the effectiveness of the attitude in daily life.

9. Make out a socioeconomic questionnaire and fill in the items for some boy or girl of your acquaintance. Do not use his correct name. Analyze the information by making a summary of each group of similar questions such as (*a*) health, (*b*) social inclinations, and (*c*) chief interests. Show various ways in which such information might be useful to that student's teacher.

10. Ask several teachers of biology to give you a copy of some of the examinations which they use. Make an analysis of these on the following basis: (*a*) How many forms of questions were employed? (*b*) To what extent are they diagnostic?

11. Get a set of standardized tests in biology and analyze it as suggested in Problem 10.

12. Examine the self-tests and teacher tests that are furnished with any biology workbook and analyze them as suggested in Problem 10.

REFERENCES

1. Bauer, H. L.: "Practicum Examination in Biology and Botany Courses," *Junior Coll. J.*, 26:379–384, March, 1956.

2. Bayles, E. E., and R. C. Bedell: "A Study of Comparative Validity as Shown by a Group of Objective Tests," *J. Educ. Research*, January, 1931.

3. Bear, Robert M.: *The Social Functions of Education*, The Macmillan Company, New York, 1937.

4. "Constructing Achievement Tests," Bureau of Educational Research, The Ohio State University, Columbus, 1934.

5. Davis, I. C.: "The Measurement of Scientific Attitudes," *Sci. Educ.*, 19:117–122, 1935.

6. Diagnostic Tests for Subject Mastery:
   Cooperative Biology Test. Grades 9 to 11. Cooperative Test Division Educational Testing Service, Princeton, N.J.
   Presson Biology Test. Grades 9 to 10. World Book Company, Yonkers, N.Y.
   Ruch-Cossman Biology Test. Grades 9 to 12. World Book Company, Yonkers, N.Y.
   Williams Biology Test. Grades 9 to 10. Bureau of Educational Measurements, Kansas State Teachers College.
   Hanes-Benz Biology Test. Grades 9 to 10. C. A. Gregory Company.

7. Diederich, P. B.: "Design for a Comprehensive Evaluation Program," *School Rev.*, vol. 58, no. 4, April, 1950.

8. Dressel, Paul, and C. H. Nelson: "Questions and Problems in Science," Test Item Folio no. 1.

9. Frutchey, F. P., and R. W. Tyler: *Construction and Use of Achievement Examinations*, "Examinations in the Natural Sciences," Houghton Mifflin Company, Boston, 1936.

10. Grant, C. L., and N. Neal: *Tests to American School Biology*, McGraw-Hill Book Company, Inc., New York, 1952.

11. Gray, H. A.: "An Approach to the Measurement of Biological Attitudes and Appreciations," *J. Educ. Research*, 28:25–29, 1934.

12. Hawkes, H. E., E. F. Lindquist, and C. R. Mann: *The Construction and Use of Achievement Examinations*, Houghton Mifflin Company, Boston, 1936.

13. Kitch, L. W.: "An Experimental Study in Integrating Testing with Learning in Biology," *Sci. Educ.*, December, 1933.

14. Micheels, W. J., and M. R. Karnes: *Measuring Educational Achievement*, McGraw-Hill Book Company, Inc., New York, 1950.

15. Owens, J. H.: "Ability to Recognize and Apply Scientific Principles in New Situations," *Sci. Educ.*, 35:207–213, October, 1951. An experimental investigation in high school biology and chemistry.

16. Preston, C. E.: *The High School Science Teacher and His Work*, McGraw-Hill Book Company, Inc., New York, 1936.

17. Remmers, H. H.: *Educational Measurement and Evaluation*, Harper & Brothers, New York, 1943.

18. Ross, C. C., and J. C. Stanley: *Measurement in Today's Schools*, Prentice-Hall, Inc., Englewood Cliffs, N.J., 1954. Test making, types of questions, measurements, statistics.

Sources of Prepared Tests

19. Educational Testing Service, Princeton, N.J., and Los Angeles, Calif.

20. College Entrance Examination Board, 425 W. 117th St., New York 27, N.Y.

CHAPTER 7

--⟨ Materials and Equipment ⟩--

There seems to be a tradition that special equipment is necessary for chemistry and physics but that physiology, biology, botany, and zoology can somehow be taught merely from books. Too often the teachers of these subjects teach them in just that way. It is true, however, that biological subjects can be taught with but little of the equipment that is often supplied when funds are available. The most desirable type of equipment is that which has to do with the furnishing and arrangement of the room. Even this is not necessary for the successful teaching of a course in biology. Why so large a number of teachers do not realize this is hard to explain. In large part it is due to improper training and experience in their college work. The ingenuity necessary to improvise apparatus and find substitutes for materials is found active in very few, but we believe that this is something which almost anyone can acquire with a little assistance and experience. Part Two is designed for the express purpose of giving willing teachers this assistance and for putting life and interest into what is so often a dead study of life.

Much of the responsibility for the lack of necessary equipment can be placed upon the teacher of the subject. Ask a teacher who has taught several years in one school and who feels that no equipment has been provided to make out a list of the equipment which he would consider to be adequate. He will sit down with catalogues and make out an order which will cost anywhere from $300 to $900. He might agree that he could do fairly well with less, but not much less. It is a matter of fact that it is possible to take a list of this sort amounting to hundreds of dollars and by skillfully applying inexpensive substitutes efficiently to equip the same laboratory for $60 to $100. Place a request with your school board for $300, and you are almost certain to be refused; ask for $30 to $50 twice per year, and you are likely to get it.

INEXPENSIVE SUBSTITUTES

Apparatus. How is it possible to furnish a laboratory satisfactorily with apparatus and supplies for as little as $30 or $50? One piece of equipment seems to be more generally found in the biology laboratory than any other. This is an aquarium. It is sometimes present when almost no other equipment is to be found. As useful and desirable a provision as it is, little use is generally made of it other than as a place to house a few goldfish. Several aquaria should be used, and they may provide an exceedingly valuable set of student problems (see Chap. 11, for complete suggestions). Even the small glass-sided commercial aquaria cost $3 to $10 each. Three such aquaria would approximate $15. But deep enameled pans or buckets, large jars, small wooden tubs or kegs, or a homemade tank may usually be provided for less than $1 each and are quite as useful as the more beautiful but expensive commercial product. One-quart, two-quart, and one-gallon preserving jars are excellent for small experiments and can be obtained for nothing, since students will bring these from their homes. Many such articles that are thrown into the trash barrel are very useful in the schoolroom.

A reasonable supply of beakers, watch glasses, flasks, and specimen jars will cost $10 to $20, but common tumblers, jelly glasses, cheese and mayonnaise jars, castor cups (coasters), and a few test tubes will cost less than $3 and for almost every purpose will serve quite as well. In Chap. 11 there are many suggestions of this character which, if used as a guide and enlarged upon according to individual needs, will aid materially in placing a neglected biology classroom in satisfactory working order for an unbelievably small outlay. If you have any considerable amount of money to spend, put it into more permanent equipment such as a microscope or some other useful apparatus for which there is no easy substitute.

Teachers often ask what to do when not even one microscope is provided for their class. There are two possibilities in such instances. In the first place, a course in general biology can be taught in a very interesting and profitable manner without the use of a compound microscope. There are many fundamental principles in biology that are of great value to students, the understanding of which does not depend upon the use of the microscope. Such material as the cross sections and longitudinal sections of stems, seeds, and fruits, various preparations of the tissues of animals, and bacteria and protozoa, for all of which a microscope is valuable, do not need a microscope to be fairly well understood. Their general characteristics may be readily comprehended from more gross preparations. In the second place, there are several ways to substitute for the lack of a microscope. In most communities there can be found an individual, such as a physician, naturalist, or retired professor, or some kind of institution which has a microscope that will be loaned to the school for a short time or brought for a personal demonstration. If it cannot be borrowed for any length of time, it may be necessary for the teacher to plan its use carefully so as to concentrate upon a few points such as showing definite cell types and microorganisms.

One of the good high-powered hand lenses, some of which magnify 10 or more diameters, will serve quite well for many kinds of low-power magnifications. Another very satisfactory substitute for the school microscope is a projection lantern of some sort. Slides of many tissues and organisms can be purchased which are made from high-grade photomicrographs in color showing staining. These, when thrown on a screen, will give the entire class a view quite like what each might see if looking through a microscope. Care must be taken when selecting slides to get photomicrographs and not diagrams. Diagrams are no better than drawings in textbooks or on wall charts. Good photomicrographs may be obtained from reliable supply houses if the equipment for preparing them is not available. It is a mistake to spend money for lantern slides of birds, flowers, and insects or of anything which may be seen with ease out of doors or in the laboratory. Good slides of microscopic objects are a splendid substitute for the microscope when it is not possible to have one (see Chap. 8, Visual Education).

Living and Preserved Materials. There are various reasons why so little material is used in general science, biology, and physiology classes and why so little living material is used in botany and zoology. It seems that the teachers regularly expect that these supplies should be furnished by the schools. This may not be done. It would be better if the school could provide the necessary materials by allowing the teacher a sufficient amount of time with a conveniently arranged schedule so that he might provide them himself. If the administration were wise, it would make this possible and then insist that the teacher do his part. The school would profit considerably in money saved on supplies. The teacher would profit considerably in becoming more familiar with the materials of the subject which he is teaching. And the students would profit immeasurably by better teaching, by contact with the plants and animals about which they read and hear, and by seeing them in their natural habitats as well as in the laboratory. It should be the business of every biology teacher to provide personally as much of the material needed for his class as is at all possible. This should also be a part of the work of the students. They need to see where these organisms live and how they behave in their natural environments, to collect some of them, returning with them alive to their schoolroom, and to preserve others for use later. The extent to which this may be carried out varies with the location of the school. Obviously, a teacher in a school located in the center of a large city may experience more difficulty in making such an arrangement than one located in a rural or suburban district. But there are distinct advantages in large cities not available to those in rural communities. Greenhouses are present where a great variety of plants may be obtained even at times when plants out of doors are at a minimum. In these same greenhouses are forms of unusual plants and plants in bloom or in fruit out of season. Parks and parkways with trees, shrubs, streams, and lagoons are within reach of almost all city schools. Often the lawns, boulevards, shade trees, gardens, and flower beds of the city show better than does the countryside the ravishings of insect pests and plant diseases or the effect of insufficient light or water. The city may also provide a conservatory, a zoological park, an aquarium, or a museum. These are the show places for out-of-town visitors, but how often are they used by those who live in their environs?

In the city are commercial hatcheries, packing houses, pet shops, and infestations of household pests. There is always the food market from which may be secured a wide variety of fish, mollusks, and lobsters. The lobsters sometimes come packed in a mass of seaweeds, and there is also the regular supply of food plants at all seasons of the year. It is true that the teacher who has a class in chemistry, physics, and geography as well as biology will experience greater difficulty in devoting sufficient time and energy to his materials than the teacher who has five classes of a single biological subject, but there is no substitute for living material, and there is no tolerating the continued use of the time-honored and over-persistent assignment of text followed by recitation as the only method for a biological science.

In the more advanced and specialized subjects, such as physiology, there is even less excuse for complaint about the lack of materials and equipment since there are numerous sources of these and ways of conducting the course without making it a book course. For the anatomical studies the parts of larger mammals such as are commonly used for food, like the cow, pig, and sheep, are so nearly like man as to be quite suitable for illustrative material. For functional use the smaller mammals, such as rats, mice, guinea pigs, rabbits, cats and dogs, and the other vertebrates, such as turtles, frogs, and fish, are always to be had. The student himself is about the most valuable laboratory specimen one could get.

For the botany, zoology, or general biology class there is a piece of equipment known as the Wardian case or terrarium (see Chap. 13 for its construction) which is one of the most generally useful articles that one may have. These small containers can be made from materials that may be obtained at practically no cost, and in them may be reared plants and animals of many kinds. One such case may be used as a desert habitat, another as a woodland habitat, another as a swamp or marsh habitat, and by use of a heating device (a light bulb is sufficient) a tropical habitat may be maintained. Materials from these cases could supply many of the living organisms for student use as well as illustrations of ecological units. They need not be kept merely as ornaments. It may not be especially easy for the teacher to get started upon a program of collecting, culturing, and preserving materials for class use, but a little persistence and study will convince the beginner of the value and the possibilities which it offers for successful teaching. Part Two, and especially Chap. 12, is designed as a guide to aid the teacher in getting this start.

LACK OF LABORATORY SPACE

Economy and lack of skillful planning prevent many schools from having the amount of laboratory space and equipment that is desirable for the satisfactory teaching of a science. The rooms provided for general science and general biology are seldom much different from those provided for language or mathematics; in fact, they are frequently the same rooms. The obsolete permanent seats and the chairs in rows are still prevalent. In some schools the science room is provided with a larger and higher teacher's table which in special cases is equipped with water and gas and sometimes electricity. These rooms are the outgrowth of the strictly demonstration type of teaching. When properly used, they have many advantages. A still later type of room is furnished with a number of small tables and chairs for the students. These offer additional advantages. Regardless of the type of equipment, the teacher often finds the room overcrowded with nearly every foot of floor space occupied with an excess of students, and there is little opportunity for individual work or use of laboratory supplies. This condition is deplorable and often quite beyond the teacher's control, but one of the reasons for its continuance is that the teacher accepts the situation and does not continually insist upon better facilities. This has to be done tactfully to be sure, but it sometimes pays.

In a certain school, a class in general science was held in a small, narrow, dark room with several rows of chairs crowded together. The teacher's desk was an old kitchen table. There was no gas, no water, and no available electrical outlet. There was no cupboard or storage space, and none was needed since there was no apparatus. The reason for having the class in this room was that this made it easy for students to transfer from one class to another in the course of the day's schedule. This was an administrative problem. It is an error, however, for the teacher to form the habit of blaming the administration for all such ills. In the example just given the teacher did nothing to remedy the situation. He never attempted to bring the simplest materials to class nor to provide for group discussions although the class was composed of manual arts boys. He would, in all probability, have used the same methods in another classroom since this called for the least effort and ingenuity on his part. (He later became an administrator.)

By way of contrast, there was in the same school system, another teacher whose room was inadequately equipped; the furniture was crowded together, and the room was frequently overpopulated. In spite of this there were always various kinds of potted plants growing in the room, and into one corner was literally squeezed a small table upon which were placed demonstrations and upon which were grown, in turn, numerous small boxes of plants, jars of protozoa, mice, and other living organisms whenever needed. The demonstration table was always covered with materials, largely of student contributions. The teacher was enthusiastic and resourceful in finding needed materials. This spread to her students, all of whom worked at special problems part of the time. Students with unusual abilities were encouraged to use them in connection with their biology. Several students were artistically inclined and drew large pictures which were used as class illustrations. Others doing shopwork in manual arts did some work in preparing and painting other materials for the class. Several others stuffed and mounted small skins. The students were eager, self-reliant, and genuinely interested even when the class was a sectioned slow group. They were encouraged to relate their studies to themselves and to their everyday life, and there was plenty of evidence that it went into their homes and excited interest among other members of their families.

The difference between these two classes was due more to the difference in the teachers than to the difference in the rooms and equipment. If a teacher uses a little ingenuity and is willing to work, a very poorly equipped room with little laboratory space can be made to function with success. It is the first responsibility of the teacher to accomplish this.

LACK OF BOOKS AND REFERENCE MATERIAL

In smaller schools there is sometimes a rather serious lack of suitable books and reading material. But here again as in the case of apparatus, the lack is probably not so big a problem as may seem at first. If there is a good encyclopedia in the building or school system, it can be made to serve as a small library. Most of the subjects in the high-grade sets are well written by authorities in the fields and are perhaps as reliable as the average text or reference book. If there is no such set in your school, there may be one in a small public library or in someone's private library that can be used, at least for special assignments. The teacher's own books will have some volumes suitable for reference if made available for certain students. A little campaign started for books on biological subjects, if given a proper build-up, will yield a nucleus about which a small reference library can be built. This requires careful planning and cannot take the nature of a demand. It may cause interested individuals or social groups to take some of the responsibility and give aid. Books that have been contributed need special care to see that they are treated properly and kept in good condition. In one school the teacher had her own small motion-picture film projector. She secured films on biological subjects and got permission to have little picture shows each week for admission to which any student in school paid 5 cents. The attendance was entirely voluntary. She soon had enough money to buy several groups of reference texts for the biology room.

A large number of books is not essential to the successful teaching of a biological subject. A few good general reference works in the field and such special pamphlets and articles as are generally available are adequate if the teacher is properly prepared. A small library or collection of books on biological subjects kept, if possible, in the classroom will be much more thoroughly worked by the class than an extensive collection submerged in a large library.

Selecting Books. Books and school are companion concepts and it is, as a rule, easier to get money for books than for any other equipment. When a small amount of money is appropriated, the teacher is sometimes at a loss as to what to spend it for, since there are so many possibilities. The following suggestions are offered as an aid in this problem.

It is always possible to consult numerous book catalogues to discover what the publishers have to offer. Such catalogues will have a brief description of books as to kind and content. It is, however, difficult to tell much about the desirability of a book from the publisher's description. Almost all publishers will send several books to school administrators or teachers on approval, and they may be returned if not found satisfactory. There are few schools that are so located that the teacher cannot make a trip to a library and there examine a number of books, choosing those which may be desirable for the purposes of his classes. A good librarian is always willing to assist and advise.

In large cities there are large book stores, especially secondhand book stores, near or in connection with colleges, where one may browse and see books before deciding upon their purchase. Consult other teachers in your field, especially teachers of experience, for their suggestions on books. The chief difficulty to overcome is that of spending a limited amount of money for books which turn out to be of little value.

Kinds of Books to Buy. For the small library it is best to buy books of a general reference character rather than those which deal with some very limited phase of the field. The more specialized books are also likely to be too technical in their treatment to be useful with elementary classes, and it requires a larger number of them to give the desired breadth to the collection. Books chosen for this purpose should be written, as far as possible, in an interesting and inspirational style, but they must be authoritative and scientific. Some of the more advanced texts make good reference books. At the end of each chapter of Part Two there will be found a list of references from which selections can be made for the subjects with which they deal, but the lists are rather incomplete.

Sources of Pamphlets, Booklets, and Articles. There are open to the teacher many sources of valuable reference material which may be obtained free or at little cost. The various departments of the Federal and state governments publish and send out numerous publications in their special fields of activity. Your state department of education should be able to advise you of such materials and tell you how to get them. Lists of publications and their cost, if any, may be had by writing to the Superintendent of Documents, Government Printing Office, Washington, D.C. Other sources of these articles are your state agricultural experiment station and the extension department of your state agricultural college. The literature from these government sources is reliable, attractive, and inexpensive, many papers being distributed free while others sell for 5 to 25 cents. Magazines and journals can be purchased secondhand at greatly reduced prices. Museums, scientific institutions, and commercial concerns furnish similar materials at little or no cost.

PROBLEMS

It is suggested that the following problems and others of a similar character be made the major portion of the work of student teachers or students in classes dealing with special methods in science teaching.

1. Write to your state department of education, state agricultural college, state experiment station, state department of conservation, and the Superintendent of Documents, Government Printing Office, Washington, D.C., for lists of their publications which would be useful in teaching biological subjects. Send for a representative group of these publications. Get extra copies of the lists or hectograph the one you received so that each member of your class may have one. Make a display of the samples for the benefit of the rest of the class.

2. Examine the catalogues of several equipment houses and from them make a list of all the apparatus you would think necessary for a class of 25 students. Consult Part Two, especially Chap. 13, for suggestions of substitutes for as much of the apparatus as you can find or imagine. Make a similar list of materials using the substitutes for as many as possible. From the prices given, estimate the reduction in cost which you might be able to effect by this method. Make this study available to the other members of your class and add to it any of their suggestions.

3. Collect a few animals of several different types (this will depend upon the location and the season) and prepare the necessary means of keeping them alive for one or more weeks in the schoolroom. Preserve some of them in various ways for dissection or for museum specimens. Present these to the class and answer such questions as the following: How were the animals caught? Where were they found? What kind and how much preservative was used? What kind of food and other

requirements are necessary for their maintenance? Would you collect them (as a teacher) or have your students collect them? What uses would you make of them in your teaching? (See Chaps. 12 and 14 to 23 for suggestions.)

4. Collect a few species of plants representative of the major groups such as algae, fungi, mosses and liverworts, ferns, and seed plants. Demonstrate how these may be grown in the laboratory for class purposes. Discuss methods of collecting and the habitats in which they may be found. Preserve specimens of each in suitable jars or bottles. Show how the green color of chlorophyll-containing plants may be preserved. Prepare some dry pressed specimens of a few seed plants mounted on herbarium sheets and label properly. How may such specimens be used in the classroom? (See Chaps. 12 and 14 to 23 for suggestions.)

5. Make a visit to one or more of the best-equipped schools in your city or county and consult the biology teachers and librarian for a list of the books which they have available for student reference work. Find out which books they find most useful. From the librarian get the titles and authors which the students prefer when they do voluntary reading in biology. Find out what points of advantage the different books have according to the teachers of the subject and increase your list to include some of the books which the teachers would like to buy for their classes if the money were available. Make hectograph copies (see Chap. 13) of your complete list and present each member of the class with one of these copies for his own record.

6. Chop some lean beef into ½-in. cubes in each of four test tubes with enough water to fill the tube one-third full. Plug these tubes with cotton and stand them upright in a pan of water or double boiler. Boil for not less than 30 min. When cool inoculate one tube with scrapings from the teeth, a second tube with dust from the table or floor, and a third with a drop of secretion from a sore or pimple. Do not contaminate the fourth tube, which is to be used as a check. Let these tubes incubate at room temperature for 4 or 5 days. Make a microscope mount from each tube and try to find different forms of bacteria (see Chap. 14 for technics). Need one buy bacteria slides or do without for class use?

7. In Chap. 22, Reproduction, are a description and drawing of a simple home-made incubator for hens' eggs. Assemble such an incubator, modifying it if you wish, and keep an accurate account of any expense. See how cheaply it may be made. Regulate it and then incubate a few fertile eggs for 3 days. Demonstrate and explain this to the methods class, comparing it to commercial incubators as to cost and utility.

8. Make a simple grass infusion of microorganisms (see Chap. 22). When this is well established prepare seven pure cultures of protozoa, such as paramecium, in jelly glasses (see Chap. 22). After about 10 days present your cultures to the rest of the methods class to illustrate the large number of organisms. Do not use anything in this preparation which will need to be bought; it is unnecessary. Such cultures would cost $3 to $10 each if purchased. Calculate the amount you have saved.

9. Build a Wardian case (terrarium) according to the directions given in Chap. 13. Do this from materials salvaged from a dump or scrap piles and do not buy anything. Stock the terrarium with plants and present it in class with a discussion of some of its uses for biology or botany. Could your students make these for a class which you may be teaching?

REFERENCES

1. Berg, Clifford O.: "Technique for Projecting Images of Living Animals, etc.," *Trans. Am. Microscop. Soc.,* **67**(4):384–387, plate 1, October, 1948.

2. Campsen, H. M., Jr.: "Purchase, Construction, and Use of Science Laboratory Equipment," 17th ed., American School and University, 1945. Pp. 382–385.

3. Duke, H. E.: "Providing and Adapting Apparatus and Equipment for Teaching Biology," *Am. Biol. Teacher*, **13**:128–131, October, 1951.

4. Heiss, E. D., E. S. Obourn, and C. W. Hoffman: *Modern Methods and Materials for Teaching Science*, The Macmillan Company, New York, 1951.

5. Morholt, E., P. E. Brandwein, and Alex. Joseph: *A Sourcebook for the Biological Sciences*, Harcourt, Brace and Company, Inc., New York, 1958.

6. Needham, J. G., and P. R. Needham: *A Guide to the Study of Fresh-water Biology*, 3d ed., Comstock Publishing Associates, Inc., Ithaca, N.Y., 1935.

7. Needham, J. G., et al.: *Culture Methods for Invertebrate Animals*, Comstock Publishing Associates, Inc., Ithaca, N.Y., 1937.

8. Palmer, E. L.: "Teaching with Things at Hand Locally," *Nature*, vol. 35, no. 9, November, 1942.

9. Turtox Leaflets and *Turtox News*. General Biological Supply House, 8200 South Hoyne Ave., Chicago 20, Ill. Leaflets on many useful subjects for projects and materials.

10. Weaver, R. L. "Using Outdoor Resources to Learn Science," *Am. Biol. Teacher,* **13**:54–56, March, 1951.

11. Woodring, M. N., M. E. Oakes, and H. E. Brown: *Enriched Teaching of Science in the High School*, Bureau of Publications, Teachers College, Columbia University, New York, 1941.

CHAPTER 8

--*{ Visual Education }*--

Visual instruction is as old as education itself. It was the original method in biological sciences when the naturalist devoted his study to organisms as he found them in nature. The results of his work he wrote down to be passed on to others; it was finally put into the form of books which treated of the various branches of biology. As education in this field found its way into the curricula of schools established for the training of great numbers of persons, it became more difficult to study original materials and easier to study about them from the writings of others. Part of this difficulty was overcome by the use of laboratory work with museum materials, preserved specimens, pictures, charts, and models. But the press of larger numbers of students and higher costs caused even these substitutes to be abandoned at times. The result has been that an increasingly larger proportion of the teaching of biology has been done from books and lectures. The simplicity of such a teaching procedure coupled with the ease of testing for memory of words has minimized the use of materials and visual aids to such an extent that those who are definitely concerned with essential values have revived the attention given to the visual phases of education. The rapid development of the motion picture has played a large part in stimulating a return to the use of visual means of instruction. In fact, many teachers erroneously think of visual education and picture projection as synonymous.

Visual education rightfully involves any and all means that may be employed in instruction whereby the student learns primarily by the aid of objects or materials rather than by reading or listening to lectures. In this broad interpretation the biology teacher may rightly include such technics and methods as field observations; trips to manufacturing plants, dairies, laboratories and greenhouses; the use of aquaria, terraria, microscopes, demonstrations and experiments; as well as the projection of still and motion pictures, photographs, drawings, models, charts, blackboard drawings, and the use of preserved and living organisms.

THE ESCAPE FROM VERBALISM

The escape from verbalism and the return to learning through seeing and doing mark a renaissance in education. Too few teachers realize that younger persons learn to generalize and use abstract learning through experiencing the concrete. Visual aids may do much of this sort of thing for the student. In biology classrooms the pupil learns words and phrases in quantities that are astounding, while drill in the mouthing of these expressions creates in both teachers and pupils a false assurance of value. The result is much learning and little understanding. The most valuable form of visual aid in biology is undoubtedly the specimen and, wherever possible, it should be the living specimen. The scarcest thing in some biology classrooms is the organism itself. There may be tables, chairs, books, microscopes, models, blackboards, pictures, and charts, but no plants or animals. There are teachers who have personal aversions toward such filthy things as slime molds and frogs and such creepy things as worms and insects. They encourage the development of a similar attitude in their students and excuse the failure to use many valuable materials by saying that the students do not like them. Much has been said throughout this book about the use of materials, especially living materials. In fact, all of Part Two is devoted to its encouragement.

WHY USE VISUAL AIDS?

Visual aids are used to accomplish four ends: (1) to stimulate interest and thus expedite learning, (2) to augment the learning process by providing visual experiences beyond the concepts of words, (3) to increase understanding by relating these experiences to life, and (4) to test for the application of learning.

Concerning the first of these ends we need say but little. To anyone who has taught or observed children at play, it is evident that they find greatest interest in those things which they can see or handle and which fire the imagination. This is especially true if the activity involves learning. They prefer the concrete experience. It is the thing itself which is interesting. In no area is this truer than in biology. Plants and animals are alive. What they are like and what they do hold a natural interest; hence their use as visual aids will stimulate interest in their study.

In regard to the second point, it is generally accepted that learning at the elementary level usually proceeds from the concrete to the abstract. This is not because the abstract is necessarily more difficult but because the concrete represents the object itself, the single experience, while the abstract is the result of many such similar or related experiences. Familiarity with the abstract may eventually render it easy to comprehend. For example, if you mention the word iguana to a class, the students are unable to call up any image or concept which corresponds to the word. If you explain that the iguana is a reptile, there is partial clarification since each student has had some experience involving reptiles. But if you explain further that it is a reptile of the lizard type, the meaning is still further clarified. However, all this depends upon words, words which have meaning only in terms of past experience. Suppose that you next add a series of visual aids, beginning with a blackboard sketch of some of the external peculiarities of the iguana. This would furnish some concrete visual concepts beyond your words. If you next flash upon a screen a photograph of such an animal, the experience is extended enormously. If the projection is a motion picture, there are additional experiences of the animal's behavior expressed beyond that of still imagery. But if you have a living specimen in a cage the experience beyond word concepts is again much greater. How different still must be the concept of the native who has seen hundreds of iguanas in their natural habitat, has chased and caught them, killed, prepared, and eaten them.

A biology student once brought a small yellow butterfly to his teacher and inquired what it was. He was surprised to find that it was a variety of the cabbage-worm butterfly since he had seen many white ones with spotted wings. Thereafter the words "cabbage butterfly" had an additional meaning for him. Thus visual experiences greatly enlarge the learning scope of the student.

Our third reason for using visual aids has to do with relating new experiences to life. Any educational technic which will do this is worthy of highest praise, for in so far as new experience can be related to the past it has fullness of meaning, and from such experiences come fullness of understanding on the part of the student. A biology teacher removed the tough, leathery hinge from the shell of a clam and asked members of his class to examine it and to tell of what it reminded them. There was little response. Then the teacher burned the material and fanned the smoke in their faces. There were immediate exclamations of "hair," "feathers," "burnt leather," etc. One student, a boy from the farm said, "blacksmith shop." He had smelled the pungent odor of the hoof when the hot shoe is being sealed. When requested to do so, he explained that the odor, which was an olfactory and not a visual image, brought back in a flash the details of an old blacksmith shop where he had taken the horses to be shod. There was the image of the flaming forge, the flying sparks, the great bellows, the red-hot shoe, the leather-aproned smith, all distinct visual experiences of the past which were definitely related to each other and to the smell of burning hoof. A girl explained that she had plucked and singed chickens and recalled the odor of burnt feathers. The other students had somewhat similar associations which made this new experience real. The teacher seized upon this opportunity to clinch his first objective and discussed the similarities of this new material with the better known animal products. In teaching it is always a safe practice to utilize the experiences of the student, and a wise teacher makes special effort to discover the kinds of experiences his students may have had. Likewise it is sound educational policy to choose such visual aids as will best relate or interpret the new experience in terms of the experiences of the past.

Our fourth use of visual aids is in testing for the application of learning. A visual aid may be used rightly as an illustration or additional explanation, but it may also serve as a problem to be solved and as a challenge for further study and discovery. As an example of this use, a teacher of botany had two of her students make two small wooden trays of exactly the same dimensions. These they filled with fine moist sand. They were then given 50 grains of corn which they separated at random and planted 25 in each tray. The trays were placed side by side near a window and watered equally through tubes which extended into the sand. One of the trays was covered by a box which excluded all light. During the next 10 days the class studied the factors of plant nutrition. At the end of that time they were confronted with this experiment and asked to predict what condition would be disclosed when the box was removed. The corn in the uncovered tray had grown to a height of 2 in. Various guesses were hastily offered, but when required to give reasons for their decision the students settled down to a consideration of the facts which they had acquired already through their recent study of nutrition. To some this recalled the factor of photosynthesis, and they concluded that the seedlings under the box would have grown to the extent of exposure above ground but would have died since there was no light, hence no chlorophyll, hence no photosynthesis. Others recalling food storage in seeds decided that the seedlings under cover would grow for some time above ground but would have died in a relatively stunted condition because of lacking the stimulating effect of light. These were logical applications of all the learning which the students had at the time, and the application was satisfactory from the teacher's point of view. The class was greatly surprised when the box was removed to find that the corn in the covered tray had reached a height of 4 in., which was twice that of the corn in the lighted tray, and that it was still flourishing though lacking in chlorophyll. The explanation of why plants grew more rapidly in the absence of light was lacking, and the teacher used this visual experience as a means of setting up a new problem for further study. In this way she had used the visual aid not only as a test for the application of previous learning but also as a means of stimulating interest, which greatly motivated the search for the new.

ESSENTIAL QUALITIES OF VISUAL AIDS

There are certain standards of essential qualities which may be used to determine the extent to which visual aids are of value in a learning situation. Their value depends upon the extent to which they assist in achieving the objectives of instruction and may be indicated briefly under the following heads: (1) accuracy, (2) relevancy, (3) realism, (4) comprehensibility, and (5) interest.

1. *Accuracy.* Whenever a visual aid is anything other than the organism or function which it represents, it becomes a matter of importance to determine the degree to which it is accurate in its representations. Chief among the offenders in accuracy are likely to be charts and models. It is difficult to make such aids as accurate as might be desired. The chart is lacking in the third-dimensional attributes and must always be viewed from a fixed position. The model overcomes both of these difficulties but is seldom as accurate in detail as the picture. The stereoscope has been used to advantage, offering the illusion of the third dimension plus the accuracy of the picture, which may even be photographic. However, photographic accuracy is not always an important issue, while accuracy of understanding is very important. For example, if one were teaching the principal parts of a flower by using a drawing of an apple blossom, it is of little importance whether the diagram resembles the apple blossom in every detail, but it is of utmost importance whether it shows the proper relation of such parts as ovulary, seed, receptacle,

anthers, filaments, and the like. For this reason a good diagram might be of even greater value than a photograph. It is the accuracy of the concepts produced rather than the accuracy of details in the visual aid which is important here. On the other hand, one teacher of botany used a large model of a fern prothalium in his class and then found that the students when given the actual tiny plants did not recognize them as being the same thing. The large size of the model and its lack of accurate detail were weaknesses. Another teacher used a diagram showing the vena cava from the ventral aspect as running beneath the liver. The students received the impression of the vein running into the liver and out again. In this case the use of a model giving three dimensions corrected the error. It is undoubtedly true that reasonably accurate visual aids are of great assistance to the student's comprehension, but one must constantly guard against any peculiarity of the aid which will produce incorrect concepts.

2. *Relevancy.* Our next standard of value is the extent to which any visual aid is directly related to the understanding of the subject matter. A visual aid could be accurate to the last detail, understandable, and interesting and yet be of little value because of its irrelevancy. If in the study of fishes the main objectives are to give an understanding of the characteristics of the fish group and some knowledge of their economic importance, it would be of little value to have preserved specimens of the African lung fish. They would be interesting and have some of the group characteristics, but are of little economic importance. The perch, goldfish, or herring would be far more relevant. In motion pictures one need not look at many of the educational films before finding excellent illustrations of films which are relevant and those which are not. After studying the amoeba and paramecium in class as types of protozoa, a teacher secured a film which she thought would present a number of other protozoa. When shown it was found to contain mostly amoebae and paramecia and a number of rotifers about which it gave much detail. The pictures were excellent but lost much of their teaching value because of irrelevant material.

Another film on the subject of the reactions of organisms was obtained and shown. It was a film with accompanying lecture. The pictures were good, clear, and limited exclusively to illustrating types of responses. The lecture was likewise limited to accurate explanations of these responses. This film had high educative value because of its complete relevancy.

3. *Realism.* As has been stated above, a visual aid may be anything from a crude diagram to a living organism. The crude diagram may be inaccurate, lacking in detail, unnatural in color, lacking in the third dimension, unable to move and uninteresting in appearance. Consequently it can have little realism. The living organism is entirely accurate, lacks nothing in detail, is natural in color and dimensions, may be motile, and is as interesting as it is possible for it to be. Its realism is 100 per cent. It has been said that visual aids have value in proportion to their degree of realism. This is generally true of visual aids, but as will be seen directly, it may be seriously modified by the degree of its comprehensibility. We all have had someone describe to us a particular scene in the country or a person whom we have never met. We could accurately redescribe the same scene or individual from our own image

formed from that person's description. But when we see the place or individual, we get an entirely different concept. This is verbalism versus realism. Students who are taught biology exclusively from books or lectures may do very well as measured by paper tests, but their appreciation of the reality of living things is sorely lacking. Most teachers of biology will tell you that one of their aims in teaching is the developing in the student of an appreciation of the nature of living things. If this is so, they should overlook no opportunity for making their teaching as real as possible, and this may best be done by injecting living materials and life problems into their course wherever possible. On the other hand, the degree of value of any specific visual aid is not always directly proportional to its realism. For example, a zoology teacher found that his class was experiencing considerable difficulty in locating and understanding the relation between parts of the circulatory system and certain organs even though each student had an excellent specimen. The teacher then drew a purely diagrammatic sketch upon the blackboard and explained it carefully. This clarified the difficulty because it was simple, readily comprehended and was therefore a valuable visual aid.

4. *Comprehensibility.* In the foregoing example each student was dissecting and studying the circulatory system of a good specimen, but the material was complicated. The students had little previous training or experiences that would enable them to succeed in their present undertaking. The comprehensibility of the material was not high, but otherwise the specimen had the qualities of a good visual aid. It was entirely accurate because it was the organism itself. It was entirely relevant because it was the thing being studied about. Being such, it was entirely real, and it was quite interesting to the students. It was lacking in comprehensibility since it was beyond the level of the class. A new visual aid was called into use, a rough diagram which lacked almost all the qualities of a good visual aid, except comprehensibility. Thus it supplied what was lacking, and the combination made the visual study a complete success. From such an illustration one may see that the quality of comprehensibility alone may be of sufficient importance to invalidate any particular visual aid. In other words, of what use is a visual aid if it is not comprehended by the student? In fact such an aid may become a hindrance. Therefore, in selecting and using our visual aids we must be cautious in choosing those things as aids which relate the new experience with past experience and which are within the comprehension of the students who are to use it.

5. *Interest.* The most elusive factor in education is interest. It is the will-o'-the-wisp which the teacher is always chasing. It is here and then it is gone. Its presence makes learning sought after; its absence makes learning repulsive. Its presence makes work a privilege; its absence makes work a punishment. A task that is sufficiently interesting defies time and the expenditure of effort. How can the teacher secure this interest?

One of the uses of visual aids is the stimulation of interest, but the mere use of an aid does not guarantee this interest. A good visual aid may be interesting by virtue of its other qualities. It may be accurate, possess realism, be entirely relevant, be easily comprehended and yet lack interest. But if it lacks accuracy and realism, is irrelevant, and is not understood, it is sure to be uninteresting. To stimulate interest a visual aid must be understandable first of all; second, it should have importance; third, it should be useful to the student; and, fourth, it should stimulate or satisfy his curiosity.

One could not expect students to maintain interest in something which is not understandable. To be interesting an object must have meaning. Sometimes interest is proportional to understanding. A pile of coal was just a lot of chores to one boy until he discovered that some of the pieces showed the forms of plant stems and leaves. He then spent hours searching for them and made a small collection of the better specimens. This led him to read something about the Coal Age and coal deposits. A class in physiology showed but the mildest interest in a plaster cast of the human torso until they found that it was made in sections which could be removed, disclosing all the internal organs. They were curious about the position and appearance of the lungs, liver, heart, stomach, intestine, kidneys, and reproductive organs. These things had meaning though they had never seen them. These things were important because each student possessed them. Their functioning was directly linked with the student's health, pain, and pleasure. Each one had felt his own heart throb after exercise or excitement, had felt the pangs of hunger and the pleasure of its satisfaction, had known the misery of a cold in the lungs and a pain in the colon. It was of use to him in solving some of his problems in that he had a better vision of his own mechanism, the relation of its parts and how they functioned. It was a good visual aid. It was interesting. The students were attentive while it was used. They were stimulated to ask many questions, to read books and articles. This interest is so essential to good visual aids that teaching cannot afford to be without it, and a great deal of effort should be exerted to secure such aids as may possess it.

THE USE AND MISUSE OF VISUAL AIDS

Early in this chapter we gave a partial list of visual aids. To discuss them all in any detail would require more space than is at our disposal. Entire volumes have been devoted to the subject, and some of these are recommended to the reader. It is difficult to select a few of these aids and to say that they are the more important. The value of an aid does not depend so much upon any intrinsic quality of the aid itself as it does upon the use made of it at a particular time. We have just discussed the qualities of good visual aids. We have seen that the quality of the aid is to some considerable measure a thing apart from the aid itself. No matter how perfect the aid may be, if it is irrelevant to the occasion of its use then it becomes of little value. Or it may lack some of the stated qualities of a good aid and yet become indispensable because of its relevancy or its simplicity, as in the case of the blackboard diagram mentioned above.

Some types of visual aids, however, do possess more of the desirable qualities than do others and, granting that they are used to best advantage, will assume a position of greater importance. First among these must be the living organism itself. There are times when to purchase, collect, or culture the living material would involve expense or work beyond its value, but teachers have used this more frequently as an excuse than as a legitimate reason for not providing the materials. There are times when some other type of aid may be more useful than the living organism even though it is lacking in realism. Such a case is well illustrated by special use of the motion picture. The twining of a tendril about a string, the unfolding of a flower, the incalculable beating of an insect wing cannot be seen nor understood from living specimens so well as when shown in long-interval or slow-motion pictures. It must be kept in mind, however, that such changes from the real as showing the flower in motion may in some instances produce incorrect notions in the student's mind if the subject is unfamiliar and the particular departure from normal is not carefully explained. Again the motion picture or the lantern slide may bring rare or unobtainable material to the classroom. There is a short film which presents the mammals of the Rocky Mountain region in relation to their ecology. Neither the materials nor this ecological relationship could be shown in class- or fieldwork, but the film can do this splendidly. Such usages of films have made the motion picture and sound film one of the truly great forms of visual aids. Their possibilities have just begun to be realized. There is a great future for their use educationally. The greatest difficulties lie in devising films that are real and accurate. Producers seem to have been slow to appreciate the fact that these films must be as accurate and realistic as possible rather than purely spectacular. In many states, films have been made available to schools by distribution from the state department of education, or some similar agency, at a small cost, which amounts to little more than postage and insurance. Good projection apparatus is now being produced at comparatively low cost.

These facts have given rise, however, to a danger which should not be overlooked. Teachers find that the showing of a film produces much of the excitement of the picture show and are likely to make use of it as a means of creating interest and especially as a substitute for materials and forms of classwork which might have been used to better advantage educationally. Whenever the motion picture or any other visual aid is used as a substitute for living materials or for a more suitable device, it becomes a detriment rather than an aid to good teaching. A most satisfactory type of film is one of the many short ones which may run not more than 3 to 5 min. and which fit into the teaching procedure—as a wall chart or model would do—to clarify, summarize, or emphasize a particularly important point. The short films are frequently more valuable than the longer ones. There is no reason why the motion picture should be looked upon as a lengthy entertainment extending for 15 or 20 min. The better films for classroom use produced in the future will probably be largely of the shorter variety.

Slides, filmstrips, and especially photomicrographs are valuable accessories to teaching. Photomicrographs are a means of making the still projector do the work of a large number of microscopes when microscopes are not available. Good photographs of microscopic preparations can be enlarged without loss of essential detail. These may be projected upon a screen, and each student sees what he would see if he were provided with a microscope and microscope slide. These have the additional advantage that all students see the same thing at the same time, and the photographs are usually made from uniformly good preparations. Projectors are made which purport to show images directly from microscope slides and from slides of living microorganisms. These projectors are usually expensive and of little worth in elementary teaching. They will show large or gross structure such as pollen grains or the veins of insect wings but are difficult to use for details of cell structure or microorganisms because when the image is enlarged sufficiently for room visibility the detail is lost. They may be used for a very small group, however, and are excellent for making enlarged drawings directly from microscope slides. See the list at the end of this chapter for further information and discussion, and the list of supply houses at the end of Chap. 13.

Models, charts, diagrams, and pictures have two types of uses. They may serve as aids in objectifying written or spoken words by substituting for specimens, or they may be constructed by the students as aids to their understanding. The way they are used at any time must be decided by the teacher. If the making of models and diagrams is not allowed to assume the level of mere pastime but is guided carefully as to accuracy and relevancy, the work has decided value. It need not be undertaken by all students. One sometimes witnesses the dilemma of a teacher or student making desperate effort to put certain ideas into words that will carry concepts of unmistakable significance. There results a conglomeration of phrases and gesticulations that are little short of comical, whereas a piece of chalk and a square yard of blackboard would have turned the trick with but few words. The hesitancy of teachers to use the blackboard is usually based upon a feeling of modesty because of a lack of artistic ability, but such drawing should be purely diagrammatic, not artistic. Good printed charts and diagrams may be accurate and even beautiful. If so, they can be of value in assisting the student to gain concepts that are impossible from words alone or even difficult to obtain from specimens, but it is often true that their complexity and detail may prove a source of confusion. A much more crude diagrammatic illustration built up by the teacher with chalk on the blackboard, adding each part with the development of each idea, will often be much better as a teaching aid than an expensive completed chart. The blackboard drawing plus the chart might be a valuable combination. The selection of purchased models or wall charts should be made with considerable care as to their accuracy and the degree to which they can be useful since it is possible to invest much money in such materials that are of little use. Models have the advantage of depicting objects in three dimensions, though they usually lack detail and may sometimes serve to furnish distorted and unnatural concepts. For example, a starfish could be modeled and painted so as to give a fairly accurate idea of the animal, but a clay or plaster model of a jellyfish is a sorry representation to the person who has never seen one at the seashore. The class may make its own models from water-softened modeling clay. These, when well done, may be painted, mounted, and kept for class use. With the cooperation of the fine arts and manual arts classes, it makes a good integrated project. For the use of toy models, charts, skins, and stuffed specimens in such studies as heredity, see Chap. 23.

Along this line, the teacher should not overlook the possibilities of amateur photography as an aid for biology. The teacher who is interested in photography may accumulate a very interesting and valuable library of pictures pertaining to biology or may encourage the formation of a school collection or a photography club by interested students. This has very special application to field study where unusual views or ecological situations may be obtained.

PROBLEMS

1. Write to the Bureau of Education, Department of the Interior, Washington, D.C., for a copy of Sources of Visual Aids, by C. M. Koon (see Ref. 11). After examining it carefully write a one-page summary of this pamphlet in the form of a book review. Make a set of hectograph copies and give each member of the class a copy for his notebook.

2. A class problem. Refer to Problem 1, Chap. 5. Take the units of subject matter as prepared in this outline and let each student choose one unit for which he will prepare a complete description of all the possible visual aids that might be used in its teaching. As a special assignment, two students may collect all the descriptions and have copies made to supplement the unit outlines prepared for Problem 1, Chap. 5, and either give each member of the class a copy or place a set in the library for each to copy.

3. Select a unit of subject matter from general biology and prepare all the different visual aids that you think would be used to advantage in its teaching. Present these to your methods class with a discussion of their use.

4. Make a list of 10 topics from biology. With each topic list at least one visual aid in the form of chart, model, or lantern slide. Make a second list of visual aids in the form of a list of motion-picture films that could be used with each of the topics. Make another list of aids composed of living materials appropriate for the same subjects.

REFERENCES

1. American Museum of Natural History: *Man and Nature.* Central Park West at 79th St., New York 24, N.Y. A catalogue of scientific publications for school use.

2. American Nature Association: *Nature.* 1214 16th St., N.W., Washington 6, D.C. Reproductions from magazine for science classes. Lists on request.

3. Anderson, K. E., et al.: "Toward a More Effective Use of Sound Motion Pictures in High School Biology," *Sci. Educ.,* **40**:43–54, February, 1956.

4. Arber, Agnes: *Mine and the Eye,* Cambridge University Press, New York, 1954.

5. Bachman, J. W.: *How to Use Audio-visual Materials,* Association Press, New York, 1956.

6. Berg, Clifford O.: "Technique for Projecting Images of Living Animals, etc.," *Trans. Am. Microscop. Soc.,* **67**(4):384–387, pl. 1, October, 1948.

7. Blanc, S. S.: "Evaluating Films for Teaching Biology," *Audio-Visual Guide,* **17**:14–19, October, 1950.

8. Burdick, A. B.: "Thrilling New Advances in Visual Aids," *Sci. Teacher,* **23**:237–238, September, 1956.

9. Butler, A. B.: "Reproducible Plaster Casts as Teaching Aids," *Sci. Teacher,* **19**:279–280, November, 1952.

10. Dale, Edgar: *Audio-visual Methods in Teaching,* Dryden Press, New York, 1954. Covers moving pictures, radio, television, and visual instruction.

11. Koon, C. M.: *Sources of Visual Aids and Equipment for Instructional Use in Schools,* U.S. Department Interior, Office of Education Pamphlet 80.

12. New York State College of Agriculture: *Cornell Rural School Leaflets.* Cornell University, Ithaca, N.Y. Very good science leaflets, issued throughout the year. Authoritative and interesting studies of eastern plants and animals.

13. Poole, L.: *Science via Television,* The Johns Hopkins Press, Baltimore, 1950.

14. Rulon, P. J.: *Sound Motion Picture in Science Teaching,* Harvard University Press, Cambridge, Mass., 1933.

15. Schick, R. D.: "Realistic Models of Plastic for Biology," *School Sci. and Math.,* **51**:523–526, October, 1951.

16. Science Educational Service: Science Publications. 201 N. School St., Normal, Ill. Lists of teaching materials for science teachers.

17. St. Lawrence, F. J.: "Use of Teaching Aids in Biology Textbooks," *Sci. Educ.,* **35**:77–81, March, 1951.

18. Turtox Leaflets. General Biological Supply House, 8200 South Hoyne Ave., Chicago 20, Ill. Free on request.

19. Wittich, W. A., and C. F. Schuller: *Audio-visual Materials,* 2d ed., Harper & Brothers, New York, 1957.

20. Woodring, M. N., M. E. Oakes, and H. E. Brown: *Enriched Teaching of Science in the High School,* Bureau of Publications, Teachers College, Columbia University, New York, 1941.

CHAPTER 9

⊶ How to Choose a Text ⊷

In many states there is state adoption of public school texts. Often a committee studies available texts and makes recommendations for adoptions. Sometimes a single text is adopted, sometimes two or three comparable texts are adopted, from which a school district may choose one. In these schools a teacher may be a member of the committee for selecting the text.

If a teacher has had some previous experience with texts he may be able to make a reasonable choice, but if not he will be confronted with the necessity of examining a number of books and selecting one from them. Anyone who has tried this feat will have realized the difficulties that confront him. The book which may make an appeal to the teacher may fail to stimulate any interest on the part of the beginning student. This difference is one that is very difficult to detect, and even teachers with years of experience may be surprised to find it true. The principal reasons for this difficulty lie in the fact that the teacher is trained in the field of subject matter and has come to have certain interests which he finds treated in the text. This training and interest are lacking in the beginning student. The teacher reads his own additional knowledge and experiences into the book; the student does not have this knowledge or experience. The book may use terminology or treat the subject in a manner very similar to more advanced texts with which the teacher is very familiar. These facts make the book seem easier and more desirable to the teacher but may be the very sources of greatest difficulty to the student. The fact is that a teacher cannot look hurriedly through a book and decide whether or not it would make a suitable text. Even a careful study of a book may not be sufficient.

CRITERIA FOR CHOOSING A TEXT

What, then, are the criteria for choosing a proper text? A number of sets of items have been compiled and published as guides to selecting a text. These items will be discussed, but before they can become of any use, it is essential that a very important question be answered by the teacher. How is the text to be used in your course? That is, will the text be the course? Will its contents be practically the only source of information? Will its order of presentation and its questions and exercises be followed closely? Or will the course be planned and outlined by the teacher and the text be supplemental? Will it be assigned intermittently for specific readings and information while the sequence of the subject matter, the selection of appropriate problems and projects, and the asking of pertinent questions come from the teacher and his planned course? Which courses the text will serve may make a vast difference in the character of the book to be selected.

The lists of criteria mentioned above seem, without exception, to assume the first situation to be true, that the text will determine the course. Unfortunately this happens in too many cases. Since it is so frequently true, we shall summarize six of the principal criteria. Many of these points are desirable considerations in the selection of a text however it may be used.

1. *Is the subject matter suitable to the course?* This will necessitate that the teacher have clearly in mind what major topics should be included in the course in order that the books may be examined to determine whether or not these areas are covered. It will further mean that the examiner shall not decide merely from a table of contents but shall read carefully a major portion if not all of each of the subject-matter topics in each book examined. How completely these areas are covered becomes of greater or less importance in proportion to the extent to which teacher and students are to be guided by and limited to the one text.

2. *Are the organization and presentation of the contents suitable to the level and interest of the class for which the book is being chosen?* A book may have a concise and logical organization, and yet it may differ so radically from the organization chosen by the teacher for the course that the book becomes a source of confusion unless its exact sequence is followed. On the other hand, the fact that a book reads logically from page to page or from topic to topic may appeal to the teacher with a broad background of training, but it must be remembered that for the student in an elementary course a psychological organization is usually to be preferred even when it may be less logical. The teacher should not lose sight of the fact that the book is being selected for the student and not for the teacher.

Has the author written clearly and interestingly? Does his style cause the reading to flow along? Is there an arousing of curiosity which keeps one reading on for further knowledge? Is the presentation problematic—does it present questions which are either answered by reading or solved by applying the knowledge gained from study? When a "problem" or "exercise" is given, does it explain something, have direct bearing upon the subject studied, or merely set a task to be done? When the textbook is to be the basis for the course, these points are of prime importance. The text should not be merely a compilation of factual material but should be also a director of the student's thinking. It should challenge his curiosity, his understanding, and his ability to think constructively and scientifically, as well as his memory. Its explanations should present the solution to a problem whenever possible, and this solution should be given in a lucid and logical order which will stand as an example of thinking and for further thinking.

Then for the sake of practice there should be a number of definite problems throughout the text which are unsolved but which are to be solved by the student. These should be more than questions of a review character, which are so often found at the end of each chapter, to be answered by turning back the pages of the book. Questions of this direct kind are of some value if used as a review to test the memory of the reader and may help him in his self-testing, but they are not sufficient. The real test of the learner is his ability to use what he acquires by relating his information to real situations of life and by using his knowledge in problem solving. Another procedure employed in some modern texts is a pretesting device consisting of questions placed at the beginning of chapters and units of subject matter which are intended to test the amount of knowledge of a topic which the student may already have before he begins his study from the text. These questions again are mostly for information, whereas they could just as readily be problematic, the student referring back to them after studying the subject to see if he has acquired information or learned a method of procedure which will enable him to arrive at a solution after his study, if he has been unable to do so before.

3. *Are the factual contents reliable?* While the correctness of the factual contents of a text is a matter of great importance, it is not at all likely that a text will contain many errors. Some minor mistakes may get into almost any book, but in addition to the fact that most authors are themselves authorities in their fields, it is customary to have specialists read various parts of a manuscript before it reaches the publisher. Also all reputable publishers have their own expert readers who review manuscripts for them before they are set in type. Thus, gross errors are usually avoided.

But widespread among texts on biological subjects is a different source of error that needs guarding against. This is teleology. It is the assigning of purpose or knowing intent to lower organisms where there is no evidence that such a capacity exists. For example, a textbook in general biology written by authors who are well trained in subject matter and who are teachers of repute contains a picture of a forest below which is a caption asking the student to note that the trees have all grown tall and straight in order "to reach the light."

If authors who use such explanations are questioned about the usage, they usually reply that they know that the use of words is very loose but that they see no great harm in it. The harm comes from the erroneous practice which it encourages in the student's thinking. There are known definite reasons which explain how plants come to be long and straight in subdued light or darkness. This information is due the young student, and it cannot be justly thrust aside by an explanation which assigns desire or reason to trees in a woods.

4. *Are illustrations, graphs, charts, and tables clear, attractive, and appropriate?* For elementary course work this is a very important item. A good reproduction of a photograph or a good diagram will often tell more and better in a few inches of space than twice the space devoted to words alone. Pictures appeal to children especially, but they make any book attractive when properly done and placed. Special diagrams, graphs, and tables of data are not especially attractive but are to be included because of their utility. They should not be included unless they serve a distinct purpose, and then they should be used by the student. How to compile data from observation and experiment and how to express it in tables and graphs should be a part of the early science training of the child.

The number of illustrations is of less importance than their quality, arrangement, and appropriateness. Some books seem to be actually crowded with illustrations, causing too frequent breaking up of the reading matter, while others give a feeling of distinct need for more. Nothing could be more useless than a picture, no matter how good, which has no place in the text in which it appears.

5. *Does the use of type and arrangement of the material make reading easy?* An examination of several books simultaneously will probably disclose considerable variation in the size of type used in their printing. When a book is to be studied and read at length, such things are important. The type size and spacing should be such as to make the physical part of reading easy.

In looking at the text pages do you find that the topics stand out because of paragraph headings in bold type or italics? Can you tell quickly what the general character of a chapter is, or must one read at length to gain this information? Are the pages, and thought, continually being broken up by paragraphs set in very small type or by references to footnotes which one must pause to read or completely ignore? These items are important to young students, especially in a new field of study where effort is required to follow a trend of thought even when it is clear and uninterrupted.

In this connection should also be considered the use of references and glossary. The references to other parts of the text are often valuable, and references to well-known books on special subjects should be made at appropriate places, such as by inserts in the text or by listing at the ends of chapters or units. The question of glossary usually takes one of two forms. Either a glossary is placed as an appendix in the back of the book, or words are defined wherever they first appear in the book. There is an advantage in having the word defined when used except that when it is repeated throughout the book it cannot be redefined each time. Therefore, the reader who has not read consecutively from the first pages may miss the definition. Because of this difficulty it is more likely that a glossary, when one appears, will be found as a compilation at the end of the text.

A complete index is essential to a good text. Most books contain fair indexes but some do not. Where a text is not followed from beginning to end but is used as a book of readings or reference, the index becomes indispensable. It is a noteworthy fact that even advanced students make little use of an index. It is not uncommon to see a student searching through page after page of a book for a special topic or even consulting the table of contents while a good index enumerating the exact pages is being ignored. See that your text is well indexed, and see that your students become conscious of it through frequent use.

6. *What is the appearance and the cost of the book?* Choose five books at random from a bookshelf and lay them before you on a table. Which book makes the strongest appeal to you because of its appearance? When you have chosen one, examine it to determine why it is more appealing. What does it have that is absent from the others, and what do they have that interferes with their appeal? You will find that size and proportion are of great importance. One seems too thick and short, another too long and narrow. One seems to have pages almost as large as the cover, causing it to seem ready to lose something. Another is very gaudy and cheap in its color and

material, and the title is badly stamped. The attractive book has a good grade of cover, is pleasing in color and printing, and is so proportioned as to give a feeling of substantial balance. The paper is of good quality and weight. These items are of far less importance than those which concern the contents of a book, but they make an impression upon the student sometimes without his being conscious of it. Witness the fact that when you ask a student what text he studied two or three years ago he will reply, "I can't remember but it was a rather large book with a dark red cover," which is not very helpful but shows the impression such things make. They also have some part in determining the cost of the book which, while it is of minor consideration, is a factor that will be closely watched by administrators.

If the above six groups of criteria are used in measuring the value of any text and they check favorably in almost all these respects, the teacher may feel certain that the selection is likely to be reasonably satisfactory. In addition to the above, some writers suggest checking the author of the book on such points as: what experience he has had; what degrees and honors he has gained; what investigations he has carried on; what recognition he has been given in certain publications. All such items are of no importance in choosing a book. In fact it would be highly desirable if the authors' names and connections as well as that of the publishers could be entirely eliminated in making the selection. If a book checks up to a high standard according to all six of the criteria discussed above, it is a good book regardless of who wrote it and regardless of whether his name appears in this or that reference list. You are choosing a book on its merits and not upon a reputation of its author, often gained in other ways. You are interested in the book regardless of its author. In general, the more widely authors have been recognized and honored, the more able they are and the more likely are they to have produced a good text. But if they have produced a good text it will be apparent when you check the book, and checking the author will not alter the value of the book in the least. Furthermore, it is a well-known fact that excellent teachers are sometimes poor book writers while splendid books are sometimes produced by those who lack the personal qualifications of a great teacher. So forget the author and publisher when making your selection, forget the friendly salesman who provided the examination copy and think of the book, the class, and the kind of course you would like to teach.

A REFERENCE-BOOK PLAN

All the above is recommended to the teacher who is confronted with the necessity of making book selections, and few teachers will escape this task at some time or other. It seems that this is the place at which to discuss an alternative to the usual choosing of a text for the course. To be sure, if it is so ordained by the authorities that a single text is selected and required for each student, this may have to be followed out, but even then the teacher should propose the following plan, which is in nearly all respects a far superior one to the uniform text plan.

The individual student is not provided with his own text, but a set of texts are bought and placed in the school as a part of the library. These books should be kept in the classroom if at all possible since it will often be desirable to use them during class. The books are not all alike nor are they by the same author. They consist of several (three to six) copies of six or seven different texts which deal with the field covered by the course, plus some six to ten additional reference books of a general character. Thus the limitations of one text may be offset by the others and a much wider field covered than could be possible from a single text. The students use these books during study periods and class periods. They may be signed out for home use to special students, but most of the work is done at school, as it should be, and the books are left there where several classes may make use of the same volumes. Some of the books will be found most useful while the class is studying one topic, and others will be more useful for another topic. The students must learn to use more than one book. If all copies of one text are in use, another must be chosen. The student soon learns to decide upon the book he is to use. He learns to use the indexes of all the books, and he may find it necessary to employ several volumes for a single study. He gets different points of view from different writers and finds it necessary to become critical and discriminating. The classes using this variety of books will have a distinct advantage over a class using but one text. It is an excellent plan to follow even if the rules insist upon the student possessing a single text of his own. Students take to the idea and are found reading the special reference volumes in preference to their own.

It is true that teaching a class without a uniform text is more difficult than with such a text. It requires that the teacher have a broad knowledge of the subject matter in the field. It requires that the teacher make a complete, coordinated, and detailed plan of the course to be pursued in teaching the class. He must be familiar with each subject-matter unit and with the texts available. He must weigh each topic and decide what part of the total time and effort should be devoted to it. He must plan more carefully the amounts to be done by students where there is individual variation and must above everything make possible the complete satisfaction of the students who have unusual abilities in this field. However, it is possible to make provision for these differences much more easily in such a well-planned course than where a one-book course is given in the same manner to all.

In estimating the cost of this plan of providing texts, let us use an example. Suppose that in a school there are three sections of 25 students each, all taking the one course in biology. Suppose that a satisfactory textbook could be purchased at $4.25. It would cost $318.75 to supply all students. Suppose that the alternative plan was carried out and that five different texts of high merit were chosen and 10 copies of each are provided at an average cost of $4.25 per copy. This would cost $212.50. Suppose that 10 reference books are also provided at an average cost of $6 each. This would cost $60, making a total expenditure of $272.50. These books may be divided into two or three sets and one kept in the classroom while the others are placed in the library or study hall for study purposes. Certainly it offers a better equipment for the classes than the single-book choice. The number of copies of each text provided would vary with its usefulness, and it might be possible to reduce the cost considerably.

Where the school furnishes the major texts for its students the plan need have but little financial difficulties since it costs no more or even less. The books last much longer than those which students carry back and forth between school and home and become more of a permanent part of the equipment, making the cost over a period of years much less. In schools where the students provide their own books, it is a little more difficult. Each student should have a book fee to pay which is considerably less than the cost of a book. This might amount to about what he would lose on the resale of a book at the end of the year. In the meantime the school board will have to provide an additional outlay to supply enough books for the first year, but the fees would return this amount in about three years and there would still be a fairly good supply of books in fair condition. Once established the plan maintains itself at little cost, and the supply is kept up to date by additions.

In selecting books for the reference plan of teaching the same set of criteria will be used, but the standards will be different when the teacher's plan is the deciding factor for the course instead of the plan of a text. This gives great flexibility to the course. The teacher plans the procedure and chooses what shall be done with each part. The students are given all the freedom commensurate with their needs, interests, and abilities. There is little need for considering whether all the teaching technics are provided in the text since they are provided in the teacher's plan. The text does not need to become an intricate methods book as well as a text. The attempt to make them such has greatly interfered with the value of some recent secondary school texts, and their use has handicapped and destroyed the initiative, versatility, and independence of many a capable teacher.

WORKBOOKS

With most of the texts that have been placed on the market in recent years has appeared a workbook written to accompany the text. Considering the large number of these workbooks, it is surprising that so few of them have so little of merit to warrant their use. They are composed of large sheets in a temporary binding, designed to be written in and not used over again. The most widely adopted form consists of questions, the specific answers to which are found in corresponding chapters of the text for which the workbook was written. Even the pages where the answers appear are designated for the student. It is obvious that in most cases the substance of the text chapters was transformed from a declarative statement into an interrogative form and placed in the workbook. A variation of this is a form of statement in the workbook which is incomplete, blanks being left for filling in by the student, the words to be filled in being found on designated pages in the text. They usually provide diagrams to be labeled and space for definitions or descriptions. Some contain review questions, some contain self-tests, and some are accompanied by sets of teacher tests. Most of these tests are not diagnostic and are therefore of questionable value (see Chap. 6, Evaluation).

A good workbook might be of very considerable value to both student and teacher. Instead of the student spending his class periods looking up information and filling in his workbook, he should be examining materials, recording observations, experiments, and demonstrations. The workbook should supply him with this kind of work plus references to text material upon the same subject but not to the specific answers. The work should be primarily from biological material with problematic questions calling for the application of facts learned both from reading and observation instead of telling the student to look at certain pages in the text where the complete answer is given. The self-testing program should be regularly distributed through the book, with a provision made for the student to keep the results of his tests for self-analysis and for comparison with the results of his teacher tests. The tests should measure more than memory of facts found in the text. When these poorer workbooks are used, there is the danger that the teacher will confine the student's work too closely to the workbook and text and prepare for but little student activity in class. The labeling of diagrams is likely to become a substitute for organisms and the hunting up of answers to questions a substitute for problem solving. A form of workbook, however, which avoids most of these objectionable features might well be a very useful educational instrument. Therefore, in choosing a workbook, when one is required, the teacher should use much care, selecting one on its own merits and not merely because it was prepared to accompany the text. In most instances the fact that it was specifically prepared for the text is one of its greatest weaknesses.

PROBLEMS

1. Consult the references at the end of this chapter and make out a card for judging texts according to your own ideas of what should be used. Compare with the cards made out by other members of your class and discuss.

2. Take about five or six textbooks written for the same kind of class, that is, botany, biology, zoology, and examine them carefully. Score them upon your own card. Compare the results with the scoring of others for the same books.

3. Get two or three workbooks for general biology from the library. Check two of the work units. If possible, get the author's text which it is supposed to accompany. Look up the references given in the workbook and see to what extent they answer the workbook questions without requiring thought from the student.

4. Examine several different workbooks to discover if any of them are built primarily around such activities as

    a. Student observation of material, experimentation, or demonstration

    b. Problem solving requiring application of knowledge rather than mere recall of facts

    c. Self-testing from diagnostic tests

5. Take two of the lessons from a workbook which impresses you as doing the least beyond answering questions and rewrite these two lessons in such a manner as to utilize materials and present problems for the student.

6. Using the results of Problem 5 above prepare a self-test and a teacher test that are diagnostic to accompany the revised lessons.

REFERENCES

1. Blanc, S. M.: "Comparison of the Biology Interests of Tenth and Eleventh Grade Pupils with a Topical Analysis of High School Biology Textbooks," *Sci. Educ.*, **40**:127–132, March, 1956.

2. Bray, W. J.: "The Selection of High School Science Textbooks," *Sci. Educ.,* **18**:147–151, 1934.

3. Crombie, C. W.: "Selecting Science Textbooks," *Sci. Educ.,* **35**:276–278, December, 1951.

4. Knepp, T. H.: "The Reading Choices of High School Biology Students," *Turtox News,* vol. 28, no. 8, August, 1950.

5. Lampkin, R. H.: *Variability in Recognizing Scientific Inquiry: An Analysis of High School Science Textbooks,* Bureau of Publications, Teachers College, Columbia University, New York, 1949.

6. Mallison, G. G., et al.: "Reading Difficulty of Textbooks for High School Biology," *Am. Biol. Teacher,* **12**:151–156, November, 1950.

7. National Education Association, Science Teachers Association Department: Bibliography of Reference Books for Elementary Science, 1956. 1201 16th St., N.W., Washington 6, D.C.

8. Packard, C. E.: "Most and Least Helpful Features of a Biology Text as Seen by Students in Course," *Am. Biol. Teacher,* **13**:29–31, February, 1951.

9. St. Lawrence, F. J.: "Are Heavy Textbooks Necessary?" *Sci. Teacher,* **18**:72–73, March, 1951.

10. Waterman, I. R.: "When You Choose a Textbook," *Phi Delta Kappan,* **33**:267–271, January, 1952.

CHAPTER 10

⸺⁓ Trends in the Curriculum ⸺⸺

In their early effort to educate American youth our ancestors established two types of schools. The first was the simple elementary school in which the more or less figurative ideal was the teaching of the three R's. This was designed for defeating illiteracy and for providing the common citizen with such elementary knowledge as would be of most practical worth to him in the activities of his everyday life. To be able to read, write, and do elementary calculations in numbers was a universal necessity. Life was complicated for most individuals then, and their time was mostly occupied with the labors which secured for them the very essentials of life. The leisure class was small. It did exist, however, and there were many who deemed an education above the most elementary level a very desirable provision for their children. As a result there was established a second type, the Latin grammar schools and the private secondary schools in which such subjects as the classical languages, history, literature, rhetoric, music, and art were the chief sources of culture.

During most of the first century of our national development there was a steady educational growth which was a natural result of an era of scientific discovery and invention. That period marks the development of the public high school offering higher education to all classes. Individuals and communities that were once isolated were brought into close association with the rest of the world because of rapid advances in communication. People whose grandparents once waited weeks for meager news brought by stage now read the happenings of yesterday brought by telegraph from great distances to their daily press. Natural resources with easy transportation and rapidly growing markets gave great impetus to industry and commerce. Necessities, comforts, luxuries, and wealth were the rewards. People became generally interested in the affairs of individuals whom they never saw and in the affairs of those upon whom their economic success often depended. There were unusual opportunities for individuals of exceptional talent or special training. The schools were expected to provide the special training, and there was sufficient money to give nearly everyone the opportunity for a broader education. Curricula grew to take care of the demand. Subjects not only became numerous, they became broader and deeper as well. The teacher no longer taught all the subjects, especially in the higher grades, but he became a supposed authority in one or two fields. In these he taught and sought to create public interest. New subject-matter fields were being added rapidly because of a demand for student training in many areas. This encouraged specialization in the training of teachers, and the result was more and more departmentalization of the schools until it sometimes reached into the earliest *grades*.

The interest in nature and life was given a mighty impetus in the latter part of the nineteenth century by the controversies which followed the publications of Darwin, Huxley, Wallace, and Spencer in regard to evolution. This conflict continued to be fanned into flame periodically until it culminated in the famous Dayton, Tennessee, trial (1925) of the school teacher convicted of teaching evolution contrary to state law. Since that time the mention of evolution has scarcely produced any visible concern in the public mind. Attention, however, has been focused more and more upon those questions of biology which are related to health, public welfare, and social and personal behavior.

THE DEVELOPMENT OF DEPARTMENTALIZATION

Almost the entire educational system became imbued with the spirit of efficiency, and the means of obtaining it was by specialization. To this was added a demand for speed. More discoveries, new inventions, greater efficiency were demanded. Even the common laborer became a "specialist" and took pride in being so thought. The fine arts, literature, and philosophy struggled along but scarcely could be said to keep pace with mechanized industrialism. It was customary to organize the course in each field in such a fashion that any student could become specially trained by pursuing a sequence of courses in that subject, or he could be made ready to follow them still further in college. Industrial and commercial training courses were enlarged for those not contemplating college education. But what of the young student? He was not yet a specialist. He was being worked upon by a group of specialists. He had not yet chosen a field of special effort; therefore he was material for any field. Though the student could not become a specialist in all fields, he was treated educationally as though he could. He might choose a sequence of subjects to make him a specialist in one field, but he must pursue a similar sequence in all other fields if he were to study in them at all. The error became apparent and a reaction developed against it.

THE REACTION AGAINST DEPARTMENTALIZATION

A new interest in psychology, especially in its application to learning and educational procedure, aided somewhat the changes that came about as a result of the reaction. The idea of the junior high school began to take root, and this was an important step toward a much more psychologically sound administration of the physical and mental differences and needs of students at puberty as compared with those of more advanced adolescence. It made for a clearer understanding of the problems of education aside from those of subject matter or content. There is now a widespread acceptance of the principles of the junior high school and of the organization and the administration of such schools, but there is not always a clearness of understanding of those principles among the teachers in junior high schools. The subjects are taught in much the same way, the class routines are gone through, and there is sometimes little difference between the junior and senior high schools in general treatment. The senior division most generally is segregated from the junior division but not always. Sometimes the separation is primarily one of administration. The true meaning of the junior high school period of the student's life and how it may best be handled should be clearly understood, and those teachers who are adept at this most difficult type of teaching should be properly compensated and honored so that it will no longer be considered an "advance" to change to higher grades. In most instances the junior high school curriculum remained as departmentalized as that of the senior high school.

Then the reaction set in which attempted to break down the lines of departmentalization. Like most reactions against well-established ways of doing things, it came gradually. Changed emphasis was a dominant factor in instituting such a reaction. So long as the aim of training in science was the learning of detailed information, departmentalization served well enough. But when the emphasis shifted from *what* to *why* and *how* a closer correlation between fields of learning became necessary. These changes in emphasis necessitated changes in the preparation of teachers.

1. The teacher had to become somewhat of an authority in a number of fields. Formerly he might learn the facts of his field and rest secure upon his knowledge, but if he was now to be required to explain these facts, if he must know *why* and *how* as well as *what,* then he must be reasonably familiar with all closely related fields. The botanist, for example, must know some zoology, the zoologist some botany, and both must know some chemistry and physics, etc. The biologists soon recognized these necessary relationships, and training in related sciences became usually a part of the prescribed courses for biology teachers in the better training schools. Some of the other fields have been less ready to recognize this relation. It was some time before sociologists recognized biology and genetics as proper background for social studies in addition to psychology and before psychologists recognized physiology and anatomy as fundamental to psychology. The most recent tendencies toward complete integration in subject-matter fields are requiring a still broader training on the part of teachers in that the teacher must visualize his special field as an integral functional part of the life problems of his student.

2. The teacher had to be versatile and adept at interpreting and relating facts. This, of course, was but part of the need for diversity of training. Theoretically, the more widely the teacher was trained, the better he should be in these respects. Of course this does not follow necessarily. The ability to correlate facts and to interpret phenomena in terms of properly coordinated causes and effects may vary with innate abilities and with types of training. The reaction which brought about the necessity for broader and better training in subject matter also placed a premium upon these abilities as well.

THE TENDENCY TO INTEGRATE

The results of this reaction against departmentalization have crystallized into several types of integration, first of which is the *combined* or *mixed course,* second, the *core course* of the *fused-subjects* type, and third, the *integrated* or truly *unified-subjects* course.

1. *Combined Courses.* At its peak, departmentalization had established astronomy, botany, chemistry, physiography, physiology, physics, and zoology as high school sciences. The tendency to integrate brought in general science as a mixture of all these. Early texts, and many recent ones, were so organized that a small amount of space was devoted to chemistry, a small amount to physics, a small amount to biology, and so on, the subjects still taught separately but in much less time. The usual objection was raised at once. The new subject was a hodge-podge with not enough of any science to warrant the name. This was countered with the excuse that few students completed enough years of school to be able to learn anything in most of these fields unless they received it as general science. Both of these objections were true, and the situation has not been completely solved as yet, though there has been a move in the right direction in the recent tendencies toward true integration. In general science there has been a minimum of biology and a trend toward building natural science into a subject coordinate with the physical sciences, chemistry, and physics. This has resulted in a major decrease in human physiology, botany, and zoology as separate subjects. When this combination was first begun, the authors of texts and the teachers saw little else in the new arrangement than the necessity for taking what had been taught as botany, zoology, and physiology and reducing them to about one semester of botany and one semester of zoology and appending the new title of biology. There was much dissatisfaction on the part of the teachers who, trained under a strict departmentalized procedure, were unable to teach both subjects well. The result was that most of the biology was either botany with a smattering of zoology or vice versa. The early biology texts were written mostly by college professors who were botanists or zoologists, and the texts were decidedly unbalanced. But biology as a combined subject has taken a newer form based upon those principles which apply to living things generally. It seeks to emphasize the features of personal health and public welfare and to teach fewer isolated facts but more generalizations. It has a decidedly valuable place in the high school curriculum and in its newer aspect has frequently found a place as a survey subject in colleges. In high schools it is rapidly gaining the prestige that heretofore has been granted to such sciences as chemistry, physics, and mathematics, and since its significance is as great or greater than any of these, there is no reason to suspect that it will not continue to be given its rightful place in the curriculum.

2. *The Core Course (Fused Subjects).* As a second outgrowth of the reaction against departmentalization there was suggested the so-called core courses. In general these are attempts to tie together certain subject-matter fields of closely related interest by centering several courses around one course recognized as the core. Frequently this was the social science course

toward which such other subjects as art, literature, political geography, and sometimes biology were supposed to contribute. This idea of fused subjects did not obliterate the departmental lines but cut across them and in some cases subjugated certain of them. For example, in a junior high school an attempt was made to establish a core course by fusing several subjects. In this case the main course was American history. Around this were fused the subjects of American literature, general science, and geography. The history course dominated the thought of all lessons. American literature was approached from its historical aspects, and what the student received from the literature side was largely a list of authors with dates and titles of their writings. General science resolved itself into a history of science especially in America. Too much emphasis was placed upon the lives of a few scientists with a few facts concerning their works. One or two special papers prepared by students upon the relation of scientific discoveries to industrial development were quite valuable. The geography lent itself well to the historic aspects of all the subjects, and the contributions of a very capable teacher emphasized the geographic influence in the development of the nation.

This attempt at a fusion course had much of value beyond the usual separate courses. Yet it was but a slight step away from the departmentalized procedure, since certain days were set aside when the science teacher took the class and certain days when the English teacher held sway, and the course plan was almost completely dominated by the historical coloring. These methods did not allow so much breakdown of departmental viewpoint for the student as should have been the case. He still was conscious of the fact that he was studying political history, American literature, etc., as separate subjects.

Such a plan was often more logical than workable. As will be seen readily, the success of any such coordination will depend upon the degree of cooperation among the teachers in the fields involved and upon the extent to which the contributions of each department are definitely integrated into a meaningful whole for the student. These two points, unless successfully carried out, were of sufficient importance to wreck many a well-meant attempt at fusion courses.

3. *The Integrated, or Truly Unified, Courses.* A variation of the core idea known sometimes as integrated or unified courses has been attempted in an effort to secure a better balanced relationship between the subjects involved. These may be considered as still representing experiments, efforts to find a means of coordinating the subject matter for the student's sake without disrupting the departmental organization or allowing one field to dominate the course out of proportion to its importance. The underlying principle upon which such an integration is based is educationally ideal. The most modern methods employed in accomplishing these results have to do with the organization of the content around the real problems of life which lie within the actual experiences of the student.

How Floods Are Controlled and Water and Other Natural Resources Conserved

1. General aim: the study of water conservation and its relation to the life and industries of a region

2. Special topics that will probably be included in the studies made by students:
   a. Rainfall, weather, and the work of the weather bureau
   b. Soils, soil formation, and drainage
   c. The relation of surface water to ground water
   d. Natural vegetation of a region
   e. Animal life of the same region
   f. Rock formations and their relation to soil and drainage
   g. The relation of rainfall and drainage to plant and animal life
   h. Ways of conserving water
   i. Dam construction
   j. Dams and conservation of wild life
   k. Dams and agriculture, irrigation
   l. Dams and their relation to power; hydraulic and electric
   m. Power and industrial development, etc.
3. Age level: seventh to ninth grades
4. Departmental areas associated in studies: physics, chemistry, agriculture, social sciences, manual arts, general science, biology, and geography

Such problems are being used as "How our community attempts to control epidemics and maintain the public health," "What is the organization and work of our chamber of commerce?" "How are floods controlled and water and other natural resources conserved?" For purposes of further clarifying the way in which this method works, suppose that we follow a brief explanation of the last problem as it might be carried out logically in a rural consolidated school of the Mississippi River valley.

THE APPROACH

The desire of the teacher is to make the subject of practical value and to make it as real as possible by objectifying the principles involved. Energy transfer is so vital to all phases of life and activity that it is best understood in its relation to natural phenomena and to man's industries. The sources of energy and their conservation are, therefore, a key to the study project. As many problems as one could wish may be undertaken in connection with the study. A point of entry may be the study of early sources of energy in a country such as pioneer America. When water power has been discussed, the stage is set for the beginning of the project proper. A suggested method of doing this is to allow individuals or small groups to choose certain vital elements (problems) of the project. Such problems may be: (1) How can the water of any region be conserved? (2) How are small and large dams constructed? (3) How is water power utilized? (4) How is a water wheel constructed? These may be formulated after conferences with other teachers, students, or interested persons outside the school, or after reading in the field.

After considerable interest has been aroused, the teacher now asks whether the group would like to undertake a program in which it would actually carry out in construction the items which have been chosen as problems. The construction of a small dam, the conservation of water through the reservoir method, the construction of a water-driven power plant, the utilization of this power in various ways by transforming it into electricity, heat, light, and motion may be studied. The great number of other conservation problems which might also be involved will soon suggest themselves. General grouping of some of these has already been mentioned in the outline on the preceding page, under "2. Special topics."

The teachers will have to make a survey of the possibilities of the region. First, there must be a steady source of water. This may be a spring or an artesian well on a hillside or a brook in a gully or even a small creek which seldom runs dry. Second, they must make sure of being able to use it for a school project, with full permission of others who might be concerned, such

FIG. 10.1   A truly integrated science project in a rural area. This project could and should last for years.

as the farmer who owns the land that would be used; the location and its accessibility; the use of a small adjacent tract of land for other purposes; and the possibility of other materials needed to carry out the project. The property involved does not need to be so large as might be supposed at first.

One can easily think of several ways of beginning the work and of carrying it on. In general the social cooperative method of planning by conference is advisable. The teachers should meet with the groups and conduct the early meetings. Later they may organize and form an engineering society, with special selected duties and responsibilities. Since all the problems in the project are intimately interwoven, it will be impossible for anyone to go along without becoming thoroughly acquainted with what all others are doing. Frequent round-table discussions for planning are a necessity and a splendid way of inculcating the spirit of cooperation necessary in most of life's activities.

THE PLANNING

After several meetings and discussions, the group is ready to put its preliminary plans on paper. This done, a tour of the site is made. The location is definitely established and some elementary surveying done which makes use of some of the mathematics learned in the classroom. The results of this should be a general map and layout of the physical phases of the project. When the areas of each problem have been definitely agreed upon and mapped, the actual work may begin.

THE EARLY CONSTRUCTION PHASES

There now follows a number of work problems such as the staking out of the dam and each of the other structural features; the selecting and securing of needed structural materials; the construction work on the dam and other units, such as the power wheel, the power shed, the runways and ditches, etc. There follows an extended period of cooperative construction. The chief function of the teacher now becomes that of anticipator of difficulties which he places before the "engineers" as questions, leaving it largely for them to solve. Above all, the teacher must refrain from becoming a dictator and a constant source of information. He must step into the program only upon emergencies. One of the main objects of such a project is to arouse the independence, resourcefulness, and initiative of the student. He must be required to do much of his own thinking.

The dam, runs, and ditches should be constructed according to specifications. The type of water engine must be chosen, constructed, and installed, with reports made to the society. The power lines to be attached may be set up and a shed constructed in which such things as the electric generator and storage batteries are housed. Simple machines, heating and lighting devices may be constructed and installed as illustrations of the physical principles involved in such apparatus so commonly used in home and industry today.

The area above the dam needs to be carefully "explored" and mapped to determine the topography, drainage, soil condition, vegetation, and probably the fauna. Plans for soil and plant conservation must be made and a planting program worked out, even if it cannot be carried out, or must be restricted. A survey of the animal inhabitants can be made just as extensive as the program would permit. Changes in both fauna and flora which naturally follow the dam construction should be carefully recorded. New animals such as fish, crayfish, insects, turtles, and frogs may be "planted" in the reservoir. Fish culture can here be given a special study, including a study of artificial propagation and government hatcheries.

A small tract of land below the dam should be prepared for irrigation from the water used as power. If the land is rugged, this should be done by terracing a steep slope and cultivating the terraces. Planting may be carried on upon a small scale. Much is to be learned in connection with this agricultural phase of the project. Studies of a great variety can be introduced for report and discussion, though it may not actually be possible for them to be carried out locally. Trips to near-by dams, conservancy projects, water supply systems, light and power plants, and fish hatcheries are important parts of the studies.

All reports and surveys should be done finally on a uniform size of paper, and this material, together with maps and photographs, bound in some fashion as a record of the progress of the project. The last item should consist of a general summary prepared jointly by all members, designating the general principles deduced and values derived from the project as a whole.

One may readily conceive of such a unified project as the above being expanded to the extent of embodying the major portion of the entire curriculum. However, this is quite unnecessary. It has been outlined in a broad inclusive manner. It need not be carried out in all its implied phases. It could be greatly restricted and still be useful. In a suitable rural community, it could well be undertaken on a large scale and would involve much careful planning and steering with close cooperation among departments or departmentalized faculty members. On the other hand, the construction phases could be reduced to an enlarged sand table or model problem, with the school laboratories substituting for the power shed, field surveys and mapping substituting for fauna and flora studies, etc. Such modifications would permit this type of integrated study to be used in village or in city schools. It is evident that in any event the work is not centered in chemistry, biology, manual arts, general science, or any departmental area, nor need it emphasize any one of these. The students study in all areas because all areas are essential factors of a group of genuine problems related to and part of life in the community.

The teachers become departmentalized to some extent by their specialization, but by virtue of this they should become efficient as well. They must be broadly trained to visualize properly the interrelationships of the unified courses, and they must be capable of maintaining a balanced, workable relation with all other teachers involved. The student profits by the coordinated character of his studies and becomes practiced in understanding the relation of one field and another to a central problem. *The problems of the student's life are not problems of history, problems of chemistry, or problems of biology—they are nearly always problems of such scope that they involve chemistry, biology, and history and sometimes many other fields.* Strict departmentalization tends to make the student piece together the substances of the segregated fields, while integration tends to train the student to attack his problems from whatever angles may be advantageous.

In many of the larger city schools where the teacher instructs five or more sections in the same subject daily and departmentalism is rigidly administered, there are many obstacles to integrated teaching. It is often far easier for teachers in smaller schools and rural communities to carry on projects such as that suggested above, and it is there that many excellent opportunities lie for carrying out the best of modern education and for establishing advances in progressive teaching instead of following the standards of methods and technics of the highly formalized, large city schools.

There is one complaint heard from those who still advocate strict departmentalization—that the student frequently gets just a smattering of information so that he is unable to do much with any of the integrated fields. This is a very valid objection and is one of the most serious criticisms against integration and individualization in education. It must be dealt with and carefully guarded against. However, because integrating tendencies may mean insufficient factual learning, it does not mean that such a result must follow. It requires a continuous series of such studies to cover a comparable amount of subject matter, and it is true that when facts are learned in relation to their true bearing upon a problem those facts have real meaning in terms of life and that meaning gives a high degree of understanding to the student, greatly enhancing his retention.

As to what is the best type of integration for any level of teaching or any kind of subject area, there is at present no answer. The more recent trend is toward integration in some fashion. There have been many disappointments and failures in the attempts made, but there have also been numerous successes. The principle is sound, at least for the more elementary levels, and the difficulties that have hampered integration have been largely those inherent in the departmentalized character of the precedent plan of teaching and in the inabilities of the teachers and administrators to organize and carry out a balanced and effective program. Integrated teaching is decidedly more difficult than drifting along in the same highly departmentalized fashion to which both the past organization and methods are adapted. There is much to be said for departmentalization and much for integration, and the wide-awake teacher will consider both carefully before condemning either. There may well be a place for some of both types of teaching.

The past has shown numerous changes in educational theory coordinate to some extent with the rise of science, invention, and industrialism. The present shows another revolution arising, in some respects the greatest yet, greatest because of the extensive growth of general education and greatest because of the depth to which it is striking at many of the fundamentals of education. Progress will be slow, and the outcome will be a new educational philosophy and new technics.

Confusion in the teachers' minds, with tendencies to adhere to what has been and the fear of the uncertainty of the future, as well as the tendency to leap off with each untried new theory and then to abandon it at the first falter, must be avoided. A change in many ways is mandatory. Just where it will lead during the next quarter of a century is difficult to predict at present. Its course will be dominated by science at first. It will produce a scientific educational procedure in that our progress will become experimental and our results carefully evaluated. The conflicts and confusion of the present will resolve themselves into a sounder scientific education of the future which the younger teachers of today will have the pleasure of seeing and the satisfaction of knowing that they had a part in its building.

PROBLEMS

1. Outline the subject matter of a general biology course by making a list of topics. Make a set of problems based upon the life in a rural community such as would be found in your part of the country. Select two of these problems and expand them, showing how they would be handled if taught by a completely integrated procedure.

2. Repeat the problem as given in 1 above, but use a village community as the type.

3. Repeat the problem as given in 1 above, using a large urban community as the type.

4. Inquire in the schools of your city or county for examples of integrated, or core, courses. Interview the teachers concerned with these courses. Interview some of the students. Observe some of the classwork. Make a report with your own analysis to your methods class.

REFERENCES

1. Baker, A. O., and L. H. Mills: "Biology Today," *Secondary Educ.*, **12**:5–6, April, 1945.

2. Benjamin, H.: *American Education in the Twentieth Century—Second Half*, Third Yearbook of the American Association of Colleges for Teacher Education, Oneonta, N.Y., 1950.

3. Brandwein, P. F.: "Studies in the Teaching of Biology," *School Sci. and Math.*, **42**:243–250, March, 1942.

4. Brubacher, J. S.: *Modern Philosophies of Education*, McGraw-Hill Book Company, Inc., New York, 1950.

5. Bullington, R. A.: "What's New in the Teaching of Biology?" *School Sci. and Math.*, **54**:253–255, April, 1954.

6. Bullington, R. A.: "Trends in the Teaching of High School Biology," *School Sci. and Math.*, **56**:100–108, February, 1956.

7. Davis, J. L.: "New Aspect for Biology," *Peabody J. Educ.*, **33**:350–351, May, 1956.

8. Glass, H. B.: *Survey of Biological Progress*, vol. 3, Academic Press, Inc., New York, 1957.

9. Heiss, E. D., et al.: *Modern Science Teaching*, The Macmillan Company, New York, 1950.

10. Huxley, T. H.: *Science and Education*, vol. III, Appleton-Century-Crofts, Inc., New York, 1894.

11. Larson, E. A.: "Opportunities for Exploration and Discovery," *Am. Biol. Teacher*, **17**:259–261, December, 1955.

12. Laton, A. D., and S. R. Powers: *New Directions in Science Teaching*, McGraw-Hill Book Company, Inc., New York, 1949.

13. Mallinson, G. G., and J. V. Buck: "Inductive Method in the Biology Laboratory," *Am. Biol. Teacher*, 17:102–104, March, 1955.

14. Martin, W. E.: "Present Status of Instruction in General Biology," *Am. Biol. Teacher*, 13:149–157, November, 1951.

15. McFadden, M. G.: "Recent Trends in the Teaching of Biology," *Sci. Educ.*, 34:47–51, February, 1950. Bibliography with recommendations relative to the development of a course of study.

16. Mees, C. E. K.: *The Paths of Science*, John Wiley & Sons, Inc., New York, 1946.

17. Miller, J. V.: "Biology, 1949 Model," *Am. Biol. Teacher*, 11:101–104, April, 1949.

18. Mullen, J. A.: "Observations on the Teaching of Biology," *School and Soc.*, 65:142–144, Feb. 22, 1947.

19. National Science Teachers Association, 1201 16th St., N.W., Washington 6, D.C. Plan for science teachers now includes free teaching packets for members. Details furnished on request.

20. National Education Association, Science Teachers Association Department: *Science Teaching Today*, 1950–51. 1201 16th St., N.W., Washington 6, D.C.

21. Office of Education, Science Education Division, Federal Security Agency, Washington 25, D.C. Recent and up-to-date literature for secondary-school science teachers.

22. Overbeek, J. Van: "Biological Education in Secondary Schools," *Science*, 109:210, Feb. 25, 1949.

23. Spencer, Herbert: *Education*, Appleton-Century-Crofts, Inc., New York, 1909.

24. Trowbridge, H.: "How to Strengthen the Teaching of High School Biology," *School Sci. and Math.*, 43:563–566, June, 1943.

25. United Nations Educational, Scientific, and Cultural Organization: *Suggestions for Science Teachers in the Devastated Countries*, Columbia University Press, New York, 1948.

26. Walsh, M. P.: "Careers in Biology," *Am. Biol. Teacher*, 16:176–178, November, 1954.

--*{ Part Two }*--

SOURCES, PREPARATION,
AND USES OF MATERIALS

CHAPTER 11

Examples of Student Projects

The method of teaching by projects is widely accepted as a desirable procedure in education. It is especially useful in the sciences where many of the materials are of the so-called laboratory and field types. The project method also offers the student the opportunity of learning by activity, seeing, doing, and handling.

This method requires the highest type of teaching in every respect. It necessitates more detailed planning, more foresight, more skill on the part of the teacher. In short, it is more work and therefore more frequently shunned. To the teachers of real ability who are alive in their field of subject matter and are teachers at heart, there is no substitute for the method. Anything else is dull and woefully inadequate by comparison. Students, once trained in the method, are likely to be dissatisfied with anything else.

Often teachers speak of using the project method when the "project" consists of little more than the making of special reports on library readings or the assignment of minor individual problems. These are worthy procedures, but isolated problems of this sort are not projects. A project includes a series of related problems and may cover a small portion of subject matter or an entire course. The problems are usually so begun that those attempted first suggest or even demand those which follow.

The five types given here as samples are intended to be of the more extensive variety. No one may care to follow one of these exactly as outlined, but a careful examination of them should suggest the possibilities that lie in this method. Such factors as the location of the school, the number of students in a class, and the number of classes per teacher may modify materially the course pursued and the extent to which individual work may be carried on. But any trend toward the method is likely to result in a distinct advance in the teaching of the course.

AN AQUARIUM PROJECT

In any biology course an aquarium can be made to play an important role. Most of the fundamental principles of biology are found inherent in either a balanced or unbalanced aquarium. The dependence of animals directly or indirectly upon green plants for their oxygen and food supplies is a striking case. The relation of carbon dioxide and light to photosynthesis and resulting products; food synthesis, food storage, respiration, digestion, growth and reproduction of both plants and animals, the relation of bacteria to the nitrogen, phosphorus and sulfur cycles; parasitism and saprophytism, the relation of one kind of animal to another; food cycles;

succession of one population by another, especially under unbalanced circumstances; temperature and water relations, etc.; all may be considered.

A well-directed aquarium project may be used very successfully at the beginning of the course as a center about which practically all the fundamental principles of biology may arise spontaneously from the student as problems which he elects to solve. Through skillful guidance of a teacher, the student may be led to the realization of the problems involved, may suggest ways to solve them, and finally make broad applications to the world about him, even including human society. Although this procedure may make a carefully prepared course of study difficult to follow in its logical order, the method is certain to be far more economical scholastically in that the student feels that the problems are his and that he must solve them. This at once removes lagging interest. The economy in learning is far greater, since he made the discoveries himself and was not merely told of them by the teacher.

From the above discussion it is apparent that such a project may be used to introduce the problems of an entire course. However, this same project may be used much later in the course to tie together all the subject matter which has been considered before. It is of great value when considering the interrelationships of organisms in nature. Also well-stocked aquaria will supply living organisms of various sorts for laboratory use throughout the course.

How to Prepare a Balanced Aquarium. *The Aquarium Tank.* A commercially built aquarium of about 5-gal. capacity is not an absolute necessity, although more or less ideal. Numerous other watertight containers may be substituted. One very nearly like the commercial tank may be built in the manual training shops by the students at little expense. If this is not feasible, fruit jars (quart and half gallon), or wide-mouthed gallon pickle jars, enameled pans, etc., may be used satisfactorily. If larger aquaria are desired, 5-gal. carboys (such as those in which distilled water is sold), wooden tubs, buckets, or barrels cut into halves will serve satisfactorily.

The Substratum. An inch or so of sand or soil should be added as a source of minerals, a medium in which plants may be anchored and animals may burrow. Well-washed sand offers fewer difficulties at the start since water over it soon clears. However, mud may be used, and the water will eventually clear. Especially in the latter case, if a sheet of paper is laid on the mud and water poured on it rather than on the mud, roiling will be prevented to some extent, and the soil surface left level.

The Water. Ordinary tap water, well water, water from springs, ponds, or streams may be used satisfactorily. Water from natural sources may contain numerous other organisms which will be interesting to establish in the aquarium. However, their presence may not be realized for some time. A glass lid may be placed on the aquarium to prevent excessive water loss. This is not a necessity, however.

The Plants. Plants such as elodea and eel grass (*Vallisneria*) are about ideal as submerged green plants to establish in the aquarium soil. Both are excellent oxygenators, grow rapidly, are good food for fishes, and may be used in various experiments in the laboratory. Algae are likely to be introduced especially in pond, spring, or stream water, in the mud or sand, and also sticking to the animals and the large plants used. Algae are good oxygenators and are very important as food for various animals. Bacteria and protozoa, water mold, etc., may come from the same sources, and in addition may fall in from the air. A dense mat of plants of any kind should not be introduced since sufficient light may not penetrate, resulting in a low rate of photosynthesis, and eventually starvation and death. This debris may soon develop into a disagreeable, decaying mass, and a long time is required for balancing. A little experimenting will soon determine the right number to use.

The Location of the Aquarium. This must be given some attention. A north window exposure is best. If this is not available other exposures may be used if care is taken to set the aquarium where direct sunlight will not fall on it for long periods. This is especially important when a glass lid covers the aquarium. Heat may be trapped to such an extent as to kill the organisms. The side next to the window may be painted or paper may be glued on it to prevent entrance of too many direct rays. In steam- or hot-water-heated laboratories a radiator is likely to be found beneath windows. If an aquarium is to be placed over one, care should be taken to see that there is plenty of ventilation between the aquarium and the radiator. If sufficient light is not available from a window, an electric light may be suspended a foot or so above the tank. The bulb should have a capacity of 100 to 150 watts. For tropical fish, in laboratories where the temperature is allowed to drop at night, an electric aquarium heater may be necessary. It can be obtained at aquarium supply stores, or may be constructed by some mechanically inclined student.

Presentation of the Project to the Class. *The Feeling of Choice.* Depending upon where the project is used in the course, the approach to it will vary. If the aquarium is used to furnish a source for most of the problems taken up in the study, it may be necessary for the teacher actually to start some phases of the preparation in order to arouse curiosity on the part of students. If the use of the aquarium comes at a point in the course following the study of many of the biological phenomena, then the class may suggest the making of an aquarium. In any event it is the express duty of the teacher to see that the class elects to construct and study the aquarium so that they feel that the work is of their own choosing. This must be done even when the teacher finds it necessary to "sell" the idea to the class. The feeling of choice is an important psychological element in teaching, especially where the problem-project procedure is used.

Setting up the Aquarium. So far as the teacher is concerned, the details of setting up an aquarium have already been given above, or he may have had experience in doing this. It would be poor teaching technic, however, if the teacher began by telling the class how an aquarium should be prepared. The preparation should furnish a series of problems which the class should have to discuss and decide upon since the principal problems involved are the keys to the very fundamental biological principles which should be clearly established in the student's mind when they are settled.

Suppose that the class has decided to construct and study an aquarium. The next logical step for the teacher would be to have the members of the class suggest the problems that would have to be solved if the aquarium is to become a reality. Writing the suggestions on the blackboard as they are received always encourages more thinking and suggestions from the class. Certainly such problems as the following would be found in the list:

1. What shall we use as a tank?
2. What kinds of plants shall we use?
3. Where can these plants be obtained?
4. What kinds of animals shall we use?
5. What other materials should be placed in an aquarium?
6. What kind of water should we use?
7. How often should the water be changed?
8. What food should be given to the animals?
9. Where should the aquarium be placed in the room?

If some time is devoted to a discussion of each of the problems, a great deal of interest is aroused. The list should be compiled first and each point settled later. For purposes of illustration let us consider some of the problems in the list of suggestions.

1. What shall we use as a tank? Water plants and animals do not normally live in beautiful glass-sided tanks; yet many schoolrooms go without an aquarium

because such a tank is not provided. A large vessel of almost any kind can be used, and smaller containers such as pans and jars are quite satisfactory for special problems. Let the class decide what it can provide. If a glass aquarium is available use it, but why not let some students use a small wooden tub and have two or more aquaria?

2. What kinds of plants shall we use?

3. Where can these plants be obtained? Perhaps aquatic plants have already been studied and can be named. Some students will suggest buying a supply from a store or shop dealing in plants. But expense must be kept low. This will probably result in an offer to bring some plants from an aquarium at home or from a fish pool. If this is not possible, what is left? Surely someone will think of going to a pond or stream and collecting something. If the students do not think of it, they can be made to do so by being asked where these plants come from originally. After all, the bringing of materials from a lagoon in the park or a pond or stream on the way to school is much better educationally than buying them from a shop. Thus they have, by their own discussion, settled what plants are to be used and where they are to be obtained.

4. What kinds of animals shall we use? Fish are inseparable in our minds from aquaria. The consideration of kinds of fish that could be used, however, may constitute a very good problem and call for some study or experimenting. The use of such other animals as tadpoles and snails will be suggested, and finally, a large number of relatively uncommon species may be called to their attention. Any decision on such a matter will have to be based upon some knowledge of their structures and habits. For example, students will probably be much surprised to find that a frog will drown if it is in deep water and cannot get out at any point.

5. What other kinds of materials should be placed in an aquarium? Here is a question that may not be readily solved. Some will suggest shells, castles of porcelain, stones, sand, and mud. It is an excellent question, since the answer distinguishes between ornament and necessity and, further, decides relative values and importance of mud, stone, and sand as sources of minerals. The absolute necessity of these materials could be tested by some student preparing several small aquaria alike in all respects as to size and materials with the exception of the substratum of mud, sand, etc. Other ways in which the substratum is of importance may be decided also.

6. What kind of water should we use?

7. How often should the water be changed?

Questions 6 and 7 may be considered jointly since the matter of changing at all may be linked with several other factors. If the students seem to be unable to start a discussion of these points, they should be asked why change or source of water needs to be considered. This brings out the chemical content and chemical treatment of city supplies, the organic content of natural waters and the presence in them of bacteria and other microorganisms. The changing of the supply suggests the accumulation of wastes, the relation of plants to animals, the relative amounts of flora and fauna, the relation of organisms to space and the sources of food and other necessary materials. Water from creek, pond, well, spring, or supply system varies in mineral content and organic content. Simple analyses of the water may be made and a number of small jar aquaria set up to test for quantity, relationships, and population.

8. What food should be given to the animals? This requires some study of food habits and requirements. It will depend somewhat upon the answers to questions in 6 and 7 above. It is directly related to changing of water, pollution, microorganisms, etc. Whether the plants used in the aquarium can also serve as food for

any animal may have to be determined experimentally by testing in small jars with and without these plants and with and without additional feeding.

9. Where should the aquarium be placed in the room? Here are problems of temperatures, both mean and extreme. Should it be near a heater, near a window, in direct sunlight, etc.? What organisms are affected by possible temperature changes? There are the problems of light. Should the direct rays of the sun be permitted to strike the aquarium? How little light will suffice for the plants used? Does light have any effect upon any of the animals used? Can or should artificial light be employed and if so under what conditions? Photosynthesis gets full consideration here.

The foregoing is but a very sketchy review of the possible problems arising and their discussion. It will, however, be quite apparent that if the aquarium project is employed as a means of setting up a series of related problems early in a course there will be brought forth nearly all the basic problems of biology especially in their ecological and social aspects. This becomes even much more apparent in the study made during the unbalancing process which follows. The unbalancing of the aquarium should not be overlooked since it offers excellent opportunities for additional problems. If the aquarium is used only as an illustration for subject matter already covered and is presented late in the course, it still offers excellent opportunities for the student to make specific application of facts and generalizations to concrete situations—a very important step in education and one that is too frequently omitted.

Observations on the Balanced Aquarium. Soon after the aquarium is established, students are likely to notice that growth is taking place in the plants. New roots, leaves, and runners are developing. This opens up many problems concerning growing organs. Young and mature elodea leaves may be examined with a microscope. The student finds that such structures are divided into compartments which he learns are cells. By higher magnification he discovers that cells are more than boxlike compartments, that they have contents. He learns to recognize cytoplasm, nuclei, vacuoles, and chloroplasts. At this point, the question as to the nature of protoplasm is likely to arise. He would soon learn that protoplasm is composed of the nucleus and cytoplasm of a cell; that, physically, it is a colloidal suspension of a system of substances such as protein, fats, and carbohydrates; and that the system of substances has the *unique* property of being alive. One of the most common properties associated with something which is alive is that of movement under its own power, at least under certain conditions.

In the following paragraph, elodea is suggested as an aquarium plant, a leaf of which when examined with the aid of a microscope reveals not only that cells are the units of structure of the elodea leaf, but that the protoplasm in each cell may be in motion—cytoplasmic or protoplasmic streaming. This observation is enhanced in elodea by the presence of green plastids, the chloroplasts, which are oval, more dense masses of the cytoplasm, bearing the green pigment, chlorophyll. It is far better educationally to allow the student to develop a concept of a cell, including the protoplasmic system rather than to try defining the unit of structure—which cannot be done satisfactorily. After examining both young and mature leaves he concludes that the mature leaf has larger cells than the young and that a leaf grows by cells enlarging. He may even decide that new cells have developed. If the study is carried on to roots, it becomes quite evident that cell division occurs. The study may be enhanced by specially prepared root-tip slides which show various stages of cell division, or sporogenous masses from young anthers of a lily may be prepared to show the various stages (Chap. 14). Many tissues of both plants and animals, including tissues from our own bodies, may be studied for cell types. The inevitable conclusion that "cells are the units of structure" is the result.

While these studies are going on, numerous observations may be made on happenings in the aquarium. It is obvious that all these cannot be taken up to their fullest extent immediately as observed. The teacher may suggest that careful notes of all observations be recorded and that they will be considered as rapidly as time permits and enough information has accumulated and principles have evolved to enable students to carry them out successfully. While studying elodea cells, cytoplasmic streaming (cyclosis) is observed. Later, when food translocation in plants is being studied, it is found that this fact may be applied in solving certain other problems. While examining the same cell, someone may become interested in the green pigment of chloroplasts. Possibly the teacher may ask this student to accumulate all the information he can concerning chlorophyll. He will be asked to report on his findings when the process of photosynthesis is considered.

Someone finds a transparent, jellylike mass on the aquarium wall. Several slightly opaque dots can be seen within the mass. A question arises as to its identification. Some may be of the opinion that these are fish eggs; others may say they are snail eggs, insect eggs, something which was included in the soil, etc. The teacher does not confirm any of the opinions, but asks, "How can you find out?" Someone suggests books. Another wants to observe the mass for several days and see what happens. The teacher urges a combination of these methods. The next day more of these jellylike masses may be discovered, and are observed under the microscope. It is found that the dots appear to have several divisions (cells), and that older masses have dots with more cells in them. In the meantime someone finds a description of snail egg masses in some references supplied by the instructor. Within a few days the dots change and appear as miniature snails. These observations may serve as a basis for studying reproduction in animals, and even may be carried over into plants. Reproduction of guppies in the aquarium may be observed and followed in the same way. It may lead to a morphological study of a fish, in which dissection is done.

While the above observations are in progress it is noticed that the aquarium walls are not so clear as originally, and finally become so opaque that fish in the aquarium cannot be observed readily. Microscopic examination of this material introduces students to a study of algae, both unicellular and multicellular. *Cladophora* is a common filamentous, branched form likely to be found. Zoospore formation may be discovered. This forms a basis for beginning studies on reproduction in plants. Preserved reproductive material or slides of *Ulothrix, Spirogyra, Oedogonium* (green algae), etc., may be presented finally to introduce the fundamentals of sexual reproduction. These forms enable an inexperienced teacher to deal successfully with a subject which is often difficult to present.

From time to time chains of bubbles may be noticed escaping from some of the plants and rising to the water surface. The student assigned to read references on chlorophyll may be asked to report of his readings. He finds that chlorophyll plays an important part in photosynthesis and that a simple (hexose) sugar such as glucose and oxygen are products of this process. Someone suggests that the bubbles may be oxygen escaping. Some of the gas is collected and tested with a glowing splinter. The glowing splinter bursts into flame, or glows more brightly, indicating that the gas is oxygen. Someone wants to know if the bubbles often seen rising from mud in ponds are also oxygen. He is asked to test some gas collected from such a source. He finds that a flash is produced when the glowing splinter is inserted. It is evident that the gas is not oxygen but acts like illuminating gas (methane or marsh gas). This fact may be used later in the study of bacteria. An explanation of the relation of oxygen loss from green plants and aeration of an aquarium, microcosm, and oxygen supply of the atmosphere and to all living organisms immediately follows.

The question of sugar production may arise, which was reported from the literature on chlorophyll. Someone suggests testing the aquarium water for glucose. Methods for such a test are given by the teacher. Negative results are obtained. From the same report it was learned that sugar may be converted very quickly after its production into starch in leaves and other parts of a green plant. A student asks if there is a chemical test which indicates the presence of starch. The iodine test is described by the teacher. Numerous starch tests are made successfully on various green plants, including the aquarium forms. The synthesis of other foods is also considered. Since the algae on the aquarium walls were growing rapidly and reproducing, it is realized that considerable energy as well as foods must be necessary in building new cell materials. Also the algae are not on soil but on glass. In this way the class soon concludes that foods for plants must be carbohydrates, proteins, and fats just as for an animal body, and that in plants they are actually manufactured. Drilling on this conclusion will probably be necessary since so many assume that "plants get their food from soil." Fish nibbling at the algae or other aquarium plants reveal their food source. In this way food cycles may be emphasized.

"What becomes of the food used by plants and animals?" is a question which should be emphasized. It is best that the question arise spontaneously from the students, if possible. Digestion is suggested. This leads to a study of enzymes and digestion in general. A study of diffusion becomes necessary, also circulation in animals, and the stem and root structures of plants. Attention is soon centered on how energy is obtained from the digested foods. Experiments demonstrating respiration then follow. Heat energy may be measured and tests made for carbon dioxide release (Chap. 19). From certain of these experiments it becomes evident that oxygen is necessary in this process in both plants and animals.

The problem of necessity of new materials in the structure of cell walls and protoplasm is apparent from the above. This initiates the problem of assimilation. Observations of many such substances along with stored foods are made. The relation of these materials to man leads invariably to interesting and complex applications to human society. For example, the demand for spices and other tropical products in Spain led Columbus to explore for a shorter route to India. Accidentally he discovered America. The vast resources of this new land have revolutionized the civilizations of the world.

PROJECTS ON ECOLOGY AND CONSERVATION

The trouble with these data is that they constantly become out of date, partly because of an astounding rate of increase in human population throughout the world. In the United States about 8,000 new consumers appear at the dinner table every day (Ref. 31). These newcomers, equaling the population of three cities the size of metropolitan Cleveland, Ohio, join our families each year, and they must be fed and clothed. It is estimated that by the year 2,000 there will be available but ½ acre of land to each individual in Ohio.

In addition to the rapid population increase, the expanding economy of the United States annually diverts over 2 million acres of farm land to other uses. Added to this diversion of land from the production of food and fibers, great losses occur annually because of poor land-use practices and the futile destruction of fertile topsoil by water and wind erosion.

Better methods must be devised to meet this crisis of agricultural land shortage before it is too late. To be solved satisfactorily, it must be in terms of a continuous, plentiful food supply for the ever-increasing population. Radical improvements in all phases of agriculture must be achieved, and the populace must be made conscious, appreciative, and cooperative through education by the biological sciences.

This mad race will still be lost unless the control of world population is soon put into practice.

Improvement in visualization on the part of the student is a constant challenge accepted by the better science teachers. Direct observation of the real thing has no equal in effecting visualization and in vitalizing learning. The biological sciences are fortunate in this respect, in that the subject in many instances may be directly observed. Conservation is an excellent medium by which these sciences may be transmitted, with meaning to all. This significance results because the subject deals with current human problems, which can be solved by the application of scientific principles (Ref. 14).

Suggested Projects Related to Conservation

Through field trips become familiar with the common weeds found in lawns, gardens, and fields. Why are they regarded as pests? How may they be controlled (Ref. 63)? How many kinds of insects are found? What do they feed upon? How may they be controlled? Are birds and other animals present? How do they affect these areas?

If possible, visit some local areas where native plants still exist. Identify as many trees, shrubs, and herbaceous plants as possible. Prepare a list of these. Note the habitat where each occurs. What animals are to be found?

In cooperation with the owners, visit a productive farm where good land usage has been in continuous practice. Visit another farm with similar acreage on which poor land usage has been the custom. Compare the production and quality of the products from the two farms. What could be done to bring the marginal farm and abandoned areas back into good production? If severe erosion has occurred, how can this be overcome? Compare soil profiles on the two farms. If your area has a soil conservation district, the soil conservationist in charge will be of great aid to you in such studies.

On the marginal farm mentioned previously, gullies may have developed by water erosion, cutting back into croplands or pastures. A larger gully with a considerable drainage area may be stopped by constructing a dam, forming a pond. Look into the possible uses for such ponds. Do not overlook the possibilities of fish culture for recreation or for commercial purposes. Ponds constructed on abandoned farm land in Alabama are known to produce annually 800 lb. of fish per acre by proper management, including the application of fertilizer for increasing the growth rate of algae. This is better food production than is usually obtained from an acre of good bluegrass pasture in terms of beef production.

Serious erosion may be controlled by planting black locust trees, if the terrain is suitable. Black locusts of appropriate size make good fence posts and similar rough timbers. This species is a leguminous tree, on the roots of which nitrogen-fixing bacteria grow parasitically and fix free nitrogen from the atmosphere. How does this fact fit into conservation of the area? In other marginal areas it may be possible to grow several hardwood species of trees used in the manufacture of paper pulp. In southern Ohio, a good-sized industry is developing on land not suitable for other types of agriculture. Some of the marginal land areas may be suitable for the growth of species of pine and spruce, with the idea of marketing these as Christmas trees. With the proper management, 5 to 8 years after planting time, a profitable annual return may be realized from what was previously a marginal or abandoned area. At the same time, soil erosion is controlled and the soil is being improved.

An outdoor laboratory can be a valuable adjunct to the biological sciences taught in the public schools and may, in addition, serve as a community recreation center. One example may be sufficient to illustrate the possibilities of this type of project. The city charter of a small town provided a 100-acre tract of land for school purposes. This area is bounded on the west by a river, the school is located near the east end, and the south side is bordered by a state highway. An arboretum is being developed in the area near the river, with nature trails extending through it. This portion is in use as an outdoor laboratory and a source of plant and animal species for study by classes in nature study, general science, and biology. No educational procedure is so vital in learning as the direct observation of the real thing in its usual environment. A conservation club of young people of the city have greatly aided in the planting, in cooperation with the classes and teachers interested in the project. The plan was initiated and is being supervised by three public-spirited conservation-minded residents and parents in the community. The area serves as an ideal recreation center for the locality.

As cited in the introduction to this part on conservation, in addition to the loss in fertility caused by erosion and poor land-use practices, the number of arable acres per person is being reduced by other agencies. The rapid increase in human population and the diversion of farm lands to other uses are occurring at an alarming rate. The average student probably knows much more about the biology, geography, history, and economics of a number of foreign nations than he does about his own country and state. Find out how many acres of farm land is being diverted annually into urban areas in your county or state. Collect data on the number of acres of agricultural lands being converted into superhighways, defense establishments, and other uses.

In your county or state, what is being done about flood control? If your county has a soil conservation district, the conservationist in charge will be of great aid in relaying information as to what is being done in the way of flood and soil control. He can suggest numerous field trips where these efforts can be observed in action. He can make many suggestions for learning about soils and how they are formed.

The biological sciences bear a tremendous responsibility in solving numerous crises with which human society is confronted. In biological education it is essential that means be contrived by which more adequate training is made available not only in the training of specialists, but in addition, the biological sciences must be "sold" to school administrators and other public officials, convincing them of the important contributions which this area can make to general education. It is quite essential for the public to have the proper understanding and appreciation of the values which accrue from these studies, in order that biological scientists may realize their maximum potential in the shortest period of time. Verify this point by recalling the great time lapse between the actual discovery of some fundamental scientific principle and the time it is put into action, solving some human problem.

Of all the land areas of the earth's surface, only about 11 per cent, or 4 billion acres, is suitable for food and fiber production. It is estimated by the United Nations that there are 2.7 billion human beings living today. They are dependent upon these tillable areas for their foods and fibers. This means that there are available to each person less than $1\frac{1}{2}$ acres, or about nine average city lots, upon which his necessities of life may be produced.

Did glaciation occur in your area? If so, what evidence is locally available which indicates that an ice sheet a mile or more in thickness once crept down from the far north over your locality? Are there granite boulders scattered over the landscape? Where did they come from and how did they get to their present place? Why are there moraines containing gravel in some areas and not in others? What is the origin of many lakes, ponds, swamps, and bogs? Get the latest information on how much time is thought to have elapsed since the glacier moved over your locality. What is the depth of the glacial drift in your county? How can this glacial material be explained? What agencies are responsible for the changes which took place in the drift material, converting it into fertile agricultural land? What is humus and what is its origin? How can you detect humus and what are its properties? Can it be increased in amount? How may it be destroyed? Why are the regions known as the prairies and great plains regarded as the center of agricultural industries?

Conservation of Soil and Water. A striking and instructive project on the conservation of soil, water, and life can be performed by a class with relatively little apparatus besides that which can be made by students. This study of soils, runoff, retention, and vegetation may be fairly simple, or may be extended to great length. Figure 11.1 shows the essential elements of equipment. In addition, a small scale and a volumetric measure for liquids, reading either in ounces or cubic centimeters, are necessary.

The trays *A, B, C,* etc., are made of wood or metal. They are all exactly the same in all dimensions. They are filled to the same level with various soils. For example, *A* may contain unwashed sand, *B* may contain clay, *C* may contain

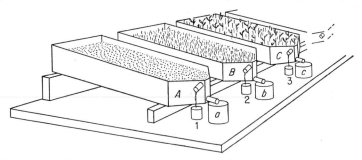

FIG. 11.1   A set of trays such as these may be used in studying the conservation of water, soil, erosion, effects of planting, temperature, and evaporation.

humus, and so on, using as many types as desired. The size of the boxes may be regulated by where the experiments are run—larger if out of doors. Each day a measured amount of clear water is sprinkled over each box, being very careful not to spill any outside the box. The following questions may serve as a guide to a simple study:

1. Which soil produces the most runoff? (As shown by surface puddles at the lower end of the boxes or by runoff collected in vessels 1, 2, 3, etc.)

2. Which soil retains moisture best? (As shown by the amounts of seepage collected in *a, b, c,* etc.)

3. Which soil produces the most sediment? (In vessels *a, b, c,* etc.)

4. Which soil remains in suspension longest? (As shown by water in *a, b, c.*)

5. Which soil is the most soluble? (As shown by evaporating measured filtered samples of water from vessels *a, b, c* and weighing the residues.)

The project can be extended by planting various seeds in the soils and comparing the results obtained after the vegetation has grown with those results obtained with soil alone, or by using several boxes of the same soil and planting different kinds of seeds in each box. Is one type of plant cover better than another when checked against the above questions?

Many other problems and questions can be added if desired. In all cases insist upon accuracy and reason and guard against drawing conclusions of a general character from too meager evidence. Introduce other modifying factors such as temperature, evaporation, slope, and wind.

The relation of water to diffusion of foods and minerals in both plants and animals, water as an end product of respiration, water as a raw material in the photosynthetic process, the presence of water in the blood stream, etc., lead to studies of water relations of both plants and animals (see Chaps. 17 and 20). This may be followed by ecological studies dealing with the distribution of plants and animals. Soon after such studies are begun it is realized that other factors besides water relations must be considered in plant and animal relationships in nature. The class may be led to see how industries are determined by ecological situations, how man fares under these varying circumstances, that he is a part of nature and is playing an important role. Too often his part is a destructive one, upsetting balances which result in floods, droughts, soil depletion, erosion, and famine. Even he may be forced to migrate to a more favorable situation or die, as soon as competition with the rest of nature becomes too great. Studies in conservation may follow.

Variation in plants and animals may be brought out when studying aquatic, swamp, bog, and other ecological situations. Parasitism, saprophytism, symbiotic relations, etc., all come in for their share of attention. The great number of species is a striking fact. The mention of the relationship of industry to ecological situations may suggest a study of some of the mineral deposits about which certain industries thrive. Even a superficial study of coal, peat, limestone, etc., brings out the fact that these are of plant and animal origin. The question of fossils and the kinds of plants and animals which have existed in the past is sure to arise. Comparisons with present-day forms show that great variations have occurred throughout vast periods of time. This may lead to the study of heredity and evolution.

Throughout the project the student should be allowed to make discoveries for himself as far as possible. The presentation of situations which stimulate the students to investigate a problem is a worthy technic not to be overlooked. Many clever maneuvers and plans may be required by the teacher. However, results in learning economy will more than pay for efforts exerted if the student is allowed to make his own discovery of facts, build definitions from them, and induce general principles.

The Unbalancing of One of the Aquaria. If the teacher has been careful in guiding the establishment of the aquaria, it is almost certain that they will be found in a balanced condition. As previously shown, most of the fundamental problems and principles of biology will have been raised from the balanced condition. There should now follow a period of progressive unbalancing which will furnish many illustrations of additional problems and show a biological foundation for many of our social problems.

Overpopulation. By allowing students to make promiscuous additions to one of the aquaria, all the problems solved in balancing it are again produced. If more fish, tadpoles, crayfish, dragonfly nymphs, water bugs, turtle, frog, leech, or even an excess of some of the filamentous algae are added, the unbalancing will begin. It may tend to correct (balance) itself again if certain very unfavorable conditions do not arise, that is, if unfavorable conditions beyond the endurance of some of the organisms do not develop. As soon as some of the conditions become sufficiently detrimental, certain organisms will be unable to survive. The ecological and social implications of such a situation are unlimited. Succession in a community made up of a mixed population of plant and animal species is a thoroughly established ecological principle. Let us consider some of the possible steps in such a succession with ways of applying them.

1. The addition of a number of individuals of a single species of animal is an increase in population. If the balanced condition was closely adjusted, the increase of population will mean a food-supply problem since the demand has greatly increased. If the animals are plant feeders, there will be a rapid decrease in plant population, with improper nourishment and eventual starvation and death. It further means an increase of waste products and rapid pollution. It may mean a deficiency of oxygen supply and an increase in microorganisms, especially bacteria. Most of the original problems of the aquarium have to be solved again. In addition, there is the possibility of increase by reproduction and a renewal of the problems, plus cannibalism in some cases. If the teacher is at all skillful and plans his questions carefully, the class will be able to bring out most of the above points without being told. When human society is substituted for the fauna of the aquarium, they will find many social problems duplicated. Overpopulation, involving food supply, immigration, birth control, and health, calls for pertinent points to be considered.

2. Do not correct or interfere with the unbalancing process. Add animals of other species, and you have problems of a mixed population arising. Competition of one species with another for food, homes, and places to rear their young follows. The preying of one species upon another, the relations of plant feeders to plants, of flesh eaters to plant feeders, and the cycles of interdependence become important. The use of tadpoles, crayfish, snails, and clams may tend to effect some balance since they are scavengers and aid in removal of pollution.

3. The death of any organism furnishes material for the additional growth of molds, yeasts, and bacteria. Some of these organisms furnish food for protozoa and small crustacea. Others such as water mold (*Saprolegnia*) may attack living animals, especially if they have been injured. It will grow, for example, upon the fins, gills, and eyes of fish. Those organisms which encourage or cause decay produce obnoxious and often poisonous gases and substances dissolved in the water. Students may well become aware of their presence and their activities from the odors and the change in appearance of the water, which loses its clearness, becomes milky or dark in color. They can examine preparations on microscope slides and make cultures on agar plates, in broth tubes, etc. The application of sanitation to health is clear.

4. Suppose that a bloodsucking leech is added to a heavily stocked aquarium. Parasitism is suggested, possibly death. This suggests the examination of some organisms for internal parasites. A grass frog is an excellent host for lung and bladder flukes, intestinal roundworms, and protozoa. The material should be alive. The sight of living parasites within the organs of their host gives a vivid impression. The distribution of blood parasites by bloodsucking animals and the succession of hosts depending upon preying for their distribution are introduced. The meat-packing industry, sanitation, and food inspection are parts of the study.

5. An unbalanced condition may be produced by addition of too many plants. If a dense mat or algae or other plants is added which is far out of proportion to the volume of water, death and disintegration usually follow. Density of the mat may prevent entrance of light. The plants which do not get sufficient light die of starvation, since photosynthesis cannot occur. If the photosynthetic rate is too low, there may not be sufficient oxygen released to keep the animals from suffocating. Toxic materials released by the decaying plants may also kill many of the remaining plants. A high concentration of carbon dioxide is an example. Under such conditions oxygen may be removed rapidly, presenting a serious problem to all the organisms involved. Murky water developing as a result of such conditions reduces the entrance of light still further. Bacterial action increases at a rapid rate in such an environment.

A Project on Transition or Succession in a Mixed Plant Population of a Newly Seeded Pasture

As stated elsewhere, succession in a community made up of a mixed population is an established ecological principle. This principle has been applied in agriculture for many years in crop rotations and in the conversion of a newly cultivated field into a bluegrass pasture. Figure 11.2 demonstrates the results of succession in a mixed population, starting with a newly prepared plot, seeded with a mixture of red clover, white clover, bluegrass, orchard grass, redtop, timothy, and meadow fescue. It shows graphically an analysis of the mixed population by percentage, starting with seedling stage of first season, through a 5-year period. With relatively little effort, experimental plots may be prepared for testing the above principle and the results, shown graphically by R. G. Wiggans for the State of New York. Two

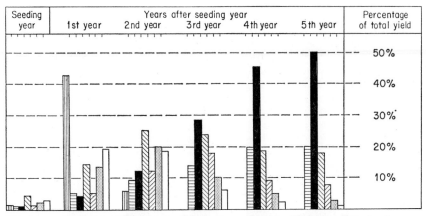

Red clover   White clover   Blue grass   Orchard grass   Red top   Timothy   Meadow fescue

Fig. 11.2   This chart represents succession or change in composition of a mixed population of pasture plants. The same principles apply to native plant communities. (*Redrawn from R. G. Wiggans.*)

3 by 6-ft. plots of good soil which can remain undisturbed for several years are necessary for the experiment. One plot is planted with the mixture of pasture plant species listed above, and the other is left without being purposely seeded. A "nurse" crop of wheat, rye, or oats should be planted with the seven pasture species for protection of the seedling plants during the year of seeding. The unplanted plot will undoubtedly have dormant seeds of numerous species already in the soil, and others will likely be carried in by wind or other agencies, resulting in a mixed population quite different from the first. These plots may continue as good teaching material for several years. The experiment may be varied greatly at the discretion of the teacher. In the Southern states, the Southwest, and Western areas, it may be necessary to select different mixtures of the pasture species which will grow more satisfactorily in these situations. Some care may be taken to eliminate shrub or tree species such as elm, which if allowed to persist will soon dominate the herbaceous species by shading, resulting in starvation. It is possible that the plot left unplanted, except by natural agencies, may eventually be dominated by bluegrass.

Ecology of a Limited Area

The relation that this project may have to the entire course can be varied from its use as a small study covering not more than 2 weeks time to such proportion that it may well serve as the basis for an entire semester or year of work. It can be used as an individual project, group project, or class project. The manner suggested here for its presentation indicates its use as a class project for at least several weeks.

It might serve equally well for a class in botany, zoology, general biology, or general science. It might also be an excellent method for integrating several courses, such as biology with geography or chemistry or mathematics. As in all the projects suggested, this one should be modified so as best to suit the conditions where it is used.

Choosing a Region to Be Studied. There are a number of important considerations to be made in beginning such a project, as accessibility, variety of habitats, variety of population.

Accessibility. A location must be selected that can be reached conveniently at all necessary times. If, for instance, the project involves an entire class, the region must lie near enough to the school so that the entire class can visit it at least some of the times. If it is to be an individual or small-group project, the distance could be much greater and time and transportation arranged for the students to visit the location.

Variety of Habitats. Enough variation in the landscape and physical features of the area must be present to furnish a number of different situations and a variation in the flora and fauna. Such ideal combinations as the following should be sought for when possible:

1. A wooded hill sloping down to a meadow with a pond or stream
2. A wood lot with a pond or small stream
3. A meadow with a creek which has tree-lined banks
4. A steep-sided valley running mostly east and west, giving north and south slopes for comparisons

However, while these conditions may be ideal, they are not necessary. A carefully husbanded park with plantings and lagoons can be used or even a cultivated garden plot or back yard. It is quite apparent that such a region as combination 1 above would furnish a wide variety of possible habitats. The differences in elevation of hill, meadow, and stream; the differences in flora of woods, meadow, and stream; the differences in light intensities, moisture retention, temperature variation, and character of the soil would all have marked effects upon the population in different parts of the area.

Variety of Population. This is essential in an extended study. It offers opportunity for introducing students to the elements of ecology in that they have occasion for correlating the plant, animal, and physical factors of each habitat.

Mapping the Area. Once the location has been selected, it is a distinct advantage that the area be mapped, even if it is done crudely. Get some general measurements of the major distances, such as length and width, elevations and depressions. This is where some valuable and practical applications of geometry or trigonometry may be made. A simple homemade surveying transit can be constructed and used to advantage, or a surveyor may be willing to instruct the class in the elements of surveying technics and make the measurements. These should be laid off on paper and rough maps constructed from them. A general observational examination of the area will suffice to give the location of principal features such as the extent and position of woods, pond, hill, etc., and how each may be placed on maps.

Types of Maps. Several maps may be found useful as the study progresses. One showing definite topographic features, one showing vegetation areas, one showing the areas of soil variation, and one showing animal distribution could be constructed to advantage. A vertical section showing elevations exaggerated to emphasize the physical relief and the depths of water also would be valuable. These maps should be marked into zones. A very useful relief map may also be made from clay or plaster. If constructed on a large scale the various plant zones and many animal habitats may be added. All vertical sections and relief maps should have the relief features exaggerated about twice (Figs. 11.3, 11.4, 11.5).

Collection and Detail Study. The intensive study from the purely biological standpoint should have many possibilities.

Plants. An examination should be made of the principal plants found growing in the area. These can be identified and their distribution recorded upon the map.

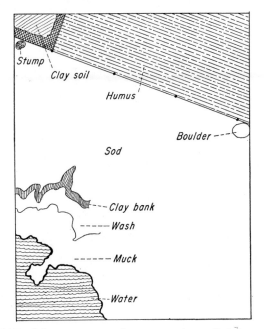

Fig. 11.3   Substratum map of an area to be studied for ecology.

They may be collected and made into a school herbarium. Their economic importance and whether they are wild or cultivated, native or introduced may be determined. Certain forms may be transplanted for cultivation in the classroom (see Chap. 12). Such a survey of the vegetation may be used as a basis for a course in botany or for such amount of study as may be desired on their structure, physiology, taxonomy, or importance to man.

Animals. A similar examination for the animals living in the area should be made. These may be recorded upon another map. A record should be kept for all forms collected, giving such information as the name of the animal, exact location where found, the conditions of the environment where collected, time of day and time of year (date). All such information should be marked upon each specimen or container and kept as a school collection and for further study later in the laboratory. Much living material may be transferred to the laboratory and cultured there (see Chap. 12).

Laboratory Study. If the field work is started and continued during the autumn, enough material and information may be collected to furnish laboratory and discussion material during most of the winter when field work is less readily carried on. Some study should be done in the field during the winter, however, to show how and where many organisms spend this portion of their lives in nature. If they are present in the fall and the spring, they must have spent the winter somewhere in some form. Preserved specimens of both plants and animals should be provided from the survey for class use. Living forms can be cultured in the laboratory, and this will save a lot of money spent for their purchase and give the students a far greater understanding of their structure and physiology, which they will find invaluable later in making ecological correlations and deductions. These materials may furnish a means for carrying out many demonstrations and experiments either indoors or out, the results

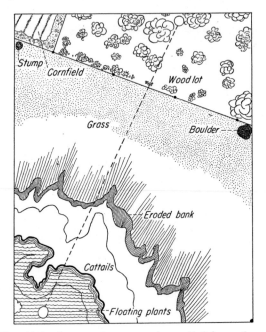

FIG. 11.4   A vegetation map to be studied for ecology.

of which should assist the students in their analyses of problems and in testing their hypotheses.

Summary and Correlations. In such a program as this, the teacher, of course, has in mind a picture of the complete study. The teacher must remember, however, that no such view of the whole exists in the minds of the students who are working piecemeal from day to day. Consequently, it becomes a matter of first importance that something be done to assure their obtaining such a picture by the time the work is finished.

Completion of Composite Maps. This concept of meaning which is so desirable for the student can best be introduced by the construction of a composite map or a series of such maps. Illustrations of such maps might be

1. The superimposing of a vegetation map upon a soils map
2. The superimposing of an animal distribution map upon a vegetation map

3. The correlating of drainage features with plant distribution

4. The correlation of plant or animal distribution with depths of water in pond or lake

5. The correlation of light intensity with the distribution of certain plants and animals

6. Many other relationships may be included and two, or more, placed upon one map

Correlation of Data and Generalizations. From such efforts there will be impressed upon the student a realization of the interrelationships of environmental factors and their effects upon the distribution of organisms. Many inductions are possible from such data, and the student is given practice in thinking correctly and in generalizing from his conclusions.

Application of These Generalizations to Life Situations. One of the tests of the real value of study and knowledge to the individual is his ability to apply the learning to other situations so as to understand new facts and to interpret and solve other problems. The type of biology studied above should make possible much of this for the students. Social behavior of all organisms, including man, can rightly be

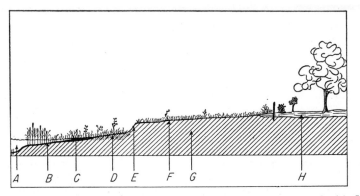

FIG. 11.5   Vertical section of an area to be studied for ecology: *A,* pond with floating plants; *B,* cattails; *C,* shore line with sedges; *D,* wash clay with weeds; *E,* eroding clay bank; *F,* grass; *G,* clay and gravel; *H,* wood-lot humus.

explained upon the basis of ecology. Industrial problems are inseparably joined with ecological situations. For example, the location of factories often depends upon the mineral resources, the rainfall and water power, the character of the soil, the kinds of plants or animals reared or existing naturally, the topography, etc. It is a chain of connected and interrelated factors existing as causes and effects often much after the fashion of the nursery rhyme about the old lady whose pig would not jump over the stile. The kinds of domestic animals that a farmer rears for profit may depend upon his nearness to a market, or upon the kinds of crops that he can grow, which in turn may be determined by the character of the soil, or the length of the growing season, or the mean annual temperature, or the extremes of annual variation of temperature, or the mean rainfall, or the distribution of rainfall in time, or any combination of these and other factors. The student should realize these relationships and their significance in interpretation of many social and personal problems.

The state and Federal governments supply free or at little cost numerous bulletins and maps showing many correlations of this nature.

A PROJECT ON DOMESTICATED PLANTS AND THEIR PRODUCTS

Corn is selected here as an example for discussion. However, any one of several other crop plants could be substituted according to the local situation involved. The following are suggested as other possibilities: soybeans, wheat, flax, tobacco, cotton, sugar cane, rice, tomatoes, apples, grapes, potatoes, peanuts, sweet potatoes, beans, pumpkins, squashes, gourds, pineapples, bananas, and citrus fruits (see references).

History and Economic Importance. Corn, or maize, is one of the world's most important cultivated plants. A great human population is dependent directly or indirectly upon this plant and its products. It is indigenous to the New World. The natives had selected out the chief endosperm types, and probably had grown them for centuries before Columbus discovered America. Many improvements have been made since its introduction into modern civilizations. A great array of products are available now from corn, and the number is being added to constantly. Because of the great economic importance and interesting history, its story offers a valuable project for group study. Following are some suggestions of major importance which may be considered. Numerous others may be selected for the project, according to the situation at hand.

Manufactured Products from Corn. Numerous corn products are now in use in many industries. Only a few of the more important ones will be considered here.

1. The possibilities of industrial alcohol from corn is one of its most promising products. The need of an efficient fuel to save and even take the place of our rapidly diminishing petroleum supply for gasoline is one of the greatest international problems of chemistry. A study of alcoholic fermentation and distillation emphasizes the importance of carbohydrates, especially starch, as sources of stored energy. Origin of the carbohydrates involves a study of photosynthesis. This process, in turn, involves leaf, stem, root, and grain structure. Facts and principles concerning diffusion and condensation of glucose to starch or other carbohydrates, storage, etc., are necessary in understanding the problems. Preparation of the starchy materials for fermenting, the action of yeast on the starch, and the products produced play a very important role. If desirable, acetic acid fermentation may also be studied. Distillation of the fermented alcoholic material requires knowledge of principles of still structure and operation. Concentration of the alcohol, resulting finally in the preparation of absolute alcohol, requires the use of several chemical and physical principles, all of which are within the range of the average laboratory. The ingenuity of the student is challenged. He is offered a chance to make use of many general principles developed during the course. He is awakened to the fact that industrial problems depend upon these principles for their solution.

2. Dextrose is an important corn product. It is an excellent human food and is often recommended in infant feeding. It is manufactured by heating cornstarch in the presence of weak hydrochloric acid (about 3 per cent) in a closed vessel. The acid is neutralized by sodium carbonate after conversion has occurred. Here chemically inclined students are given a chance to show their ability in making at least a crude sugar solution. Investigations may be made of the various uses of dextrose, its value as a food in the human body, involving a study of physiology.

3. Other manufactured products such as dry dextrin, corn oil, cornstarch, adhesives, sizing compounds for textiles, glue, corn nitroglycerine (mositol), plastics, corn sirup, corn molasses, protein plastic, lactic acid, sodium and calcium lactate, acetone, butanol, nitrocellulose lacquer, hydrogen, methanol, formaldehyde, carbon dioxide, etc., offer other possibilities for investigation. Many of these are found in use in

industry and in nearly every home and often are not suspected as having originated from corn.

4. In the above investigations the student learns that corn with starchy endosperm is most profitably used in the alcoholic fermentation process. This may lead to a collection of various corn types as starchy, sweet, flint, pop, and waxy endosperm forms. This may be expanded to include several varieties of each. The ear specimens may be shellacked or otherwise treated to prevent insect injury and mounted in cases or glass jars for permanent display. Through seedsmen and county or state fair association secretaries, much help may be received in obtaining specimens.

5. Knowledge of the various types of corn and their numerous varieties may raise questions as to their origin. This will bring out the fact that the Indians, in their primitive ways, had selected the fundamental types and were growing them when Columbus discovered America. A study of the uses for food and ceremonial purposes by the aborigines is a fascinating study of history. Many of these practices are still carried out by Indians of the Southwestern states and in Mexico.

6. Contact with the various corn types may arouse interest in heredity of these forms. A collection of the various endosperm types may be made. Collections of specimens showing xenia are of interest and of practical significance. Details of how xenia occurs involves an understanding of sexual reproduction in seed plants as well as endosperm formation. The growing of albino corn seedlings (Chap. 23) obtaining a 3:1 ratio is very worth while since this ratio and its derivatives are so fundamental in the study of heredity in many sexually produced organisms. This leads to a consideration of hybrid field corn and hybrid sweet corn and their uses in modern corn production. Charts may be prepared showing why only the hybrid, or F_1 generation, is of value. This is certain to arouse interest in an agricultural community, even outside the school.

7. Work with any of the divisions of this project will raise the question of corn ecology. The "corn belt" is often referred to. Preparation of distribution maps outlining the belt are very worth while in understanding the relation of corn growing to the environment. Enumeration and study of environmental conditions which determine this distribution will emphasize the importance of environment in the distribution of any organism. The distribution of corn determines the centralization of a large human population throughout the corn belt and determines the location of the most important hog- and cattle-producing areas. Extension of the range of corn-growing localities through breeding and selection adds another important phase for study. Government publications as well as numerous books will supply such data.

A PROJECT ON RADIATION BIOLOGY

Ever since the explosion of the first atomic bomb it has been readily apparent that man has demonstrated his ability to release and control tremendous energies heretofore not comprehended by the masses. It is equally apparent that these energies are not merely destructive forces but give promise of becoming the greatest boon to man's future growth and the evolution of his society. Already great potentials in the fields of agriculture, medicine, and biological research have been recognized. It is important that some understanding of radiations and their effects be given to students in science classes at as early a point in their schooling as possible.

Such radiations, however, are not harmless forces that can be manipulated by students, and not even by teachers unless they have had adequate training and experience to guarantee personal safety to themselves and their students. When using isotopes, the following points are musts;

1. Use only compounds emitting soft rays.

2. Be sure that all materials and equipment are so kept that only the experienced teacher can possibly have access to them.

3. Procure isotopes in quantities small enough to be used up completely when the demonstrations are over.

4. Use isotopes with short half-lives.

5. Have a carefully laid-out plan for the disposal of all materials at the end of each demonstration.

6. Take every prescribed precaution during the conduct of a demonstration.

Carelessness and lack of experience are the greatest sources of danger. If proper care is taken, these demonstrations can be made very enlightening to the students and will provide an excellent source of interest and enthusiasm.

Radioisotope Methods in Biology

Experiments and demonstrations with the use of radioactive isotopes can be performed with relative ease in the high school classroom. A minimum of equipment such as X-ray film, a survey meter, or a Geiger counter are necessary to carry out these experiments adequately.

In many experiments or demonstrations a combination of two detecting devices can be used, such as film and a Geiger counter. The use of these two devices in one of the suggested experiments for use in high school biology classes makes for more accurate and comprehensive measurements and thus a more complete experiment.

If two goldfish about 3 in. long are used, two experiments can be performed as outlined below. The experiment with fish no. 2 involves rapid careful weighing of internal organs and is more difficult.

Experiment with Fish No. 1. *Objectives.* (1) To determine if iodine (I^{131}) is absorbed by a goldfish from the water in which it is being kept. (2) To determine where the radioactive iodine concentrates in the body of the fish. (3) To make these determinations by the use of radioautographs.

Materials. Laboratory coat; surgeon's rubber gloves; aquarium approximately 6 by 6 by 12 in., or jar of similar capacity; aquatic plants (such as elodea); X-ray film, film holder, black paper, film developer, and fixer; 100 cc. of 10 per cent solution of potassium iodide; dissecting pan; Saran wrap; aluminum foil, to cover table tops or trays used in handling radioactive materials; dissecting kit—scissors, pithing needle, forceps; Geiger counter and scaler; 10 microcuries of I^{131} (maybe in the form of iodinated serum albumin); 2 dozen planchets (aluminum milk-bottle caps can be used); two goldfish, 3 in. long.

Procedure

1. Add 2 liters of water to the aquarium.

2. Remove 1 cc. of water and add it to a planchet. Let the sample dry. Determine the radioactivity of the sample with the Geiger counter. Record the result.

3. Quickly determine the radioactivity of the goldfish by placing it beneath the Geiger tube for a period of 1 min. Record the count.

4. Add 10 microcuries of radioactive iodine to the 2 liters of water in the aquarium. Remove 1 cc. of water and place it on a planchet. Let the sample dry and determine the radioactivity of the sample with the Geiger counter. Record the result.

5. Place some elodea in the aquarium with the two small goldfish and allow them to remain there for 3 days.

6. Next, remove one goldfish from the aquarium with a small net or by a hand covered with a rubber glove. Hold the fish in running water for 3 or 4 min. to

remove surface contamination, or rinse in three separate beakers of 1-liter capacity each. Rinse the fish in a dilute solution of potassium iodide further to decontaminate the surface.

7. Wrap the fish securely in Saran wrap.

8. Take the fish and all other photographic material to the darkroom to prepare the autoradiograph.

Autoradiograph Preparation

1. Place the fish on a sheet of Saran wrap and carefully enclose it so that fluids from the body will not leak out and contaminate the film and obscure the picture.

2. Prepare a cassette with film. Place the wrapped fish on the film, close the cassette and place it in the refrigerator for 3 to 6 hr. The time of exposure for best results will have to be determined through experience. See Fig. 11.6 for a modified film and fish holder that could replace the cassette, made from two smooth blocks of wood.

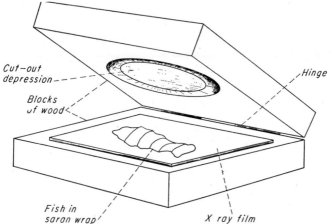

FIG. 11.6   A cassette may be made according to this illustration: two blocks of wood, one with depression; two hinges; X-ray film; Saran wrap; black paper to wrap around cassette.

3. Remove the cassette from the refrigerator and take it once again to the darkroom. Remove the film from the cassette without moving the fish. Place the film on a solid surface and with a pin or stylus mark the outline of the head or tail by scratching the film. Remove the wrapped fish and place it in waste container in the darkroom.

4. Develop the film according to directions obtained with the X-ray developer. After developing, the film should be placed in "fixer" for about 10 min., washed in tap water for an hour and then hung up to dry.

5. Interpretation of the autoradiographs will improve with time and experience. Autoradiographs are particularly good for many kinds of plant material, especially leaves and stems. For plant material choose any fresh growing twig or seedling, such as a bean seedling, and place it in a beaker, flask, or jar containing the solution of I^{131} (or P^{32}) and allow it to stand where *it cannot be upset* for 2 days. Remember that the plant and its juices are contaminated. Remove a leaf with forceps and proceed as with the fish.

6. The laboratory being used for radioisotope experiments should have a separate sink where low-level radioactive solutions can be disposed of and diluted many times with running water. It is particularly valuable to have a survey meter to

check all areas where radioactivity was used to locate any possible sources of contamination.

7. One of the most important and helpful procedures is to get all the materials together and go through every step of the experiment *without radioisotopes*. This enables one to learn the importance of planning ahead and having everything ready. Every step of the procedure should also be memorized so that it is not necessary to turn pages of books with contaminated hands.

Experiment with Fish No. 2. *Objectives.* To determine the uptake of I^{131} by various organs of the goldfish.

Materials. Goldfish; good analytical balance (if available); dissecting instruments; concentrated nitric acid (HNO_3); hot plate and aluminum foil; planchets or aluminum milk-bottle caps; masking tape; Geiger counter and scaler.

Procedure. This experiment is best carried out with at least two persons. The whole procedure should be gone through at least once without using the radioactive material. It is especially important to be completely familiar with the internal organs of the fish and the best way to remove them.

1. One person should remove the fish from the aquarium, prepare it for dissection and removal of the organs. The second person should number and weigh the planchets and make a record on a table (see below). Be ready to weigh the organs as soon as they are removed from the fish. The same number of planchets should be weighed as organs to be removed.

2. The wet weight of each organ removed should be determined as quickly as possible.

3. After all organs to be studied have been removed and weighed, the planchets containing them should be transferred to a chemical hood. Several drops of concentrated nitric acid (HNO_3) should be placed on each organ still on planchet. The digestion of the tissue can be speeded up by placing the planchets beneath a heat lamp in the hood and allowing the vapor to come off slowly.

4. After all the HNO_3 is evaporated and the tissue samples are dried, they can be placed one at a time beneath the Geiger counter and their relative radioactivity determined.

5. If a ditto machine or some other duplicating device is available, one could make a number of sheets for recording the data of an experiment such as the one just described. Select any number of organs. It is not necessary to use all of them.

No.	Organ	Planchet wt.	Planchet wt. organ wt.	Organ wt.	Counts	Time, min.	Counts/ min./mg.
1	Gill						
2	Heart						
3	Brain						
4	Intestine						
5	Kidney						
6	Liver						
7	Muscle						

6. Counts will indicate whether some organs retain more I^{131} than others. Discussion should follow to suggest how isotopes can be used as tracers in biological experimentation and human medicine.

Experiment with Irradiated Seeds

Another instructive demonstration of radiation effects can be performed without the use of isotopes, and therefore without danger of contamination, by planting irradiated seeds. See Irradiation Facilities below for sources of these materials. Find out what is available before ordering.

Objectives. (1) To determine the effects of irradiation upon the time of germination of seeds. (2) To determine the effects of irradiation upon growth. (3) To determine other visible effects such as leaf shape, coloration, and branching as compared with check plants grown from nonirradiated seeds. (Be sure that you have checks grown under identical conditions.)

Materials. Sufficient number of irradiated seeds to grow at least 20 plants of each type, as well as checks. Seeds may be irradiated by Co^{60} to produce such numbers as 1,000 r, 10,000 r, 20,000 r, 40,000 r, etc. Flats, or trays, with soil for planting seeds; separate tray for each amount of irradiation.

Procedure

1. Plant each kind of seed in separate trays, using equal amounts of soil in each tray and equal numbers of seeds per tray.

2. Mark each tray clearly so as to distinguish the amounts of irradiation.

3. Water each tray every day with equal amounts of water.

4. Watch each tray daily for germination and record the time after planting.

5. Measure the growth rates and record these daily.

6. Make a table for recording data. Later, make graphs where possible.

7. Watch for other differences such as coloration, leaf shape and size, branching.

This experiment could be extended by growing plants to maturity and getting seeds which could be planted again to see if any of the noted effects are hereditary.

Irradiation Facilities. Irradiated materials may be obtained from the following sources:

The Argonne High Level Gamma Irradiation Facility, Argonne National Laboratory, 9700 South Cass Ave., Argonne, Ill.

Oak Ridge Atom Industries, 845 Chicago Ave., Evanston, Ill. Irradiated flower and vegetable seeds can be purchased from this organization.

The Ransom Seed Company, 9056 E. Arcadia Ave., San Gabriel, Calif. Two pages of their catalogue are devoted to several kinds of irradiated seeds of flowers, vegetables, field crops, fruit trees, and forest trees. This list is accompanied by some discussion and photographic illustrations, indicating the importance of use of such material as projects for biology in schools.

Radiation Equipment. Equipment may be obtained from the following companies:

Nuclear Chicago Corporation, 333 E. Howard St., Des Plaines, Ill.

Landsverk Electrometer Co., 641 Sonora Ave., Glendale 1, Calif.

Radiation Counter Laboratories, Inc., Nucleonic Park, Spokie, Ill.

A PROJECT ON CHROMATOGRAPHY

Chromatography began with a botanist, M. Tswett, who found that when he packed a glass cylinder with certain powders and then poured a green plant extract over it, separate bands of differently colored pigments would develop as the solution flowed down the tube. In this way he could separate and identify the several green (chlorophylls), yellow (xanthophylls), and other pigments found in green plants. In 1906 he named the technique "Chromatography" since it graphically separated colored materials. Gradually it became possible also to isolate uncolored materials if these could be made visible by ultraviolet light or, more commonly, by the use of locating reagents which reacted with desired materials forming colored products. Not until 1944 was paper chromatography first described, but this important simplification in technique has all but supplanted column chromatography.

We may define paper chromatography as a technique for separating and identifying selected components of a drop of sample deposited as a spot on filter paper. When a mixture of two or more solvents is caused to flow slowly across the paper and past the spot, the soluble components of the sample will be moved along by the solvent flow to varying distances, depending on their different solubilities. Ideally each component will be deposited as a separate spot according to its solubility, but in complex mixtures some components may not separate from each other with a given solvent mixture, but can be isolated by then applying another solvent at right angles to the first, resulting in a "two-dimensional" chromatogram. Finally the desired components are made to appear as colored spots by the use of an appropriate locating reagent.

Because of the very small amounts of material needed for chromatography, it has found many uses in biology. By this procedure it is possible to isolate and identify the specific amino acids or soluble carbohydrates (sugars) present in a bit of plant sap, nectar, the blood of an insect, or the urine of man. We find that the appearance of certain abnormal sugars or amino acids (readily detectable by chromatography) in human urine denotes serious pathological conditions such as advanced liver damage or muscular dystrophy. As we shall see, the taxonomy of insects can be assisted by studying chromatographs of their blood amino acids. Chromatographs of ink particles from the signatures on documents have been used to prove forgery of those signatures. However, the most extensive use of chromatography is in the field of biochemistry where it has been used particularly to follow the appearance or disappearance of vital life substances (organic metabolites) in the metabolism of living organisms.

In the demonstrations which follow, the beginning student can see for himself how mixtures of colored inks or dyes can be separated into their component dyes or how colorless amino acid or sugar mixtures can be similarly separated and then "developed" as colored spots by means of the locating reagents.

Demonstrations

Colored Materials. Locate different colors and brand names of ink, then dilute one drop of each color with 9 drops of water in separate containers (or on a spot plate). Also dilute a mixture of the several inks with 9 parts of water. Now place one or two drops of diluted ink in the center of a filter-paper circle placed on a smooth clean surface or in a petri dish. Prepare separate filter papers for each color or combination. In an hour's time some of the filter papers will show rings of more than one color corresponding to the number of component dyes present. Note that some commercial inks are mixtures of dyes and that not all blue-black inks give the same ring diagram. The student may wish to extend this procedure to pure food colors, determining by trial the best dilutions to use. However, he will get better results by using these colored materials in a modification of the cylinder technique next described. (Water would be the solvent and no locating reagent would be needed.)

Sugars. Paper chromatography is generally accomplished on filter-paper strips or sheets. The 8¾-by-6-in. sheets called for in this procedure may be cut from the large sheets of Whatman no. 1 or Whatman 3 MM paper or from 27-cm. circles of Whatman no. 1. The 3 MM paper is especially prepared for chromatography. After the sheets have been cut, draw a pencil line lengthwise of each sheet 1 in. from the bottom edge. Mark this line with eight neat dots at 1-in. intervals to show where the sample spots will be placed. The diluted sugar samples (1 per cent sugar in a 10 per cent isopropanol solution) are applied to the dots with a flat-tipped glass stirring rod or a chromel wire loop. The wire loop has the advantage that it can be quickly flamed between samples, whereas the glass rod must be carefully rinsed between each sample and deposits less accurately controlled droplets. It is helpful to dry the spots as they are applied by the use of a hair dryer. This will keep them small in size. Start at the left with glucose and continue with sucrose and the mixtures, labeling each spot with pencil beneath the line. Now carefully staple or Scotch tape the ends of the sheet together near the top and bottom to form a 6 in.-high cylinder with the line of spots near the bottom. The staples are placed so that the ends of the paper are held close together but without actual contact or overlap. As soon as the spots are thoroughly dry, the cylinder is carefully lowered into a quart-size wide-mouthed Mason jar containing 30 ml. of the solvent (80 per cent isopropanol). It is important to avoid tipping the jar or wetting the cylinder on the way down. In this way the solvent will rise evenly all the way around the cylinder as it wets the paper. After about 2 hr. the cylinder will be wetted all the way to the top and is ready to be removed for drying. Drying is best accomplished by hanging the cylinder in the draft of a chemical fume hood. Lacking this, one may use a hair dryer or fan in a well-ventilated room. When the cylinder is thoroughly dry (at least 30 min.), the stapled ends are separated and the sheet is flattened. It is then sprayed or dipped with the sugar locating reagent (aniline-diphenylamine-phosphate) and again dried in the hood. The colors will appear after several hours at room temperature or within minutes in a 100°C. oven. If a hot oven is used, be sure the inflammable solvents (from the locating reagent) have been removed in order to avoid fire. Also the paper should be observed frequently in the oven to avoid its becoming overdone. A successful chromatograph will show discrete colored spots, one for each single sugar and more than one for each mixture.

Three kinds of clues can be followed in identifying the component sugars of a mixture: (1) Match the color and height of the spots with those of the single sugar samples, e.g., glucose and sucrose. (2) Check the height of the spots above the base line relative to the height of the glucose spot (R_g values) in Smith's text, p. 167 (see Ref. 55). (3) Compare the color of the spots with the notes given by Smith. By using this procedure the sugars present in several samples of honeys and sirups can be identified and compared. Preservation of the chromatographs is difficult as the whole sheet will gradually darken and soften, especially in the light, until the spots are finally obliterated. It is best to circle the spots and record their best colors while the sheet is fresh.

Amino Acids. The 8¾-by-6-in. filter-paper sheets are cut and marked as for sugar chromatographs. Glycine is suggested as a standard amino acid since it is the least expensive to purchase and also is commonly found in normal human urine. It should be made up as a ¹⁄₁₀th to ½ per cent solution in 10 per cent isopropanol. Other amino acids are equally suitable and are likewise diluted. The standard sample or any other dissolved samples are applied as described for sugars. Insects make good subjects for this technique since their blood or hemolymph is relatively high in the number and concentration of free amino acids present. Live small insects, such as mosquitoes, *Drosophila*, houseflies, or aphids, are killed by wrapping them in a piece of gauze or cheesecloth and dipping them in boiling water for 2 min. This precipitates interfering proteins. Each specimen is touched lightly to cleansing tissue to blot it dry and then crushed directly on the chromatograph dot with a flat-tipped glass stirring rod. Drying is hastened with the hair dryer. Larger insects, such as cockroaches or moths, are killed and blotted as above and then, minus legs and wings, each is placed in a 10-ml. syringe. By pressing the syringe plunger, several drops of fluid are expressed from the crushed specimen, enough for several spots. After all spots have been applied, dried, and labeled, the sheet is formed into a cylinder as before and carefully lowered into a jar containing 30 ml. of solvent mixture (butanol 12 parts, glacial acetic acid 3 parts, and water 5 parts). After 2 hr., or when the solvent has *nearly* reached the top, the cylinder is removed and dried. When thoroughly dry it is opened and sprayed with a ninhydrin dispenser. After drying and brief oven heating the violet ninhydrin—amino acid spots will appear. There is not much color variation in the spots, except for proline and hydroxyproline, which are yellow. As with sugars, the amino acid spots can be identified by comparison with spots from known acids, such as glycine, run at the same time, or by comparing R_f values as found in Smith Ref. 55, or other sources. The R_f value for a given spot is defined as the ratio: distance from base line to spot center/distance from base line to solvent front. R_f values, like R_g values for sugar chromatography, are useful because they are reasonably constant even though the exact positions of the spots will vary from run to run depending on temperature, time, water content of the paper, and other variables. Notice that in comparing insect blood chromatograms it is not even necessary to identify the spots in order to discover reliable differences or similarities between the spot patterns.

Separation of Pigments Found in Green Leaves, by Paper Chromatography. Treat about 1 g. of fresh green leaf tissue (spinach, found on the vegetable market is quite satisfactory) in boiling water for about 3 min. to kill the cells. Remove the boiled leaves, blotting off the excess water with paper toweling. Place the leaf material in a mortar with about 1 g. of fine-grained quartz sand and 15 ml. of a mixture of 50 parts petroleum ether to 1 part of methyl alcohol, and grind thoroughly until the solvent mixture is reduced to 4 or 5 ml. Repeat this procedure twice more. Pour 1 ml. of the pigment extract into a test tube. Cut a strip of filter paper narrow enough to be readily inserted into the test tube, and long enough to reach the bottom, with enough outside the tube for support. By capillarity the extract moves up the filter paper strip, with color bands developing. At lower end of the strip chlorophyll *b* forms the first band since it is absorbed more strongly than chlorophyll *a*, which appears next and above chlorophyll *b*. The carotenes (yellow and orange) pigments will collect at the top of the strip as the solvent evaporates.

Column Chromatographic Separation of Chloroplast Pigments. Absorption column chromatography is based on the differential absorption of solutes on a nearly inert support. The inert support used in this exercise is ordinary cornstarch. The procedure is as follows: Fit one end of a piece of glass tubing of 37 mm. diameter and 30 cm. length with a one-holed rubber stopper. Insert a 10 cm. length of 5-mm. tubing into the rubber stopper projecting it a millimeter or so through the stopper. Place a small amount of glass wool into the large glass tube all the way down to the stopper. This will prevent the cornstarch from entering the small tubing. Next add dry cornstarch one spatula full at a time to the open end of the column. After each addition, tap the column on some solid surface. The starch will pack evenly and tightly. (Be cautious about how hard you tap the column.) Leave a 6-cm. space at the top of the column. Attach one end of a rubber hose to the small tube at the bottom of the column and the other end of the hose to a water aspirator or a vacuum pump. (If a vacuum pump is used, attach a Gooch filter flask in series with the pump and column to trap fluid passing through the system.) Keep the vacuum applied during the following procedure. After the starch has been packed by the pressure created by the vacuum, pour 50 ml. of petroleum ether into the top of the column. After this solvent has passed through the column, the chloroplast pigments may be added.

The chloroplast pigments are extracted fresh or dry green leaves (fresh spinach is excellent material) in a Waring Blendor (or other efficient grinding system) using a mixture of 80 per cent acetone, 15 per cent methyl alcohol, and 5 per cent water as a solvent. A suitable ration is 25 g. of leaves and 100 ml. of solvent. Filter the solids out of the solvent and mix the solvent (which now contains the pigments) with an equal amount of petroleum ether in a separatory funnel. Gently rotate the funnel for several minutes and allow the solvent layers to separate. Discard the lower solvent layer. Wash the petroleum ether extract several times by adding equal volumes of distilled water, gently shaking by rotation, allowing the layers to separate and discarding the lower layer. Transfer the petroleum ether extract to a small bottle, add 1 g. of anhydrous sodium sulfate, stopper and allow to stand 5 min. Pour 10 to 20 ml. of the petroleum ether extract into the top of the column. Apply mild vacuum and after the last of the extract passes into the starch begin adding pure petroleum ether. The carotenes will be almost completely dissolved in the petroleum ether as it passes down the column. The chlorophylls will remain near the origin. If the carotenes are allowed to pass on through the column there will be a separation near the top of the column as follows: xanthophyll at the top, then chlorophyll *b*, and finally chlorophyll *a*.

Materials. Glass stirring rod; medicine droppers; filter-paper circles (11 cm. diameter suggested); filter-paper sheets (Whatman 3 MM suggested); quart-size wide-mouthed Mason jars and lids;[1] stapler or Scotch tape;[2] hair dryer (desirable);[3] chemical fume hood (desirable); incubator oven (desirable); chromel wire (bacteriological inoculation loop) (desirable); 10-ml. tuberculin syringe (optional); distilled water (to be used wherever water is called for); isopropyl alcohol (isopropanol); *n*-butyl alcohol (butanol); glacial acetic acid; sucrose (cane sugar),[1] glucose (dextrose), honeys and sirups,[1] and glycine (aminoacetic acid). (The last four are made up as dilute solutions in a solvent made up of water 9 parts, isopropyl alcohol 1 part. The alcohol is a preservative.) Colored inks and/or pure food coloring;[1, 2] live insects;[4] ninhydrin-acetone dispenser;[5] aniline–diphenylamine phosphate dispenser;[5] test tube; mortar and pestle; fine quartz sand; fresh spinach;[1] ordinary cornstarch;[1, 6] glass tubing of 37 mm. diameter and length 30 cm.;[6] one-holed rubber stopper;[6] glass wool;[6] rubber hose;[6] water aspirator or faucet vacuum pump;[6] Gooch filter flask;[6] Waring Blendor (desirable);[6] separatory funnel;[6] anhydrous sodium sulfate;[6] methyl alcohol; petroleum ether.

Except for the noted items, the above supplies, if not already at hand, can be secured through almost any laboratory supply house.

REFERENCES

1. Admundson, C. L.: "Biology Fair," *Am. Biol. Teacher,* **12**:129–131, October, 1950.

2. Alan, P. F., and C. N. Davis: "Ponds for Wildlife," *U.S. Dept. Agr., Farmers' Bull.* 1879, 1941.

[1] Grocery items. [2] Stationery items. [3] Hardware items. [4] Live insects usually can be captured locally. [5] These Chromo-Spray aerosol dispensers are available from Schaar & Co., 7300 W. Montrose Ave., Chicago 34, Ill. If they are not used, one must prepare the following locating reagents: For sugars—aniline 1 ml., diphenylamine 1 g., acetone 100 ml.; just before use, add 10 ml. concentrated (85 per cent) phosphoric acid. For amino acids—ninhydrin 0.2 g., acetone 100 ml.; just before use, add 1 ml. of 2 per cent pyridine in water. [6] Materials for column chromatography.

3. American Tree Association: Charts and Pamphlets on Tree Conservation. 1214 16th Street, N.W., Washington 6, D.C.

4. Ames, C. E.: "The Use of a Display Case for Science Education," *School Sci. and Math.,* vol. 50, no. 7, October, 1950.

5. Audubon Society of Canada: Conservation and Natural History Pamphlets. 177 Jarvis St., Toronto 2, Canada.

6. Ayers, Quincy C.: *Soil Erosion and Its Control,* McGraw-Hill Book Company, Inc., New York, 1937.

7. Blaydes, Glenn W., and L. V. Domm: "The Effectiveness of Our Schools in the Teaching of Biological Sciences," *Sci. Teacher,* **15**:57–58, April, 1948.

8. Blaydes, Glenn W.: "The Romance of Domesticated Plants," *Ohio J. Sci.,* **53**:193–215, 1953. Also reprinted in *Smithsonian Repts.,* 1954, pp. 317–366. Deals with the origin of domesticated plants, genetic variation in seeds, hybridization and somatic mutations with 41 photographic illustrations (2 in color).

9. Block, R. J., E. L. Durrum, and G. Zweig: *A Manual of Paper Chromatography and Paper Electrophoresis,* rev. 2d ed., Academic Press, Inc., New York, 1958.

10. Briggs, L. J., and K. F. Weaver: "How Old Is It," *Natl. Geog. Mag.,* **114**:234–255, August, 1958. Deals with the discovery and application of the radiocarbon (carbon 14) method of dating organic remains.

11. Browning, J. C.: "Live Animal Projects in the Teaching of Biology," *Junior Coll. J.,* **27**:407–408, March, 1957.

12. Bullington, Robert A.: "Winter Field Experiences for Biology Teachers," *Am. Biol. Teacher,* vol. 21, no. 1, January, 1959.

13. Camp, W. H., V. R. Boswell, and J. R. Magness: *The World in Your Garden,* National Geographic Society, Washington, D.C., 1957.

14. Carter, Vernon Gill: *Man on the Landscape,* National Wildlife Federation, Washington, D.C., 1949. Deals with the fundamentals of plant, animal, soil, and water conservation. Contains a wealth of ideas and suggestions to the teacher of conservation and ecology.

15. Chase, Grafton D.: *Principles of Radioisotope Methodology,* Burgess Publishing Company, Minneapolis, 1959.

16. Clark, S.: "Use of Projects in Biology," *Am. Biol. Teacher,* **16**:212–213, December, 1954.

17. Comar, C. L.: *Radioisotopes in Biology and Agriculture,* McGraw-Hill Book Company, Inc., New York, 1955.

18. Davis, R. K.: "Farm Pond Management," *Ohio State Univ., Agr. Ext. Service, Extension Bull.* 374, 1958.

19. Davison, V. E., and J. A. Johnson: "Fish for Food from Farm Ponds," *U.S. Dept. Agr., Farmers' Bull.* 1938, 1943.

20. DeKruif, Paul Henry: *Microbe Hunters,* Harcourt, Brace & Company, New York, 1926. Deals with lives and scientific achievements of Pasteur, Koch, Bruce, Ross, Reed, and others.

21. DeKruif, Paul Henry: *Hunger Fighters,* Harcourt, Brace & Company, New York, 1928.

22. DeKruif, Paul Henry: *Men Against Death,* Harcourt, Brace & Company, New York, 1936.

23. DeLaubenfels, M. W.: *Pageant of Life Science,* Prentice-Hall, Inc., Englewood Cliffs, N.J., 1949. A pictorialized survey of biology, leavened with many curious facts.

24. Devoe, A.: *This Fascinating Animal World,* McGraw-Hill Book Company, Inc., New York, 1951. Questions and answers most often asked about mammals, birds, insects, snakes, etc.

25. Edminister, Frank C.: *Fish Ponds for the Farm,* Charles Scribner's Sons, New York, 1947.

26. Francis, G. E., W. Millegan, and A. Wormall: *Isotopic Tracers,* University of London, The Athlone Press, London, 1954.

27. Friends of the Land: Conservation Materials for Secondary Schools. 1368 N. High St., Columbus 1, Ohio.

28. Glasstone, Samuel: *Source Book on Atomic Energy,* D. Van Nostrand Company, Inc., Princeton, N.J., 1958.

29. Gustafson, A. F., H. Ries, C. H. Guise, and W. J. Hamilton: *Conservation in the United States,* Comstock Publishing Associates, Inc., Ithaca, N.Y., 1940.

30. Hadorn, E., and H. K. Mitchell: "Properties of Mutants of *Drosophila melanogaster* and Changes During Development as Revealed by Paper Chromatography," *Proc. Natl. Acad. Sci.,* **37**:650–665, 1951.

31. Heft, Floyd E.: *Ohio's Conservation Story—On the Land.* The Ohio State University, College of Agriculture, Columbus, Ohio, 1956. An excellent source of information as to the effects of a rapidly increasing population, land diversion to other than agricultural purposes, and soil depletion on land conservation in Ohio.

32. Hillcourt, W.: *Field Book of Nature Activities,* G. P. Putnam's Sons, New York, 1950. Suggestions for projects, nature study, nature collections for teachers.

33. Jackson, H. W.: "Weed Control in Small Ponds," *Virginia Agr. Expt. Sta., Bull.* 425, 1949.

34. Johnson, A. M.: "The Use of the Weed-patch in the Teaching of High School Botany," *School Sci. and Math.,* **23**:127–132, 1923.

35. Johnson, Carl S.: *Planning School Forests,* Ohio Forestry Association, Columbus, Ohio, 1955.

36. Kastrinos, W.: "Biology Projects for High School Students," *Am. Biol. Teacher,* **18**:251–254, December, 1956.

37. Keeler, Alma A.: "The Value of an Observation Hive of Honeybees in the Teaching of High School Biology," *Ohio J. Sci.,* **32**:539–543, 1932.

38. Lacroix, D. S.: "Yeast Experiments for the High School Student," *Am. Biol. Teacher,* **11**:86–87, March, 1949.

39. Leeming, J.: *Real Book of Science Experiments,* Doubleday & Company, Inc., Garden City, N.Y., 1954.

40. Lichtenwalter, M. C.: "Plant Projects with or without a Greenhouse," *Am. Biol. Teacher,* **18**:97–98, February, 1956.

41. McAtee, V. M.: "Some Class Activities in Biology," *Sci. Educ.,* **28**:50, February, 1944.

42. Micks, Don W., and F. J. Gibson: "The Characterization of Insects and Ticks by Their Free Amino Acid Patterns," *Annals Entomol. Soc. Am.,* **50**:500–505, 1957.

43. Millar, C. E., and L. M. Turk: *Fundamentals of Soil Science,* John Wiley & Sons, Inc., New York, 1954.

44. National Education Association, Science Teachers Association Department: *If You Want to Do a Science Project.* 1201 16th St., N.W., Washington, D.C., 1955.

45. National Education Association, Science Teachers Association Department: *Encouraging Future Scientists: Student Projects.* 1201 16th Street, N.W., Washington 6, D.C., 1954.

46. National Education Association, Science Teachers Association Department: *Let's Take a Field Trip.* 1201 16th St., N.W., Washington, D.C., 1956.

47. Otto, J. H., and S. S. Blanc: *Biology Investigations,* Holt, Rinehart and Winston, Inc., New York, 1956.

48. Patton, A. R.: "Quantitative Paper Chromatography for Students," *J. Chem. Educ.,* **28**:629, 1951.

49. R.C.A. Service Company: *Atomic Radiation,* Camden, N.J., 1958.

50. Richardson, J. S., and G. P. Cahoon: *Methods and Materials for Teaching General and Physical Science,* McGraw-Hill Book Company, Inc., New York, 1951.

51. Schneider, E.: *All About Aquariums,* Doubleday & Company, Inc., Garden City, N.Y., 1956.

52. Science Clubs of America: *Details on Participation in the National Science Fair and Other Activities Sponsored by the S.C.A.* 1719 N St., N.W., Washington 6, D.C.

53. Sibley, H.: *72 New Bird Houses and Feeders,* Goodheart-Wilcox Co., Inc., Chicago, 1957.

54. Simmons, M. P.: "Model Bathysphere," *School Sci. and Math.,* **42**:157–159, February, 1942.

55. Smith, Ivor (ed.): *Chromatographic Techniques: Clinical and Biochemical Applications,* Interscience Publishers, Inc., New York, 1958.

56. Swingle, H. S., and E. V. Smith: "Management of Farm Fish Ponds," *Alabama Polytech. Inst., Agr. Expt. Sta., Bull.* 254, 1942.

57. Transeau, E. N., H. C. Sampson, and L. H. Tiffany: *Textbook of Botany,* rev. ed., Harper & Brothers, New York, 1953. Useful for study of all processes, ecology, and survey of the plant kingdom.

58. Treuting, H. R., Jr., and H. M. Fuhrman: "Natural Pond in the Classroom," *Am. Biol. Teacher,* **17**:127–130, April, 1955.

59. Tyson, Joe W.: *Atomic Radiation in the High School Science Class,* Tyson—Old Friends Books, Austin, Tex., 1959. The best single book for the classroom.

60. U.S. Fish and Wildlife Service, Department of the Interior, Washington 25, D.C. Bulletins on care, control, conservation, etc., of fish, birds, and wild animals.

61. U.S. Government Printing Office: *Teaching with Radioisotopes,* 1958. Washington, D.C. Valuable and at low cost.

62. U.S. Soil Conservation Service, Department of Agriculture, Washington 25, D.C. Literature and pictures on soil conservation.

63. Vance, B. B., C. A. Barker, and D. F. Miller: *Biology Activities,* J. B. Lippincott Company, Philadelphia, 1954.

64. Vogt, William: *Road to Survival,* William Sloane Associates, Inc., New York, 1948.

65. Weatherwax, Paul: *Indian Corn in Old America,* The Macmillan Company, New York, 1954.

66. Wiggans, R. G.: "Studies of Various Factors Influencing the Yield and the Duration of Life of Meadow and Pasture Plants," *Cornell Univ. Agr. Expt. Sta., Bull.* 425, 1923.

67. Wilson, S. O.: "Biology Classroom Zoo," *School Sci. and Math.,* **43**:345–351, April, 1943.

68. Yothers, L. R.: "Biology Clubs and Projects," *Am. Biol. Teacher,* **17**:109–111, March, 1955.

CHAPTER 12

⁕ Collecting, Culturing, and Preserving ⁕

There is probably no greater problem for the teacher of biological subjects than the necessity of providing suitable materials for class use. In this chapter an attempt is made to suggest to the teacher (1) typical ecological situations (habitats) where such materials may reasonably be expected to be found, (2) types of materials that may be secured which will be of use in the classroom, and (3) methods of collecting, culturing, and preserving such material.

For the student to think of plants and animals in relation to their natural environment is an important part of training in biology. When trips afield are at all possible, they should be arranged because they result in the production of attitudes not otherwise possible. Too frequently students know that laboratory or demonstration materials come out of cans or bottles but are unable to trace them farther. The recognition of organisms in the out-of-doors is a long step toward the appreciation of nature and of life itself. The elements of ecology may be made quite simple and quite interesting for beginners, and an attempt has been made here to formulate type situations which are common and to avoid technical terms and minute distinctions.

A good collector and a successful field trip conductor must know at least a few of the fundamentals of plant and animal distribution. He is aware of the fact that such environmental factors as water supply, light, temperature, oxygen supply, hydrogen-ion concentration, and fertility of the soil determine the types of plant communities to be found, and, consequently, the types of animal forms likely to be encountered. He knows that certain forms are found only about ponds, swamps, or bogs; many species found in a beech-maple forest are not found in oak-hickory associations, swamp forest, or grasslands, etc. The careful observer will have noted gradual changes of one type of community into another as environmental conditions change. Any farmer can tell something of the changes brought about by drainage. The landscape of our agricultural regions has been changed notably by such procedures. An area once covered with frog ponds and cattail swamps may become dry grasslands or grain fields. The wildflower enthusiast can readily relate instances of favorite forests being lumbered, resulting soon in the disappearance of the usual spring, summer, and autumn flowers. He may also have noted that after a certain forest type was removed it was often succeeded by a different kind of forest if the area was not further disturbed. Conversations with the older inhabitants of a community often will reveal many interesting facts concerning vegetation changes.

Many teachers are confronted with the problem of being surrounded by agricultural lands on which most of the original vegetation has been destroyed. Too often they regard the situation as hopeless as far as field work is concerned. However, if the region is carefully studied, pastured grasslands, wood lots, ponds, and streams are likely to be found. Quite a variety of species can be listed from these. The shrewd teacher will be able to substitute many local forms for the standard ones of biology texts. There are always waste areas along roads and railways which offer possibilities to the biologist. Abandoned fields or vacant city lots will yield numerous possibilities especially in the study of plant succession. A comparison of the vegetation on a series of similarly located waste areas will bring out the extremely interesting phenomenon of one plant and animal population succeeding another as the environmental conditions change. A study of weeds, insects, rodents, birds, fur-bearing animals, game, cultivated and native trees, shrubs, and plant and animal diseases of an agricultural region will arouse interest. And, after all, knowledge concerning these are of fundamental and immediate value to the student living in these particular surroundings. When a teacher once realizes that an available jungle of native vegetation is not necessarily a prerequisite to successful field trips, he may become aware of the numerous possibilities of his particular community.

Other methods of collecting, culturing, and preserving which are quite useful may be known to the teacher. Those selected here are intended to be suggestive rather than comprehensive.

ANIMAL ORGANISMS

Protozoa

General and Mixed Cultures. *Habitat.* In the extent to which they are distributed, the protozoa are exceeded only by the bacteria and molds, and perhaps certain algae. They are, with but few exceptions, aquatic in their active and reproductive stages. They may be driven about in the wind on dust and debris, but unlike bacteria, are seldom obtained from the quiet air of rooms. Most debris from out-of-doors, however, will contain spores or resting stages of protozoa. The most fruitful sources are usually the remains of plants of various kinds, especially those which have grown or have collected in ditches or depressions that are sometimes filled with water. The water, the surface scum, or the bottom ooze of ponds, pools, and ditches may yield numerous forms of protozoa.

Collecting. If water or material from a pond or pool is collected, bottles with stoppers or jars with lids are needed for the collecting trip. If dry culture materials are to be collected, sacks, cans, or almost any kind of container will be satisfactory to hold the dead grass, leaves, sticks, stones, or other material collected. If water containing protozoa is secured, it is advisable to fill the container not more than one-half full and to unstopper the bottles as soon as possible after returning to the laboratory to permit aeration.

Culturing. After material has been brought to the laboratory the preparation of cultures for later use is simple.

Place a quantity of the grass, leaves, etc., in quart jars or enamelware pans and add enough water to more than cover the material. Allow this to stand in a warm place but not in direct sunlight. If examined at intervals of about 24 or 48 hr. the changes in population will be found to be very marked, from almost no protozoa at the beginning to an exceedingly dense population in 10 to 15 days and then a steady decline to a very small population. Also, there will be a decided sequence of types appearing and disappearing during this time.

Preserving. Sometimes an unusually good or rare culture is discovered, and it may be desirable to preserve some of it for future use. This material is often useful to give the student a better understanding of detail of structure which cannot be so readily seen in the more rapidly moving forms. In general, however, a living culture is more instructive and should not be entirely replaced by preserved specimens.

Not all forms can be preserved equally well in all preservatives. A 10 per cent solution of formalin is about as good a universal preservative as any. Another good one consists of

50 per cent alcohol	90 parts
4 per cent formalin	5 parts
Glacial acetic acid	5 parts

This acts as a killing and fixing agent, and if the protozoa are left in it they will keep indefinitely. The addition of a little glycerin tends to keep the animals from becoming too brittle. Use an amount of glycerin equal to 5 parts of the above. (See also special methods under Pure Cultures below.)

Important. In killing and preserving microscopic animals use the following procedure. Be sure that the culture is good. Draw up a medicine dropper or tube full of the culture and look at it under some kind of a lens to be sure that numerous animals are present. Run the culture material quickly into a dish or bottle containing about two to five times as much preservative as you have culture medium. Otherwise the medium may dilute the preservative to the point where it is not effective. It is usually best not to run the preservative into the culture but the culture into the preservative. If the specimens are to be kept in a vial or bottle the cork should be dipped in melted paraffin or petroleum jelly to prevent evaporation. Dipping the cork and end of the vial in collodion also makes an excellent seal. A still better vial has a plastic screw cap. The inside of the cap may be coated with paraffin before screwing it on to the vial.

Pure Cultures. At intervals during the life of a mixed culture of protozoa certain forms become abundant for a while and then decline. For example, there is usually a period of paramecium dominance. During such times as this it is possible to have certain forms separated out and pure cultures started. See Chap. 22 for the method of making this separation. Very little practice is necessary in order to do this successfully.

Amoeba (Sarcodina). Amoebae are not found in cultures of mixed protozoa as frequently as one might hope. When they are found, they seldom seem abundant and are usually on the bottom of the container or on the surfaces of leaves and stems. They feed upon other minute protozoa or one-celled plants; therefore a culture medium is necessary which will furnish these food organisms. The most successful culture medium for *Amoeba proteus* is made as follows: Into a shallow dish (such as a butter dish) pour about 100 cc. of water (distilled is best but not necessary); add to this 3 grains of rice. When soaked, contaminate the water with saprolegnia (water mold) and then place in the culture medium some monoidia or other small protozoa which are usually abundant in most infusion cultures of mixed character made from dead grass and leaves. Select a few amoebae as suggested above, under Pure Cultures. Add them to the culture medium and set it aside in a warm place for a week. It can be covered to prevent evaporation, but do not seal it. The small flagellates reproduce abundantly, and the amoebae feed upon them and will also become abundant. The amoebae sometimes become so numerous as to form a white film over the bottom of the dish. Once started, this method is easy to continue. New cultures should be started about every 3 or 4 weeks since they run out in time.

Paramecium (*Infusoria*) (and many other ciliates) are the easiest forms to culture. Use the method described in Chap. 22 to start new cultures about every 2 weeks in order to avoid loss.

Euglena (*Phytomastigina*). It is desirable to have this chlorophyll-bearing organism for class. It may be cultured in abundance by the following method. Place about 1 g. of sheep manure or dry chicken manure in a vessel with 250 cc. of water and boil for 10 min. When it has cooled let it stand open to the air or blow some dust into it so that it will become contaminated with bacteria. After about 36 or 48 hr. it can be inoculated with euglenae. They increase rapidly in number, causing the medium to become green in appearance. Euglenae are sometimes found in practically pure culture in small pools or ditches. If the water in such a place appears greenish in color, examine it carefully. It is likely to be due to algae, but may be caused by euglenae instead.

Another successful medium for euglena consists of dissolving approximately 0.1 g. of Bacto Beef extract, or peptone, in 120 cc. of distilled water and bringing it to a boil. When cooled, inoculate the medium with a few drops from a good euglena culture. The cultures do best if made in an Erlenmeyer flask stoppered with a rolled cotton plug.

Sponges

Fresh-water Sponges (Spongillidae). *Habitat.* All sponges are aquatic and mostly marine, but there are a few forms that live in ponds, lakes, and streams. They are not very conspicuous organisms, appearing as soft white or brownish slimy blotches on sticks, stones, and other objects submerged in the water. They may be a fraction of an inch to more than an inch in diameter. Sponges are not usually recognized unless they are being watched for specifically.

Collecting. Any can or bucket used for collecting aquatic forms may serve to convey sponges back to the laboratory. They must be kept submerged in the water in which they were found.

Culturing. Fresh-water sponges are not easy to keep in aquaria for long periods but may be kept a short time for class use. Place in balanced aquaria or in an out-of-door fish pool.

Preserving. The stick or object to which the sponge is attached may be dried and kept in something such as a mounting box. The sponge will dry and become very crumbly, falling apart if touched. Preserving in liquid, such as 5 per cent formalin, is much better. If 70 per cent alcohol is easier to obtain it may be used instead of formalin.

Worms

Planaria (Turbellaria) (fresh-water flatworms). *Habitat.* The common flatworm *Planaria* is widely distributed in ponds and streams of all sizes. They can be found attached to the surface of stones or other objects and being strongly negative to light are nearly always on the underside. Sometimes they occur on the submerged portion of aquatic plants. There are different species with corresponding differences in size and color. They may vary from 1/8 in. to 1/2 in. or more in length. In color they vary from white through brown to black. They are commonly dark gray.

Collecting. Upon visiting a pond or stream turn over stones, boards, sticks, etc., examining their undersurfaces carefully. Usually, but not always, planarians are to be found in groups and clusters. They may be washed off into a bucket, jar, or other collecting vessel. If the vessel is small they may be removed and transferred to it upon the point of a penknife. The collecting can or jar should be closed until you reach the laboratory.

Culturing. Planarians may be kept in aquaria if stones are placed in the bottom and a considerable amount of plants and mud is allowed to accumulate in the bottom. A simpler and more certain method is to place the planarians in a shallow dish or porcelain pan with 1 in. of fresh water. Cover the pan to exclude the light. Two or three times a week they must be fed. This is done by laying a small thin slice of liver in the pan. The planarians will cluster upon it and feed. At the end of 1 hr. the liver should be lifted out and all worms washed off or lifted off the liver with a dull knife blade. Make a complete water change to avoid fouling of the culture. Worm cultures kept in this manner may run several years. They may also deposit egg capsules at times, which if carefully watched will produce numerous young planarians in 2 to 3 weeks. Planarians should be studied alive if possible. After general observations of the moving animal, it may be flattened between two microscope slides and examined under the microscope. Place the worm in the middle of a dry slide and lay another slide upon it carefully to avoid crushing.

Preserving. Planarians may be preserved and kept for future use when it is not convenient to culture them. Place one or more worms near the middle of a microscope slide and cover with a second slide (other pieces of glass may be used if slides are not to be had). Put enough pressure upon the upper glass to flatten the worms out thinly, being careful not to crush them. Place the slides and their worms in a shallow dish or pan and pour over them a solution of 5 per cent formalin. If the glass slides are slightly tilted, the preservative will run in between them and fix the worms. Allow them to remain submerged for a period of 2 hr. or more. If the plates of glass are removed, the worms will be found preserved and sufficiently thin for microscope use. They can be left between the slides until used if so desired, or removed and preserved in vials. They are very delicate and if the above method crushes them, try heating very slowly in water until killed and then drawing off the water and adding preservative. They do not preserve and handle well unless mounted on microscope slides in balsam. (For regeneration experiments with planaria, see Chap. 22.)

Parasitic Flatworms and Roundworms (tapeworms, Cestoda; flukes, Trematoda; roundworms, Nematoda). *Habitat.* The more common parasitic flatworms and roundworms are widely distributed, and among their hosts are members of most of the other phyla of the animal kingdom. Naturally some hosts, because of their habitats, habits of feeding, and nature of their food supply, are more frequently found to harbor these parasites and therefore offer good sources of the material. Some of the most readily available hosts for most localities are (1) the common grass frog found in brooks, pools, ponds, and streams; (2) birds, especially the common chicken, terns, gulls, and other fishing birds; (3) fish, those which prey upon other fish are usually the most likely sources; (4) snails; (5) insects (not common); (6) snakes, turtles; (7) rats, pigs, sheep, dogs, cats, horses.

Collecting. Naturally those cavities of the body of the host which open to the outside are best suited for sites which parasites may infest. Consequently, in searching for material always look in the lungs. Amphibia, reptiles, and birds may have both flatworm and roundworm parasites in their lung cavities. A hand lens or microscope may help in locating them.

The stomach, small and large intestine, and the cecum are likely sites for these worms. Sometimes the worms may be encysted in the walls of these organs or may be attached to the surface from which they project into the body cavity.

The urinary bladder may also harbor parasitic worms, and they sometimes enter the liver and kidneys. Certain forms are occasionally obtained from the blood, but these are not easy to find.

In the insects, the abdomens of grasshoppers, beetles, and roaches frequently possess the very long threadworms which are often called "horsehair snakes." The same parasites are also sometimes found in pools, drinking pans, and watering troughs where they may have escaped from their host.

If a visit is made to a slaughterhouse or packing house and the fresh entrails of pigs and chickens are obtained, there should be little difficulty in securing a large quantity of tapeworms and roundworms. This is an almost never-failing source.

Culturing. If worms are obtained soon after the slaughter, placed in normal salt solution, and kept warm they may remain alive for 2 or 3 days. Not a great deal is known about culturing parasitic worms easily. It is known, of course, that if the bladder worm stage of a tapeworm is found in a rat liver it is possible to feed the liver to a cat and rear the adult tapeworm in the cat. A much more practical method for obtaining material from the intestines of chickens or pigs is to wash the contents thoroughly and place a few of the worms in boiled normal saline to which has been added enough glucose to make a 0.2 per cent solution of the glucose. If the solution is kept slightly warm (about 35 to 38°C.) and changed once every day, the worms may live a week or more.

Preserving. It is usually better to kill all forms of worms before preserving them. Some way of killing them in a relaxed condition is best. The two simplest ways of accomplishing this are as follows: (1) Place them in water and heat it slowly until the worms are limp and motionless. Then drop them into 6 or 8 per cent formalin. (2) A small amount of grain alcohol may be added to some water containing worms. After a few minutes add a similar amount of alcohol and continue until the worms are anesthetized. Then preserve in formalin.

Segmented Worms (earthworms, Annelida). *Habitat.* One of the most widely distributed and easily collected animals is the common earthworm. There are several species that are numerous. They are generally found wherever there is an abundance of decomposing vegetable matter and moisture in the soil. Digging with a spade in the soil or turning over an old manure pile or a heap of last year's dead leaves is likely to yield worms. They are usually available in warm manure piles or under straw stacks even in weather when the ground is frozen. Heavy rains, especially late at night, frequently wash many worms from elevated lawns or terraces out upon the sidewalks of city streets. A few minutes spent in collecting at such times may save hours of work later.

Collecting. Most boys have stalked the large night crawlers used as fish bait. All one needs is a flashlight and a can of earth. If the grass is sprinkled heavily in the evening or later afternoon of a warm spring or summer day, the night will yield its supply of worms. Walk very lightly and examine the grass carefully with the flashlight. The worms lie stretched in the grass with their posterior ends still in the opening of their burrows. Grasp the worm quickly and firmly and pull slowly. A jerk will more than likely pull the worm in two, but a slow steady pull will get it. If you miss the animal on the first snatch you should start looking for another, because there is no time for a second chance, so quickly do they retract within the burrow. A little practice will be necessary before you become a successful worm catcher. If the teacher cannot handle the "nasty" worms, the students will do it for the fun of it.

Collect some of the mud, leaves, sticks, and other debris from the bottom of a quiet pool or shallow pond and let it stand in a pan or jar for a few days until it is clear and settled. Examine the surface of the mud for tiny waving hairlike worms. They are minute relatives of the larger earthworms and mounted in a drop of water show well under a microscope.

Culturing. In these as in any culture methods those conditions which most nearly approximate the conditions of the habitat in which the animals are found in nature are likely to be most satisfactory for keeping them in captivity. The larger forms of earthworms should be kept in soil containing considerable humus or in a soil that has a layer of leaves over the top. A large box or a garbage can with numerous small holes in the bottom may serve as a suitable container. The holes must be so small that the worms cannot escape. A wooden box is better. The container may be placed in a pit dug in the ground or kept in a cellar. In any event it must be kept where the temperature will not become high. A good range is 45 to 65°F. A large number of foods have been tried for the feeding of worms, and several may well be recommended. If the soil in which they are kept does not contain much humus, the food may be scattered over the surface. Corn meal has been used for this and also common vegetable garbage from the table or kitchen. Not much can be used at a time, and it must be rather carefully removed. A small can of evaporated milk may be diluted with water and sprinkled on the surface twice per week. If there is much humus in the soil, feeding becomes almost unnecessary.

Preserving. Any annelid may be killed by slowly heating in water or by anesthetizing in alcohol as described above under the preserving of parasitic worms. To preserve large worms so that the internal organs will be in perfect condition and so that the worms will be fully extended, use the following procedure: heat the worms in warm water as in killing or stupefy them with weak alcohol until they become relaxed. Lay the worm on a table and insert a hypodermic needle or fine glass needle through the body cavity. Care should be taken not to strike the needle into the intestinal tract. Be sure that the needle is pointed well anteriorly (forward) before injecting. Slowly force the preservative into the body cavity (6 per cent formalin containing a little glycerin). Maintain the pressure until the segments are fully extended. Withdraw the needle and insert it again about 10 segments posteriorly to (behind) the first point and inject again. When the entire worm has been injected lay it in a pan and pour over it enough of the preservative to cover it. Let this stand overnight and the worm will be in excellent condition for keeping or dissecting. If the glass injection needle is used, the body wall should first be pierced with a large needle or pin to make a hole into which the glass needle may be inserted.

Mollusks

Snails (Gastropoda) and Clams (Pelecypoda). *Habitat.* Snails, clams, and oysters are among the more common mollusks and are widely distributed. Snails and clams of several kinds can be found in most creeks and ponds, while oysters may be obtained at markets in cities. In some places land snails are abundant. Of course people living near the seashore are familiar with a great variety of marine mollusks.

Clams are usually at least partly submerged in muck or sand and in the water, though sometimes they may be found in mud flats. Snails attach themselves to stones or to sticks and stems of growing plants. Land forms are commonly under stones, logs, or in leaf mold on the ground. Sometimes they climb up on trees and shrubs.

Collecting. Usually mollusks will be collected along with numerous other animals or plants. The containers for mollusks alone, however, may consist of jars with stoppers or screw caps. Something larger will be necessary for clams if large ones are captured or if very many are to be brought back alive. Snails are best gathered by hand. If returned alive they should be placed in some of the water from which they are taken or the soil or leaf mold in which they are found. A rake or pronged hoe with long tines is convenient to rake up clams from sand or muck.

Culturing. After snails have been captured in the field, do not leave the lids of the containers closed any longer than is absolutely necessary. By no means allow the containers to stand in the sun. This is a very common error of the inexperienced collector and applies to all other forms collected alive. Most of the common snails found in ponds and streams will survive without further attention if placed in an ordinary aquarium. A deep pan or bucket of water with water plants in it is sufficient if a regular aquarium is not available. If numerous plants are present, no feeding is necessary. Land snails usually may be kept in dampened leaf mold or may be fed on lettuce leaves. Most grocers or food markets will furnish enough of the outer cast-off leaves free.

Clams are not so easy to keep but sometimes survive for a long time in large aquaria that are well stocked with algae and other plants. It is best to have several inches of muck, sand, or gravel on the bottom of the aquarium.

Interesting studies may be made upon mollusks. Reproduction and development of the snail, the pattern and winding of shells, and the composition and structure of shells and of the animals themselves make good problems.

Preserving. Snails may be killed by heating them in water. If done slowly this often causes them to protrude from their shells. They also may be dropped directly into 6 to 8 per cent formalin. Clams should have the edge of the shell broken and a peg driven between the valves to allow the formalin to penetrate thoroughly. The breaking of the edge may be done by pounding with a hammer or stone.

Arthropods

With the animal kingdom as a whole divided into 10 to 18 customary parts, or phyla, it is a surprising fact to find that well over half of all the known species of animals belong to this one phylum, the Arthropoda. One almost never finds a child, and seldom an adult, who does not have a very considerable interest in its members. Because of its definite economic importance to man and its biological significance, it is well deserving of special consideration and time in a biology course. Because of the great diversity of forms it is necessary here to treat it in general aspects which have wide application.

Insects (Hexapoda). Since in the class known as insects we find most of the species of arthropods, it naturally follows that this class also contains most of the animal kingdom.

Habitat. When one attempts to speak of the habitat of insects it becomes necessary to describe almost every possible type of environment, for practically no situation exists which will not harbor some form of insect at least in some stage of its life history. In the ooze at the bottom of lakes and ponds and under and upon the rocks or streams and waterfalls live the young of many species, while others swim freely in the water or glide swiftly over its surface. The depths of the soil furnish homes for innumerable forms and every stone, board, or log may be a hiding place. Over the heated sands of beaches and deserts, in dry clay banks, in the crevices of rocks, and in and upon every plant they swarm. Cold regions well above the Arctic Circle, the peaks of lofty mountains, fertile temperate valleys, and regions under the heat of tropical sun are all occupied. Some suck the juices of plants and the blood of animals, some thrive in the decomposing masses of dead organisms, others penetrate and feed upon living hosts, while not a few stalk and capture small prey. Thus has the most numerous and diversified group in the animal kingdom survived for many millions of years.

Collecting. Though collecting is not difficult there are certain provisions which should be made in order to do it successfully. Some of these are the following.

Collecting Equipment. 1. Cyanide bottle. Crush some sodium cyanide and place it in small lumps in the bottom of a jar with a wide mouth and a good stopper or tight lid. Put enough chopped cork, sawdust, or dry plaster of paris over the cyanide to make the surface level. Pour about ½ in. of plaster of paris over this and set it aside to dry. When dry, close the jar tightly and keep it so except when opened to use. Cyanide is so deadly poisonous to all animals that it has to be handled with care. If you cannot purchase it, your druggist will likely make up the bottle for you. Each bottle should be labeled "Poison."

2. Carbon tetrachloride bottle. A totally harmless and rather efficient killing bottle may be made as follows: Cut a small hole through the cork of the bottle and insert in this hole a small glass tube. Fasten a wad of cotton to the bottom of the cork so that the glass tube will reach the cotton (see Fig. 12.1). The cotton may be saturated through the tube with carbon tetrachloride which is nonpoisonous and nonexplosive. A small bottle of the killing agent may be carried along on a trip and added to the cotton at times through the small hole in the cork.

3. Chloroform bottle. Because of its capacity for absorbing chloroform, rubber is made use of in another type of killing bottle. Place a small handful of rubber bands in the bottom of a jar and cover them with chloroform. Let it stand overnight; then pour out all remaining chloroform and wedge a piece of cardboard over the bands. The rubber will have absorbed enough chloroform to keep the air in the bottle filled with fumes (see Fig. 12.1).

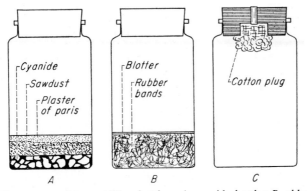

FIG. 12.1   Three types of insect-killing bottles: A, cyanide bottle; B, chloroform bottle; C, carbon tetrachloride bottle.

4. Net. A good and rather inexpensive net may be made from marquisette sewed into the form of a bag and fastened to a heavy wire or rod frame which is circular in form. This frame is attached to a handle, such as a broom or mop handle, as shown in Fig. 12.2B.

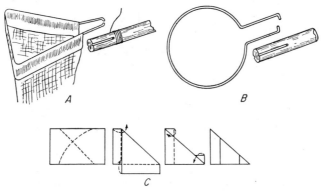

FIG. 12.2   Collecting equipment: A, straight-edged dip net for collecting in water and mud from bottom of ponds; B, frame for insect sweeping net; C, method of making paper folds for butterflies, moths, and dragonflies.

5. Sieves with fine wire bottoms are very handy to carry on a trip when collecting from water. Mud can be dumped into it and washed through, straining out the larvae which live in the ooze at the bottom of a pond or stream.

6. Paper folds for keeping butterflies, dragonflies, and damselflies until you return to the classroom are often a convenience. If a good specimen is left in the killing bottle it becomes frayed and broken when new insects are added. The fold can be made as per diagram (Fig. 12.2C). This keeps the scales from rubbing off and the wings from breaking. They may be laid aside and if they dry they can be relaxed in the relaxing chamber and spread (Fig. 12.3).

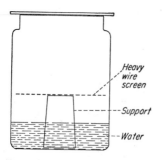

FIG. 12.3 Relaxing chamber for dry insects so that they may be spread or pinned.

7. Vials of alcohol may be taken on a collecting trip. Sometimes beetles survive long periods of exposure in killing bottles. If they are dropped into alcohol, however, and pinned while wet, they are sure to be killed. A few drops of toluene on the body of a moth or butterfly kills it almost instantly and is better than a killing bottle since the wings are not broken by beating.

8. A light trap is an interesting apparatus for students, and its construction and use make excellent projects. By grouping its catch into insect orders or families an idea of night flying insects may be obtained. Any variety of simple trap is effective. One kind is suggested in Fig. 12.4.

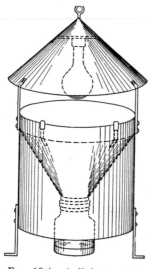

FIG. 12.4 A light trap for insects.

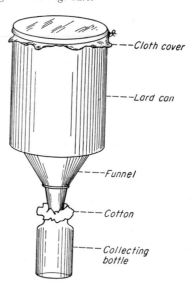

FIG. 12.5 The Berlese funnel for collecting from grass, leaves, and debris.

9. The so-called Berlese funnel is also a convenient apparatus for getting small insects, as well as other animals, which conceal themselves in leaves, grass, and debris that collect on the ground. Figure 12.5 shows such a funnel. A large can, such as a lard can, has a hole cut in its bottom and a big funnel soldered over the

hole on the outside. A false bottom made of heavy large-mesh wire net is placed inside the can, which is then loosely filled with leaves, grass, weeds, etc., and covered with a piece of cheesecloth tied tightly. At the end of the funnel is placed a wide-mouthed bottle or jar, sealed with a cotton plug. As the materials in the can dry out, the inhabitants will move down and eventually be trapped in the jar. If a little alcohol or formalin is placed in the jar the catch will be preserved as caught.

Aquatic Forms. Collecting from streams, pools, and ponds is easy and yields a great variety of insects.

1. On the surface in warm weather one usually finds swarms of actively swimming insects, such as the whirligigs (*Gyrinidae*) and water striders (*Gerridae*). To capture such as these, a dip net is advisable. Such a net can be made without too much difficulty, as shown in Fig. 12.2*A*. Its straight edge makes it useful for dredging bottoms also. When these surface forms are to be returned alive, they may be kept in vessels of the water or placed in wet grass or sphagnum moss until they reach the laboratory. They must be closely caged, or they will escape in transit. When placed in an aquarium they must be covered with glass or a screen to prevent their escape (Fig. 12.6).

2. Beneath the surface of water. Some insects such as diving beetles (*Dytiscidae*), back swimmers (*Notonectidae*), and giant waterbugs (*Belostomatidae*) may be found beneath the surface at various depths, always coming to the surface at intervals for air. These may also be captured by the dip net and returned to the schoolroom in the same manner as the surface forms. (Fig. 12.6*C, D, E.*)

3. Clinging to the surface of rocks, especially the underneath surface, are such common larval (or nymphal) forms as Mayflies (*Ephemeridae*), caddisflies (*Trichoptera*), midges (*Chironomidae*), and stoneflies (*Plecoptera*). These usually cling to the rock when it is lifted from the water and may be caught with forceps and placed in bottles or small jars half filled with water. (Fig. 12.6*F, O.*)

4. In the mud and sediments in pools, slowly flowing streams, and lakes may be found immature stages of Mayflies and dragonflies (*Odonata*). Thrust the dip net, flat side down, into the sediment and drag it toward the shore. Lift the net full of debris to the surface and slush it about to wash as much of the fine mud through the net as possible. Lay the net on the ground and search through the remaining material for larvae. One also may find submerged forms in this material. (Fig. 12.6*R, S.*)

5. Flying above the water or in its immediate neighborhood or resting lightly upon the nearby vegetation may be found graceful airplane-like insects commonly known as snake feeders. These are the dragonfly and damselfly adults, the nymphs of which may be found in the water or in the ooze at the bottom. They are extremely active and difficult to catch even with the light sweeping net which should be used.

On the Leaves and the Tender Stems of Herbaceous Plants. Here are found numerous insects which at first seem to be doing no particular harm to the plant. They may be collected directly in bottles or killing jars, or the capture of the more active ones may require a net. They feed upon the juices or fluid contents of the plant by inserting their sucking beaks beneath the surface. If the ventral surface of the head of such an individual is examined carefully, the piercing structure may be found. Such insects are most properly called true "bugs" (*Hemiptera, Homoptera*). (Fig. 12.7*A* to *D*.)

Upon the Bark and Leaves of Shrubs and Trees. Many of the insects found upon herbaceous plants, as well as upon the bark and leaves of shrubs and trees, do visible damage by their feeding. They eat holes in the leaves, cut off the tender stems near the ground, remove the leaf surface, or bore into the bark or stem. An examination of the mouth parts of such forms shows the presence of short, rough-

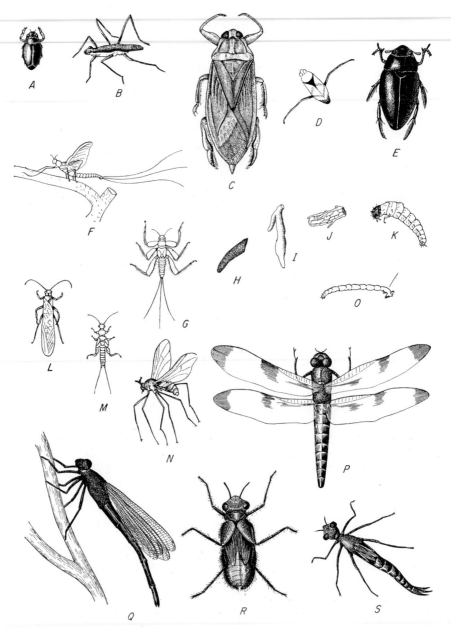

Fɪɢ. 12.6 Group of insects found on, in, and around water: *A*, whirligig beetle; *B*, water strider; *C*, giant water bug; *D*, back swimmer; *E*, diving beetle; *F*, adult Mayfly; *G*, Mayfly nymph; *H, I, J*, cases of caddisfly larvae; *K*, caddisfly larva; *L*, stonefly adult; *M*, stonefly nymph; *N*, midge; *O*, midge larva; *P*, dragonfly adult; *Q*, damselfly adult; *R*, dragonfly nymph; *S*, damselfly nymph.

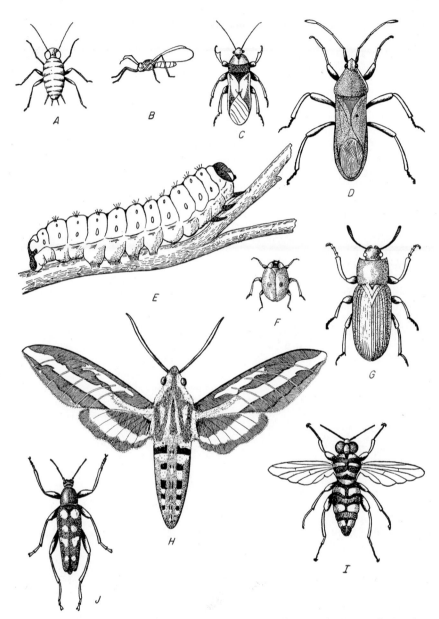

Fig. 12.7 Insects found upon the stems, leaves, and flowers of plants: *A, B,* plant louse (aphids); *C,* chinch bug; *D,* squash bug; *E,* luna moth caterpillar; *F,* ladybird beetle; *G,* ground beetle; *H,* sphinx moth; *I,* syrphid fly; *J,* pollen beetle.

edged hard jaws or mandibles with which they chew the tissues. Some of these are adults and others are larvae. They may be collected in the same manner as the juice suckers. (Fig. 12.7.)

Insects Common in Flowers. In the minds of everyone there is a ready association between blossoms and such insects as bees and butterflies. These are our best-known insects and everyone knows where to find them. Flowers secrete nectar and odorous substances which attract insects and, what is much less well known, also produce pollen which is fed upon by many other insects. Some of those which are not so well known may profitably be collected as a part of the study of insect importance. They may be swept into a collecting net or may in most cases be caught directly in a bottle or a killing jar if not wanted alive. Small beetles are abundant in flowers and are usually pollen feeders; some flies may be caught while visiting flowers; small *Hymenoptera* of various kinds other than the common honeybee and bumblebee are to be found there; some of the sphinx moths suck nectar through a long tube, remaining on the wing while feeding and often being mistaken for humming birds. Some syrphid flies, because of their color and size, so closely resemble honeybees that they are distinguished with difficulty. Such forms as these may be collected from any front- or back-yard flower garden or from the wild blossoms of the open field or roadside. (Fig. 12.7.)

Within the Fleshy Parts of Fruits and Vegetables. Here one finds the young stages of insects of a number of kinds. These often are known as "apple worms," "peach worms," etc., but usually are the caterpillar stage of a moth (*Lepidoptera*) such as the codling moth, Oriental peach moth, etc. In most cases they enter the fruit while it is very young, feeding and growing as the fruit matures and eating their way out after the fruit has reached full size. Thus, the holes found in fruit are usually the exits rather than the points of entrance of the insect. This means that one cannot select what is usually spoken of as "damaged" fruit as a source of the material. It is best to look for these insects by picking out an old or uncared for tree and cutting the fruit before it is ripe. Walnuts, hickory nuts, chestnuts, etc., may yield material of this character also. The young larvae of such insects are best preserved by dropping them directly into alcohol of 80 to 90 per cent strength. Larval stages preserve much better after being killed in hot water. This kills bacteria in and on the body and also stops enzyme action. Store in 70 per cent alcohol. They may be kept in formalin if the alcohol is not available. A few common types are shown in Fig. 12.8.

Insects That Live in the Ground. The ants (*Formicidae*) are the most abundant and most widespread of this group; in fact, they are the most abundant of all insects. Ants may be found in almost any locality, so that a trip in the field to any sort of location will furnish ants as one of the forms that can be captured. They may be killed in the killing bottle, dropped into 80 per cent alcohol, or brought back alive if you wish to establish a colony. It is always desirable to dig into the nest and get some of the forms other than the workers. Queens, sometimes drones, pupae, larvae, and eggs are usually present. If a domesticated colony is to be established, be sure to collect some of all forms. Place them in a jar with a cloth tied tightly over the mouth. Other forms that are not abundant but are interesting when found are the scarab beetles (*Scarabidae*), or "tumblebugs." The commonest are the May beetles (sometimes called June bugs). The young live in the ground, feeding upon the roots of grasses, sometimes becoming a pest upon cultivated crops such as corn and small grains. In the young stage they are often used as fish bait and are known as white grubs. One also may find such insects as bumblebees (*Bombidae*), mason wasps (*Sphecidae*), and the pupae of the Colorado potato beetle (*Chrysomelidae*), and of some butterflies (*Lepidoptera*) in the ground.

Insects that suck the blood of other animals are found everywhere. The commonest example of this type is the mosquito (*Culicidae*), usually thought of as being parasitic upon man and a great variety of other animals with "warm blood." Mosquitoes may be most easily obtained in spring and summer when they are breeding and laying their eggs in pools, puddles, ponds, and such containers as tin cans and barrels. If any rearing is to be attempted, it is advisable that the eggs or at least the larvae (wrigglers) be taken along with an abundance of the water in which they are found, since this contains food upon which they may be able to mature. Next in abundance are the bloodsucking flies such as the deer flies (*Tabanidae*), stable flies (*Muscidae*), and sand flies (*Chironomidae*). Mammals and birds are attacked by these insects, and they sometimes become a scourge. The horseflies (*Tabanidae*) and stable flies (*Muscidae*) may be found near stables or where domestic animals are quartered. Deer flies may occur in moist places where there are tall weeds and plenty of decaying vegetation in which the young feed. Sand flies are abundant along beaches, where they frequently annoy bathers. They are very small and difficult to combat. Bedbugs (*Cimidae*) are not so easily found, but whenever they are located they should be preserved for use later. They sometimes establish themselves in chicken houses, rabbit and guinea-pig hutches, as well as bedrooms. If dropped into 85 per cent alcohol, they keep well and are flat enough to be mounted upon microscope slides. However, if they are to be mounted it is better to add a

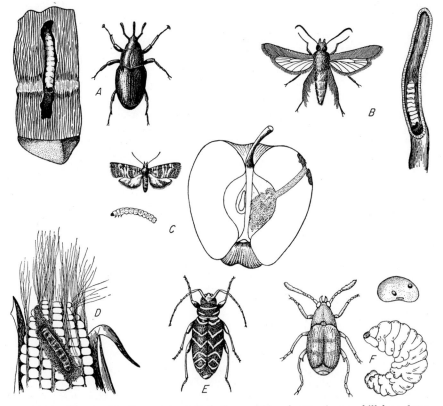

FIG. 12.8   Insects that live much of their lives within plants: *A,* corn bill bug, larva in corn stalk; *B,* squash vine borer, larva in stem; *C,* codling moth and larva; *D,* corn earworm, a moth larva; *E,* locust borer; *F,* bean weevil, adult and larva.

little glycerin or to place them between two slides and clamp these tightly with rubber bands before preserving. This makes them very thin.

Insects that capture prey are not uncommon. Many ants may do this even though they do not live entirely by this means. Flies, maggots, caterpillars, and even large insects such as locusts and cicadas (seventeen-year locust) may be attacked and overcome by them. Some of the wasps, notably the mud dauber (*Sphecinae*), capture spiders which they sting into a helpless condition and then seal into the cells of their nest along with their eggs. It is the growing young that feed upon the spider instead of the adult which captured it. Break open a new mud nest and find the stored spiders. Solitary wasps make similar provision, using caterpillars. The dragonfly nymph (*Odonata*), which has been mentioned above under aquatic insects, is a ferocious insect known to capture and feed upon many forms of animals. It eats other insects, including smaller individuals of its own kind, small fish, tadpoles, worms, etc. Adult dragonflies capture insects on the wing. One of the best known predators of the insects is the antlion (*Myrmeleonidae*). These larvae are known to many as "doodle bugs." They are always found in sand or loose dirt where they excavate small funnel-shaped pits and bury themselves at the bottom. They may be found by carefully lifting out the sand and spreading it out, or they may be made to come out of concealment if a disturbance is made in their pit with the end of a small twig or straw. If an insect tumbles into the pit, it is pounced upon by the antlion which pierces it with its needlelike jaws. The aphis lion, larvae of the lacewings (*Chrysopidae*), and the larvae of the ladybirds (*Coccinellidae*) feed upon aphids (plant lice, *Aphidae*) and scale insects (*Coccidae*). The assassin bugs (*Reduviidae*) belong to the predators also. They attack other insects with soft bodies and thrust their hard beaks into their victim, sucking out the body fluid and other soft parts (Fig. 12.9).

Insects that live on carrion, such as the burying beetles (*Silphidae*) and the flesh flies (*Calliphoridae*), sometimes called blowflies, are to be found wherever there is a dead animal, or they may be easily attracted in almost any location if a large piece of stale meat is placed out of doors on the ground. The bait should be protected from cats and dogs. The adult flies can be captured with a net or an ordinary fly trap. They will lay their eggs upon the meat, and these may be kept and hatched to obtain the very small larvae. If they are fed upon meat they will mature and pupate, or the older stages of the maggots can be taken from the bait. For methods of rearing the blowflies see below in this chapter. Silphids and staphylinids are beetles that commonly visit carrion or meat bait and can be captured by turning over the bait. They may be killed and pinned or preserved wet in the usual manner for insects.

Some insects become household pests, living in the habitations of man or entering it to forage.

1. Ants, which are perhaps the most common offenders of this sort, seldom build their homes in the building but enter to search for food. Some ants, however, will move into the crevices of the building.

2. The so-called white ants, or termites (*Isoptera*), are a still less pleasant visitor at times. They live in wood, and sometimes they eat out tunnels in the wood structure of dwellings and cause them to become so weakened that they may collapse. Tunneling as they do within the wood they may be overlooked until a lot of damage has been done. Where wood framework or supports make actual contact with the ground there is always danger, and the removal of such possible means of entrance is essential to their elimination whenever there is danger from infestation. They are interesting forms, and it is a good idea to have some for the sake of giving students an opportunity to become familiar with their appearance so that they may be recognized.

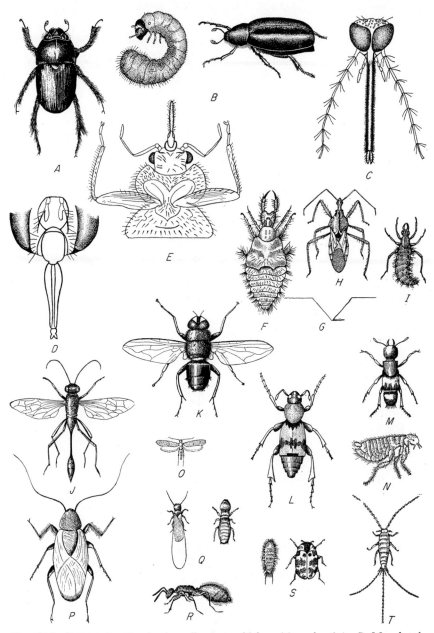

Fig. 12.9 Insects that live in the soil: *A,* tumblebug (dung beetle); *B,* May beetle. Insects that suck blood: *C,* mosquito; *D,* stable fly; *E,* bedbug. Insects that capture prey: *F,* antlion; *G,* antlion sand pit; *H,* assassin bug; *I,* aphis lion; *J,* wasp (mud dauber). Insects that feed on decomposing flesh: *K,* blowfly; *L,* rove beetle; *M,* burying beetle. Insects that are household pests: *N,* flea; *O,* clothes moth; *P,* cockroach; *Q,* termites, winged and wingless; *R,* ant; *S,* carpet beetle, larva and adult; *T,* silverfish.

3. The housefly (*Muscidae*) is such a well-known pest that little need be said about it, but a study of its breeding places and their elimination is well worth while.

4. Another very common insect pest is the cockroach (*Blattidae*). There are several species all of which look sufficiently alike to be readily recognizable. They nearly always frequent damp places such as kitchen sinks, cellars, restaurants, dairies, and the like. They are scavengers so that they can be caught in traps made of jars, milk bottles, and lard cans which have had some old bread or meat placed in them for bait. A simple trap is shown in Fig. 12.10. Careful elimination of all food and the placing of an insecticide for roaches in cracks and along their runways are common remedies. There are many commercial household dusts and sprays that are effective. This is an insect that is not difficult to keep alive for considerable periods of time and it can be found in heated buildings throughout the year.

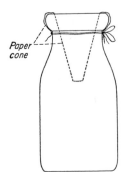

Paper cone

FIG. 12.10 Roach trap. Paper cone tied into milk bottle. Bait is placed in bottle, which is laid on its side.

5. The silverfish, fish moth, or shiner (*Lepismatidae*) is a common household form so named from its shiny appearance. They may be located in books, papers, and sometimes clothing. They move with great speed and agility. It is interesting as a representative of a group of insects that are wingless, not having degenerate wings but apparently a group that never had wings. In this respect they differ from bedbugs and fleas. (Fig. 12.9*T*.)

6. The clothes moth (*Tineidae*) is known to everyone, at least by its work. The small adults (miller moths) enter the house and deposit their eggs upon woolen cloth, fur, or feathers. When hatched the young are so small as to be unobserved, and consequently the first evidence of their presence is a hole in the garment. If a badly infested piece of cloth or fur is discovered, it may be placed in a large can or jar and covered by a piece of muslin tied tightly over the opening and the moths reared. Sometimes several generations can be obtained. Naphthalene, moth balls, and similar remedies are beneficial merely to repel the adults. They do not kill the moths once an infestation is started. Carbon bisulfide or carbon tetrachloride may be used in a closet or very small room or in a large box prepared for the purpose. If a flat dish of either substance is placed upon the shelf near the ceiling and the door tightly closed for a few days, the moths will be killed. All garments should be hung as loosely as possible. A collection of the moth and its work is a desirable display for students to see. The adults usually may be found in a collection of small moths taken at random. (Fig. 12.9*O*.)

7. The buffalo moth (*Dermestidae*), dermestid beetle, and its close relative the carpet beetle are generally well known. The name "buffalo moth" comes from the appearance of the larva, which is a hairy object and conceals itself in woolen cloth and in woolen carpet. They usually work deep in the cloth and are difficult to see until they have done considerable damage. They are also easily reared, if one wishes, in either woolens or meal. Heat and extreme cold are sometimes used effectively against these beetles and also against the clothes moth. Fumigating with hydrocyanic acid gas is the best method when it can be used by someone who understands its dangerously poisonous character and how to safeguard against it. (Fig. 12.9*S*.)

8. Once in a while fleas (*Siphonaptera*) become extremely numerous in a dwelling and greatly annoy its occupants. They can nearly always be traced to the presence of a cat or dog and are often found in the cellar where such an animal has been quartered for a time. They may be caught in large numbers because they are

usually more or less concentrated in the bedding where the animal sleeps. Drop the bedding into a can or jar that can be tightly closed and pour in some carbon tetrachloride or carbon bisulfide before closing. Later the fleas may be shaken out upon a white cloth or paper and collected. Children are usually willing to make a special examination of their pets at home for a few individuals for class use. Most pets have them even when the owner is emphatic in his denial of their presence. If a cellar should be infested, it is usually possible to get rid of them by burning all old clothing, rags, and papers that are in the cellar and thoroughly washing down all the side walls and floor with a strong jet from a garden hose. Clean up all dirt, since flea larvae breed in it. Also purge or get rid of the cat or dog. In bad cases fumigation of the house is necessary, but this is not often. The peculiarities of the flea structure make interesting study.

Insects That Live within Other Animals, Parasitic Forms. Some insects parasitize other insects, while others attack animals higher in the scale. They gain entrance in various ways. In some cases the female has long sharp ovipositors by means of which she can pierce the surface or the entire body wall of the host and deposit the eggs within the host where they hatch and the larvae feed until mature.

1. The ichneumon flies (*Hymenoptera, Ichneumonidae*) and the syrphids (*Diptera*) attack other insects. Others lay their eggs upon the surface of the host; when hatched, the young burrow into the body tissues.

2. The warbles (*Oestridae*) or botflies (*Gastrophilidae*) attack cattle and other mammals. Botflies lay eggs which are swallowed, and the larvae attach themselves to the digestive tract and feed upon the food of the host. Horse-stomach bots (*Gastrophilus intestinalis*) may be found during middle and late summer in the stomachs of horses that have died or been killed and may be had at fertilizer factories. The warbles which attack muscle and tissue beneath the skin are sometimes found in rabbits and other game, but more often in cattle.

3. Once in a while one finds a large caterpillar which has upon its back a lot of small white seed-shaped objects, usually standing upon end. These are likely to be mistaken for eggs of the caterpillar which, of course, they could not possibly be, since the caterpillar is sexually immature and since it would be impossible for it to lay its eggs upon its own back. They are, on the contrary, the cocoons of the tiny parasites which have been living within the caterpillar's body and which have pupated on the outside. They may be collected and reared, or the caterpillar may be preserved in alcohol or 6 per cent formalin (Fig. 12.11*A*).

Culturing. There are many insects which can be kept alive in captivity for a considerable length of time, and others that may be reared through complete life histories and sometimes many generations. Such are the meal worm beetle, wax moth, cheese skipper, and fruit fly. For suggestions on these see Chap. 22. In addition to these, it is often desirable to keep some of the aquatic forms in the laboratory or classroom.

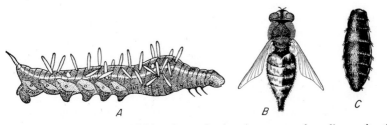

A   *B*   *C*

Fig. 12.11   Insects that live within other animals: *A,* cocoons of small parasite that lived in tomato worm; *B,* botfly; *C,* botfly pupa.

1. The water striders and whirligig beetles may be placed on the surface of an aquarium which is covered tightly with wire screen. If flies or other insects are thrown in occasionally, they will be devoured by the aquatic captives.

2. The large aquatic bugs, such as the giant water bug and the back swimmer, will sometimes capture tiny fish, worms, tadpoles, or other insects and feed upon them. Therefore, they can be kept in a good aquarium for considerable lengths of time.

3. The common flesh-eating flies (blowflies, bluebottle flies, greenbottle flies) are abundant in most parts of the United States and demonstrate an interesting type of insect reproduction, complete metamorphosis, and a very short life history. Many uses could be found for them in the biology course. Aside from their usefulness as laboratory material in teaching, the larvae and adults may serve as food for many of the other animals which require living food, such as frogs, toads, lizards, salamanders, and some kinds of fish. They may be reared throughout the year. Modifications of the method may be advisable according to need and convenience.

Materials needed for growing these flies are a cage for the adults, drinking fountain, feeding dishes such as saucers, tin-can lids, or petri dishes, tubes or bottles for growing the maggots, a jar or can for pupation. The cage for the adults may be of almost any type. Approximately 1 cu. ft. capacity is suggested as being large enough and is convenient to handle. A manual arts project of preparing the cage would be a good chance for cooperation in school. If one or more sides are closed by a pane of glass, it makes a better display for the class.

The drinking fountain is made by inverting a small jelly glass or beaker containing water in a saucer which has a piece of filter paper or paper towel under half the glass. This keeps the paper soaked so that the flies have water at all times, and it prevents the water standing where the flies may drown. It should be renewed every 2 days and the glassware thoroughly cleaned. The feeding dishes are saucers or tin lids. The food consists solely of dry sugar (granulated or lump) and fresh lean meat. The sugar is kept in the cage at all times, and the meat is fed once every other day. It can be left in the cage for a few hours and then removed. The adults will not lay eggs until several days (3 to 6) after the first feeding of meat. The eggs are laid upon the meat at feeding time, and they may be discarded or saved to start a new culture.

Culture tubes or bottles should be furnished with a small amount of lean meat. Care must be taken to add only about 50 eggs to a tube so that it will not become overcrowded with maggots. Each tube or bottle should be plugged with a snug-fitting rolled cotton plug to prevent the escape of the maggots and allow ventilation, which is quite necessary. When the maggots are about full grown, the tubes should be placed in the pupation jar described below and the plugs removed. There will be some odor from the meat as it ages, making it necessary to keep the tubes where they will not offend when not being used. A room that is little used, an air shaft, or a box attached to a chimney are excellent places to grow larvae.

A pupation jar or can should contain sand or crumpled paper. The culture tubes are placed in the pupation jar when the maggots are about full grown (3 to 4 days) and the stoppers removed. Cover the opening of the jar with cheesecloth or, better, with muslin. The fully fed maggots will migrate from the tubes and come to rest in the sand, where they will pupate. The pupae may be removed later and used or placed in a jar or bottle plugged with cotton and when emergence begins may be placed in the cage for a new stock of adults.

4. Diving beetles (*Hydrophilidae* and *Dytiscidae*) are scavengers and may be kept upon most any organic food or upon prepared goldfish foods.

5. Meal moths (*Phycitinae*) are readily kept in quart jars half filled with bran or

cornmeal. They will reproduce continuously and run several generations in the jar. The culture must be covered with a piece of thin cloth instead of a lid. Tie the cover on with strings, do not use rubber bands.

6. Dragonfly nymphs can be kept in small amounts of water and will feed freely. Small worms, insects with soft bodies, and pieces of earthworm may be used as food. When the food is held in front of the nymph with a pair of forceps, it will seize the food and devour it. This is an interesting sight for students and illustrates the feeding activities of these voracious insects. If reared in this manner the shedding of the skeleton and emergence of the adult may also be observed. Do not place dragonfly nymphs in aquaria with other insects, worms, tadpoles, or very small fish because the dragonfly nymphs may eat them.

7. Colorado potato beetle (*Chrysomelidae*). This is the 10-lined potato beetle which can be secured in unlimited quantities any summer wherever the white potato is grown. These beetles may be reared as easily as the milkweed bug and in much the same manner. Their food may be supplied by placing small pieces of common potato tubers in the culture dish. A flat-covered butter dish is a good container. The insects will feed upon the tuber, deposit egg masses, and pass through their complete life cycle. If 1 in. of sand is kept in the bottom of the dish, the mature larvae will burrow into the sand to pupate.

As the larvae reach about half size, give an occasional leaf of potato plant or stalk from a sprouted tuber. Unless they get this, they may not be able to complete metamorphosis. To start a new culture, capture a copulating pair and place in a dish with a potato or a leaf or stalk. These insects are hardy, will grow all winter with the above treatment, and are useful for laboratory material as specimens of Coleoptera and as reaction material for demonstrations. (Fig. 12.12*B*.)

8. Milkweed bug (*Lygaeidae*). This insect is widely distributed, easily obtained in late summer and early autumn from milkweed, and can be kept for indefinite periods of time during the winter months. But one provision need be made, and that is the winter food supply. This is done in early autumn by gathering a large number of milkweed pods. They may be secured before they burst and start the dispersal. The seeds are removed from the pod and placed in the culture dish as needed. An excellent culture dish is a flat-covered butter dish. Place seeds in the dish with several female bugs. Add a small wad of cotton saturated with water. This furnishes sufficient moisture, but it must be changed regularly to prevent growth of mold and bacteria. The water must not run out in the dish. The milkweed seeds supply food and a place for depositing eggs which will hatch into tiny red nymphs. The nymphs also feed upon the seeds and develop into mature bugs. Very little work is involved in providing and caring for these insects, which make desirable laboratory material.

Preserving. The almost universal method of preserving insects is by thrusting a pin through the body of the insect after it has been killed but before it has dried. When the insect has dried thoroughly, it will be firmly fastened to the pin. The usual method of pinning insects is to place the pin through the thorax, as shown in Fig. 12.12*C*. In the case of beetles, however, the pin is thrust through the right elytra, or wing cover, as shown in Fig. 12.12*D*. Very small insects which cannot be pinned are usually mounted with glue on a heavy paper "point," as shown in Fig. 12.12*E*. These should be laid on their side unless two specimens are available, in which case they may be mounted by gluing one dorsal side up and the other ventral side up. Butterflies and moths and sometimes grasshoppers are spread before drying. The spreading board is shown in Fig. 12.12*H*. A very simple form of spreading board can be made from a flat cardboard box, as shown in Fig. 12.12*I*.

1. Collection boxes. Convenient boxes for keeping pinned insects may be made from a variety of materials. A heavy cardboard box, such as a candy box, can be

A

B

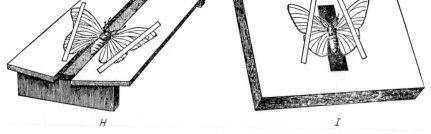

F   Wood blocks   Metal plates

G   Box

Metal plate

H

I

Fig. 12.12   Insects that may be easily cultivated are: *A*, milkweed bug; *B*, Colorado potato beetle. Methods of pinning insects for a collection are shown in *C, D, E, F, G* and method of spreading large insects in *H* and *I*.

used, and cigar boxes, especially the better grade of box, are convenient. The best manner for preparing the collection box is to place a layer of sheet cork on the bottom and glue over it a layer of white paper. Sheet cork may be had as scraps and cuttings at furniture stores, or it can be purchased as pads for hot dishes at five-and-ten-cent stores. When pins are thrust into it, they stay firmly set and stand upright. If cork is not to be had, however, a sheet of heavy corrugated box may do as a substitute. The heavy, loose-fiber wallboard also does very well instead of sheet cork (see Fig. 12.13B for construction).

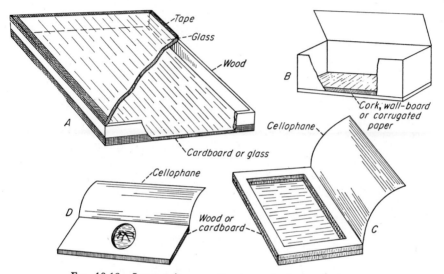

Fig. 12.13   Inexpensive mounting boxes for insect specimens.

In many schools it should be possible, and very commendable, to work out a joint project between the biology class and the manual arts in which pinning boxes, display cases, and many other articles are prepared by students in manual arts for use in biology.

2. Pinning. When a box has been filled with insects, all the insects or paper points should be at the same height. To secure this it is necessary that the height be regulated at the time of pinning, since it is not possible to change the height after the insect dries. Several devices called "pinning blocks" have been invented to regulate the pinning height. Two such devices are shown in Fig. 12.12F, G.

3. Two other methods of mounting insects for display should be mentioned. Large forms such as moths and butterflies can best be kept in good condition by placing in so-called Riker mounts, which are cardboard boxes with glass tops. The box is filled with cotton, which holds the insect in place and makes a contrasting background. Riker mounts are expensive. A good substitute can be made by taking narrow strips of wood and constructing a frame from them.[1] Tack or glue a heavy cardboard back on the frame and place a glass plate (old photographic plates are excellent) over the top. This may be fastened by a glued tape around the edge (see Fig. 12.13A).

The other method of mounting for display consists of cutting frames from heavy cardboard. These may be made of any desired size. Thickness is obtained by laying

[1] The A. I. Root Company, of Medina, Ohio, makes and supplies the narrow wood-frame material in an excellent form and at very low cost.

two or more frames on top of each other. Sheet cellophane is glued over one side of the frame. The insect is placed inside the frame and stuck fast to the cellophane with glue or cement (cellophane cement can be purchased) and the other side of the frame closed with another sheet of cellophane (see Fig. 12.13C, D). When mounted in this manner the specimen may be viewed from either side. Very small forms may be placed in thin frames and examined under the microscope. The materials are inexpensive, and the mounts will last for a long time.

4. Relaxing dry insects. If moths or butterflies become too dry to spread the wings, they may be softened readily in a "relaxing chamber." Such a chamber need be nothing more than a jar or can that may be tightly closed and partly filled with water (Fig. 12.3). The insect is placed over the water, the air in the jar soon becomes saturated and the insect absorbs sufficient moisture in 24 hr. to soften so that it may be spread on a spreading board and pinned. A small amount of carbolic acid is usually added to the water to prevent mold growth on the specimens.

It is desirable to have a quantity of some insect which is abundant, such as grasshoppers or May beetles (June bugs), in order that each student in the class may tear one apart and examine its structures. For this purpose insects preserved in liquids are preferable. Formalin (6 per cent) with glycerin (20 per cent) is a good preservative. Alcohol (80 per cent) is also commonly used. Rubbing alcohol is cheap and when used full strength does quite well for such animals.

5. Collection pests. No matter in what type of container dried insects are stored, there are likely to be pests which will find their way into it and destroy the specimens. As a precaution against them, it is necessary to place a small bag or fold of cloth in one corner of the box in which have been placed some flakes of naphthalene or a single moth ball. If a pinhead is heated and immediately pressed against a moth ball it will melt its way into the ball and then quickly "freeze" fast. This is a convenient way of securing the ball into one corner of a box. This acts only as a repellent and will not kill the pests that are already installed. To kill them it is necessary to fumigate the boxes that are infested. Open and place the collection boxes either in a larger box that can be closed tightly or in a small closet. Pour into a flat pan or dish some carbon bisulfide or carbon tetrachloride. Place the dish in the upper part of the closet or box as the fumes are heavier than air and tend to settle. Close the lid or door tightly and allow the collection to stand for 2 days or longer. This is usually sufficient to kill the pests.

6. Preserving colors. Frequently specimens such as caterpillars are captured which have a brilliant green color. If preserved, the collector is usually disappointed later to find that the color has faded almost entirely. This often can be avoided by placing the fresh specimen in either formalin or alcohol to which has been added some copper salt, such as copper sulfate or copper chloride. Allow the larvae to remain in the copper solution until they are thoroughly colored. This may take as long as several days in some cases. Then remove them from the coloring solution and preserve in either formalin or alcohol. The green color of the copper salt is usually slightly different from the natural color of the organism, but it is much better than faded specimens.

Other Arthropods

Crawfish or crayfish (Crustacea), water fleas (Cladocera), and sow bugs and pill bugs (Isopods) are among the more widespread arthropods which are not insects and which make excellent material for class use.

Habitat. All these forms may be found in water. The isopods and crayfish are ordinarily situated under stones in streams. The crayfish usually live where the water is not very swift, and the isopods cling to the undersurface of rocks where the water moves freely, as in rapids. Crayfish may be found in water surrounding reeds and eel grass as well. Land isopods, such as pill bugs, are frequently found under boards in damp places (Fig. 12.14*A*). The water fleas are more frequently found in very quiet lagoons of streams and in ponds and even very small pools (Fig. 12.14*B*).

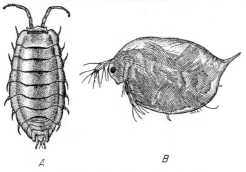

FIG. 12.14 *A,* sowbug; *B,* water flea.

Collecting. For collecting crayfish the flat-sided dip net is convenient when the animals are not concealed under large rocks. When they are under the rocks, the collecting becomes a matter of capturing each individual separately. This may be done by hand or in a very small short-handled net. Lift the stone with much care and as the crayfish swims swiftly backward place the net in such a position as to cause the crayfish to swim into it. A can or bucket that has a perforated lid is a convenient container for returning them alive to the school.

Isopods are easy to collect as they adhere to the rocks and may be removed with forceps. The land forms may be picked up with the fingers.

Water fleas are sometimes so numerous that they can be had by dipping the water containing them. They may be concentrated by dipping with a very small hand net or tea strainer (see Fig. 12.15).

Culturing. Any of the aquatic forms may be kept alive indefinitely in aquaria. Running water and plenty of water plants are a distinct advantage. Temperatures around 60 to 70°F. are best. Crayfish will eat worms or small pieces of meat but should be removed and fed in a separate pan of water to avoid polluting

FIG. 12.15 Small aquarium net made from a tea strainer.

the aquarium. When kept in the same water with fish or tadpoles, the crayfish will often try to capture them and sometimes succeed. At least they tear the fins with their claws. Water fleas should be cultured in a separate vessel, in water to which has been added a little boiled bone meal, sheep manure, or pulverized boiled egg (2 oz. of dry material per gallon of water). Bacteria thrive in such a solution and the water flea lives on the bacteria. Land sowbugs may be cultured in a jar containing moist soil and rotting pieces of wood.

Preserving. In preserving crayfish, first puncture the hard shell over the back with a small knife blade or sharp nail to allow the preservative to penetrate readily into the body. The best preservative is 6 per cent formalin. The isopods and water fleas may be preserved in 4 per cent formalin or in alcohol.

Spiders, mites, and ticks (Arachnoidea) are arthropods which are known collectively as "arachnids." The spiders especially are well known to everyone, and their habits are interesting for study.

Habitat. Spiders are almost as widespread as insects but not so varied in their adaptations. They may be found wherever food is available. Much interest centers around their web-weaving activities. They live in trees and other plants, in the ground, and under stones. Some spiders seldom build webs but stalk their prey. The web weaving is sometimes restricted to spinning cocoons or nests for eggs. For interesting details see *The Spider Book,* by Comstock.

Collecting. An orb collection is both fascinating and instructive. Get some sheets of black-surfaced cardboard and cut them into rectangles of different sizes. These cards can be carried along when the orbs are to be collected. When an orb has been located, blow a cloud of talcum powder from the palm of the hand so as to coat the web with dust. Prepare a card by painting the edge of it with shellac. For this purpose a small bottle and camel's-hair brush are needed. If the card is then pressed gently against the web, the radiating strands will adhere to the edges of the card. As soon as it has dried sufficiently, the web may be cut loose from its original moorings and carried away. These cards may be framed under glass or cellophane wrapped to protect them. If an atomizer is carried along and filled with a solution of very thin shellac and whiting, the orb may be sprayed before being fastened to the card. Such sprayed webs are much more easily seen on the black background. Small wood framework may be constructed and the webs attached in the same manner, thus leaving the orb swinging free instead of stretched over the black card. In either case the spider which made the web may be collected, and after it has been spread and dried so that the legs are in a natural position, it may be attached to the orb to enhance the demonstration. If notes on the location and habits of the spiders are taken as collected, they may be attached or filed, and the project becomes very instructive.

To collect the spiders take along small vials or bottles of 85 per cent alcohol and a pair of forceps. Drop the spider directly into the alcohol. It may, however, be placed in an insect killing bottle and used dry for mounting. Very large spiders with abdomens full of soft material become shriveled upon drying. This may be avoided by slitting the ventral wall, scraping out the contents, and stuffing with cotton.

Culturing. Some spiders can be kept in captivity for years. They should be placed in large jars with cloth covers instead of caps or in small screen cages. Some enclosures, such as a small box with a hole in it or part of a mailing tube, can be added to provide a place for hiding, but this is unnecessary and is a hindrance to observation. Any small insect such as flies, meal worms, or moths can be added every few days as food. If a small pad of cheesecloth or cotton is suspended from the cloth cover and moistened regularly it will provide sufficient moisture. Under such conditions of captivity they sometimes lay eggs and hatch young. Of course one must obtain a female that has already been fertilized or have both sexes to expect offspring.

Preserving. If spiders are collected and killed by dropping them into jars containing 85 per cent alcohol, they may be tightly stoppered and kept for any length of time. As suggested above, they also may be killed in the same manner as insects and placed in mounts, either Riker mounts or in cardboard or cellophane mounts.

Vertebrates

The vertebrates (backboned animals) are those with which students are most familiar. The common ones are the fishes, the amphibia, the reptiles, the birds, and the mammals. It will be best to take each group in turn and consider some examples of what can be done in their study.

Fish. *Habitat.* Since almost any permanent creek, river, pond, or lake contains fish, and even many brooks with pools which do not dry up contain fish of some kind, it is possible to find them and to capture them with a seine or trap. If seining or trapping is prohibited, it is usually possible to get special permission from your state division of wildlife to collect for educational purposes. The five-and-ten-cent stores, bait stores, and pet shops all have goldfish, minnows, guppies, and other varieties that keep readily in captivity. A study of nesting habits and breeding places of fish or of the kinds of situations where different species are found is very instructive and interesting.

Collecting. Fish caught on the conventional hook are often damaged too severely to be satisfactory for an aquarium but would be quite suitable to preserve. It is much better to use a net or trap. Small hand nets can be used for minnows in pools or small streams. By using a small trap in a brook or narrow part of a stream the minnows can be driven into it. In larger bodies of water a lift net is successful for minnows and may be set and baited as shown in Fig. 12.16E by placing bread crumbs on the water over the net. When the minnows are feeding, lift the net quickly. Fish for laboratory use may be obtained at fish markets at relatively low cost and preserved in formalin or used fresh. Small fish for aquaria or bowls are available at pet shops, bait stores, and five-and-ten-cent stores. Familiarize yourself with your fish and game laws before seining or trapping for game fish. Very large minnows or small bait fish may be purchased from a bait store already preserved.

Culturing. Most states have literature to send out on the fish hatcheries and fish culturing which is done for commercial stocking. Anyone can rear goldfish, guppies, etc., in a bowl or aquarium. Have plenty of water plants and feed very little. If water plants are not used, it is necessary to feed prepared fish food and to change the water frequently to prevent fouling. If plants are used and little or no prepared food is added, it is unnecessary to change the water. Keep the aquarium out of direct sunlight but near enough to a window for the plants to do well. A north window is best if available. The addition of a few water snails helps keep down pollution and retards the growth of algae on the sides of the aquarium, although the algae do no harm other than to impede vision.

Preserving. Fish are best preserved in formalin. If very many are placed in a jar or can it is best to leave them in a 5 per cent solution for about a week and then transfer them to a fresh 5 or 6 per cent solution. This is true for bulky animals of any kind as they greatly dilute the preservative and may spoil. Be sure to slit the ventral body wall with a knife or puncture it in some way when the fish is first placed in the preservative in order to let the preservative into the cavity. If this is not done there may be a lot of decomposition before the formalin penetrates to the internal organs. The addition of 15 per cent glycerin to the formalin prevents the fish from becoming very stiff.

Amphibia. *Habitat.* Amphibia, as the name implies, live a sort of double life, and therefore their distribution is varied. They are well known to all. One naturally goes to the pond, creek, or swamp for frogs and tadpoles. In damp places under stones or in pools and brooks small salamanders can be found. Mud puppies or water dogs (salamanders) are more frequently found in creeks and rivers, while the toads live on dry land and may be seen in gardens, yards, or woods. The tree toads as their name suggests are most commonly found in trees where they so closely resemble the bark that they are seen with difficulty even when their call tells of their presence.

The frogs and salamanders have smooth wet skins because of the secretion of mucus from glands in the skin, and they cannot live long without moisture. Hence, they are seldom seen far from water. The toads have a dry horny skin which resists evaporation. and hence they live in places often well removed from bodies of water or streams. They need only an occasional wetting which serves as a "drink." Toads do, however, lay eggs in water, and their young are tadpoles similar to those of the frog.

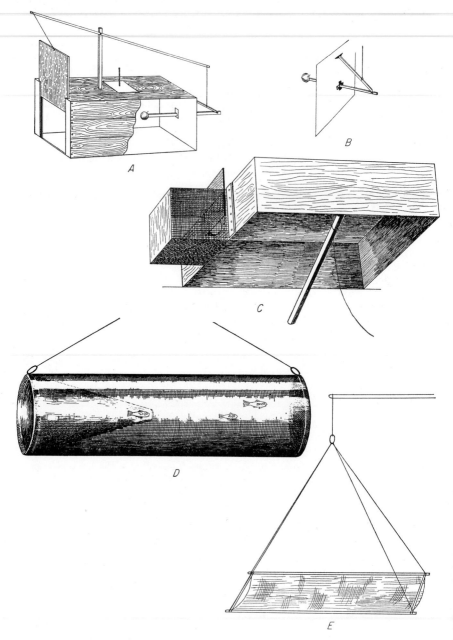

Fig. 12.16 Traps for small vertebrates: *A*, figure-four trap; *B*, details of the figure-four trigger; *C*, bird trap; *D*, small fish trap; *E*, lift net for minnows.

Collecting. There is not much to learn about collecting amphibia. Frogs and toads have to be approached cautiously and captured individually. A hand net with long handle may help in this. Frogs may be more easily caught at night by directing a flashlight beam upon them. They are apparently unable to escape and sit quietly while the hunter approaches. (This method of hunting is sometimes prohibited by law.) They may be quickly seized, or a small net may be placed over them. Salamanders that are found in small pools can be caught by hand or in a net or sieve. Those under stones and logs are caught by hand or in jars. Mud puppies and water dogs are usually not seen unless caught on a hook while fishing. They may bite the captor and should be handled with care. Contrary to popular opinion, the salamanders in the northern United States are not poisonous.

Culturing. Adult frogs are not completely aquatic and should not be forced to stay in water. They do not get along well in an aquarium and will drown unless stones are provided which protrude above the water. The best arrangement is a cage or box with a large flat pan of water in one end. The frog dries out rapidly and will die from lack of water in 1 to 3 days. Sand on the bottom of the cage prevents a rough bottom from injuring the frog's legs as it hops about. The same arrangement is very satisfactory for toads. Salamanders vary from aquatic forms with external gills on the neck to terrestrial forms which will drown if kept in water. A box or aquarium of damp sand and a few large flat stones so placed as to make it easy for the salamanders to conceal themselves under them is a good habitat for land forms. Newts, the small aquatic salamanders, can be kept in an aquarium like goldfish. Any of these amphibia may be fed an occasional earthworm or live insect. Frogs will also eat small crawfish.

Preserving. Any of these animals are large enough so that the body should be slightly opened to allow the preservative to enter quickly. A penknife blade stuck into the side is sufficient. Formalin, 7 per cent, is the best preservative. The addition of 15 per cent glycerin will help keep them soft for dissection.

Reptiles. *Habitat.* Reptiles are not so limited in their distribution as fish and amphibia because most of them can resist drying and are independent of water. Turtles (*Testudinata*), lizards, and snakes (*Squamata*) are found everywhere; alligators and crocodiles (*Crocodilia*) live only in southern streams.

Snakes attract more attention and excite more interest than any other type of animal. This is partly due to the age-old misconceptions that have been almost universally taught. It is the duty of the biology teacher to dispel as far as possible this attitude toward snakes and to emphasize the facts that most snakes are harmless and that many are decidedly beneficial; that most snakes fear man and do not go about ready to pounce upon him. In regions where rattlesnakes, copperheads, and other poisonous forms are likely to be met, it would be advisable to have preserved or stuffed specimens so that students may learn to recognize them at sight.

Land turtles are not frequently met with in most localities but can be found or purchased. They are easily kept alive by feeding them small pieces of meat and thus are highly desirable for school use. Small ornamental turtles may be purchased at pet shops or five-and-ten-cent stores. They keep fairly well in aquaria. The larger aquatic forms which are found in ponds and streams are not so desirable because they require some care unless a large tank is available.

Small alligators may be found in the streams of the Southern states and are available from several supply houses. They are not very expensive, live well in captivity if kept above freezing temperatures, and can be made both interesting and instructive. They may be fed fresh meat.

Lizards, such as the common little pine lizard (*Sceloporus undulatus*) and the so-called chameleon (*Iguanidae*) are readily kept in captivity. They can be captured in the woods, where it requires sharp eyes to detect them on the dull bark of tree trunks or among the green leaves. Their peculiarity in changing color in such a manner that they blend into the immediate environment is well known and serves to make collecting difficult. They also may be purchased.

Collecting. Not much need be said about methods of collecting reptiles. They must be located and captured individually. Snakes are best caught with a forked stick, as is generally known. This is an assurance against being bitten, unless the collector is certain of his species. A long stick with a fork at one end is used and when a snake is found the stick, fork down, is thrust over the snake's neck. This will hold it in a manner which prevents coiling and offers time to maneuver the captive into a box or can.

Culturing. Most reptiles are carnivorous and feed upon such small prey as worms, insects, small rodents like mice and shrews, birds, eggs, fish, frogs, and sometimes they can be fed upon fresh meat such as beef or liver cut into small pieces. If alligators refuse to eat over long periods of time, as they sometimes do, they can be forced to swallow small pieces of beef or earthworms by thrusting it down their throat on the end of a pair of long forceps. Turtles must not be kept in aquaria with fish or other aquatic animals. The turtles are likely to kill or injure them. Lizards and snakes should be kept in small cages, preferably with a sand bottom and a piece of branching tree. They can usually be fed on insects such as meal worms and beetles.

Preserving. Snakes may be skinned and the skin dried and preserved with an arsenic salt. Alligators may be skinned and the skin stuffed and preserved in a similar manner. Any of the reptiles may be preserved entire in formalin the same as other animals. About a tablespoonful of sugar added to a quart of formalin is an aid in preservation of color.

Birds. *Habitat.* Because of their migratory habits it is more difficult to speak of birds in terms of definite distribution than of some other animals. The time-honored method of bird study involving the recognition of birds by their plumage and songs is, of course, a desirable and essential feature. However, it might well be combined with several other angles of study in such a way as to be all the more instructive. Considerably more than the usual amount of emphasis should be placed upon the habitats of the various species common in the locality studied. In making a record of the census, particular attention should be paid to the type of immediate environment in which the bird is usually found, the habits of its nesting places, where, how, and upon what it feeds as an adult, and what it feeds to its young. Its relation to other birds, mammals, amphibia, and fish and to the crops and wild plant life of the vicinity should be noted. If the trips afield or the entire survey is made on the basis of feeding habits or nesting habits, etc., it will add a great deal to the study besides mere recognition.

Collecting. The collecting of birds is something that should be undertaken only after due consideration of all the laws and regulations governing birds. Some collecting should be done, however. For this purpose a simple fall trap is all that is needed, and a great deal of interest can be aroused in students. It can be undertaken by the students as a project at their homes or at school. A low cage of some such type as that shown in Fig. 12.16C is set upon a stick which is attached to a string for tripping. The board is baited with such foods as bread, grains of all sorts, pieces of suet, or cakes of cracklings. It is best to allow birds to feed for several days or a week unmolested before dropping the trap. A little care will ensure no injury to the birds, and an examination made in the small cage will make it possible to release any that may not be legally kept.

Banding. A bird-banding permit including bands and directions may be obtained from the Banding Office, U.S. Department of the Interior, Fish and Wildlife Service, Bureau of Sport Fisheries and Wildlife, Patuxent Research Refuge, Laurel,

Md. This is a very interesting hobby for a class to have and will do a lot to stimulate interest and will put a lot of zest into the study of birds. It also makes a survey and seasonal record possible. If continued for several years, many birds which were banded one or two years before may return to the trap. This will arouse interest that will soon permeate a large portion of the school.

It is difficult to keep most birds alive in captivity and to do so is illegal for many birds in most of the states. Chickens may be incubated as a home or school project. Sometimes state departments of conservation offer a bonus for the hatching and release of such game birds as the pheasant and grouse. Get the free literature from your state department of conservation.

Preserving. Birds, like other animals, may be preserved in formalin of about 7 per cent strength. However, this is satisfactory only for purposes of dissection, and other methods of preserving are usually resorted to. Preserving the skins and stuffing them and the technic involved are discussed in this chapter under the general head of Taxidermy.

Mammals. *Habitat.* What is done in the study of mammals will depend to some extent upon the location of the school. If it is distinctly suburban or rural, it will be easier to study mammals out of doors. Rural children are generally familiar with the *Rodentia,* rabbit, squirrel, chipmunk, and woodchuck. The raccoon and opossum are not so often seen. Muskrats are sometimes abundant along streams. Prairie dogs and beavers are abundant only in certain parts of the country. Field and wood mice are rather widespread. Field mice, chipmunks, and woodchucks normally live in burrows dug in the ground and in relatively open places. Muskrats burrow into the banks of streams at about the water level and, in marshy ponds, build houses of sticks and reeds. Rabbits are usually found during the day in fields of clump grass and weeds or in thickets and piles of brush. Raccoons, opossum, and squirrels are tree inhabitants. Deer and fox are seldom seen in most parts of the country, but the Virginia deer is abundant in many Eastern states and may be seen in woods and fields. Your state department of conservation of wild life may have check lists and literature on the mammals of your region.

Collecting. Although most mammals may be hunted with a gun, at least during certain seasons specified by law, the better method is to trap them. This can be done with little injury and the specimen used alive, and if the skin or skeleton is wanted (see Taxidermy below) it is usually in better condition if the animal has been trapped. The commercial mouse and rat traps, including the steel trap, may be employed. Specimens so captured are likely to be dead when found. The ordinary wire rat trap does not injure its captives, and the "figure-four" trap can be constructed by almost any child (see Fig. 12.16*A,B*). Some of the references cited at the end of this chapter give details of problems met in collecting mammals. Be sure to consult your local and state laws on trapping.

Culturing. Keeping wild mammals alive in captivity is not easy in most cases and is quite likely to end in disappointment and in the death of the animal. Many wild types refuse to eat if closely confined, and even if this is not the case one must be certain of the kind of food which they eat. For most school purposes it is better to use the living animals as soon as possible and then kill them for mounting or set them free if they are not harmful. If kept alive, mammals require continuous and regular attention such as feeding once or more times every day and regular cleaning and sterilizing of the cages.

Preserving. See the following section on taxidermy for preserving skins and bones and also the section on embalming.

If it is wished, the entire body of a mammal may be preserved in the same manner as any other vertebrate. The abdomen is opened by a knife or scissors just enough to allow the preservative to enter quickly. See that it does enter; otherwise the specimen will spoil. Formalin, about 6 or 8 per cent, is the best and cheapest preservative. Always be careful not to dilute the preservative by placing too many specimens in one container.

Taxidermy

Because of the amount of space required, and to avoid unnecessary repetition, the art of skinning, preserving, stuffing, and mounting of vertebrates is reserved for the single topic of taxidermy. Although but two or three illustrations will be reviewed here, they may well serve as samples for the preparation of many other types of animals.

A Small Mammal Skin. *Skinning.* Select a specimen that is in good condition and has not been torn by a trap or in shooting. Lay the dead animal on its back and make one straight cut in the posterior half of the median ventral surface (see Fig. 12.17). Be careful not to cut anything but the skin, and extend the incision to the base of the tail. Lift the edges of this incision and cut away the thin tissue that connects the skin to the muscles of the abdomen. Work the skin loose to one side until the base of the leg is reached. Dry corn meal is used freely between the skin and flesh to absorb blood and to prevent sticking. Now cut down into the muscles at the hip and separate the bones at the joint. Pull the leg out through the opening in the skin, carefully removing the skin from the leg muscles. When the heel is reached, cut the muscles free from the leg bones. If the animal has much of a pad under its paw, it will be necessary to cut through the bottom of the foot and remove the fleshy tissue. Remove the other leg in a similar manner. This leaves the skin from the hind legs turned inside out with the leg bones protruding from the ends of the skin. Leave these bones attached. Remove the tail in a similar manner, being careful not to tear the skin.

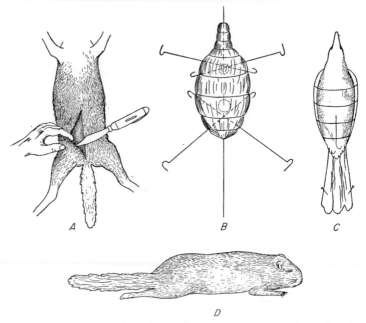

A   *B*   *C*

D

Fig. 12.17   Preparation of skins for study or mounting: *A,* loosening skin from muscles; *B,* cotton form to be inserted in skin; wires for appendages; *C,* tied bird skin after stuffing; *D,* finished study skin.

With the hindquarters free, it is rather easy to pull the skin forward toward the shoulders. Cut whenever necessary, to avoid stretching the skin. At the shoulders proceed with the front legs just as you did the hind legs, and continue removing the skin until the ears are reached. Cut the ears loose from the skull, leaving them in the skin and attached to it. As the eyes are reached, unusual care must be exercised in order to get the lids loose from the skull without tearing or cutting them. The same care is necessary for the lips. The cartilage of the nose is cut close to the bone and left attached to the skin. When the skin has been freed from the head, it is completely inside out. It should immediately be turned right side out again and any blood on the hair must be washed off at once.

Preserving. When the above procedure is accomplished, the skin is again turned wrong side out and all fat, muscle, or other tissue scraped free from the surface. It is now ready to be preserved and poisoned. Use a rubber or leather glove for the handling of the poison. Take a handful of the arsenic alum mixture and scatter it thickly over the raw surface of the hide. Rub this powder thoroughly into the skin. Continue until all parts of the surface have been thoroughly treated. Do not forget the tail or the inside of the paws, if they were cut. If formula 1 or the liquid form of formula 2 is used (see under Formulas below) it may be applied by a paint brush. If the skin has dried, it should be dampened before the arsenic alum is applied.

The skull is to be returned to the skin; so it must be detached and the tongue and jaw muscles cut off. The brain is mashed thoroughly by a wire inserted into the opening at the base of the skull, and it may then be shaken out or washed out by a water jet.

Stuffing. The leg bones are now wrapped with thin strips of cotton or cloth until they have assumed the same proportions that they had before the muscles were removed. The bulges must come in the same places. The cotton may be tied on with thread. The clean dry skull is inserted into the skin again and enough cotton added to the cheeks to replace the muscles removed. The skin is next turned right side out. Take a piece of soft iron wire and insert it into the tail. It may be necessary to wrap cloth about the wire to fill out the tail completely. The wire should be long enough to extend part way into the body, where it ends in a small loop inside the body filler which is next inserted. Make a bundle of excelsior or cotton of as nearly the same shape and size as the trunk and neck as possible. Insert this into the skin through the slit and adjust. Do not attempt to stuff the body with small pieces, but bind them into a single form and tie with thread. When the legs and head are all arranged properly sew the slit shut neatly. Lay the animal ventral side down on a board and leave it to dry (Fig. 12.17D). Sometimes it is advisable to take a stitch in the lips to hold them together. Also the final appearance of the specimen will be improved if you brush the hair into place before it dries.

A Bird Skin. In preparing bird skins use almost the same method and procedure as for a mammal, with a few exceptions and precautions. Be especially careful about blood on the feathers, removing it with corn meal. In handling and skinning do not break any of the tail or wing feathers.

The treatment of the skull in skinning a bird is different from the treatment of a mammal's skull in that it is never completely removed because the beak is attached to it. When the skin has been brought forward from the skull to the base of the beak, the eyes are removed from the sockets and the muscles cut away from the jaws. The brain is then removed from the skull. When the skin has been thoroughly treated, the skull is pushed back into it.

A single long roll of cotton is used to stuff the neck. It is held by forceps and thrust into the skull cavity and should extend back into the body. A larger wad is used to fill the body, and the skin is held in shape by tying a string around the body and wings until it has thoroughly dried. A stitch is taken through the nostrils and lower jaw after the throat has been filled lightly with cotton. The tail feathers are slightly spread and held by pins until they dry.

Mounting. A complete mount of a specimen differs from the above study skins in that artificial eyes are placed in the sockets and the animal is fastened to a board, tree limb, or other suitable substratum in as lifelike a pose as possible. This requires some essential differences in wiring and stuffing, such as those shown in the diagrams of Fig. 12.17*B*.

Beside wiring the tail, wires are used in each leg or wing. They are inserted upward through the bottoms of the feet and thrust through the body of excelsior. Then a loop is made in the end of the wire and it is drawn back into the bundle of excelsior as in the diagram (Fig. 12.17*B*). A bird should be wrapped about with string when completed to hold wings in position until the specimen is thoroughly dry.

Supplies Needed for Small Skins. If taxidermy is gone into extensively, there are many useful tools and materials that one would find convenient and for certain types of work essential, but the actual equipment required by the beginner to make a few study skins in the fashion described here is small.

Cutting Tools. A well-sharpened penknife with a rather pointed blade is by all means the most essential tool. A scalpel, or dissecting knife, is useful but not mandatory. A pair of small pointed scissors is a very helpful addition to the penknife. These too may not be necessary. A pair of pliers with wire cutter should be supplied and a small flat file.

Stuffing Equipment. A pound of absorbent cotton, some strips of cotton cloth bandage such as gauze, cheesecloth, light muslin, or surgeon's gauze are of first importance as well as needles and several colors of strong thread. A pair of long forceps are useful at times, and iron wire is a necessity.

Preservative. The one universal preservative is a mixture of white arsenic and powdered alum in equal parts. See the formulas below for suggestions and uses.

Accessories. A quart or more of very dry corn meal is almost an essential to a good job of skinning. The meal is used liberally between the skin and flesh wherever a blood vessel is cut, to prevent flowing blood from soiling the hair or feathers. This may sometimes be taken care of by cotton or gauze packs, but the meal is better and cheaper. A towel or large cloth for the hands and a vessel of water for sponging soiled hair or feathers are needed. A small brush for hair is also convenient.

Additional Supplies for Complete Mounts. If one wishes to mount a skin completely in some lifelike pose, other material is required, as described in the discussion above. Artificial eyes, glue, colored wax and excelsior, various sizes of soft iron wire, and pieces of thin soft wood are necessary.

In mounting skeletons of a larger size, such as a cat, large rabbit, or dog, in fact anything too large to be glued together, a small hand drill is required for making holes in the bones so that joints may be wired together. Boards, frames, and pieces of limbs or trunks of trees may be found proper to complete the mount.

Formulas. *To Preserve Skins.* (1) White arsenic 1 lb. dissolved in 1 pt. of water and painted on the inside of the skin. (2) White arsenic mixed with powdered alum in equal proportions and dusted heavily over the inner surface of the skin while it is still moist. After protecting the hands with rubber gloves, it may be rubbed into the skin and the excess dusted off after it dries. This may be made into a solution and painted on the skin if preferred. The solution is best if the skin has become too dry to hold the powder.

To Prepare Bones. 1. Add 4 lb. of baking soda to 1 gal. of water and bring to a boil. Cool and add 1 lb. of chloride of lime. Keep the container corked and in a closed box to exclude the light. Submerge bones in the liquid until bleached, if possible. If it is not possible to submerge the bones, paint the liquid on the bones freely and frequently. This, however, is not very satisfactory. Wash thoroughly in clear water after bleaching.

2. A 10 per cent solution of hydrogen peroxide makes a satisfactory bleaching solution for bones.

3. When bones are freshly cleaned, they may be greasy or contain fat. To remove this material place the bones in a fat-dissolving substance such as benzene or carbon tetrachloride, the latter being preferable as it is noninflammable. After a few hours remove the bones and wash in warm water before bleaching. Soaking in strong solutions of commercial washing powders helps to clean and whiten bones.

4. To prepare bones for mounting a skeleton, first scrape off all the flesh that will come off easily without cutting the ligaments at the joints or scratching the bone surface. Then place the bones in a vessel and cover completely with water. After a few days the muscle will be softened enough to come off by brushing briskly with a stiff brush. This will leave the bones fastened together by ligaments. If the skeleton is large, it should be disarticulated and the bones reassembled by wires or rods. The addition of a weak solution of caustic soda or Clorox to the water will remove the ligaments and cartilage, but the solution must be watched and thoroughly washed away as soon as the ligaments are removable.

Embalming

Larger Animals. When animals larger than a rat or guinea pig are to be preserved, especially if they are to be used for careful dissection, they are best embalmed. Details for embalming animals such as a cat or dog can be found in a number of books (see also *Turtox Service Leaflet* 21). The gist of the process is as follows:

Preparation. Have all instruments and materials ready at the start. These should generally consist of dissecting scissors, scalpel or sharp knife, forceps, injecting syringe and needles, thread, embalming fluid, ether, chloroform or jet of gas (or other anesthetic), and a spreading board or device.

The animal is slowly anesthetized until it is thoroughly limp. If you are inexperienced in keeping animals under an anesthetic, it is best to give enough to kill it, as shown by the heart beat. Proceed immediately to the work of embalming, stretching the legs out and the head up on the spreading board while the animal is limp. Cut the skin on the inner surface of the thigh and separate the muscle bundles carefully to expose the femoral artery along the bone, taking care to get the artery and not the vein. Expose the artery for an inch or two. Get the injecting needle and syringe ready and then tie a thread loosely around the artery, making a slip knot for tightening later. Insert the needle into the artery pointing it toward the body. Some workers prefer to cut carefully through the wall of the thorax and inject directly into the aorta just above the heart. Apply the pressure on the syringe very slowly and steadily and continue it until the body assumes a swollen or turgid appearance. Be sure to tie the thread tightly as soon as the needle is withdrawn.

Embalming Fluid. A satisfactory embalming fluid which will preserve and yet keep the muscles pliable is made as follows:

Formalin (3 per cent)	880 cc.
Glycerin	100 cc.
Carbolic acid (melted crystals)	20 cc.

If heavy cloth is saturated with the solution and wrapped around the embalmed animal and the specimen kept in a closed can to prevent drying, it will keep indefinitely.

Injecting

By injecting into the circulatory system, or parts of it, a substance which will solidify and impart a striking color to the vessels, their tracing and study are made much easier. Complete injection, especially with differential coloring, requires considerable practice. The colored-starch injection method will be described briefly here, as it is the one most commonly used.

The injection medium may be prepared as follows:

Formalin (40 per cent)	100 cc.
Glycerin	100 cc.
Cornstarch (1 lb.)	450 g.
Water (1 qt.)	950 cc.

Mix the starch and liquids slowly and thoroughly and strain through a thin cloth. Add enough finely powdered carmine (for red) or lead chromate (for yellow) to impart a bright color.

The animal to be injected should be freshly killed and the injection made immediately, before the blood becomes clotted. The injection needle should be placed into the carotid artery of the neck pointing toward the heart or in the aorta or the femoral artery. A thread is used to tie the needle into the vessel and then drawn tight when the needle is removed to prevent the injection mass from leaking out. There must be no lumps in the fluid.

Complete injection of a system may be accomplished by this method if the mixture is carefully prepared and the animal is quite fresh. Apply pressure gently at first, as a sudden force may rupture a vessel and all injection past the break would be impossible. Watch such places as the gums, undersurface of the tongue, and eyelids (if present). When they show a definite color it means that the injection has reached the capillaries. This method usually forces most of the blood into the veins and causes them to appear dark and well filled. If a color is desirable in the veins it is necessary to inject directly into the veins, such as femoral vein, jugular vein, or hepatic portal.

Both embalming and injecting are scarcely suited to general secondary school uses, but for the use of the teacher or for special and advanced projects they have been included. It is recommended that the technic be studied carefully before it is attempted.

Fossils

Making a School Collection. The making of a collection of fossils and the studying of the kinds of organisms that produced them and their significance in evolution offer an interesting problem. Some regions present excellent and varied materials, whereas others do not. Most limestone regions will furnish the more abundant forms of fossils such as brachiopods, corals, gastropods, crinoids, and sometimes trilobites. Soft coal, coal ball, and accompanying formation when split nearly always give indications of fern fronds, stems, spores, roots, and leaves. In general, sandstone and shales are regarded as poor sources of fossils although they sometimes yield excellent specimens.

The collecting should be started by a field trip and a talk on the age of the fossils, and a definite place such as a cabinet should be provided for keeping the better specimens. Once started on the hunt, students will continue to search for and bring in additional fossils, and a good collection can be built.

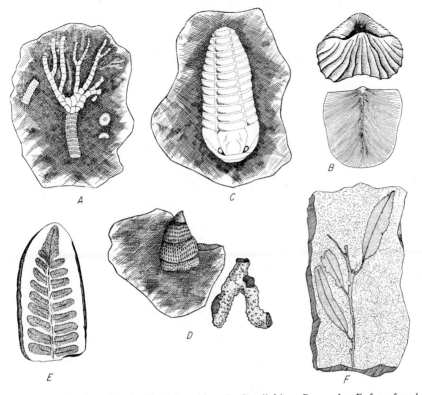

FIG. 12.18   Fossils: *A,* crinoid; *B,* brachiopod; *C,* trilobite; *D,* corals; *E,* fern frond; *F,* willow.

PLANT ORGANISMS

Bacteria

Permitting the student to make his own observations, draw his own inferences, based on experiences with living organisms, and finally come to some conclusion is far superior to *telling* him all the answers. All teachers who read this recall the thrill and "lift" experienced upon the discovery of something made entirely through their own efforts. This is the kind of experience that is not readily forgotten and the carry-over is high; the transfer residue from too many of our educational experiences is pitifully low.

An easy way to start a study of bacteria is to suggest examining a drop of liquid taken from directly below the surface of a hay-infusion culture (see Collecting and Culturing on page 152), first with the medium-power objective of the microscope and later under the high-power objective. While under the lower magnification, it probably will not be necessary to ask, "What do you see in this mount?" Someone says, "Things are dashing around." Under the high power, they appear to be moving even more rapidly. The students decide that the things they see are composed of but single cells and that they have swimming organs. At length someone notices that they are "eating" (engulfing) some very small particles. When asked what these moving bodies are, which they can see quite well under the medium-power lens, they are likely to answer, bacteria. They may then be shown some good illustrations of protozoa or *unicellular animals*. They saw them feeding upon some much smaller structures, which they could scarcely see under the medium power but were much more apparent under the high power—these are the bacteria. It may be suggested that they observe their mounts carefully to see how much they can discover about the bacteria. They will eventually decide that some are rod-shaped (bacillus type), others are spiral-shaped (spirillum type) or spherical-shaped (coccus type). They are likely to discover that some are motile (move under their own power) and others are nonmotile. They may have some difficulty in distinguishing between Brownian movement and actual motility. The teacher may aid in this difficulty by setting up a demonstration of Brownian movement, using nonliving material. The class may then be informed that *they have discovered* the most fundamental structural characteristics of bacteria, which was first discovered by a Dutch lens grinder Leeuwenhoek on Sept. 12, 1683.

From the same hay-infusion culture the students may be asked: Where do the bacteria get their food? What effect do the bacteria have upon the dry grass used in the hay-infusion culture? Before this, someone has probably raised a complaint about the foul odor emitted by the culture. The alert teacher will take advantage of this reaction in terms of learning that *decay* or *fermentation* has occurred. How does decay occur? Soon it is apparent that external *digestion* has taken place by enzymes diffusing from the bacterial cells, some enzymes digesting the cellulose of cell walls, converting the carbohydrates to sugar, which in turn is used as food by the bacteria and oxidized. Fats are digested, also external to the bacterial cells, and result in the presence of fatty acids and glycerin, and these are used as food. Proteins are digested, with the formation of amino acids. Some of the amino acids may be oxidized, resulting in the formation of ammonia and hydrogen sulfide, often detected in the odor of decaying organic materials. How does man benefit from decay caused by both bacteria and the fungi? Under what circumstances does man make an effort to prevent or retard the processes of decay?

In addition to the hay-infusion cultures, the common saprophytic bacteria may be studied from a somewhat different point of view, by pouring a thin layer of sterile nutrient agar into sterile petri plates. If the standard glass disk-shaped petri plates or dishes are not available, substitutes may be fashioned from heavy-duty aluminum foil, available at all supermarkets. Incidentally, the biology teacher will find many other uses for aluminum foil in the laboratory. Allow the sterile agar plates to cool and jell before asking the students to inoculate them with bacteria. Where will they get the bacteria for these inoculations? The instructor may suggest that some merely remove the lid or cover and expose the sterile agar to the air for 2 or 3 min.; others may lightly streak the agar with the point of a pencil, cough into the agar; touch the agar with the finger tips, shake a powder puff over the agar, sprinkle a few soil particles over the agar; or if a housefly can be persuaded to walk about on the agar, the results may be highly instructive. After the inoculation, the lids are replaced on the culture plates, and these are then set in a table drawer or other dark place at room temperature (about 70°F.) for 24 to 48 hr. When observed at the end of this period, *colonies* of bacteria will likely be evident. Many of these colonies will be almost perfectly disk-shaped, some with slightly wavy margin, some with a slick or glazed surface, others rough or crusty in appearance; most colonies are white or gray, ranging to almost transparent; and occasionally yellow, red, and purple colonies may appear.

A slide prepared from a symmetrical disk-shaped colony, by touching it with a dissecting needle, washing the needle point in a drop of water on a microscope slide, covering with a cover glass, then examining it with the microscope, will reveal a number of facts which by inferences drawn will solve a number of problems. Where are bacteria to be found? How do bacteria reproduce? What is the maximum potential rate of reproduction? Does this maximum rate of growth and reproduction continue indefinitely? What are the factors which prevent the maximum rate of reproduction from continuing for only a very limited period? How do you explain the regularity as to shape and color of a given colony of bacteria? Are the characteristics of a given bacterium hereditary? How could you demonstrate this feature?

It is likely that after about 72 hr. other colonies will begin making an appearance; these are obviously different from the bacterial colonies studied. They are composed of filaments which are multicellular instead of unicellular as for the bacteria. The filaments usually are apparent to the unaided eye; with aid of the microscope, one discovers that the filaments are either divided by cross walls or that they are tubular and without cross walls. In either case they are multicellular. These plants are representatives of another large group of nongreen plants—the fungi. Those occurring in the plates are likely to be the common household molds (mildews). If they are bluish-green in color, it is likely to be *Penicillium;* if black, with a sootlike appearance, it is probably a species of *Aspergillus;* if the colony has a cottonlike appearance with black specks scattered through it and if the filaments (hyphae) are tubular and branched, it is probably *Rhizopus,* a common bread mold. These petri-plate cultures, started specifically for a study of bacteria, lead directly and naturally to the study of the fungi.

Another point, which should not be overlooked, is the change that has taken place in the mixed population of a 48-hr. culture compared with that of the same culture at the end of 2 weeks. This is plant succession occurring within the boundaries of a petri dish and is fundamentally the same as found about a well-established pond or lake, or a flood plain through which a stream is flowing, or for that matter, a vacant lot in your city. Refer to Chap. 11 on student projects, the portion dealing with ecology and conservation.

Respiration (biological oxidation) in most, if not all, bacteria is incomplete. That is, the end products may exhibit other substances in addition to carbon dioxide and water as well as released energy. For example, when fermented (hard) cider or any other fruit juice is exposed to air for 2 to 3 weeks, the juice becomes vinegar. The alcohol in the fermented juice has been converted to *acetic acid* by acetic acid bacteria. The souring of milk is caused by the lactic acid bacterium converting milk sugar into *lactic acid.* Rancid butter and meat are usually due to the presence of *butyric acid* formed by the butyric acid bacterium. Some bacteria under anaerobic conditions incompletely oxidize carbohydrates, with methane (CH_4) as a resulting end product. This is marsh, or natural, gas. In a pond it often can be observed that when a stick is pushed into the mud, bubbles of marsh gas rise to the surface. The bubbles may be collected in a test tube and tested with a lighted match; if methane is present, an explosion instantly occurs. About 80 per cent of the power used in some sewage-disposal plants comes from methane collected from the decaying sewage.

There is another group of bacteria which live as parasites in contrast to the saprophytic bacteria which cause decay. These parasitic bacteria are the causative agents of some diseases of man and other animals. A few representative diseases caused by pathogenic bacteria are anthrax, tetanus, typhoid, tuberculosis, pneumonia, diphtheria, scarlet fever, septic ("strep") sore throat, and fire blight of pear and apple trees. Under most circumstances living cultures of pathogenic bacteria should not be used in the laboratory or classroom because of the danger involved. They may be studied satisfactorily from stained slide preparations, without the risk of a serious accident.

Antibiotics. Since 1939, when penicillin, the first "miracle" drug to be generally accepted, became available, numerous other antibiotics have been discovered.

Penicillin is a respiration end product of a common blue-green mold or mildew known as *Penicillium notatum;* streptomycin is a product of *Streptomyces griseus,* another fungus; streptothrian from *Streptomyces lavendulae;* Chloromycetin from *Streptomyces venezuelae;* Aureomycin is elaborated by *Streptomyces aureofaciens;* and subtilin comes from a common bacterium *Bacillus subtilis,* which is likely to be seen in the hay-infusion culture studied previously.

To demonstrate the action of these antibiotics, some sterile petri plates containing a thin layer of bacto yeast dextrose agar will be needed. Place 1 ml. of sterile water in a test tube. With a transfer needle inoculate the water with *Bacillus subtilis* or *Serratia marcescens,* a common pigmented (red) bacterium. Pour the inoculated water into a petri dish containing the sterile agar. Tip the plate back and forth so that the agar surface is covered by a thin film of water. This should ensure an even inoculation of the entire agar surface. Cut some ¼-in. disks from filter paper. Saturate the disks with a 100 p.p.m. aqueous solution of streptomycin sulfate, or a sodium salt of penicillin. Place a saturated disk in the center of the inoculated plate. Allow the plate to incubate in a warm room for 24 to 48 hr. At the end of this time there should be an obvious halolike area about the paper disk, which is free of bacteria. Beyond the halo, bacteria should be growing abundantly. To increase the effectiveness of this demonstration, prepare similar agar plates, but instead of the filter-paper disks carrying the antibiotic, inoculate the approximate center of the plate from a living culture of *Streptomyces griseus* or *Penicillium notatum,* the sources of streptomycin and penicillin. The inoculation in either case is accomplished by touching the pure culture of either fungus with a sterile transfer needle and transferring the spores or mycelia to the center of an agar plate already inoculated with bacteria. Allow these plates to incubate for 48 hr. or longer. The same kind of halo should surround each mold culture.

Pure cultures of bacteria and fungi may be obtained from some of the biological supply houses, or from the American Type Culture Collection, 2029 M. St., N.W., Washington 6, D.C. The antibiotics streptomycin sulfate and penicillin may be obtained from Nutritional Biochemicals Corporation, Cleveland 28, Ohio. Already prepared filter-paper disks impregnated with various antibiotics may be purchased from Difco Laboratories, Detroit 1, Mich., suppliers of many kinds of nutrient media.

General and Mixed Cultures of Bacteria. *Habitat.* Bacteria occur in greater numbers in most places than any other known living forms. They may be obtained for general study from almost any situation. Decaying plant or animal matter and soil particles contain them in vast numbers. Also many may be found on skin surfaces, teeth, mucous membranes, etc., of human beings.

Collecting and Culturing. Mixed forms including many common species. A handful of decaying grass or weeds placed in a container with water in a warm (about 70°F.), dark room for 7 to 10 days will produce vast numbers of bacteria. Motile and nonmotile rods (bacilli), spheres (cocci), and spirals (spirilli) are likely to be found.

A handful of dead dry honeybees or flies placed in a container with water will produce a good culture of bacteria, many of them being large motile rods which can be seen with the medium-power lens (16 mm.) of a microscope. Spores may be seen in some of them with the high-power objective. Bees may be obtained from a local beekeeper by sweeping up dead ones near the entrance of a hive or after an infected colony has been killed. The bees may be thoroughly dried and stored indefinitely.

Pure Cultures of Bacteria. *General Culture Methods.* To obtain pure cultures of bacteria it is necessary to have sterile medium on which to culture the desired form, a transfer needle, test tubes or petri dishes, and a steam sterilizer. In some cases sterilized slices of white potato are satisfactory as a medium. Place the potato slices in petri dishes, one in each dish, set the covered dish in the double-boiler sterilizer, and boil the water for about 1 hr. Usually this is sufficient to sterilize the piece. Cool, and do not lift the dish lid until ready to inoculate. Nutrient agar medium is best for most purposes.* For general purposes this may be made by the following method:

1. To ¾ lb. of ground lean beef add 710 cc. of water and let stand in a cool place overnight.

2. Strain off the juice, removing as much as possible by squeezing through a muslin cloth.

3. Make the volume total 750 cc. by adding more water.

4. Boil for 15 min. to coagulate albumin, and filter through a layer of absorbent cotton in a funnel.

5. Add 7.5 g. of peptone and 3.7 g. of sodium chloride (common table salt). Stir until these are dissolved. This beef broth may be used as a liquid medium for growing bacteria. The liquid is placed in test tubes or small flasks, the tube or flask mouths are plugged with cotton, and the tubes are sterilized (see steps 10 and 11 of this procedure).

6. Heat 300 cc. of the beef broth to the boiling point, and add 4.5 g of agar-agar.

7. Boil until the agar is dissolved. Filter through absorbent cotton. Wet the cotton with boiling water before pouring the agar.

8. Make up the volume of 300 cc. with water. At this point professional bacteriologists usually adjust the medium to a definite pH (hydrogen-ion concentration). However, for use in general botany or biology classes, this procedure usually is not necessary.

9. Pour the agar into test tubes, filling them about one-fourth full. Be careful not to get the agar on the wall of the tube above the liquid level.

10. Plug the tubes with cotton (Fig. 12.19). The plug should be sufficiently tight to support the tube when lifted up by the cotton. Be careful to prevent agar from getting on the plug.

11. Set the tubes in an upright position in the double-boiler sterilizer and boil for 1 hr. If the medium shows contamination after 24 to 48 hr. repeat the sterilizing process.

12. To slope the agar for cultures, lay the sterilized tubes at about a 30° angle in a cool place until the agar hardens.

The medium is now ready for inoculation. To do this a transfer needle is used. A 3-in. piece of nichrome wire (no. 24) is necessary. An electric heater unit may be used as a source of nichrome wire. Units for electric irons and heaters may be obtained from five-and-ten-cent stores. The wire is fastened to the end of a glass rod. One end of the rod is heated until soft, the wire inserted into it about ¼ in. and cooled. An aluminum rod about ⅛ in. in diameter and 5 in. long also makes a good handle. With a chisel or knife cut a slit in one end of the rod, insert one end of the nichrome wire into the slit and hammer the halves of the rod tightly about the wire. Before making a transfer always heat the nichrome wire to a red heat in a flame to sterilize it. Allow the needle to cool before touching it to the culture to be transferred to the sterile medium.

Remove the cotton plug from the culture tube or flask, holding it between the third and fourth fingers of the left hand. Be sure that the end of the cotton plug, which is to be placed in the culture tube, does not touch anything. Hold the tube in a slanting position between the thumb and first finger of the left hand. Heat the

* Bacto Yeast Dextrose Agar, sold by Difco Laboratories, Detroit 1, Mich., is satisfactory for most purposes. It is very convenient to prepare by following directions given on the package.

mouth of the tube in a flame for a few seconds. Dip the sterile needle tip in the culture to be transferred, holding the needle in the right hand. Insert the needle into the sterile tube, touching the agar slope near the bottom and streak it by drawing the needle to the top of the agar. Do not dig into the nutrient medium. Flame the needle before laying it down. Flame the mouth of both tubes (stock culture and that just inoculated) and insert the cotton plugs. It is often advantageous to flame the plugs before replacing. Store the inoculated tubes in a dark warm situation (room temperature to 98°F.). Colonies should appear in most cases within 24 to 48 hr.

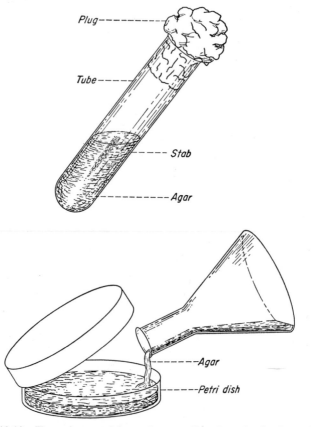

Fig. 12.19   Test tube containing culture medium for culturing bacteria.

Luminous Bacteria. *Habitat.* Several species of bacteria have luminous properties under certain conditions. This phenomenon is of rather common occurrence in decaying fish along ocean beaches, if observed during the night. Occasionally it is also seen in decaying wood in a forest after nightfall. Butchers commonly observe it on old meat (ham and beef) in refrigerators which retain a temperature of 45 to 50°F. Such meat can be obtained occasionally from them for demonstration purposes. If the infected meat is placed in a darkened room (a little light is necessary) luminous patches may be observed. For best results observers should remain in the darkened room for a few minutes until the eyes become accustomed to the darkness.

Nitrogen-fixing Bacteria. *Habitat.* Nitrogen-fixing bacteria are of inestimable value to nearly all other organisms since they, along with approximately forty species of blue-green algae, are probably the only living organisms which can fix free nitrogen of the atmosphere and transform it into compounds usable by green plants in protein synthesis. If it were not for these organisms the entire nitrogen supply eventually would be unavailable and practically all organisms would die of malnutrition. One of the easiest places to observe these forms is in nodules commonly found on the roots of leguminous plants. The white clover of lawns, red clover, sweet clover, alfalfa, vetch, soybeans (Fig. 12.20), shallow roots of black locusts, etc., all produce excellent nodules.

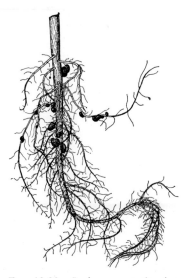

FIG. 12.20   Soybean root showing nodules caused by nitrogen-fixing bacteria.

Collecting and Preserving. Carefully dig up the root system of one of the above plants. Wash away adhering soil. When present the nodules are readily apparent. Select one of the larger nodules and wash thoroughly, cut open, and smear the cut surface on a clean side. Add a drop of water and observe with medium and high powers of a microscope. The bacteria are rods which may be straight, club shaped, Y shaped, etc. Usually favorable material can be obtained during the winter months from white clover, red clover, sweet clover, and the black locust. If desired, they may be preserved in 7 per cent formalin solution or in formalin-acetic acid-alcohol preservative.

Sulfur Bacteria. *Habitat.* In regions where sulfur springs are available the sulfur bacterium *Beggiatoa alba* may be found. It appears as white masses or scum on rocks or other debris in such springs. A mount of this material will show long

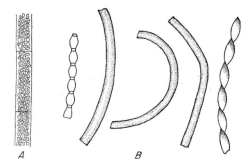

FIG. 12.21   Bacteria: *A,* sulfur bacteria; *B,* iron bacteria.

slender filaments with refractive granules inside (Fig. 12.21*A*). These granules are amorphous sulfur. Hydrogen sulfide from the sulfur water is oxidized and the resulting energy released causes carbon dioxide and water to combine, with a simple sugar being synthesized. In the living cells, the sulfur may be converted to sulfuric acid, which is neutralized by calcium or other basic materials, resulting in the formation of sulfates. These sulfates may be used by green plants in the synthesis of certain proteins which contain sulfur. When the bacterium dies, these sulfur granules are left as a residue. Many sulfur deposits may have been formed in this way. This species of sulfur bacterium, and others similar to it, are unique in that they use hydrogen sulfide as a source of energy instead of sunlight. This process is known as *chemosynthesis*.

A purple pigmented sulfur bacterium is often found in sewage-laden waters or in any other decaying organic mass. It occasionally appears in aquaria which are overstocked with mud and algae. The bacteria thrive in sunlight, which is a unique character among bacteria. Some of this group are very large, motile, and spiral in form.

Iron Bacteria. *Habitat.* In most regions iron springs are to be found. They are made conspicuous by the presence of rusty, flocculent masses in the water. Microscopic examination of this material will show comparatively large amber-colored rods, some of which may be spiral shaped (Fig. 12.21*B*). These are the iron bacteria. They use certain iron salts as their source of energy. Other iron compounds are deposited in their sheaths. It is thought that these organisms are responsible for some iron-ore deposits. They also are of interest because they are one of the few types which can use inorganic substances as a source of energy—chemosynthesis.

Algae

Culturing Algae. Algae are assuming greater importance as understanding of the many species increases. The possible use of green algae, through cultural methods, as a source for greatly increasing the supply of human food may be of great significance in the future. Understanding the food-chain relationship in aquatic habitats has led to profitable commercial fish culture in artificial ponds and lakes on abandoned land. The need for control of the growth of algae in municipal water supplies, in order to deliver more potable water, is of increasing importance.

With a little effort on the part of the teacher, it is possible to provide students with living fresh-water algae in the laboratory. An alert teacher who has had a little training in the observation of algae can collect a surprising number of species from almost any locality. These may be used directly for class use. However, most of them will not keep satisfactorily for more than a few days in the laboratory, and their abundance varies greatly with the environment, particularly with seasonal changes. This difficulty may be overcome by preparing cultures which may be maintained indefinitely in the laboratory. Pringsheim's soil-water culture method is one of the most useful and is applicable to a large number of the fresh-water algae (see Ref. 148). Convenient containers for such cultures are 8-oz. glass jars or ½-pt. wide-mouthed bottles. Wash the glassware thoroughly. Place in each container half of a level teaspoonful (1 g.) of calcium carbonate and cover it with ½ in. of garden soil. Add 6 oz. of tap water in a gentle stream down the side wall. The jar or bottle may be stoppered loosely with cotton or a small glass plate. The culture containers should then be sterilized by steaming (without pressure) at 100°C. for 1 hr. on three successive days. Allow the culture containers to cool and clear by settling, before inoculation. With a dissecting needle, algae filaments may be isolated and transferred to the soil-water culture medium. If unicellular or small colony forms are to be isolated, a micropipette, made by drawing a piece of glass tubing to a fine point and fitting a medicine dropper bulb on the opposite end, is useful. Cultures of many algae species may be maintained in the light from a north window. An artificial light source, such as that from a fluorescent light tube, delivering an intensity of 100 foot-candles may be used during the short days of the winter period. For more complete directions, see Ref. 148. If the algae species desired are not found locally, they may be purchased at a very reasonable price from The Culture Collection of Algae, Department of Botany, Indiana University, Bloomington, Ind.

Methods for Preserving Algae. *Formulas for Preservatives.* 1. Most algae may be preserved very successfully in Transeau's algal preservative. This is made up of 6 parts water, 3 parts 95 per cent grain alcohol, and 1 part commercial formalin. This preservative will be referred to as *six-three-one solution.* For marine algae use sea water in making up the formula. Medicinal (rubbing) alcohol may be substituted for the pure grain alcohol, making the preservative less expensive and more easily obtainable. The formula must be adjusted as follows if this substitution is made, since medicinal alcohol is usually 70 per cent. The substitute formula should contain 47 cc. water, 43 cc. medicinal alcohol (70 per cent), and 10 cc. commercial formalin.

2. The green color of chloroplasts may be preserved by saturating the above preservative with copper sulfate. The copper salt may be dropped in along with the specimens if desired. However, any excess copper should be removed after saturation. After the green color develops to its proper intensity the specimens should be transferred to a copper-free solution of this preservative.

3. Many algae and most other plant species are preserved very satisfactorily in formalin–acetic acid–alcohol solution (referred to hereafter as F.A.A.). The formula calls for 5 cc. of commercial formalin, 5 cc. of glacial acetic acid, and 90 cc. of 50 per cent grain alcohol. A variation of this, which is in common use, is 10 cc. of commercial formalin, 5 cc. of glacial acetic acid, and 85 cc. of 70 per cent alcohol. Medicinal alcohol may be used also as a substitute for the pure grain alcohol. In the first F.A.A. formula the 50 per cent alcohol may be made from medicinal 70 per cent alcohol by adding 30 cc. of water to each 70 cc. of alcohol. In the second F.A.A. formula this dilution is not necessary. The green color of chlorophyll may be preserved by adding copper sulfate to either of these formulas, the same as for Transeau's algal preservative. After color fixation the specimens may be transferred to copper-free F.A.A. without loss of green color.

Concentrating Unicellular and Small Colonial Forms of Algae. 1. A funnel-shaped plankton net made of bolting silk (20 mesh) is desirable, but expensive. The nets may be purchased from biological supply houses or may be homemade. Water containing the desired forms is strained through such a net, the organisms collecting in the bottom. The concentrated material may be emptied then into preservative.

2. A simple and inexpensive method of concentrating microscopic forms is to add about 100 cc. of a saturated copper sulfate solution to 900 cc. of algal culture. Flocculation of small organisms will occur often within 5 min. The precipitated material is allowed to stand for a few minutes longer, during which time they will rise to the surface or settle to the bottom. The mass is separated by decanting the water. The concentrated organisms are then preserved. The adsorbed copper is sufficient to preserve the green color. A saturated solution of alum may be used instead of the copper sulfate. If this is used, and a green color is desired, copper sulfate must be added to the preservative.

Blue-green Algae

In recent years, it has been demonstrated that at least 40 species of blue-green algae are capable of fixing free nitrogen. They probably are of considerable importance in wet habitats, such as rice fields, because of this feature; heretofore nitrogen fixation was known only among certain bacteria. *Nostoc* particularly is being studied in this respect.

Rivularia and Gloeotrichia. *Habitat.* These forms are commonly found floating in ponds or lakes or growing attached to submerged seed plants. They also may be found in mixed scums on lily-pool walls.

Collecting. Colonies of these genera often appear as brownish globules, floating or attached (see Fig. 12.22*A, B*).

Culturing. These forms may be kept from a few days to several weeks in a gallon-size aquarium filled with pond water.

Preserving. Use six-three-one solution.

Nostoc. *Habitat.* This form (Fig. 12.22*C*) is common in ponds, lakes, wet-weather pools, and limestone ledges which are wet for long periods. It also occurs as an inhabitant of *Anthoceros* gametophytes and several lichens, especially *Collema*. See the collecting notes under these forms.

Collecting. Some species of *Nostoc* occur as blue-green mucilaginous globules floating in water or attached to some other aquatic plant. Other species form sheets of irregular blue-green mucilaginous masses on soil or rocks in wet-weather pools. When these become dry the *Nostoc* appears as bluish-black sheets. After soaking in water for ½ hr. it may be dissected and easily examined under a microscope. It may be kept in the dry condition until needed. When growing in *Anthoceros* it forms dark colored spots in the gametophyte thallus. These can be dissected out with a needle. If *Collema* or some other lichen is used as a *Nostoc* source it must also be dissected.

Culturing. *Nostoc* may be kept several weeks in an aquarium. Also it may be stored dry outside the laboratory for several weeks. Soaking for a few hours will bring back much of its normal appearance.

Preserving. Use six-three-one solution.

Anabaena. *Habitat.* This genus (Fig. 12.22*D*) is often mistaken for *Nostoc*. It differs from the latter in that very little gelatinous matrix is produced. It often occurs as a scum on water surfaces and is commonly found associated with *Coelosphaerium*. It is also found in the intercellular air spaces in the floating fern *Azolla* and in the coralloid roots of cyads, such as *Zamia*.

Collecting. Collecting of light, gelatinous scums from water surfaces often yields this form. Also see the notes on collecting *Coelosphaerium*. In *Zamia* coralloid roots it forms blue-green layers often extending halfway into these organs. When the scalelike leaves of *Azolla* are dissected, they nearly always yield a few trichomes of *Anabaena*.

Culturing. A growing *Zamia* plant with some of the surface roots uncovered and cultures of *Azolla* are simple sources of living material. See notes on culturing of these two plants. Also, if a glass container such as a quart fruit jar is partly filled with sifted wood ashes, kept very moist in north window light, cultures of this organism will often occur. These cultures may appear as dark-colored globules, and are a good source of spores.

Preserving. Use six-three-one solution.

Oscillatoria. *Habitat.* This blue-green (Fig. 12.22*E*) is commonly found in waters heavily laden with organic materials, in wet-weather pools, on the surface of stones, dams, etc., over which water is running, stock tanks on farms, very moist soil in greenhouses, etc. Its color ranges from blue-green to a dark purple. The purple forms are usually large, which enhances its value as a form for study. It is commonly found on very wet soil.

Collecting. The slippery masses may be picked from rock surfaces, mud, etc. Often in sluggish streams or ponds, mats of it break loose from the bottom and float. These clumps may be easily dipped up with a net or one's hand.

Culturing. Small clumps placed in aquaria may grow for a long time.

Preserving. Use six-three-one solution.

Gloeocapsa. *Habitat.* This form (Fig. 12.22*F*) often occurs abundantly as a floating form mixed with other floating types, forming a scum. However, one of the best places to get it in abundance is on moist sandstone cliffs in shaded recesses.

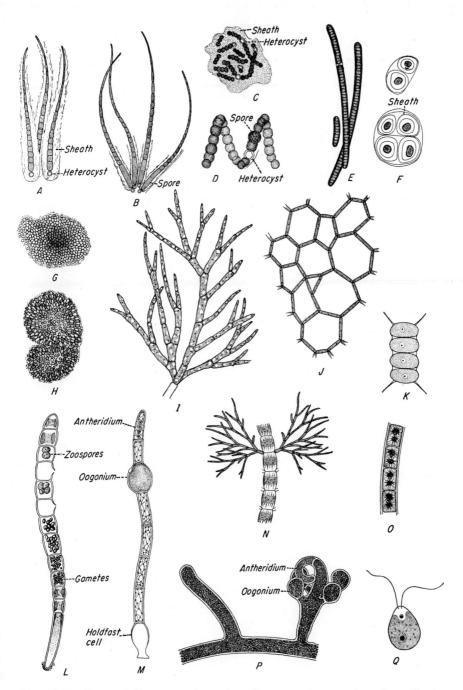

Fig. 12.22 Types of blue-green algae *A* to *H*, types of green algae *I* to *Q*: *A*, *Rivularia*; *B*, *Gloeotrichia*; *C*, *Nostoc*; *D*, *Anabaena*; *E*, *Oscillatoria*; *F*, *Gloeocapsa*; *G*, *Microcystis*; *H*, *Coelosphaerium*; *I*, *Cladophora*; *J*, *Hydrodictyon*; *K*, *Scenedesmus*; *L*, *Ulothrix*; *M*, *Oedogonium*; *N*, *Draparnaldia*; *O*, *Zygnema*; *P*, *Vaucheria*; *Q*, *Chlamydomona*.

Here it may occur in almost pure form in irregular, crumbly, light bluish-green gelatinous masses. Scrapings from the walls of a cement lily pool often contain great numbers of this plant.

Collecting. Scum may be skimmed from pond surfaces with a silk tow net or some container. A spoon is useful in collecting it from walls of pools or cliff faces.

Culturing. Occasionally when a small globule is placed in a quart of water and set in light from a north window it will grow and reproduce for many months.

Preserving. Use six-three-one solution.

Microcystis. *Habitat.* This blue-green (Fig. 12.22*G*) is often found as bluish-green to gray-green floating bits in ponds and sluggish streams.

Collecting. Often the masses are no larger than a pinhead. A silk net is very serviceable in straining it out. However, any container may be used in skimming it from the water surfaces.

Culturing. Occasionally it will live and reproduce for several months if kept in water in a north window exposure.

Preserving. Use six-three-one solution.

Coelosphaerium. *Habitat.* This floating form (Fig. 12.22*H*) often occurs in ponds and lakes in great quantities. When in abundance it gives water a blue-gray appearance.

Collecting. May be skimmed from the surface with a cup or fruit jar. A plankton net of very fine bolting silk is useful. *Anabaena* often occurs with it.

Preserving. Use six-three-one solution.

Green Algae

Chlamydomonas. *Habitat.* This interesting unicellular motile alga (Fig. 12.22*Q*) is widely distributed in ponds, lakes, and wet-weather pools. It sometimes occurs in great numbers during very wet weather in farm yards where there is an abundance of organic material. In water-lily pools it occasionally occurs abundantly after the addition of fertilizer.

Collecting. If a scum is formed it may be easily skimmed from the surface. However, it is more likely to be found well distributed through the water, offering a problem of concentration. This may be done easily with copper sulfate or alum solutions.

Culturing. Small amounts may be kept for several weeks in quart jars in a cool situation. Scrapings from walls of a water-lily pool, where it is known to occur at certain times, are a favorable source of inoculating material. Place the scrapings in glass jars filled with pool water to which has been added a little Knop's solution (about 10 cc. to each 100 cc. of water). Keep the scrapings in a warm, light situation. Cultures can be maintained on clean quartz sand in flower pots. Pour a culture over the sand. Set the pots in shallow containers with water. Moisten the sand surface with Knop's solution once or twice a month. When a culture for laboratory use is desired, transfer some of the sand to a quart jar filled with water. Set this in a well-lighted situation. Motile cells are likely to appear in a day or so.

Preserving. Preserve in six-three-one or formalin–acetic-acid–alcohol solution. The addition of copper sulfate to either of these gives excellent results with *Chlamydomonas.*

Scenedesmus. *Habitat.* This common green alga (Fig. 12.22*K*) is found as a floating or submerged species in many ponds. It often occurs in aquaria along with other forms.

Collecting. Surface skimming of ponds or pools with a plankton net or fruit jar is usually an easy way to obtain this alga. Scrapings from the underwater surfaces of a lily pool often show it in abundance.

Culturing. Scenedesmus may be kept alive for some time in cool shaded aquaria.

Preserving. Sparse cultures may be concentrated by the copper sulfate method. Preserve in six-three-one solution.

Hydrodictyon (water net). *Habitat.* Water net (Fig. 12.22*J*) is often found in ponds and in shallow, slow-moving parts of streams. The ponds or streams may dry up during the summer. Resting spores may carry this form over to the next season.

Collecting. Both large and small nets should be collected to show different stages of development. The floating mats may be picked up readily from the water.

Culturing. Water net will keep for weeks and even months in aquaria. If given additional light (electric) during the late fall and early winter it may be kept through to spring. If a few mature nets are placed in a shallow dish (petri dish is about right size) filled with water, then allowed to evaporate until nearly gone, the large cells (coenocytes) may show zoospore and new net formation.

Preserving. Use six-three-one solution containing copper sulfate.

Protococcus (Pleurococcus). *Habitat.* The commonest place to find this species (Fig. 22.2) is on tree trunks in a moist shaded side. It appears as a bright-green layer on the bark. It often occurs in such locations as an almost pure culture. It may be found in dense forests or on isolated lawn trees in a city.

Collecting. Cut off pieces of bark covered with the green layer. If the bark is moistened for a few minutes, the *Protococcus* may be scraped or brushed off fairly free of debris.

Culturing. Pieces of the bark may be kept in a laboratory for months from which the living alga may be obtained when needed. It may reproduce if kept in a moist chamber in diffused light.

Preserving. Use six-three-one solution with copper sulfate.

Ulothrix. *Habitat.* This interesting alga (Fig. 12.22*L*) grows attached to stones or other debris in streams, ponds, or lakes. It usually occurs in early spring and often lasts in good condition for a short time (2 or 3 weeks).

Collecting. Scrape the material off with a knife or other instrument and catch in a tea strainer.

Culturing. It is difficult to keep alive in a laboratory for more than 3 or 4 days. Stones from streams in midwinter will occasionally develop small quantities if placed in a container with water in a warm, light situation.

Preserving. Use six-three-one solution with copper sulfate.

Draparnaldia. *Habitat.* This alga (Fig. 12.22*N*) is commonly found in small streams attached to stones. It is of a bright-green color and very gelatinous to the touch. It may be found somewhat sparsely in late winter, in abundance in the spring, and as occasional tufts during the summer and fall.

Collecting. A tea strainer or net of some type is almost necessary because of the slickness of the filaments. They may be scraped loose with a knife and caught in the strainer.

Culturing. This alga is difficult to keep longer than a few days in a laboratory. Zoospores may be obtained by keeping the filaments in a refrigerator for 10 to 12 hr., then exposing to room temperature (70°F.) for 30 to 60 min. before use.

Preserving. Use six-three-one solution containing copper sulfate.

Spirogyra and Zygnema. *Habitat.* These usually occur in floating masses in slowly moving streams, ponds, lakes, roadside ditches, and wet-weather pools. They rarely reproduce sexually in shaded places, but commonly in brightly lighted situations. In the vegetative state they usually have a dark green color, and when reproducing a yellowish-green shade appears.

Collecting. Usually *Spirogyra* (Fig. 22.9) and *Zygnema* (Fig. 12.22*O*) may be collected in midwinter from springs which do not freeze over. They occur most abundantly in late April to early June. They may be found abundantly in any fresh-water aquatic situation where currents do not carry them away. In the field usually they can be identified readily by the fact that they feel like silk. *Spirogyra* has spiral ribbon-shaped chloroplasts, while *Zygnema* chloroplasts are roughly star shaped. To get *Spirogyra* in the reproductive phase in good condition, examine a few filaments of yellowish masses with a microscope every few days until the desired stages are found. It disintegrates rapidly after conjugation occurs. Sufficient masses may be scooped up with the hand, a stick, or dip net.

Culturing. Small mats may be kept in aquaria in the laboratory for several weeks. If too many are placed in a single container they disintegrate rapidly, often in a day or so. They should be kept in a light, cool place.

Preserving. Use six-three-one solution containing copper sulfate.

Desmids. *Habitat.* These are found in pond and lake scums, in small pools about springs, and on moist cliffs. One is most likely to find them sparsely mixed with other forms. *Staurastrum* (Fig. 12.23A), *Closterium* (Fig. 12.23B), and *Cosmarium* (Fig. 12.23C) are three common genera which are excellent for study.

Collecting. Almost any mass of scum from a pond surface will probably show a few forms.

Culturing. Ordinarily it is difficult to culture in pure form. Occasionally *Cosmarium* occurs sporadically in aquaria. It forms light-green flocculent masses.

Preserving. Use six-three-one solution containing copper sulfate.

Diatoms. *Habitat.* These unique algae (Fig. 12.23) are found abundantly in nearly all streams, ponds, and lakes. They may occur as floating forms, epiphytes on other water plants, or as a slick, brownish scum on stones, sticks, and other debris in flowing streams. Some forms apparently can reproduce rapidly at nearly freezing temperatures. Many forms are usually found in every algal collection.

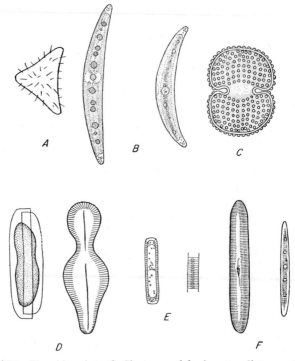

FIG. 12.23   Desmids: *A* to *C*. Six types of fresh-water diatoms: *D* to *F*.

Collecting. Stones, sticks, etc., in small streams during the winter often have a brownish gelatinous layer on their surfaces. A drop of this material is likely to show many forms. Scrapings from moist rock-cliff surfaces, floating scums on ponds, etc., usually are rich in many species.

Culturing. Numerous forms will survive in aquaria if not overcrowded.

Preserving. Use six-three-one solution containing copper sulfate.

Cladophora. *Habitat.* This common alga (Fig. 12.22*I*) is often abundant in rapidly flowing streams. It grows attached to rocks and other debris in rapids on rock surfaces of falls and dams. Also, it may occur in ponds and lakes. Sexual reproduction is rare, but reproduction by zoospores is common.

Collecting. Carefully scrape material from rocks to retain holdfast cells. Small quantities may be kept in aquaria for a long time.

Culturing. If the right balanced condition is attained in an aquarium, this alga may grow and reproduce for years. It often becomes a pest in fish aquaria.

Preserving. Use six-three-one solution containing copper sulfate.

Vaucheria. *Habitat.* This alga (Fig. 12.22*P*) is commonly found as dark-green velvety mats about springs and their brook outlets. It often is found as a green velvety covering of moist soil in greenhouses and fields during very wet seasons.

Collecting. The mats may be held in running water to wash away adhering mud. They must be handled carefully to prevent crushing of the delicate filaments. It can usually be obtained in midwinter about unfrozen springs.

Culturing. If a small clump of *Vaucheria* is placed in a glass container with about twenty times its volume of water in a light cool situation, zoospores are likely to be found in a few days. These as well as oospores may also be found germinating. If the organic mass is not too large for the volume of water, considerable development may be attained.

Preserving. Use six-three-one solution containing copper sulfate.

Oedogonium. *Habitat.* This interesting alga (Fig. 12.22*M*) is found commonly in quiet pools, ponds, and lakes. It grows attached to other water plants, stones, and debris. It may be found during the early spring, summer, and fall.

Collecting. It often appears as a thin mat of fine filaments on submerged parts of cattails, water-lily petioles, sticks, and stones. Small pieces of these objects may be collected or the filaments may be scraped loose.

Culturing. This alga is usually difficult to keep for many days in the laboratory. However, occasionally cultures may appear among other algae in aquaria. After fruiting starts the filaments rapidly disintegrate.

Preserving. Use six-three-one solution containing copper sulfate.

Slime Molds—Myxomycetes or Mycetozoa

Slime molds have two phases in their life cycle which are quite unlike. The phase known as a plasmodium is a naked multinucleate mass of protoplasm with no cell walls. It is derived indirectly from germinating spores. An oval flagellated cell escapes from each spore as it germinates. These cells swim for some time; then the single flagellum is withdrawn and the cell becomes amoeboid. Groups of these ameboid cells fuse, forming a plasmodium. Food is engulfed and digested by the plasmodium, assimilation converts the food into more protoplasm—and so the plasmodium grows. This phase is quite animallike. Under the proper conditions, probable lack of food, exposure to light, and slow desiccation, it may be transformed into a very different phase. This stage is nonmotile and bears spores, which is a plant characteristic. In other words, the slime molds have the characteristics of both plants and animals.

Fuligo, Lycogala, and Stemonitis. *Habitat.* In general a swamp forest containing many decaying logs and stumps is one of the most favorable situations for numerous slime molds. Beech forests, pine woods, and flood plains also are suitable habitats for many. *Fuligo* (Fig. 12.24*A*) is common on decaying wood and old apple pomace about cider mills. *Lycogala* (Fig. 12.24*B*) is particularly common on decayed beech and pine wood. *Stemonitis* (Fig. 12.24*C*) may be found on numerous species of decaying logs.

Collecting. Many species may be taken throughout the year, but seem most abundant in the autumn. A heavy knife to cut out pieces of wood on which the specimens are located is a necessity. Boxes and glue should be taken into the field and specimens glued immediately in boxes. Since they are very fragile this method prevents much breakage and loss. Usually they are stored dry. If plasmodia are taken they must be preserved if they are to be kept long. Usually plasmodia brought into the laboratory will produce sporangia overnight.

Culturing. One common species of slime mold *Physarum polycephalum* has proved to be the most satisfactory for plasmodium cultures in the laboratory. In this species, the plasmodium is of lemon-yellow color and may be found on decaying logs and even on lawn grass during periods of wet weather. Carefully remove a piece of the decayed wood, or other substrate which bears a concentrated mass of the plasmodium, and transfer it to the laboratory or other situation where it may

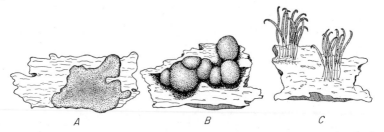

Fig. 12.24   Representative types of slime molds: *A, Fuligo; B, Lycogala; C, Stemonitis.*

be air-dried quickly. If this procedure is carried out successfully, a crusty, tan-colored, granular mass results which is known as a *sclerotium*.

Prepare a culture container similar to that shown in Fig. 12.25. The bottom or lid of a petri plate is inverted and wrapped with a piece of filter paper, folding it under edge of the petri plate. Set this in a larger finger-bowl type of culture dish, with a piece of window glass for a lid, or use a transparent plastic box with a cover. Add enough water to cover the bottom of the larger container so that it comes in contact with the filter paper covering the petri plate bottom. The filter paper becomes saturated with water by capillarity. Place a piece of the sclerotium approximately in the center of the filter paper covering the petri dish. Add three to four pieces of raw rolled oats (common breakfast cereal), placing the pieces near the sclerotium. Cover the outer glass or plastic container with a lid or piece of glass, and set in a cool, dark place.

If the sclerotium is viable, an active plasmodium will develop in 24 to 48 hr. It should have a glistening lemon-yellow color and an amoeboid movement which can be seen with the aid of some magnification. The mass soon becomes reticulated and is often somewhat fan-shaped in outline. It engulfs the rolled oats, digesting the food and converting it to new protoplasm (plasmodium material). Under the proper conditions, the plasmodium may approximately double in volume within 24 hr. The culture should be fed a few grains of rolled oats once each day. Overfeeding will likely result in a bacterial infection, and the plasmodium may die. However, by this time it is likely that the plasmodium will have moved over the whole area of the filter paper and out on the water to the wall of the enclosing dish. With a scalpel or spatula, uninfected portions of the plasmodium may be lifted out and transferred to another culture dish and a new, active culture started. This is an excellent example of regeneration, or somatic (vegetative) multiplication.

If a blank, microscope slide is placed on the petri dish, near the protoplasmic strands (pseudopodia), the plasmodium will likely creep upon the slide. Lift the slide bearing the small mass of branched strands, breaking it free from the main plasmodium, and transfer it to the stage of a microscope. Cover the plasmodial portion with a thick film of water and allow it to recover for 5 to 10 min. With the medium power objective of the microscope, one may observe protoplasmic streaming, with granular masses tumbling along in the stream.

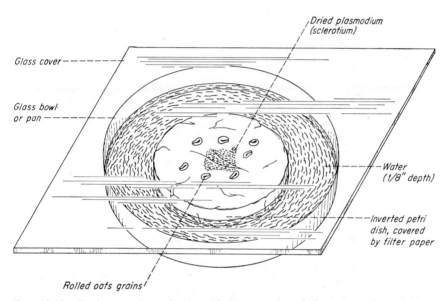

FIG. 12.25   Equipment for culturing *Physarum polycephalum,* a common Myxomycete or Mycetozoan (slime mold).

When a culture is growing vigorously, masses of the plasmodium should be removed and placed on clean filter paper, and dried rapidly in open air at room temperature. Sclerotia will form from each dried mass. When air-dry, the sclerotia may be stored for future use. These sclerotia may remain viable in dry storage for 2 years and possibly longer.

The culturing of slime mold plasmodia, as a demonstration of living protoplasm, unencumbered by cell walls, may be presented by the instructor, or used even more effectively as a student project. Numerous possibilities for experimentation will become apparent to both the teacher and students. Some of the biological supply houses have available agar cultures of slime mold plasmodia.

Preserving. As stated above, sporangia usually are preserved dry, glued in small boxes. However, they may be preserved in F.A.A. solution or in 7 per cent formalin. Clusters of young sporangia whose walls are not broken should be selected for preserving. Plasmodia may be preserved in F.A.A. solution by placing a piece of the substrate bearing the plasmodium in the solution. It must be carefully protected and the jar not crowded to prevent crushing.

Fungi—Phycomycetes

Plasmodiophora brassicae (club root of cabbage). *Habitat.* This destructive fungus (Fig. 12.26*E*) is commonly found in market-gardening regions. It occurs commonly on roots of cabbage and several other mustard species. If infection occurs while a plant is young, it rarely lives to maturity.

Collecting. Stunted, unhealthy-looking plants are symptoms of the disease. If infected, the roots will be greatly enlarged and malformed.

Culturing. Start seedlings of Chinese cabbage or common cabbage in disease-free soil. After they are growing vigorously and are 2 or 3 in. tall, transplant to pots or flats of soil containing the club-root organism. Keep moist and in a warm location. Within 5 or 6 weeks good-sized infected roots will appear. If thin freehand sections are made of the diseased tissues, mounted in water, and examined under the high power of a microscope, spore masses are commonly found within cells. If the roots are young and still developing, amoeboids cells may be observed crawling about within living host cells. The infected soil may be kept from season to season for culture purposes.

Preserving. Preserve in F.A.A. solution. If green parts are attached to the roots, the green color may be retained by adding a small amount of copper sulfate.

Rhizopus nigricans (bread mold). *Habitat.* Spores of this mold (Fig. 22.2) are abundant about any habitation.

Collecting and Culturing. Smear pieces of bread across a table top. Moisten the bread and keep it in a closed container in a dark warm place for 24 to 48 hr. Several pieces of bread should be started at the same time since other molds such as *Penicillium, Aspergillus* (green and black molds), *Monilia* (a pink mold), etc., may dominate some of the cultures. When a colony of pure bread mold is found, transfer some of the spores to sterilized potato agar, made as follows:

1. Pare and slice 100 g. of white potatoes. Add 250 cc. of distilled water. Mark the level of the liquid in a cooking pan.

2. Put 9 g. of plain agar in 250 cc. of distilled water. Use an ordinary double boiler. Mark the level of the liquid.

3. Cook 1 and 2 separately for 1 hr.

4. Add distilled water to each vessel to restore the water lost by evaporation.

5. Strain off the clear liquid of 1 and 2.

6. Add 10 g. of dextrose to the combined liquids and boil for 1/2 hr.

7. Filter through a layer of cotton or several layers of cheesecloth.

Pour the filtered medium into test tubes, plug with cotton, and sterilize. The inoculation is made by using a sterile transfer needle. The same precautions to prevent contamination must be used as for bacteria.

Preserving. Use F.A.A. solution.

Saprolegnia (water mold). *Habitat.* Water mold (Fig. 22.2) is a fungus occurring in nearly all ponds and streams. It is a common parasite of fish. Tropical and other aquaria fish often become infected with it. On fish it appears as cottony masses attached to the scales and fins, often causing death. It commonly occurs on insects which have fallen into water.

Collecting and Culturing. Since this form of mold produces zoospores in abundance and infection takes place by means of these, one may grow cultures by placing a few dried bees, flies, or grasshoppers in a large container (1 to 5 gal.) of pond water. Good growth usually results in about 1 week. Zoospores are likely to be found in abundance. Within 5 to 14 days sexual stages (oogonia and antheridia) may be found occasionally. The same cultures may show bacteria, paramecia, vorticella, and numerous other forms.

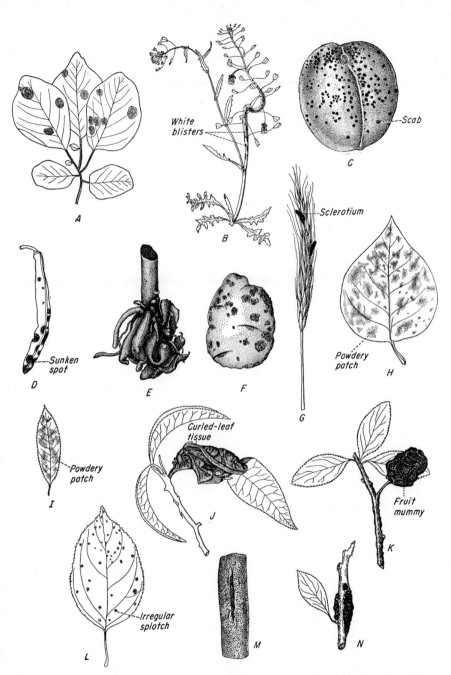

FIG. 12.26   Some common plant diseases: *A*, early blight of potato; *B*, white blister of shepherd's purse; *C*, peach scab; *D*, anthracnose of bean; *E*, clubroot of cabbage; *F*, common scab of potato. Some common ascomycetes causing plant disease: *G*, ergot on rye; *H*, powdery mildew of lilac; *I*, powdery mildew of willow; *J*, peach-leaf curl; *K*, brown rot of plum; *L*, apple scab; *M*, chestnut blight; *N*, black knot of plum.

205

Preserving. A good preservative for *Saprolegnia* is F.A.A. solution.

Cystopus candidum (Albugo candida, white blister). *Habitat.* This disease-causing organism (Fig. 12.26*B*) is common on shepherd's purse (*Capsella bursa-pastoris*), a common weed in lawns, gardens, and fields. It may occur on several species of mustard and one species on salsify (oyster plant). It is much more common during moist periods since infection takes place by zoospores. Infected plants in advanced stages show white blisterlike pustules and often swollen tissues. Infected shepherd's purse is usually available in May and June. The powdery mildew (*Peronospora parasitica*) looks superficially like *Cystopus* and may occur along with it. However, it does not show the blisterlike pustules.

Collecting and Preserving. Pressed specimens show the general macroscopic characteristics very well. Material preserved in F.A.A. solution or in 7 per cent formalin is better for the conidia and sexual stages. The oogonia, antheridia, and zygospores are usually found in stems which are swollen and beginning to show a dark discoloration.

Fungi—Ascomycetes

Saccharomyces (yeast). *Habitat.* Wild yeast (Fig. 22.2) species are common almost everywhere, causing alcoholic fermentation.

Collecting and Culturing. Apple juice allowed to stand for a few days in a warm room will usually produce an abundance of yeast cells. The scum on the liquid over kraut (that made and kept in open containers) and dill pickles often shows fine cultures. Also a few crumbs from a commercial yeast cake dropped into a 2 per cent glucose solution will usually produce a good growth within 24 hr. if kept in a warm room.

Preserving. Use F.A.A. solution. Mix the formalin, acetic acid, and 95 per cent alcohol, then add enough of the culture to equal the volume of alcohol. This prevents too much diluting.

Exoascus deformans (peach leaf curl). *Habitat.* Peach leaf curl (Fig. 12.26*J*) is a very common fungal disease of peach trees during moist periods of early summer. It occurs soon after the leaves develop, causing them to be curled and otherwise distorted. The infected leaves soon die and drop off. Sections through the distorted tissues will show ascospores.

Collecting and Preserving. The infected leaves and twigs should be picked when found in good condition and preserved in F.A.A. solution containing copper. Fine museum mounts may be prepared in this way.

Microsphaera alni (powdery mildew of lilac). *Habitat.* This common powdery mildew (Fig. 12.26*H*) may be found on most lilacs in the central states during the late summer. It appears as powdery patches on the leaves. Late in the autumn, perithecia appear as very small black dots to the unaided eye.

Collecting and Preserving. The leaves may be pressed or preserved. The appendages on pressed material become very fragile, and most of them break off within 2 or 3 years. Preserved material may be retained satisfactorily much longer. F.A.A. solution with copper sulfate is a satisfactory preservative.

Uncinula salicis (powdery mildew of willow). *Habitat.* This mildew (Fig. 12.26*I*) is a common parasite on willows, especially *Salix discolor* (wild pussy willow). Perithecia appear late in the autumn.

Collecting and Preserving. Same as for *Microsphaera.*

Aspergillus (black mildew). *Habitat.* The black mildew (Fig. 22.2) is widely distributed and occurs on many substances. It causes fruit decay, occurs commonly on home-canned fruits and jellies, may be found on clothing and leather goods stored in a moist place, etc.

Collecting and Culturing. Bread kept in a warm, moist chamber for 2 or 3 days often will produce good cultures. It may be grown readily in pure culture (for method see bread mold above and Chap. 22, Reproduction).

Preserving. Cultures grown on a liquid medium such as a sterile beef broth (see page 191) are best for preserving. This eliminates a solid substrate. Preserve in F.A.A. solution.

Penicillium (downy mildew). *Habitat.* This downy mildew (Fig. 22.2), sometimes called "green mold," is widely distributed. It occurs commonly on home-canned fruits and jellies, causes decay of oranges, grapefruits, apples, is the common mildew of clothing and leather goods stored in moist places, and is used commercially in the manufacture of Roquefort and Camembert cheeses. *Penicillium notatum* is a source of the important antibiotic *penicillin.*

Collecting and Culturing. Same as for *Aspergillus.*

Preserving. Same as for *Aspergillus.*

Venturia inaequalis (apple scab). *Habitat.* Apple scab (Fig. 12.26*L*) is one of the commonest and most serious apple diseases in most apple-growing regions. The fruits and leaves are attacked.

Collecting. Perithecia containing mature ascospores are not found until early spring during moist periods. They develop on old leaves on the ground. They appear as black specks just discernible to the unaided eye. Spores from these perithecia infect young leaves of the apple as they are unfolding. This infection causes slightly irregular, roundish brown spots on leaves and fruits. The spots on the fruits may become quite irregular as the fruit grows. Conidia develop on these spots and cause reinfection during the summer.

Preserving. If the old leaves with perithecia are dried and curled, they may be moistened, straightened out, pressed, and redried. The fresh leaves with conidial stages may be pressed or preserved in F.A.A. solution with copper sulfate to give them a green color. Fruits may be preserved in the same way. Excellent demonstration specimens may be prepared from such materials. If old leaves bearing perithecia are boiled in potassium hydroxide, the tissues will clear considerably, making the perithecia more easily visible. Rinse the leaves thoroughly in water and preserve in 7 per cent formalin or F.A.A. solution.

Sclerotinia fructiginia (brown rot of plum). *Habitat.* Brown rot (Fig. 12.26*K*) is a common disease of many varieties of plum. The fruit is the chief part attacked. The disease becomes prominent about the time of ripening of the fruits.

Collecting. The rotting plums usually show brown pustular spots scattered over the fruit surface. The diseased plums may hang on the tree far into the winter or spring. They may be collected any time. Early the following spring those which are on the ground may produce small stalked cups. These contain ascospores.

Preserving. A solution of 7 per cent formalin is effective for both stages. If a stem with leaves and diseased fruit is desired for demonstration purposes, it may be preserved in F.A.A. solution with a little copper sulfate.

Plowrightia morbosa (black knot of plum). *Habitat.* This disease causes distorted wartlike growth on twigs (Fig. 12.26*N*) of many plum varieties and occurs commonly on the Blue Damson. It infects only woody parts.

Collecting. Conidial stages are found in the late spring and early summer. They may become so abundant that a brownish velvety surface is produced on the wartlike hypertrophies. Perithecia develop about midsummer or later. These papillae may be located with a hand lens. The asci do not develop until during the winter and the ascospores ripen during midwinter or later. A thin transverse section through the infected portion will disclose the perithecia, if present.

Preserving. A solution of 7 per cent formalin is satisfactory. Specimens may also be kept dry. If demonstration specimens are desired with leaves in place, preserve in F.A.A. solution containing copper sulfate.

Claviceps purpurea (ergot of rye). *Habitat.* Ergot (Fig. 12.26*G*) is a common disease of rye, but is not of serious importance as far as the host plant is concerned.

Collecting. Black sclerotia are produced where grains should be. It is easily detected in rye just before harvest time. The whole heads should be collected with the sclerotia in place. Year-old sclerotia on soil, usually early in the spring, may produce sporophores which are mushroomlike bodies ranging from ¼ to 1 in. in length.

Culturing. Sclerotia occasionally may be made to produce sporophores by planting them in a marked place on moist soil and being allowed to overwinter there. Close watch during the following spring may result in finding the sporophores.

Preserving. Infected rye heads may be dried for class use, or they may be preserved in 7 per cent formalin. Fruiting sclerotia should be preserved in F.A.A. solution.

Endothia parasitica (chestnut blight). *Habitat.* Chestnuts of all the chestnut-growing regions of the United States are infected with this disease. In many areas it is so serious that all mature trees are dead or nearly so. At present it looks as though our native chestnut may be exterminated by this organism (Fig. 12.26*M*).

Collecting. Dead crown or clusters of branches are symptoms. Close examination of these will show areas of the bark becoming cankerous and covered with numerous small reddish-brown pustules. From these spores may be escaping continuously. A saw is useful in cutting out diseased segments.

Preserving. Usually specimens are kept dry. Small pieces may be preserved in 7 per cent formalin for dissection.

Morchella (morel, or sponge mushroom). *Habitat.* This mushroom (Fig. 12.27*C*) is the most highly prized edible form. It is widely distributed throughout the Central and Northern states. It appears early in the spring during moist warm periods. Its fruiting time lasts but 2 or 3 weeks as a rule. It is found in moist woods of several types, old uncultivated orchards, hawthorn thickets, stream banks, fence rows, and grasslands which are not heavily pastured.

Collecting. For the inexperienced this is a most difficult form to see because of its light brown to dark gray color blending it into the surroundings. After one has found one or two it is much easier to find more. Often raking aside dead leaves and grass will reveal more specimens. When a good collecting place is found, visits there every other day for a week or so will repay one with specimens. Specimens will range from 1 to 5 or 6 in. in length.

Preserving. Preserve in F.A.A. solution.

Peziza, Bulgaria, Urnula (cup fungi). *Habitat.* Some species of the cup fungi may be found in many situations. Moist woods of various types seem to be the best locations. The genus *Peziza* (Fig. 12.27*B*) may be found either on soil or decaying wood. *Bulgaria* (Fig. 12.27*D*) and *Urnula* (Fig. 12.27*A*) always occur on wood. Moist periods favor their development.

Collecting. The scarlet cup *Peziza* occurs early in the spring. It develops on decaying wood. The inside of the cup is colored a beautiful scarlet. Some species of *Peziza* are nearly white and others usually of a light brown color. *Bulgaria* is quite fleshy and contains considerable mucilaginous material. Deep shaded woods seem to be the best situations for it. It fruits about midsummer during moist periods. *Urnula* is almost black in color, urn shaped, and usually about 3 in. tall. It occurs in moist woods in early spring.

Preserving. Preserve in F.A.A. solution or in 7 per cent formalin.

Cladosporium carpophilum (peach scab). *Habitat.* This is a widely distributed peach disease which affects fruits (Fig. 12.26*C*), leaves, and twigs.

Collecting. It appears as numerous blackish spots, usually circular, on the fruits.

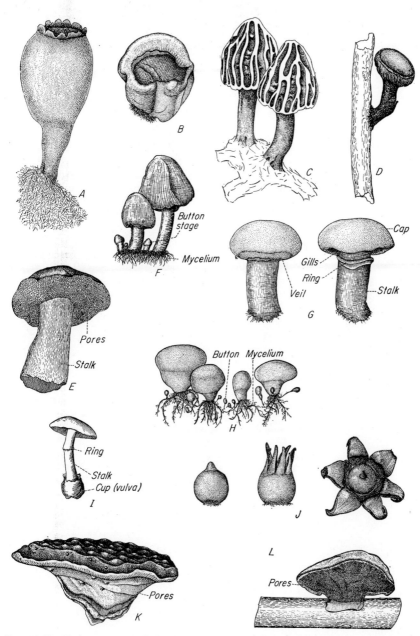

Fig. 12.27 Some common fleshy ascomycetes: *A*, Urnula; *B*, Peziza; *C*, Morchella (Morel); *D*, Bulgaria. Common fleshy basidiomycetes: *E*, Boletus; *F*, Coprinus (inkcap mushroom); *G*, Agaricus (field mushroom); *H*, Lycoperdon (puffball); *I*, Amanita (death angel); *J*, Geaster (earth star); *K*, Fomes (shelf fungus); *L*, Polyporus.

The spots may fuse with one another, forming large irregular patches. Cracking of the fruit may result from the infection.

Culturing. Diseased fruits may be kept a week or so in a cool, dry place, or indefinitely in a refrigerator.

Preserving. Fruits, stems, or leaves may be preserved in 7 per cent formalin or in F.A.A. solution with copper sulfate.

Lichens

With the exception of a few species, lichens belong to the Ascomycetes. They are characterized by the presence of some alga upon which the fungus is parasitic. The alga usually belongs to the blue-green group or *Protococcus* (*Pleurococcus*) of the greens.

Peltigera (mad-dog lichen). *Habitat.* This lichen (Fig. 12.28*D*) usually occurs on moist soil, decaying logs, or on sandstone ledges.

Collecting. *Peltigera* is a thallose lichen, usually brown, ranging to a bluish-green in color. The fruit bodies are brown, shaped somewhat like a fingernail, and occur at the tips of the thalli.

Culturing. Mats of the thalli may be kept alive in a cold frame or cold moist chamber for many weeks.

Preserving. Plants may be kept dry, preserved in F.A.A. solution or in 7 per cent formalin.

Collema. *Habitat.* This genus (Fig. 12.28*E*) is a thallose lichen occurring on tree trunks and limestone cliffs in moist situations.

Collecting. When dry this lichen is nearly black. When moist it is blue-green in color and more or less gelatinous. The fruit bodies are brown, shallow *Peziza*-like cups about 1/16 in. in diameter. This algal host is *Nostoc*, which can be dissected out readily and observed under a microscope.

Culturing. *Collema* may be kept alive for several weeks in a moist, cool place.

Preserving. Use F.A.A. solution with copper sulfate.

Parmelia. *Habitat.* The commoner *Parmelia* (Fig. 12.28*F*) species are large thallose types occurring commonly on tree trunks, large boulders, and sandstone masses.

Collecting. These lichens are usually yellowish to bluish-green in color. When moist, especially after a heavy rain, they may be peeled free of the substrate. However, it is usually safer to cut out the piece of bark to which they are attached.

Culturing. These forms may be kept alive for several weeks in a cool, moist place.

Preserving. They may be kept dry or preserved in F.A.A. solution with copper sulfate.

Physcia. *Habitat.* This is a common lichen (Fig. 12.28*G*) occurring on the bark of hickory, elm, black walnut, etc., and occasionally on rocks.

Collecting. This lichen is usually gray in color, thallose, rather small, and often fruits abundantly. Asci can be dissected readily from the cups (ascocarps). The alga present is *Protococcus.*

Culturing. *Physica* may be kept alive several weeks on pieces of bark placed in a cool, moist situation.

Preserving. Keep dry, and moisten when ready to use, or preserve in F.A.A. solution with copper sulfate.

Cladonia cristatella. *Habitat.* This lichen (Fig. 12.28*A*) is distributed extensively. It is commonly found in abandoned fields and pastures on poor soil. Also it may be found on decaying wood.

Collecting. The fruit bodies of this *Cladonia* are scarlet when fresh, ranging to brown when old. They are borne on upright branches often an inch in height. The vegetative portions are grayish-green in color. They may be collected any time of year, but are usually most abundant in the winter and spring.

Culturing. Plants may be kept alive for many weeks in a cool, moist place.

Preserving. Specimens may be kept dry or preserved in F.A.A. solution with copper sulfate.

Graphis. *Habitat.* This interesting crustose lichen (Fig. 12.28*B*) is usually found on tree trunks. Butternut, tulip tree, and blue beech (*Carpinus*) are among the most favorable trees on the bark of which they are commonly found.

Collecting. Good specimens may be taken at all times of the year. The lichen forms gray patches often circular in outline. The fruiting pustules appear as pencil marks over the surface. With a heavy knife or ax, pieces of bark bearing the specimens may be removed.

Culturing. Material may be kept alive for several weeks in a cool, moist place.

Preserving. Usually such specimens are kept dry, but they also may be preserved in F.A.A. or 7 per cent formalin.

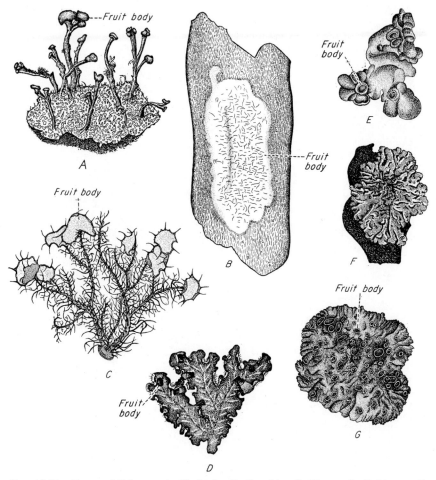

FIG. 12.28   Types of lichens: *A*, Cladonia; *B*, Graphis; *C*, Usnea; *D*, Peltigera; *E*, Collema; *F*, Parmelia; *G*, Physcia.

Usnea (goatsbeard lichen). *Habitat.* This lichen (Fig. 12.28*C*) grows attached to branches of various trees. Well-developed specimens are found only where the atmosphere is continually moist. The genus is widely distributed but is often rare locally.

Collecting. Cut off small branches or bark pieces with the *Usnea* attached. If dry, moisten before packing to prevent breakage. Collect plants which are fruiting. The apothecia are disk shaped. This species is used commonly as a fruticose type.

Culturing. Plants may be kept alive in a cool, moist place for several weeks.

Preserving. The goatsbeard lichen may be stored dry and moistened when needed for class use. It also may be preserved in F.A.A. solution with copper sulfate or in 7 per cent formalin.

Imperfect Fungi

Actinomyces scabies (potato scab). *Habitat.* This disease is widely distributed and very common wherever growers are careless about planting disease-free tubers (Fig. 12.28*F*).

Collecting. Infected tubers have conspicuous rough, corky pits over a large portion of the surface. Diseased tubers may be obtained from growers or on sale in vegetable markets.

Culturing. Diseased tubers may be kept several months if stored as for healthy potatoes.

Preserving. They may be preserved in 7 per cent formalin.

Alternaria solani (early blight of potato). *Habitat.* This important potato disease occurs almost throughout the potato-growing region of the United States. It usually is found from the latter part of June to the end of the growing season. Severe droughts check its growth.

Collecting. The disease is distinguished from others by appearing as brown circular spots (Fig. 12.26*A*) with prominent concentric rings on the leaves.

Preserving. Infected leaves may be collected and pressed for laboratory use, or they may be preserved in F.A.A. solution with a little copper sulfate.

Colletotrichum lindemuthianum (anthracnose of beans). *Habitat.* Anthracnose of beans (Fig. 12.26*D*) may be found wherever beans of any variety are grown. The fungus attacks leaves and stems but is more conspicuous on the pods. The spots are brownish in color, the central portion becoming dark and sunken.

Collecting and Preserving. Collect infected bean pods about the time they are old enough to shell. Preserve in F.A.A. solution with copper sulfate to give green color.

Fungi—Basidiomycetes

Puccinia graminis (black stem rust of wheat). *Habitat.* The black stem rust (Fig. 12.29*B*, *C*) is found on wheat stems and sheaths in many localities. One stage is also found on the common barberry (*Berberis vulgaris*). It does not occur on the Japanese barberry, which is now commonly planted as a hedge. The common barberry was introduced by the New England pioneers from England. It was grown as an ornamental plant, and its fruits were prized for jelly making. It escaped from cultivation and became widely distributed. For several years the Federal government developed eradication campaigns against this species. In many areas specimens are now difficult to locate because of these control measures.

Collecting. The urediniospore, or red rust stage, is usually abundant at harvest time. Plants which are badly infected have a rusty appearance due to many pustules filled with numerous reddish-brown one-celled spores on the stems and sheaths. Another species, the leaf rust of wheat, may appear on the leaf blades. Soon after harvest time, and sometimes before, black pustules with amber-colored two-celled spores appear. These may be found on old wheat stubble and in straw stacks during fall, winter, and early spring. These winter spores (teliospores) usually germinate on soil and produce a mycelium about four cells in length. This stage produces the spring spores (basidiospores). Germinating winter spores and spring spores are difficult to find. The spring spores can infect only the common barberry and some of its close relatives. This infection occurs early in the spring, often just as the barberry leaves are unfolding from buds. This infection usually results in orange-colored spots on the barberry leaves. When these spots are examined under the microscope, they are found to contain orange-colored spores called "barberry spores" (aeciospores). These are carried by wind and if they fall on young wheat plants will cause infection which later results in summer spores (urediniospores). Grains from infected and uninfected plants should be collected for comparison. Shriveled grains from infected plants readily show effect of the disease. Usually dried specimens of straw with summer and winter spores, infected barberry leaves, and slides of each will be loaned more or less permanently to teachers by the U.S. Department of Agriculture, Division of Barberry Eradication. Extension offices in the various wheat-growing states usually have a supply of these.

Preserving. The simplest way of preserving the spores of the summer, winter, and barberry spore stages is by drying. The barberry leaves should be pressed and dried quickly to prevent molding. The spores of the summer spore stage should be dried thoroughly in an oven. If they are not thoroughly dried, the winter spore stage may develop. Care must be taken not to scorch the straw. If the green color of the straw of the summer spore stage and barberry leaves is preferred, the spores may be preserved in F.A.A. solution with a little copper sulfate added.

Gymnosporangium macropus (apple rust). *Habitat.* In some of the central and eastern apple-growing regions this disease becomes serious if high humidity prevails. Brownish-orange spots are found on apple leaves (Fig. 12.29*D, E, F*) and fruits. Spores (aeciospores) from these infections may be transferred to red cedar trees. The infection appears as galls, averaging about 2 cm. in diameter, the so-called cedar apples. In early spring during moist periods orange-colored gelatinous finger-like masses extrude from the cedar apples. Teliospores are found in these masses. These germinate, producing the basidial stage. Basidiospores infect apples in the vicinity.

Collecting and Preserving. Infected apple leaves may be collected and pressed, or they may be preserved in F.A.A. solution with a little copper sulfate to give a green color. Infected fruits may be preserved in the same way. Cedar apples with the orange-colored gelatinous masses last for only a few days in good condition. They must be picked from the trees and preserved in either 7 per cent formalin or F.A.A. solution.

Puccinia sorghii (corn rust). *Habitat.* Corn rust (Fig. 12.29*A*) is a fairly common disease of corn, especially of sweet varieties. It appears first as reddish-brown pustules on the leaf blades. Later, black pustules containing teliospores appear. These overwinter on dead leaves. Aeciospores are produced in the spring and summer on *Oxalis stricta* (sour clover, or sour grass).

Collecting and Preserving. All stages may be pressed or preserved in F.A.A. solution with copper sulfate to give leaf tissues a green color.

Culturing. Collect and dry a few corn leaves with teliospores present. Store them where they will be exposed to low temperatures in the winter season. In the spring plant *Oxalis* seeds, collected the previous season. After the seedlings are growing vigorously place some of the old infected corn leaves near the young *Oxalis* plants. Keep all in a moist condition. Within a few weeks infections are likely to appear on the sour clover and appear as orange-colored spots on the leaflets. These spots will produce the aeciospores. The aeciospores, if carried to corn, will cause infection.

Ustilago tritici (loose smut of wheat). *Habitat.* The loose smut of wheat (Fig. 12.29*I*) is widely distributed and common throughout wheat-growing regions. The spores mature as the wheat heads begin to appear out of the sheaths.

Collecting. Infected plants may be detected by the sooty appearance even through the sheaths. Specimens should be collected just as the heads are about to appear from the sheaths since the spores shatter readily when uncovered.

Preserving. The collection may be dried or preserved in F.A.A. solution with a little copper sulfate.

Ustilago avenae (loose smut of oats). *Habitat.* This common oat disease (Fig. 12.29*G*) is found wherever oats are cultivated. It matures at about the time of flowering of the oat plants.

Collecting. Infected plants can be detected easily as the oat heads (panicles) are growing out of the sheaths. This is the best stage to collect specimens since the sheaths help prevent loss of the spores.

Preserving. Specimens may be dried satisfactorily for laboratory use. If the green color of the leaves, sheath, and stem is desired, the specimens may be preserved in F.A.A. solution with a little copper sulfate.

Ustilago zeae (smut of corn). *Habitat.* This disease occurs wherever corn is grown. The flowers, stems, and leaves may be affected (Fig. 12.29*H*).

Collecting. Diseased portions of the corn plant become enormously enlarged. Before spore formation the abnormal swellings have a grayish-white appearance. By the time spores are forming, the host tissues break down and leave great pockets of spores. Spore formation occurs usually from flowering to fruiting time of the corn.

Preserving. Pieces of the corn plant with smut in place may be dried successfully. However, the smut masses shatter easily and scatter spores. A 7 per cent formalin or F.A.A. solution with a little copper sulfate may be used if specimens are to be preserved in liquid.

Agaricus campestris (common field mushroom). *Habitat.* This is a common edible mushroom (Fig. 12.27*G*) which is often found in pastures and on lawns during moist summer and fall seasons. It is the same as the common cultivated mushroom of the United States sold on fruit and vegetable markets during the fall, winter, and spring.

Collecting. These mushrooms range from a white to gray in color. The gills are pink when young and almost black when old. The stipe, or stem, has a delicate collar (annulus) attached just below the gills. The stem end in the soil is not swollen but of about the same diameter as the aboveground portion. Some of the vegetative part (mycelium) can be taken from the soil still attached to the mushroom if patience and care are taken in removing it. If wild mushrooms are to be eaten, too much care cannot be taken in determining what they are. Often only minute differences separate poisonous and edible species. Do not take a chance on them unless you are absolutely sure that you know what they are. Some are deadly, and there is no known cure.

Culturing. Either in a small or large way the first requirement in mushroom culture is a suitable place. The temperature must not go above 70°F. The room must have no strong air currents through it and be such that the atmosphere can be kept very moist. A darkened cellar with no artificial heat is preferable.

Fresh manure, free from bedding material, from grain-fed horses is preferred. This is piled in a heap, moistened, and allowed to heat for 2 or 3 days. This material is mixed and turned over, with more water being added to dry spots. This

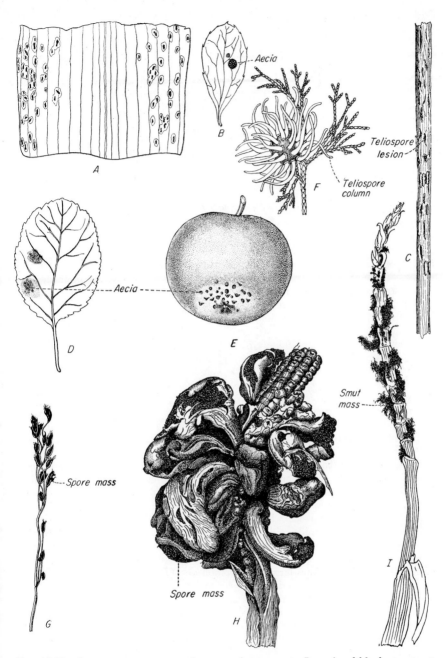

FIG. 12.29   Some common rusts and smuts: *A*, corn rust; *B*, aecia of black stem rust of wheat on barberry leaf; *C*, teliospore pustules of black stem rust on wheat stem; *D*, aecia of apple rust on apple leaf; *E*, aecia of apple rust on apple fruit; *F*, cedar apple (cedar gall) with teliospore columns of apple rust; *G*, loose smut of oats; *H*, corn smut; *I*, loose smut of wheat.

215

process is repeated for about 2 weeks or until the high temperature is lowered. Some growers add to the manure about one-third of its bulk of rich garden soil. When the mass is free from disagreeable odor and its temperature about 80°F. it is ready to place in beds. The beds should be filled with the compost to a depth of about 10 in. It should be packed down firmly and should be moist but not wet. The bed is ready to inoculate with spawn when its temperature is about 75°F. The spawn which can be obtained from seed stores in the form of a brick is broken into pieces approximately 1 in. square. These are buried to a depth of about 2 in. and about 1 ft. apart. The beds must not be allowed to dry out, nor must they be kept too wet. After about 1 week the beds should be covered with 2 in. of good garden soil. Within about 6 to 8 weeks the first mushrooms are likely to appear.

Preserving. Solutions of 7 per cent formalin or F.A.A. solution may be used successfully.

Amanita (deadly amanita). *Habitat.* Species of this genus are found usually during moist periods of the summer and fall in wooded areas. However, they occasionally are found on lawns and in open pastures.

Collecting. Most of the *Amanitas* are very poisonous. Great care must be taken to not allow even small pieces to become mixed in with specimens intended for eating. Figure 12.27*I* shows general characteristics of the group. All of them have a more or less enlarged base, which may be buried in the soil several inches. In some of the species this bulbous base breaks away from the stem (stipe) forming a cup. The name "death cup" is sometimes applied to these species. Along with the cup a collar or annulus occurs on the stem a little distance below the gills. The bulbous base, cup, and the collar definitely distinguish it as an *Amanita.* Occasionally the collar has been destroyed in some way or the bulbous base is poorly developed. Some species of *Amanita* are whitish, some greenish, some yellowish-brown to blackish-brown and the cap (pileus) smooth (*A. phalloides*); or white, ragged margin, smooth (*A. virosa*); or yellow or yellow with orange-red center, warty pileus (*A. muscaria*). The very young developing *Amanita* (the so-called button stage) might be mistaken for a puffball. However, if a longitudinal section is made through it, the internal portion is not solid as in a puffball.

Preserving. Use F.A.A. or 7 per cent formalin solution.

Lycoperdon (puffballs). *Habitat.* Puffballs (Fig. 12.27*H*) are of common occurrence in pastures, on lawns, or in wooded areas. They occur most abundantly during moist periods. Some occur on decaying wood and others on humus.

Collecting. Cool, moist periods are the most favorable times for looking for puffballs. Most of them are white, cream, or grayish in color. Before maturity they are solid on the inside and very white. As they mature the internal portion develops spores in vast numbers and becomes dark in color. Escaping spores appear as puffs of smoke. Some species rather common in pastures often develop a diameter of 4 to 6 in. and sometimes larger. A common one (*Lycoperdon pyriforme*) occurring on spongy, decayed wood rarely gets to be more than 1 in. in diameter. It commonly grows in clusters from a few to a hundred or more. It is especially fine for showing all stages of development from "buttons" the size of a pinhead to the mature form. The mycelium also can be separated easily from the decayed wood. It is quite easy to obtain excellent material for demonstrating all stages of the life cycle. The puffballs are also edible. They are used as food only when they are solid white inside. There is some danger of mistaking buttons of *Amanitas* for them.

Preserving. Use F.A.A. solution or 7 per cent formalin.

Geaster (earth stars). *Habitat.* Earth stars (Fig. 12.27*J*) are fairly common but usually not abundant. They may be found in moist woods, sandy situations, and in partly cleared areas.

Collecting. Badly decayed logs, stumps, and leaf mold seem to form good culture media for these species. Wherever found it is worth digging into the substrate and looking for various stages of the developing fruit body.

Preserving. These plants dry fairly well. Either 7 per cent formalin and F.A.A. solution is recommended as a preservative.

Coprinus (inky cap mushroom). *Habitat.* This very common mushroom (Fig. 12.27*F*) occurs on heavily manured soil and on decaying stumps and logs. Moist seasons favor its development. It may be found throughout the late spring, summer, and fall.

Collecting. This genus may be recognized by its black spores, close gills, which at maturity disintegrate into an inky mass. The species growing on decaying wood often occur in close clusters numbering many individuals. All the species are edible in the fresh condition.

Preserving. F.A.A. solution is a very satisfactory preservative for *Coprinus*.

Fomes (shelf or bracket fungus). *Habitat.* This serious wood-destroying fungus (Fig. 12.27*K*) infects several species of forest trees and is common in moist forests. It may be found on dead trees and is a perennial.

Collecting. The vegetative part of the fungus is concealed in the wood. Only the conspicuous fruiting structures occur on the surface. The bracket of several species may be shaped somewhat like a horse's hoof and is often as large. They become quite woody, which often makes a hatchet or small ax useful in removing them from the host.

The underside of a bracket is made up of many pores which can scarcely be detected by the unaided eye. Spores are borne in these pores. The surface is white to cream colored when in good condition. It is soft and will bruise or scar if care is not taken.

Preserving. Specimens may be dried successfully as laboratory specimens. They also may be preserved in 7 per cent formalin. If kept dry it is well to poison them by painting on a saturated solution of bichloride of mercury in 70 per cent alcohol to keep free of insects.

Polyporus. *Habitat.* Species of this genus (Fig. 12.27*L*) are important wood-rotting fungi widely distributed on living trees, decaying logs, and stumps. This fungus is an annual.

Collecting. Any wooded area or cut-over lands on which slashings still remain are usually productive of several species. One of the most conspicuous is a sulfur-yellow form occurring in clumps often 1 ft. or more across. It is soft when young and is edible. Another conspicuous one is brick-red in color and is of a hard, leathery texture. The undersides of brackets are spore bearing. This surface is honeycombed with vast numbers of almost invisible pores.

Preserving. These may be kept dry or preserved in 7 per cent formalin solution. If kept dry, poison to prevent insect attack the same as for *Fomes*.

Boletus. *Habitat.* Most species of *Boletus* (Fig. 12.27*E*) grow on soil and a few on wood. Their color varies through brown, reds, yellow, to purplish. They are most commonly found in moist woods.

Collecting. These fruit most abundantly from midsummer to late fall. They resemble in form the gill mushrooms, but instead of gills they have numerous pores on the underside of the cap. Some species when wounded quickly turn to a bright-blue color in the injured tissues. Some are edible while others are poisonous.

Preserving. Use 7 per cent formalin or F.A.A. solution.

Mosses

Mosses are of importance in botanical studies as forms showing a well-defined alternation of generations in which the sporophyte is parasitic upon the gametophyte to a greater or lesser extent. As a land cover they invade newly exposed surfaces following lichens. They are important soil builders and binders. The group is of little immediate economic value except for *Sphagnum* (peat mosses). In some regions peat (*Sphagnum*) is of great importance as fuel. Pulverized peat is used often in the preparation of soil for lawns and other landscape plantings. Dry *Sphagnum* will absorb water equal to about thirty-five times its dry weight. For this reason it is commonly used in packing roots of living plants for shipment. Nearly 13,000 species of mosses have been described. Only a few of the commoner species will be dealt with here.

Bryologists ordinarily dry their specimens and store them in envelopes or paper folders. They may or may not be pressed. When specimens are moistened for 2 or 3 min. they regain much of their lifelike appearance. This method enables one to store a hundred or more species, with adequate specimens of each for future examinations and records, in a shoe box. For demonstration purposes and general class use, however, material preserved in liquid is often desired. The formula for F.A.A. solution with copper sulfate, given on page 300, is an excellent preservative for *Bryophytes*. Nearly lifelike demonstrations and material for dissection may be prepared by this method.

Sphagnum (peat moss). *Habitat.* The peat mosses (Fig. 12.30*B*) grow in very wet locations, often forming bogs. In the more extensive bogs, cranberries, pitcher plants, and sundews are usually associated with it. It may be found occasionally in small clumps about swamps and in seeps on hill or cliff sides.

Collecting. Fruiting of a common species (*Sphagnum palustre*) occurs during the first half of June in Ohio. The sporophytes are globose, becoming brown with age. They are restricted to lateral branches near the gametophyte tip. The color of the gametophyte scales ("leaves") ranges from a light grayish-green to a brick-red color. The protonema is thalloid, looking somewhat like a fern prothallium.

Culturing. No very definite methods of culturing are known. However, clumps may be kept alive for several months if placed in a glass container and kept very moist and in a cool situation.

Preserving. Use F.A.A. solution with copper sulfate.

Funaria hygrometrica (cord moss, ash-heap moss). *Habitat.* The cord moss (Fig. 12.30*H*) is widely distributed, occurring in numerous habitats. One of the best situations is wood ashes which have lain in the open for some time. Ashes from burned brush and stumps on cut-over areas are likely to be more or less covered with this moss. It also occurs on old coal ashes, small undisturbed areas in greenhouses, pockets of soil in limestone quarries, etc.

Collecting. Gametophytes with antheridia and archegonia begin to appear usually in October and persist throughout the winter. The gametophytes become branched (see Fig. 12.30*G*). The tip of the main axis produces a cluster of antheridia which can be detected by the unaided eye. Soon a side branch develops, and at the tip of this archegonia are to be found. After fertilization the archegonial branch gradually breaks away and becomes established as a separate plant. From a fertilized egg at the tip of this plant a sporophyte develops and matures in the spring and early summer.

Culturing. Fill a shallow box with sifted wood ashes to a depth of about 4 in. Moisten the ashes and scatter *Funaria* sporangia over the surface or transplant a few clumps of established gametophytes in it. Cover the box with glass and keep in a cool situation in somewhat reduced light. Protonemata and young gametophytes are likely to make their appearance within 4 or 5 weeks.

Preserving. Plants of all stages of development may be very successfully preserved in F.A.A. solution with a little copper sulfate.

Atrichum (Catharinea). *Habitat.* This moss (Fig. 12.30*D, E*) is very common in beech-maple woods and deep moist ravines.

Collecting. This moss grows in rather dense clumps. It fruits abundantly in the fall. Sporophytes in good condition may be found throughout the fall and winter. Clumps may be brought to the laboratory and placed in a box out of doors in some convenient, cold, moist place until needed. A light covering with moist leaves or grass will give them sufficient protection. Male and female gametophytes may be collected in May and June in good condition for antheridia and archegonia. The male plants can be detected readily by a cuplike structure at the gametophyte tip. In the center of this the greenish-brown cluster of antheridia can be seen. Other plants in the clump not showing the cups are likely female plants. The only way to be sure is by dissection of the tips. When dissected parts are placed in a drop of water and observed microscopically, archegonia may be detected readily if present.

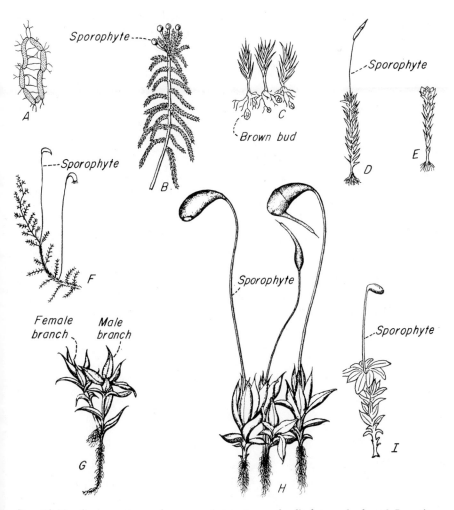

Fig. 12.30   Common types of mosses: *A,* two types of cells from a leaf, and *B,* entire *Sphagnum* plant; *C, Leptobryum; D, Atrichum,* female plant with sporophyte; *E,* male plant; *F, Thuidium; G, Funaria* gametophyte; *H, Funaria* gametophytes with sporophytes; *I, Mnium.* Types of liverworts.

Culturing. Protonemata (Fig. 22.10) of either *Atrichum* or *Funaria* may be cultured readily. The simplest method is to crush a dry sporangium and liberate the spores on the surface of some diluted Knop's solution.

KNOP'S SOLUTION

Potassium nitrate	1 g.
Magnesium sulfate	1 g.
Calcium nitrate	3 g.
Potassium acid phosphate (KH_2PO_4)	1 g.
Ferric chloride (1 per cent aqueous solution)......	2 drops
Distilled water	1,000 cc.

Dilute Knop's solution to one-third of its original strength with distilled water (tap water if distilled water is not available) and place in petri dishes or other small glass containers which can be covered. After they have been inoculated place them in light from a north window or other reduced light situation. Within about 4 weeks branched protonemata may be expected. Germinating spores may be had in about 2 weeks.

Another very good medium for culturing protonemata is a 2 per cent agar made up with diluted Knop's solution (diluted to one-third original strength). This medium is made by adding 2 g. of granulated or sheet agar to 98 cc. of the diluted Knop solution. Boil in a water bath—double boiler is excellent—until the agar melts. Filter the solution by passing it through an absorbent-cotton-lined funnel. Pour the hot solution into petri dishes to a depth of about ⅛ in. Cover and allow to cool and solidify. After cooling crush a clean sporangium, allowing spores to fall on the medium. Replace the cover and set the cultures preferably in north light. Several cultures should be made since some may become infected with molds and bacteria. Germination will occur within a week or 10 days. Buds and young gametophytes may appear abundantly within 2 or 3 months. Better cultures may be prepared by using sterile nutrient medium, sterile plates, and by sterilizing the unbroken sporangia in sodium hypochlorite (sold commercially at grocery stores as Clorox, Dag, Oxol, Chlorite, etc.). The sporangium must then be rinsed in sterile water, transferred to the plates, and broken under as nearly sterile conditions as possible. An agar made up with full strength Beyerinck's solution also gives excellent results.

BEYERINCK'S SOLUTION

Distilled water	1,000 cc.
Ammonium nitrate	0.5 g.
Calcium chloride	0.1 g.
Potassium acid phosphate (KH_2PO_4)	0.2 g.
Magnesium sulfate	0.2 g.
Iron chloride (1 per cent aqueous solution)	1 drop

Preserving. All stages of the life history may be preserved with natural color in F.A.A. and copper sulfate solution.

Mnium. *Habitat.* Most species of this genus (Fig. 12.30*I*) are found in shaded, moist woods or in deep, wet ravines. Clumps may be formed on soil, rocks, decaying logs, or stumps. Some species have very large scales which are very leaflike in general appearance.

Collecting. These mosses fruit abundantly from early to late spring. In early summer fine antheridial and archegonial plants are easily found. This form is excellent for archegonia. Some species are unisexual while others are hermaphroditic. The antheridial plants of unisexual species are easily detected by the broad flat cups at the gametophyte tips.

Preserving. Preserve all stages in F.A.A. and copper sulfate solution.

Polytrichum (pigeon wheat or haircap moss). *Habitat.* The various species of *Polytrichum* (Fig. 22.10) grow in a wide range of situations. Some are commonly found in bogs and swamps, some on very poor acid soil, others on dry hilltops and talus slopes. When growing in very favorable situations the species of this group become our largest mosses. They often form large, circular, dense mats.

Collecting. Ordinarily sporophytes are produced in May and June. At high altitudes they may not fruit until midsummer. Antheridial and archegonial plants may be collected in good condition during the latter part of May and June. The male plants can be detected readily by the well-developed cup at the gametophyte tip. The sporangia are as large or larger than a large grain of wheat and may be of about that color. The sporangia, while fresh, are covered with a conspicuous calyptra which forms a conical tip at the apex and has a ragged edge below. The name "haircap" is derived from this structure.

Preserving. Some prefer to store the sporophyte-bearing plants dry. Many, however, prefer them preserved in liquid. The F.A.A. solution with a little copper sulfate is recommended for all stages.

Leptobryum pyriforme. *Habitat.* This species (Fig. 12.30C) occurs commonly as a weed in greenhouses. It often becomes established on soil about potted plants which have not been disturbed for some time and in sand on cutting benches which is moist but not disturbed for several weeks. It rarely produces sporophytes in these situations. However, it is very fine for demonstrating brown buds and protonemata. These buds are asexual reproductive bodies.

Collecting. Under the above conditions this moss is usually not more than 1 cm. in height, forming small clusters or large mats, depending on the age and amount of disturbance. The scales are rather long and hairlike, inclined to bend, giving the mat a curly appearance. The brown buds are somewhat flask shaped, composed of several cells, and are attached by a slender axis to rhizoids, or protonemata. Under proper conditions the buds will germinate, one or more cells giving rise to protonemata. It apparently spreads by means of these structures in greenhouses as well as in nature.

Culturing. Living cultures may be had by inoculating sand mixed with a little soil and keeping it in a Wardian case (Fig. 12.33) or in a closed glass container in a shaded situation. Inoculation is brought about by placing a small clump of living plants in the sand-soil mixture and wetting thoroughly. Such cultures are also usually a good source for protonemata.

Preserving. Carefully remove the plants from the soil and wash, brushing particles of soil and sand away with a camel's-hair brush. Preserve in F.A.A. and copper sulfate solution.

Thuidium delicatulum (fern moss). *Habitat.* This beautiful moss (Fig. 12.30F) forms dense lacy mats on decaying logs or stumps in moist woods and deep shaded ravines. It is sometimes collected and used as soil containers in wire swinging flower baskets. It is an excellent representative of a pleurocarpous (sporophytes lateral and gametophyte prostrate) moss.

Collecting. The highly branched prostrate gametophytes often form a dense mat which can be pulled up from the substrate in great sheets. It fruits about midsummer. The antheridial and archegonial branches are somewhat difficult to detect. It is better to depend upon some other type for demonstration of these organs.

Culturing. Mats of living plants may be kept alive for many weeks if placed in a cool, moist situation.

Preserving. Preserve in F.A.A. and copper sulfate solution.

Liverworts

Marchantia. *Habitat.* This most widely studied form of any of the liverworts (Fig. 12.30*J*) may be found growing in several types of situations. It may be found growing luxuriantly about some bogs, swamps, deep shaded ravines, moist woods, etc. It occasionally occurs as a weed in greenhouses, in shaded lawns, and between bricks of old walks.

Collecting. Archegonial and antheridial branches occur usually in June. Gemmae cups are usually more abundant before the production of these branches. If clumps are kept in a greenhouse they will fruit usually in April in the central states.

Culturing. Marchantia may be grown successfully in Wardian cases (see Fig. 12.33) or in glass-covered cold frames out of doors. It will grow satisfactorily in a mixture of sand and garden soil or on ashes. It must be kept moist and shaded at all times.

Preserving. After washing thalli free of soil, preserve in F.A.A. and copper sulfate solution.

Conocephalum. *Habitat.* This liverwort (Fig. 12.30*L*) is usually of much commoner occurrence than *Marchantia.* It is commonly found on sandstone or limestone cliffs, talus slopes, and stream banks which are continually moist. It often covers whole cliff surfaces.

Collecting. The individual plants are often 2 to 5 in. long, ribbon shaped, bright green, and show forked branching habit. It is often mistaken for *Marchantia.* The surface is divided up into small hexagonal areas with a minute opening in the center.

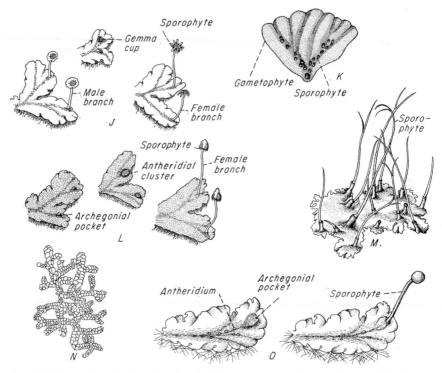

Fig. 12.30 (*cont.*) *J, Marchantia; K, Ricciocarpus; L, Conocephalum; M, Anthoceros; N, Porella; O, Pellia.*

Mature sporophytes are found about the first of April. They last for but a short time. The first week or 10 days of warm weather in spring are sufficient for development of the stalks bearing the sporophytes. The short wartlike antheridiophores are produced about midsummer. Archegonia may be found usually during July. Their location can be detected by a cone-shaped structure near a gametophyte tip.

Culturing. Conocephalum may be grown on very wet soil or sand in a Wardian case, or cold frame.

Preserving. Preserve in F.A.A. and copper sulfate solution.

Pellia. *Habitat.* This thalloid liverwort (Fig. 12.30*O*) may occur abundantly on sandstone cliffs which are continually moist. It grows luxuriantly in dripping water.

Collecting. Pellia fruits usually in early April and may be found occasionally in May. During the winter and spring the thalli are often a reddish-purple color. The plants are about 1 in. long and of a delicate structure. The antheridia and archegonia may be found in June and July. The antheridia form tiny pimples along the midribs of gametophytes. The archegonia are located in a little pocket near the anterior end of the thallus and are covered by a tiny flap of tissue. The sporangia of young sporophytes may be found protruding from these pockets in late August. The seta does not elongate until the following spring.

Culturing. Pellia may be kept alive for several weeks if placed on constantly wet sandstone or clay soil.

Preserving. Preserve in F.A.A. and copper sulfate solution.

Ricciocarpus. *Habitat.* It is frequently found in ponds and small lakes and on mud banks surrounding these situations. (Fig. 12.30*K*.)

Collecting. Only the floating form fruits. The aquatic form is roughly triangular to fan shaped, rounded on the anterior portion. A deep furrow marks the middle of each branch. The sporophytes occur embedded in the green thallus along these grooves. When mature they appear as small dark spots. Fruiting usually occurs in the latter part of May and June. A small dip net is useful in skimming these plants from water surfaces.

Culturing. Plants may be kept for several weeks in aquaria.

Preserving. Preserve in F.A.A. and copper sulfate solution.

Anthoceros. *Habit.* The hornwort (Fig. 12.30*M*) may be found on mud banks, marshy situations about springs, moist sandstone cliffs, etc. In the Illinois prairie region it is often abundant during moist seasons in clover fields.

Collecting. Fruiting seems to occur from midsummer to late in the fall. The sporophytes arise as green hornlike projections at right angles to the green semicircular thallus. They split open at the tips as they mature. The sex organs appear as pimplelike dots in the central portion of the thallus. The blue-green alga *Nostoc* may be found as an endophyte in the thalli. Bluish-green spots indicate locations of this form.

Culturing. Small clumps may be kept alive and growing for several weeks or months if kept on very wet soil in a covered glass container or Wardian case (see Fig. 12.33).

Preserving. Preserve in F.A.A. and copper sulfate solution.

Porella. *Habitat.* This is probably our commonest so-called leafy liverwort (Fig. 12.30*N*). It may be found on wooded north-facing slopes near the ground on the bases of elm trees, on flood plains commonly on the bases of elms and buckeyes, also on stones and even soil in shaded moist ravines.

Collecting. Plants with mature sporophytes are commonly found in September. The archegonial and antheridial branches may be found by midsummer.

Culturing. Plants may be kept alive for several weeks by keeping them in moist Wardian cases (Fig. 12.33).

Preserving. Preserve in F.A.A. and copper sulfate solution.

Pteridophytes

Polypodium virginianum (P. vulgare, common polypody). *Habitat.* This is a very common evergreen fern (Fig. 22.11) in sandstone regions and is occasionally found on soils underlain with shale. It often forms great clumps on cliff edges where it is shaded and moist.

Collecting. Fruiting starts about the first of July, and the sori remain in good condition throughout August. Complete specimens including roots, rhizomes, and leaves should be collected for laboratory work.

Culturing. Rhizomes may be collected during any season. When placed in moist sandy or peaty soil they will start growth within 10 days to 2 weeks. This provides an easy way to obtain coiled buds for study. If placed in a mixture of sand, peat, and garden loam in a Wardian case and kept moist, the plants mature and live for a long time.

Preserving. This form presses nicely, retaining a fairly good color if care has been used. If preserved material is desired the F.A.A. solution with copper sulfate is recommended.

Dryopteris (Aspidium, marginal shield fern). *Habitat.* This evergreen fern (Fig. 12.31*B*) is common in moist woods and deep shaded ravines. It often attains a height of 2 ft.

Collecting. The sori are borne close to the leaf margins. Fruiting occurs usually in August. The plants are usually too large to press and mount as whole specimens. Single fronds are satisfactory for most purposes.

Culturing. Small specimens may be grown in Wardian cases or terraria (see Fig. 12.33). They must be kept in shaded situations.

Preserving. Such forms are usually pressed and mounted on herbarium sheets or in special mounts. If desired in liquid, F.A.A. with copper sulfate solution is very satisfactory.

Asplenium (spleenworts). *Habitat.* These ferns (Fig. 12.31*A*) are common inhabitants of rocky woods and deep ravines. Some species occur on limestone and others on sandstone.

Collecting. Fruiting occurs about midsummer. The sori are oblong or linear.

Culturing. Spleenworts may be grown in woods soil if placed in a terrarium (see Fig. 12.33).

Preserving. Plants may be pressed or preserved in F.A.A. and copper sulfate solution.

Polystichum acrostichoides (Christmas fern). *Habitat.* A very common evergreen fern (Fig. 12.31*E*) which grows in shaded rocky woods, where the soil is commonly underlain with sandstone or shale.

Collecting. Often the plants are too large to be collected as whole specimens. The leaves are dark green and of a leathery appearance. Fruiting usually occurs in June. Sori occur on only a few leaflets near the tips of a few of the leaves. Often more than half of the total number of leaves are sterile. The shape of these is also somewhat different.

Culturing. Plants may be grown in a glass case in woods soil. Keep them in a shaded situation.

Preserving. Whole plants, or leaves, may be pressed or preserved in F.A.A. and copper sulfate solution.

Camptosorus rhizophyllus (walking fern). *Habitat.* The walking fern (Fig. 12.31*G*) may be found on moist cliffs and in deep shaded ravines. Occasionally it is found in alkaline bogs. It is commonest in limestone regions.

Collecting. This interesting species fruits about midsummer. The propagation by leaf-tip rooting is one of its most interesting features.

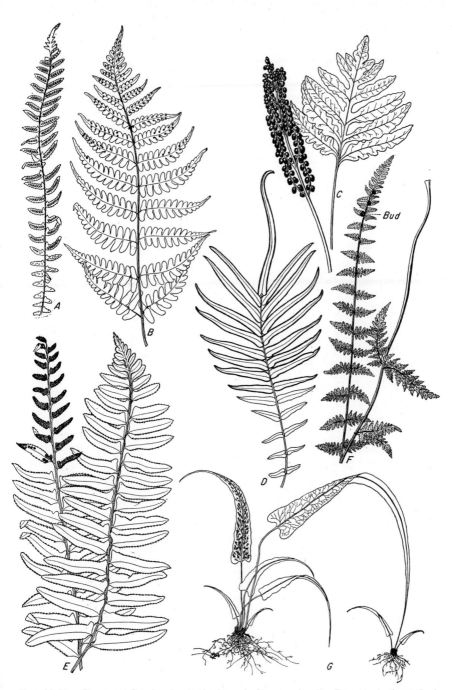

Fig. 12.31 Common ferns: *A, Asplenium* (spleenwort); *B, Dryopteris* (marginal shield fern); *C, Onoclea* (sensitive fern); *D, Pteris longifolia* (Florida brake fern); *E, Polystichum* (Christmas fern); *F, Cystopteris* (bladder fern) showing reproductive buds; *G, Camptosorus* (walking fern) showing vegetative multiplication.

225

Culturing. If soil from a woods is placed in a terrarium the plants may be kept growing for a long time. They must be kept shaded and very moist.

Preserving. Plants may be pressed and mounted as herbarium specimens, or they may be preserved well in F.A.A. and copper sulfate solution.

Cystopteris bulbifera (bladder fern). *Habitat.* This interesting fern (Fig. 12.31*F*) grows in crevices of moist, shaded limestone cliffs, and in alkaline bogs.

Collecting. This species is of particular interest because of the bladderlike buds on the leaves. These drop off, root, and grow into new plants. The "bladders" and sori may mature in July and August. Leaves with reproductive buds must be handled very carefully since the "bladders" are easily broken off.

Culturing. If plants are placed in calcareous soil and kept very moist in a terrarium, they may grow for at least several months.

Preserving. Fronds or complete plants may be pressed and mounted as herbarium specimens. It is likely that the buds will have to be glued to keep them in place. Material may be preserved in F.A.A. and copper sulfate solution.

Pteris longifolia (Florida brake fern). *Habitat.* This subtropical fern (Fig. 12.31*D*) is found in southern Florida on calcareous rocks. However, it is grown by florists as an ornamental; so it may be easily obtained.

Collecting. The plants fruit throughout the year, making it a valuable laboratory plant for a supply of spores and sporangia. As for all *Pteris* species, the sporangia are borne in a continuous line along edges of leaflets.

Culturing. This is one of the easiest ferns to grow in pots. It may be grown as ordinary house plants. However, it will grow more vigorously in a terrarium.

Preserving. May be pressed or preserved in the usual way as for other ferns. However, since it may be grown in the laboratory, fresh material may be on hand at all times.

Onoclea sensibilis (sensitive fern). *Habitat.* The sensitive fern (Fig. 12.31*C*) grows in swamps and near the edges of bogs. Occasionally it may be found in moist places along railway embankments and roadsides.

Collecting. There are two types of leaves or fronds—vegetative and spore-bearing. The fruiting fronds usually make their appearance in August. The leaflets of fruiting leaves are rolled up into roundish berrylike bodies with the sporangia inside. They are of a dark-brown color.

Preserving. May be pressed or preserved as for other ferns. The fruiting fronds may be stored dry for spores. They remain viable for at least two years.

Botrychium (grape fern). *Habitat.* The grape fern (Fig. 12.32*A, B, C*) is very common in moist woods and deep shaded ravines. *B. virginianum* fruits in May. *B. obliquum* and *B. dissectum* are common in moist beech-maple and swamp forests. They fruit in September and October.

Collecting. The complete plants should be taken. The roots are of a contractile type and are excellent for structure study. Mycorhiza are usually present. Gametophytes of this genus are subterranean and are dependent upon mycorhiza. Gametophytes with mature sex organs are difficult to locate. Collecting them requires painstaking digging and sifting of soil. Gametophytes with sporophytes attached are much more easily found since they may be detected by the green sporophyte. However, the juvenile leaf does not have quite the appearance of a mature leaf. It looks somewhat like a carrot seedling. The gametophyte is usually 2 to 4 in. below the soil; so it is necessary to use great care in removing it from the substrate. If an attempt is made to collect these, select a situation where fruiting plants are found rather abundantly. Then make a search on hands and knees. Young sporophytes attached to gametophytes may be found in September and October. A few specimens for a teaching collection are well worth the effort.

Preserving. The same procedures are used as for other ferns. The gametophyte stages should always be preserved in F.A.A. solution.

Nephrolepsis exaltata (Boston ferns). *Habitat.* The wild form (wild Boston or sword fern) grows abundantly in southern Florida hammocks. However, the cultivated Boston fern and many of its varieties may be found at any florist's establishment. The wide range of mutations in this species within the last 65 years have produced at least 240 varieties. This is one of the finest records of evolution in progress to be found among our commoner plants. Its propagation by runners (stolons) is an outstanding characteristic.

Collecting. The wild species can be easily collected in almost any fair-sized hammock in southern Florida. Many nurserymen in Florida can supply it. The common Boston fern, the oldest variety of the wild species, can be supplied by any florist. The following varieties also are commonly found on sale: *Wanamakerii, Whitmanii, Scottii, Piersonii, Compacta, Superba,* and numerous others. The spores of the Boston fern and its varieties are usually sterile.

Culturing. Ordinary pot culture methods commonly used for other house plants are satisfactory. In fact, these ferns, if given a cool shaded place, do better than most other plants usually found in homes. Rich garden soil placed in a clay pot with good drainage is all that is necessary. Keep the soil moist, but not soaked.

Azolla (floating fern). *Habitat.* This beautiful little fern (Fig. 12.32E) is occasionally found as far north as New York in ponds and lakes, but is rather rare in the Northern states. It is common in Florida. It is often sold as an aquarium species.

Collecting. For most teachers the easiest place to obtain this species is from a dealer in aquarium supplies. A small amount is inexpensive.

Culturing. It may be kept over winter in an aquarium. It will not grow vigorously during the winter, but a few plants held over will cover the surface of a small pool within a few weeks during the summer. The blue-green alga *Anabaena* usually may be found in the intercellular air spaces of the scalelike leaves.

Preserving. Preserve in F.A.A. solution with copper sulfate.

Salvinia. *Habitat.* This floating fern (Fig. 12.32F) is tropical, but it is commonly grown as an ornamental in pools and aquaria.

Collecting. Dealers in aquarium supplies and pond lilies usually can supply this form. It may produce spores any time from June until October.

Culturing. *Salvinia* can be kept satisfactorily over winter in an aquarium. It often does not grow vigorously during the winter, but the longer days of spring and summer quickly revive it. It is not hardy.

Preserving. Preserve in F.A.A. solution with copper sulfate.

Marsilea (clover fern). *Habitat.* This interesting fern (Fig. 12.32D) grows in shallow water of lakes and ponds. It may become very abundant in small ponds when introduced.

Collecting. The leaves of *Marsilea* appear somewhat like a four-leafed clover. It occurs rather rarely as a native plant. However, where it has been introduced as a pond plant it may occur abundantly. It is being used in lily pools and fish ponds. It is hardy, living over from rhizomes and roots. The fruiting structures (sporocarps) look superficially like seeds. These are borne on short stalks, often in pairs. It seems to fruit more abundantly in shallow water (2 to 4 in.). The sporocarps may be picked, dried, and stored the same as seeds. The spores inside will remain alive for several years. Fruiting usually occurs in August and September.

Culturing. A clump of plants placed in mud in an aquarium or lily pool may grow satisfactorily. The pool may be drained in winter, yet the plants will live over if there is a foot or so of mud. The leaves are likely to die in winter even if the plants are kept at room temperature in an aquarium.

If dry sporocarps are cut or cracked and placed in a dish of water, a gelatinous mass often in the form of a ring is extruded on which are located the sporangia. The microspores and megaspores will germinate in a day or so. The sperms can be demonstrated and, occasionally, fertilization can be observed. If the tiny gametophytes are kept in diffuse light and not allowed to dry out, young sporophytes will appear within 2 or 3 weeks. If these are transplanted to an aquarium they may mature.

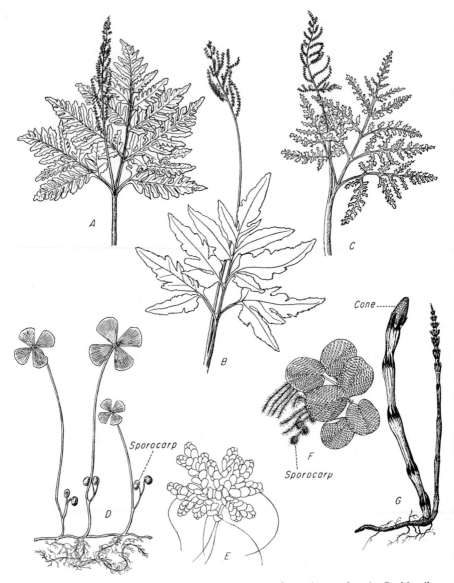

Fig. 12.32   Types of pteridophytes: *A, B, C, Botrychium* (grape ferns); *D, Marsilea* (clover-leaf fern); *E, Azolla; F, Salvinia; G, Equisetum* (horsetail).

Preserving. Complete plants may be pressed as herbarium specimens or preserved for demonstration purposes in F.A.A. and copper sulfate solution.

Fern Gametophytes (prothallia). *Habitat.* Fern gametophytes (Fig. 22.11) may be found wherever fern sporophytes are common. Moist cliff surfaces are usually most favorable from the standpoint of ease in locating them.

Collecting. Most of the gametophytes are roughly heart shaped, and large ones may be ¼ in. across. The young sporophytes grow up through the sinus or notch. Dissecting needles or a small-bladed knife are useful in freeing them from the substrate. They may be found throughout the growing season.

Culturing. Cultures of living fern gametophytes are much more satisfactory than gametophytes that are found in their natural habitat. To prepare these cultures, fern leaves with mature spores should be collected and placed in a shoe box and allowed to dry for 2 or 3 days. Cover to prevent entry of dust. Thoroughly clean a 3- to 4-in. clay flower pot and fill it with peat, sphagnum moss, pieces of newspaper, or paper toweling, moisten and pack tightly. Invert in a flower-pot saucer and fill with water. Set the pot and saucer on a piece of glass (small windowpane is satisfactory), invert a glass container such as a gallon battery jar over it (see Fig. 12.33). If a battery jar is not available 2-in. pots may be used and a large tumbler, beaker, or wide-mouthed fruit jar may be used to cover it. Shake the closed shoe box with the dry fern leaves to free the spores and jar them to one corner. With a clean, dry medicine dropper suck up some of the spores. Raise the battery jar enough to permit entrance of the medicine dropper and dust spores over the moist surface of the inverted pot. The beginner will likely do the dusting too thoroughly. The result will be a crowded growth of gametophytes with poor development. Experience will help in this matter. Place the glass-covered culture in a cool situation and reduced light such as that of a north window. Germination may occur within a few days. Antheridia may be found on young stages. The prothallia will mature in about 8 to 10 weeks. Place water in the saucer frequently. If Knop's solution is available, dilute about one-half and use this for watering purposes. It is impossible by this method to prevent entrance of mold spores and bacteria along with the fern spores. Often the mold and bacterial growth will subside in a week or so and the culture is not greatly injured. However, sometimes the whole culture is ruined. Since this is a common difficulty, it is well to set up three or four cultures at a time to be sure of a supply of gametophytes when needed. Sporophytes may begin to appear in about 8 weeks. Older cultures up to 6 months or more are likely to show them in abundance. When a root system is well developed on the young sporophytes, they may be transplanted to moist soil. They should be kept in a humid atmosphere until well established. To secure sperms, remove the glass cover from the culture and allow the prothallia to wilt but not dry out. Place a cluster of the young wilted gametophytes in a drop of water on a slide. If antheridia are present, sperms likely will be found swimming about within 2 or 3 min.

Another method, which is regarded by some as superior, is to grow the prothallia on Knop's or Beyerinck's agar. Make a 2 per cent agar solution in Knop's or Beyerinck's solution diluted one-half. Sterilize and place in sterile petri dishes, wide-mouthed bottles, test tubes, or ½-pt. mayonnaise jars. After the agar sets, sprinkle a few spores over the moist surface, using a medicine dropper as above. Plug the containers with cotton so that a diffusion of carbon dioxide and other gases can take place into the containers. Keep in a cool, shaded place. Development will occur in about the same time as for the pot method.

A simpler method is to place sifted litter (duff) from a pine woods in a terrarium. Moisten it thoroughly and sprinkle fern spores over the surface. Good gametophytes can be obtained in 4 to 6 weeks. They often become much larger

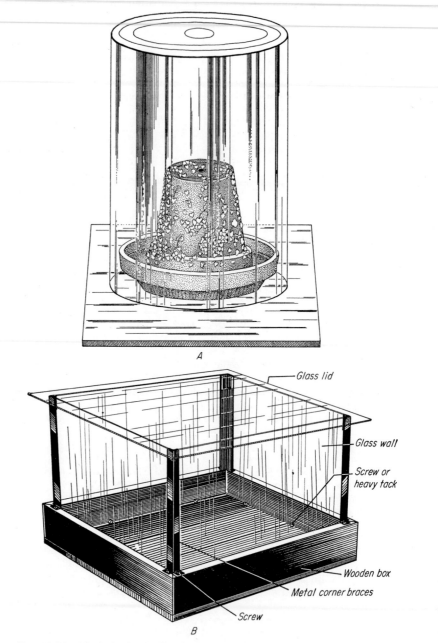

Fɪɢ. 12.33   Method of culturing fern gametophytes. Terrarium, or Wardian case.

than by the other methods mentioned. However, soil sticks to them and is rather difficult to remove.

Preserving. Fern prothallia may be preserved very successfully in F.A.A. solution. If a green color is desired add a small amount of copper sulfate. Prothallia preserved in this way may be used to make permanent entire mounts for microscopic examination.

Equisetum (horsetails). *Habitat.* The scouring rushes (Fig. 12.32*G*) or horsetails are usually found in moist habitats. However, field horsetail (*E. arvense*) is commonly found also along railway embankments and roadsides in gravel or cinders.

Collecting. The field horsetail (*E. arvense*) produces its fertile shoots in April. After these nongreen shoots appear aboveground the cones shed their spores within a few days. The vegetative (sterile) shoots make their appearance about the same time but do not reach their full development until May or June. Storage organs in the form of black tubers about ¼ in. in diameter may be found often on rhizomes of this species. *E. praeltum* bears its cones on green shoots. Their best development usually occurs in June. However, a few good cones may be found any time in the year, if a careful search is made.

Culturing. Cuttings of the vegetative shoots of the above two species will root readily in wet sand. They will grow successfully in pots if kept wet or in a wet terrarium.

For early stages of spore germination and gametophyte development fresh spores may be sown on a water surface. Complete development will occur on boiled sphagnum moss when placed in petri dishes, inoculated with fresh spores, kept moist and in the light of a north window. Several weeks is required for their development.

Preserving. Plants may be pressed as herbarium specimens or preserved in F.A.A. solution with copper sulfate.

Lycopodium (club mosses). *Habitat.* These primitive plants (Fig. 12.34*A, B, C*) are inhabitants of deep, shaded ravines, moist cliffs, and bogs. They are commoner in mountainous regions in pine, hemlock, and spruce forests.

Collecting. The shining club moss *L. lucidulum* produces its sporangia in leaf axils near the stem tips. Fruiting occurs from about midsummer until fall. Gemmae are also produced near stem tips during the same period. These break off easily and propagate rapidly. *L. complanatum, L. obscurum,* and *L. clavatum* usually produce cones in August and September.

Culturing. This group is very difficult to culture under artificial conditions. If success is to be attained, conditions closely approximating their native habitat must be produced. However, the gemmae of *Lycopodium lucidulum* will germinate and grow to considerable size in a pot of soil taken from where the parent plants were growing, if kept in a moist terrarium.

Preserving. Specimens press easily for the herbarium. They preserve well for dissection and museum purposes in F.A.A. and copper sulfate solution.

Selaginella. *Habitat.* Only three species are recorded as native of our temperate regions. Most species are tropical in their distribution. *S. apoda* (Fig. 12.34*F*) and *S. rupestris* are occasionally found in the central states region, sometimes in considerable abundance, and *S. apoda* in moist shaded situations usually on soil underlaid with sandstone. In West Virginia it may grow as a weed in lawns. *S. rupestris* is often found in much drier situations and often in crevices of sandstone rocks and in sand dunes. It occurs abundantly in the sand dunes of northern Indiana. In most instances the two or three tropical species used by florists are more readily available.

Collecting. The two native species mentioned above may be easily mistaken for mosses. *S. apoda* looks much like the moss *Mnium.* Their four-angled cones and leaf arrangement will readily distinguish them, however. *S. apoda* usually fruits in the early summer, while *S. rupestris* bears its cones in the late summer and fall.

S. kraussiana, S. emmeliana, and *S. lepidophylla* (Fig. 12.34D, E) are three species often used commercially. The first two are sold as potted plants. *S. lepidophylla* is sold under the name of "Resurrection plant." When the dried plants are placed in water they unroll and develop a bright-green color. It is native of western Texas and Arizona.

Culturing. Our native species *Selaginella apoda* may be transplanted successfully to a moist terrarium containing soil mixed with peat. Plants started in August will begin to produce cones in November if kept at room temperature or a little lower. Both *S. emmeliana* and *S. kraussiana* root deeply in moist sand. These may be potted in rich garden soil. They will grow vigorously if kept in reduced light and in a moist atmosphere. After the plants are well established, they may bear cones

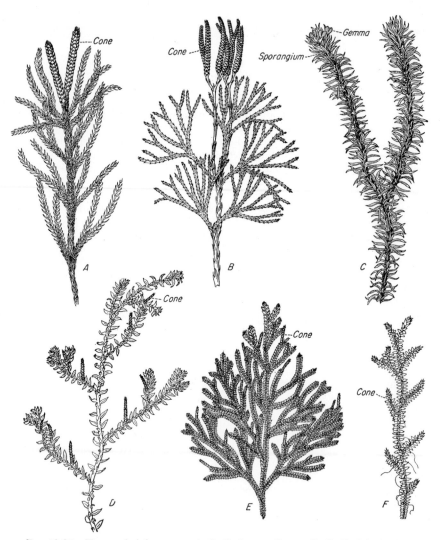

FIG. 12.34   Types of club mosses. *A, B, C, Lycopodiums; D, E, F, Selaginellas.*

throughout the year. They may begin to produce cones from cuttings within 8 to 10 weeks. Sporelings of *S. kraussiana* often may be collected from soil about the mature plant.

Preserving. Plants may be pressed or preserved in F.A.A. and copper sulfate solution.

Spermatophytes (Seed Plants)

Because of the vast number of seed plants available in any community, many of which are commonly known cultivated varieties, we will depart with a few exceptions from the foregoing scheme of discussion. Vegetative parts may be pressed or preserved in F.A.A. solution with a small quantity of copper sulfate added to retain a green color in the leaves. Fleshy fruits must be kept in preservative, while dry types may be stored in the dry condition. Suggestions for cone, fruit, seed, flower, leaf, stem, and root types will be made from commonly known and widely distributed plants wherever possible. The lists cannot be comprehensive, but are sufficient to meet the needs of most laboratories.

Gymnosperms (Conifers)

Pinus. The various species of pine (Fig. 12.35*A, B, C, D*) are usually selected as a common representative of this group. They are widely distributed and are found native and as ornamentals. The male cones mature and shed pollen about May 15. This varies with weather conditions and the region. The various developmental stages may be secured easily by collecting the male cones at earlier periods in the spring. Young female cones may be found on the same trees at the same time. The male cones last for about 2 weeks, then drop. It takes approximately 30 months for the female cones to mature to time of shedding seeds. Fertilization occurs in the female cones of Austrian pine when they are about 13 months old, or about June 1.

Stem and root material of the white pine (*Pinus strobus*) section well and show all the essential structures. Leaves of the Austrian pine are desirable for sectioning for structural studies. Seedling stages of pines may be obtained by planting seeds. However, trouble is experienced often with "damping-off" diseases. An aid in preventing this difficulty is to carry on the germination in a box or pot filled with sifted pine duff (decayed litter from pine wood) placed in a dry and well-lighted situation. If a native stand of pine is available, the seedling stages may be obtained easily in clearings during the summer.

Picea (spruce) (Fig. 12.35), *Tsuga* (hemlock), *Abies* (fir), *Taxodium* (cypress), *Thuja* (arborvitae), *Larix* (tamarack or larch), *Juniper* (juniper berry or red cedar), and *Taxus* (yew) may be used also for life history studies. All these produce their male cones about the same time as the pine, excepting arborvitae, juniper, and yew. The male cones of these three species mature during the late summer and fall, but the pollen is not shed until early spring. Female cones of all mature in the autumn of the first year. The juniper and yew are dioecious (sexes separated on different plants). The female cones of juniper are small, blue, fleshy, one-seeded berrylike structures. Yew female cones, when mature, are scarlet, fleshy, one-seeded structures with a hole in the lower end.

Ginkgo (maidenhair tree) (Fig. 12.35*O*) is occasionally planted as an ornamental shade tree. It has peculiar fan-shaped leaves. Staminate clusters are produced just as the leaves are unfolding. They last for about 10 days. Ovules may be found on separate trees at the same time but remain in good condition for early stage studies until after the leaves are fully developed. The fleshy seeds—often mistaken for fruits—mature in September. They are about the size and appearance of a small greengage plum.

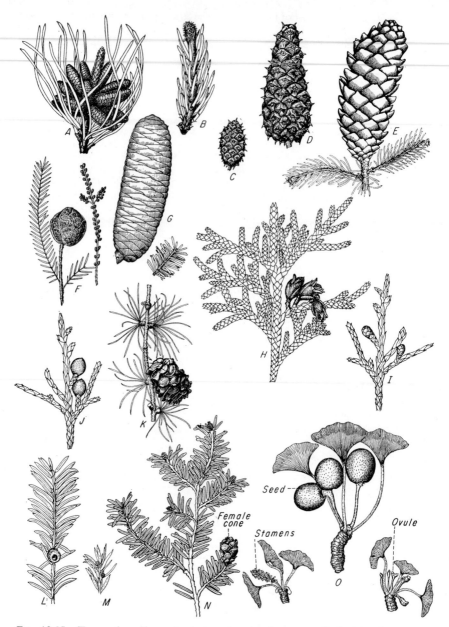

FIG. 12.35   Types of conifers: *A*, cluster of male pine cones; *B*, female pine cone at time of pollination; *C*, female pine cone at time of fertilization; *D*, mature female pine cone; *E*, mature female cone of spruce; *F*, mature female cone and male cones of cypress; *G*, mature female cone of fir; *H*, arborvitae with mature female cones; *I*, red cedar with male cones; *J*, mature female cones (juniper berries) of red cedar; *K*, mature female cone of tamarack; *L*, mature female cone of yew; *M*, male cones of yew; *N*, hemlock; *O*, *Ginkgo* or maidenhair tree, showing reproductive structures.

Zamia. This primitive group of gymnosperms is native to the tropics and sub-tropics. Two species are found rather abundantly in Florida. They grow successfully as potted plants just as ferns, except that they can withstand more drought and direct sunlight. Plants from the wild can be readily transplanted. However, they usually lose their leaves. It may take a year or more to get them started growing. After they are established as pot plants they will usually produce cones. The plants are dioecious. Nurseries in Florida often can supply them.

Angiosperms (Higher Seed Plants)

Classification systems dealing with seed plants are based on characteristics of leaves, buds, stems, roots, inflorescences, flowers, fruits, and seeds. The great variety of these organs has made an elaborate set of descriptive terms necessary. A collection of such organs carefully prepared to illustrate the various types is useful in enabling students to become acquainted with unfamiliar descriptive terms and aid them in making more accurate decisions. Leaves, inflorescences, and flowers may be pressed satisfactorily and displayed in mounts. Buds, stems, roots, and fleshy fruits are best preserved. Formalin–acetic acid–alcohol is an excellent preservative. Where it is desirable to retain green color add some copper sulfate. Many buds, stems, and roots may be dried and mounted if desired. However, if they are first preserved in F.A.A. solution containing 20 per cent glycerin for about 10 days, then rinsed in water and dried, they will not shrivel so badly. Dry fruits and seeds may be displayed in botanical mounts or in glass containers. From these same types of organs or groups of such organs, material is selected for morphological and physiological studies. The following list of types is given along with names of an example or examples and the general habitat in which they may be found. Effort has been made to select for these types, as far as possible, plants which are common and have a wide distribution.

SIMPLE LEAVES

Description	Plant name	Habitat
Cordate	*Cercis* (redbud)	Limestone regions along streams, often cultivated
Cuneate	*Portulaca retusa*	As a weed in waste places
Deltoid	*Populus deltoides* (cotton-wood)	Along streams, often cultivated
Lanceolate	*Plantago lanceolata* (English plantain)	Lawns
Linear	*Phleum* (timothy)	Cultivated and often a weed along roadsides
Lyrate	*Barbarea* (yellow spring cress)	Common spring weed in waste places
Oblanceolate	*Antennaria* (pussytoe)	Dry soil
Oblong	*Apocynum cannabinum* (Indian hemp)	Moist soil
Obovate	*Evonymus obovatus* (trailing strawberry bush)	Low shrub, in beech-maple woods
Orbicular	*Pyrola americana* (shinleaf)	Moist, shaded, acid soil
Ovate	*Fagus* (beech)	Common forest tree in central states region
Palmately three cleft	*Ambrosia trifida* (giant ragweed)	Common weed along streams and bottom lands

DESCRIPTION	PLANT NAME	HABITAT
Palmately three lobed	*Sassafras*	Common in woods on poor, acid soil
Palmately three parted	*Dentaria* (toothwort)	Moist woods
Pinnately divided	*Lycopersicon* (tomato)	Cultivated
Pinnately lobed	*Quercus alba* (white oak)	Common forest tree in central states
Reniform	*Asarum* (wild ginger)	Native of shaded, moist ravines
Runcinate	*Taraxacum* (dandelion)	Common weed in lawns and fields
Spatulate	*Mollugo* (carpetweed)	Common weed in waste places

Leaf Margins

Crenate	*Nepeta* (catnip)	Common weed about old dwellings
Dentate	*Eupatorium* (white snake-root)	Moist woods
Double serrate	*Ulmus* (elm)	Moist woods and cultivated
Entire	*Plantago* (plantain)	Common weed in lawns
Incised	*Acer saccharinum* (silver maple)	Cultivated and native of swamp forests
Pinnately lobed	*Quercus alba* (white oak)	Common forest tree in central states region
Palmately lobed	*Acer saccharum* (sugar maple)	Common tree of beech-maple forests
Serrate	*Prunus* (wild black cherry)	Common tree in moist woods, along line fences, etc.
Sinuate	*Rumex crispus* (curled or narrow dock)	Common weed in waste places
Undulate (repand)	*Amaranthus* (pigweed)	Common weed of gardens and fields

Leaf Tips and Bases

Acute base	*Apocynum* (Indian hemp)	Moist soil
Acute tip	*Aster* (New England aster)	Roadsides and abandoned areas
Acuminate base	*Amaranthus* (pigweed)	Common weed of gardens and fields
Acuminate tip	*Syringa* (lilac)	Cultivated
Aristate	*Agave* (century plant)	Cultivated
Auriculate	*Aster* (New England aster)	Roadsides and abandoned areas
Bristle pointed	*Quercus imbricaria* (shingle oak)	Dry to moist situations
Cordate	*Cercis* (redbud)	Usually near streams on limestone soil
Cuspidate	*Asclepias syrica* (common milkweed)	Waste places
Cuspidate	*Smilax herbacea* (carrion flower)	Waste places

DESCRIPTION	PLANT NAME	HABITAT
Emarginate	*Oxalis* (wood sorrel, leaflets)	Weed in gardens and fields
Hastate	*Rumex acetosella* (sheep sorrel)	Weed on acid soils
Mucronate	*Nemopanthus* (mountain holly)	Swamps
Oblique base	*Ulmus* (elm)	Tree of moist woods, and cultivated
Obtuse (tip)	*Evonymus obvatus* (trailing strawberry shrub)	Low shrub of beech-maple woods
Rounded base	*Asclepias syrica* (common milkweed)	Weed common in fields
Sagittate	*Sagittaria* (arrowhead)	Stream banks
Truncate tip	*Liriodendron* (tulip tree)	Tree of moist woods
Truncate base	*Platanus* (sycamore)	Stream banks

Leaf Attachment

Clasping	*Aster* (New England aster)	Roadsides and abandoned fields
Connate	*Eupatorium* (boneset)	Wet soil
Margined petiole	*Lactuca virosa* (wild lettuce)	Weed common in fields
Perfoliate	*Uvularia* (bellwort)	Moist, shaded ravines
Sessile	*Zinnia*	Cultivated

Venation Types

Dichotomously veined	*Ginkgo* (maidenhair tree, a gymnosperm)	Cultivated
Palmately veined	*Acer* (maple)	Cultivated or native of moist woods
Parallel veined	*Phleum* (timothy)	Cultivated
Pinnately veined	*Ulmus* (elm)	Cultivated or native of moist woods

Arrangement of Leaves

Alternate	*Ulmus* (elm)	Cultivated or native of moist woods
Opposite	*Acer* (maple)	Cultivated or native of moist woods
Whorled	*Catalpa*	Cultivated

COMPOUND LEAVES

Even pinnate	*Gleditsia* (honey locust)	Rich, moist woods
Odd pinnate	*Robinia* (black locust)	Cultivated and native in varied habitats
Palmate	*Aesculus* (buckeye)	Flood plains
Ternately decompound	*Aquilegia* (columbine)	Cultivated and native as crevice plant
Twice pinnate	*Gleditsia* (honey locust)	Rich, moist woods

BLADE, PETIOLE, AND STIPULE MODIFICATIONS OF
SIMPLE AND COMPOUND LEAVES

Leaf with blade, petiole, and large stipules, *Chaenomeles* (*Cydonia*, Japanese flowering quince).

Compound leaf with stipules and terminal leaflets as tendrils, *Pisum* (garden pea).

Simple leaf with stipules as tendrils, *Smilax* (green brier).

Petiole and rachis of compound leaf acting as a tendril, *Clematis*.

Stipules acting as bud scales, *Liriodendron* (tulip tree).

Stipules forming close, membranous sheaths (ocrea), *Fagopyrum* (buckwheat).

Stipules modified as spines, *Robinia* (black locust).

Leaf spines on some shoots, *Berberis vulgaris* (common barberry).

Phyllode development of petioles, some species of *Acacia*.

Leaves pitcherlike, insectiverous, *Sarracenia* (pitcher plant).

Leaf very glandular, insectiverous, *Drosera* (sundew).

Bladderlike leaves, insectiverous, *Utricularia* (bladderwort).

STEM TYPES

Woody, dicotyledonous. Basswood, cottonwood, fine for demonstrating stem abscission; tulip tree, papaw, apple, excellent for demonstrating grafting and budding; buckeye, oak, etc., blocks of oak wood showing transverse radial and tangential surfaces are very instructive in understanding the origin of grain in wood. A collection of commercial woods from any locality always attracts attention. Also, a cross section of a log 2 or 3 ft. in diameter smoothed off to bring out annual rings will be found valuable in a collection. Dates of important historical events which occurred during the life of the tree from which the log came may be placed on the proper rings. From such a cut sapwood and heartwood can be detected easily.

Woody, dicotyledonous vine (liana). *Menispermum* (moonseed).

Herbaceous, monocotyledonous. *Zea* (corn) and other grasses, *Lilium* (lily).

Herbaceous, dicotyledonous. *Helianthus* (sunflower), *Coleus*, *Melilotus* (sweet clover), *Pelargonium* (geranium), etc.

Rhizome, monocotyledonous. *Iris*, *Acorus* (calamus), *Poa* (Kentucky bluegrass).

Rhizome, dicotyledonous. *Menispermum* (moonseed), *Sambucus* (elderberry), *Asclepias* (milkweed), *Cirsium* (Canada thistle).

Phylloclade (leaflike stem). *Asparagus*.

Tubers. *Solanum* (potato), *Dahlia*, *Helianthus* (Jerusalem artichoke), *Dioscorea* (cinnamon vine).

Bulbs. *Allium* (onion), *Lilium* (lily), *Tulipa* (tulips), and *Hyacinthus* and *Camassia* (hyacinth) wild and cultivated.

Corms. *Arisaema* (jack-in-the-pulpit), *Gladiolus*, *Claytonia* (spring beauty).

Stolons. *Fragaria* (strawberry).

BUD TYPES AND CERTAIN STEM CHARACTERS

Terminal, large and with numerous scales, alternate laterals. *Hickoria* (hickory).

Terminal, large and with numerous scales, opposite laterals, solid cylindrical pith. *Aesculus* (buckeye) or (horse chestnut).

Terminal, large and with few scales, alternate laterals and accessory or superposed buds, chambered pith. *Juglans* (black walnut, butternut).

Terminal bud abscised, prominent axillary, alternate laterals. *Ulmus* (elm), *Tilia* (basswood).

Buds clustered at stem tip, pith solid and star shaped. *Quercus* (oak).

Buds stalked. *Alnus* (alder).

Buds with single bud scale. *Salix* (willow).

Terminal bud covered with stipule. *Philodendron, Ficus* (fig), *Liriodendron* (tulip tree), and *Magnolia*.

Naked buds. *Helianthus* (sunflower), *Coleus, Bryophyllum, Hedera* (English ivy), *Ipomoea* (sweet potato).

Adventitious buds. *Bryophyllum* leaf, *Taraxacum* (dandelion) root. Each of these should be placed in moist sand for 3 or 4 weeks to bring about their development.

Fruit spurs, flower buds, and scars left by fruit abscission. *Pyrus* (apple, pear).

Mixed buds (buds which contain both leaves and flowers). Obtained best in spring as the buds are opening, *Aesculus* (buckeye), *Hickoria* (hickory).

Flower buds (buds which contain only flower parts). Obtained best in spring as buds are opening. *Ulmus* (elm), *Acer* (silver maple).

Leaf buds (buds which contain only leaves). Obtained best when buds open in the spring. *Ulmus* (elm), *Fagus* (beech).

Buds to demonstrate transition from bud scales to true leaves. Should be collected in spring as buds are opening. *Acer negundo* (box elder).

ROOT TYPES

Fleshy taproot. *Taraxacum* (dandelion).

Fibrous roots. *Helianthus* (sunflower), *Zea* (corn), etc.

Aerial roots. *Parthenocissus* (Virginia creeper), *Hedera* (English ivy).

Adventitious roots. *Tulipa* (tulip), *Allium* (onion), *Hyacinthus* (hyacinth). Obtained after the bulbs have been in moist sand for about 10 days, also roots on stem cuttings.

FLOWER TYPES

Hypogynous. *Lilium* (lily), *Tulipa* (tulip), *Yucca*, etc.

Perigynous. *Pyrus* (apple, pear).

Epigynous. *Oenothera* (evening primrose).

FLOWER FORMS

Actinomorphic (regular). *Tulipa* (tulip), *Yucca, Lilium* (lily), etc.

Zygomorphic (irregular). *Tropaeolum* (nasturtium), *Delphinium, Lathyrus* (sweet pea), etc.

COROLLA FORMS

Chloripetalous (separate petals). *Tulipa* (tulip), *Lilium* (lily), *Yucca*, etc.

Sympetalous (petals united). *Ipomoea* (morning glory), *Convolvulus* (bindweed).

INFLORESCENCE TYPES

Catkin. *Alnus* (alder), *Populus* (cottonwood), *Salix* (willow), etc.

Corymb. *Pyrus* (apple, pear), *Crataegus* (hawthorn), *Saponaria* (bouncing Bet).

Cyathium. *Euphorbia* (snow-on-the-mountain, poinsettia).

Cyme. *Ptelea* (hop tree), *Tilia* (linden).

Head. *Helianthus* (sunflower), *Taraxacum* (dandelion), *Aster, Cephalanthus* (buttonbush), etc.

Panicle. *Poa* (Kentucky bluegrass), *Zea* (corn) tassels, *Catalpa*.

Raceme. *Robinia* (black locust), *Cimicifuga, Prunus* (wild black cherry).

Solitary, axillary. *Convolvulus* (bindweed), *Ipomoea* (morning glory).

Solitary, terminal. *Erythronium* (dogtooth violet), *Trillium,* etc.

Umbel. *Daucus* (wild carrot), *Zizia* (early meadow parsnip), *Pastinaca* (wild parsnip).

TYPES OF SEXUAL EXPRESSION

Bisporangiate (both stamens and carpels in same flower). *Lilium* (lily), *Yucca, Tulipa* (tulip), *Pyrus* (apple).

Monoecious (staminate flowers and carpellate flowers on same plant). *Zea* (corn), *Begonia, Cucurbita* (cucumber).

Dioecious (staminate flowers and carpellate flowers on separate plants). *Salix* (willow), *Morus* (mulberry), *Fraxinus* (ash), *Acer* (box elder), *Arisaema* (jack-in-the-pulpit), *Cannabis* (hemp), *Humulus* (Japanese hop), *Asparagus*.

FRUIT TYPES

Simple Fruit

Achene. *Helianthus* (sunflower), *Fagopyrum* (buckwheat).

Berry. *Vitis* (grape), *Ribes* (gooseberry), *Lycopersicon* (tomato), etc.

Capsule. *Yucca, Iris, Tulipa* (tulip), *Papaver* (poppy).

Caryopsis. *Triticum* (wheat), *Zea* (corn).

Drupe. *Prunus* (cherry, plum, peach), *Olea* (olive).

Key. *Fraxinus* (ash), *Ulmus* (elm), *Ptelea* (hop tree).

Nut. *Juglans* (walnut), *Hickoria* (hickory nut), *Castanea* (chestnut), *Quercus* (oak), *Cocos* (coconut), etc.

Pepo (form of berry). *Cucurbita* (cucumber, squash, gourd, pumpkin).

Pod. *Phaseolus* (bean), *Gleditsia* (honey locust), *Robinia* (black locust).

Pome. *Pyrus* (apple, pear), *Cydonia* (quince).

Samara. *Acer* (maple).

Aggregate fruits. *Rubus* (blackberry, raspberry), *Liriodendron* (tulip tree), *Magnolia, Fragaria* (strawberry), etc.

Multiple fruits. *Morus* (mulberry), *Maclura* (Osage orange), *Ananas* (pineapple).

PARASITIC SEED PLANTS

Leptamnium (Epifagus, beechdrops). *Habitat.* This plant (Fig. 12.36*B*) follows the distribution of beech (*Fagus*). It is parasitic upon beech roots and occurs apparently on no other species. It is often abundant in moist woods during the latter part of August until frost.

Collecting. This species is without chlorophyll, and often has a color ranging from a yellow to light reddish purple. The plant is without leaves except for scattered scales. It usually grows 3 to 12 in. in height and whenever found it is under or near beech trees. If the plants are carefully removed from the soil, attachments to small beech roots may be found.

Preserving. These, like several other parasitic seed plants, often darken in preservative. This may be prevented by first treating the specimens in a preservative such as formalin-acetic acid-alcohol containing 30 per cent sodium hypochlorite (sold for laundry purposes as Clorox, Dag, Chlorite, Oxol, etc.). After treating overnight in this solution transfer to regular F.A.A. solution. Plants also may be pressed as herbarium specimens.

Comandra (bastard toadflax). *Habitat.* This species usually occurs on dry soil, especially on hilltops among blueberries and other heath plants, and also in alkaline bogs. It is known to be at least partially parasitic upon over 50 different species of plants.

Collecting. Plants may be found in flower in May and June. Plants range in height from 6 to 15 in. There are numerous light green leaves, and the plant may be branched. The plant has an underground rhizome with roots which may be found attached to the host roots. Usually there is quite an enlargement at the point of attachment. Plants showing this attachment should be collected.

Preserving. The plants wilt very quickly after removal from the host. If dry herbarium specimens are to be prepared, they should be placed between blotters of a plant press immediately for best results. If they are to be preserved they should be kept moist and placed in the preservative as soon as possible. F.A.A. solution with a little copper sulfate is recommended.

Orobanche ramosa (broomrape). *Habitat.* This very interesting and sometimes destructive parasite is occasionally found in southern Ohio, Kentucky, and Illinois. It grows parasitically on giant ragweed, hemp, tobacco, and tomato.

Collecting. Broomrape is straw colored, the flowers yellow or light blue, and the stem is usually branched. The above-named host plants become yellowish when parasitized. Mature plants may be found in July and August.

Preserving. F.A.A. solution is recommended.

Corallorhiza (coral root). *Habitat.* Five species (Fig. 12.36E) are found in northeastern United States and Canada. They occur in woods on acid soils. Pine and hemlock forests are favorable places for this form.

Collecting. Flowering occurs from midsummer until frost. The plants are without chlorophyll, and range in height from 3 to 12 in. The rhizomes are corallike and without roots. These rhizomes are particularly fine for demonstrating internal mycorrhiza.

Preserving. F.A.A. solution is recommended.

Cuscuta (dodder). *Habitat.* The several species (Fig. 12.36C) have a wide distribution in the United States. One species is particularly destructive to red clover. Some other species are very common along streams; willow, *Dianthera,* cocklebur, etc., being common hosts.

Collecting. Tangled masses of the yellowish to orange-colored threadlike stems often may be detected at considerable distances. Chlorophyll is present in early seedling stages and in the unripened fruits. The vestigial leaves are small, scalelike structures. Stems may penetrate the host plant wherever they touch. Flowering of the parasite occurs from midsummer until frost.

Preserving. F.A.A. solution is recommended.

Monotropa (Indian pipe). *Habitat.* This species (Fig. 12.36A) is found in moist woods throughout North America.

Collecting. Indian pipe is one of the most conspicuous parasitic seed plants because of its lack of pigmentation in the fresh condition, usually appearing perfectly white. It is dependent upon fungal mycelia for its food supply.

Preserving. When placed in common preservatives, the plants change from a white to a purplish-black color. To prevent this they may be placed first in formalin–acetic acid–alcohol solution containing 30 per cent sodium hypochlorite (sold for laundry purposes under name of Clorox, Dag, Chlorite, Oxol, etc.) for about 24 hr., then transferred to straight F.A.A. solution.

Phoradendron (mistletoe). *Habitat.* This plant is the most widely known of all the partially parasitic seed plants. It may be found on several deciduous tree species including elm, hickory, and ash. It often grows on branches high above the ground. It ranges from New Jersey southward along the coast from the Ohio River southward and westward to Missouri. Usually it is limited to moist situations.

Collecting. This plant has numerous green leaves and has branched stems that often form clumps which can be recognized in tree tops at a distance of 100 yd. or more when the tree leaves are off. Specimens should show connection with the host.

Preserving. Small branches with flowers or fruits may be preserved in F.A.A. solution. A small amount of copper sulfate in the solution will give the specimen a green color.

FIG. 12.36 Types of parasitic seed plants: *A*, Indian pipe; *B*, beech drops; *C*, dodder; *D*, squawroot; *E*, coral root.

Conopholis (squawroot). *Habitat.* This species (Fig. 12.36D) is distributed from Maine to Florida. It is found usually under oaks.

Collecting. The plant is yellowish brown in color, 4 to 6 in. in height, and the stem is about ¾ in. in diameter.

Preserving. F.A.A. solution is recommended.

Plants Suitable for Aquaria

Anacharis, Philotria (Elodea). *Habitat.* This common aquarium plant is occasionally found in ponds and lakes and sluggish streams.

Collecting. This plant grows as a submerged aquatic which roots in mud in shallow water. The leaves are sessile and occur in whorls or opposite on the stem. It dries out very rapidly when removed from water. If one expects to bring it in alive it should be placed in a closed container or wrapped in moist paper. It is widely used by aquarium dealers who sometimes sell it as "water moss." In regions where the plant is not found as a native, one may resort to dealers as a source of supply. The dealers usually supply a giant species. The native species is about one-third as large. The smaller species is best for protoplasmic streaming.

Culturing. Place pieces of *Elodea* stem—roots are not necessary—in an aquarium in a well-lighted situation. It does best when the aquarium contains a layer of mud or sand in the bottom. If conditions are right roots will develop within a week or 10 days. It is very easily grown. It is an excellent oxygenator for aquaria and useful about a laboratory in numerous other ways.

Vallisneria (eel grass). *Habitat.* This is widely distributed but often rare locally. It may be found in shallow lakes, ponds, and sluggish streams.

Collecting. The plant has long linear leaves and grows as a submerged aquatic. It propagates rapidly from runners. The entire plant should be collected, transported in water, or wrapped in moist paper to prevent drying out, and placed in an aquarium or pool where it is to be grown. It is often sold by aquarium dealers.

Culturing. The aquarium or pool in which it is to be grown must contain a layer of sand or mud. The roots should be buried in the substrate. A partially shaded situation is preferred for its best growth. However, it is one of the best aquatics for withstanding extremely reduced light. Two or three plants will soon densely populate an ordinary aquarium if good conditions are provided. This plant is an excellent oxygenator for aquaria.

Sagittaria sinensis. *Habitat.* This is a southern plant, found occasionally in Florida in ponds and slow streams.

Collecting. This plant looks very much like eel grass but usually is somewhat larger. Aquarium dealers often can supply it.

Culturing. Same as for eel grass. It is a good oxygenator.

Cabomba. *Habitat.* Chiefly a southern plant found in great abundance in Florida and Texas. However, it has become established in some ponds and streams in Ohio.

Collecting. The leaves are highly dissected and occur opposite or whorled on the stems. It is a submerged aquatic. Aquarium dealers can supply it.

Culturing. Same as for *Elodea* or eel grass.

Myriophyllum (water milfoil). *Habitat.* The genus *Myriophyllum* is made up of numerous species which are widely distributed. It occurs in ponds, lakes, and slow streams.

Collecting. Most species of *Myriophyllum* are submerged aquatics. In some the tips come to the surface of the water and float, and in some species become emersed spikes. Submerged leaves are finely divided and occur opposite or whorled on the stems. These plants must be transplanted in a very moist condition. It is often available at aquarium supply stores.

Culturing. Same as for eel grass.

Ceratophyllum (hornwort). *Habitat.* The hornwort is common in slow streams, ponds, and shallow lakes.

Collecting. This plant occurs as a submerged aquatic and sometimes in such quantities that rowboats cannot penetrate the masses readily. It looks very much like *Myriophyllum,* but the leaves are very stiff and have a roughened surface.

Culturing. Same as for eel grass. It cannot be eaten by the ordinary aquarium fish species and is a fair oxygenator.

Ludwigia (false loosestrife, water purslane). *Habitat. L. palustris* and *L. glandulosa* are probably the most commonly used forms in aquaria. The genus occurs in ditches or mud flats.

Collecting. If light is bright enough the leaves develop a reddish tinge. Use the same precautions in collecting and transporting as for eel grass. It is supplied by aquarium dealers.

Culturing. Same as for eel grass.

Lemna and Spriodela (duckweeds). *Habitat.* The duckweeds are widely distributed. They may be found in almost any pond and along the margins of lakes.

Collecting. These plants are floating forms with roots dangling into the water. The flat fronds ("leaves") are lobed and often not more than ⅛ in. across. They live over drought periods on mud.

Culturing. They will grow and propagate rapidly in most aquaria. They are not of much value as oxygenators.

Wolffia. *Habitat.* This plant, the smallest and simplest of all seed plants, is widely distributed. It occurs in ponds and lakes.

Collecting. The plant is globular in shape, rootless, leafless, and about the size of a pinhead. It occurs as a floater or may be submerged.

Culturing. It will grow successfully in any well-lighted aquarium. It is often exhibited in the laboratory because of its unique characteristics.

Preparation of Herbarium Specimens

Value of a Herbarium. A collection of dried and preserved plants has an important role in any course in botany and in several other biological sciences. If living specimens are not obtainable, dried or otherwise preserved ones are next in value as teaching material. Although they are not nearly so desirable as living forms, they are far better than "just reading about them." Such a collection enables a teacher to exhibit groups of closely related species, genera, and families which are usually impossible to get together in the living state at the time they are needed. The collection becomes invaluable for purposes of comparison when new specimens are being identified. It enables one to see ranges of variation within a group, flowers, fruits, seeds, bulbs, tubers, rhizomes, etc., which may not be found on a single specimen at a given time. This is very important when studying the more difficult genera. Knowledge of the flora of the world today would be sparse indeed if man had been forced to describe plants entirely from living specimens. Most descriptions and keys have been made from dry herbarium material. The more important characters are not transitory and are often nicely retained by a pressed specimen. Those characters which do disappear upon drying and which are useful for identification may be recorded on the specimen's label. Examples of such characters are fragrance of flowers, flower and leaf color, time of day during which the flowers open (only a few species), duration of the flowers, mechanical dehiscence (as in *Impatiens* and *Oxalis*), sensitive stamens, stigmas, and leaves, stinging properties of hairs as some of the nettles, poisonous properties, etc.

A herbarium is of very great value for comparison when attempt is being made to identify a given species. After careful identification has been made a specimen becomes valuable for future consultation. The dried specimens may be allowed to accumulate and later sent to specialists for verification. Often it is not feasible to do this with living material. If a student is concerned with the flora of a certain region, there is no substitute for a herbarium collection as a record. The older these collections, the more valuable they become. This is becoming increasingly true with the disappearance of our virgin vegetation. Any student of native plants can cite numerous instances of extinction of species. Local people often ask a teacher to identify plants for them. This is an important service to a community which should not be overlooked or shunned. Such contributions will gain friends for the teacher and his school, which is something to consider. The herbarium will be of great aid in such instances.

To the layman accustomed to looking at the external beauty of plants, at the commercial value, yield of fruits and seeds, etc., a dried dead specimen may appear worthless. However, the specialists can readily glean the diagnostic characters from such remains. Some common criticisms of herbaria are that "the dried plants are uninteresting to look at," "they look different from the living specimens," "they do not have a neat appearance, too often looking like so much hay." All these objections cannot be fully removed, but much can be done to the average collection to reduce these comments to a minimum.

Methods, Materials, and Apparatus. Materials and apparatus required for preparing good herbarium specimens need not be expensive. A heavy knife of some kind is necessary for excavating specimens, cutting off branches, thorns, etc. A corn knife, such as used by farmers for harvesting corn fodder, has been highly recommended. This, however, increases the collector's burden and may present a belligerent appearance to some landowners. It is an ideal instrument for aiding the collector through briar patches and jungle vegetation, digging, and cutting. Many botanists use a specially made tin can called a "vasculum" for carrying freshly collected specimens from the field. This prevents excessive wilting during short periods. It has the disadvantage that the specimens become tangled, the leaves and inflorescences may be bent in unnatural positions, and flowers often close or abscise. For these reasons it is better to take a plant press directly into the field and to place the specimens in it as they are collected. This is more burdensome than a vasculum and takes more time from field work, so is too often neglected. Presses of various types may be obtained from botanical supply companies or may be inexpensively made by nailing a few slats together, forming a latticework. The press consists of two of these lattice pieces, each having the dimension of 12 by 18 in. Twelve pieces ¼ by 1 by 12 in. and ten pieces ¼ by 1 by 18 in. are needed for the two press halves. Two boards of approximately the slat-press dimensions may be substituted. As soon after collection as possible place the plant specimen between the halves of a folded newspaper. Along with it should be placed data concerning the plant. The newspaper folder is then inserted between the blotter driers (11½ by 16½ in.). The most satisfactory ones are specially made and sold by botanical supply companies. Ordinary blotters as used for office and study tables are usually too thin. Corrugated cardboard ventilators of same size as blotters (11½ by 16½ in.) are used advantageously above and below the two driers. Pieces of corrugated cardboard cut from packing boxes may be substituted if new material is not available. Other specimens similarly prepared may be stacked on top of the first, the sequence being drier, newspaper specimen folder, drier, ventilator, drier, etc. A stack of specimens 2 to 3 ft. in height may be satisfactorily cared for in this way. If blotters are not available extra newspapers may be substituted more or less successfully. Some professional collectors use corrugated aluminum sheets as ventilators instead of the cardboard. Sheets of aluminum 29 by 64 cm. and 0.15 mm. thick are about the right size. These are corrugated by grooves 4 mm. deep and 13 mm. wide across the sheets. The finished sheet is then about the size of an ordinary blotter drier. These are excellent but much more expensive than the corrugated cardboard. Some of the better collectors use a layer of absorbent cotton on each side of the specimen folder next to the blotters. These layers aid in the desiccation process and tend to prevent crushing of the more delicate parts. After the specimens are prepared as above they are placed in a press and pressure is applied while drying.

The simplest method of applying pressure to a press is by means of a heavy weight such as a large stone, box of small stones, or heavy cloth sack filled with sand or gravel. Any one of these is laid on top of the specimen pile, above the upper half of the lattice or board press. Many collectors prefer this, since there is constant pressure applied as the drying process occurs. The disadvantages are as follows: the weights are difficult for some to handle; if a large pile is to be treated, the weight is difficult to keep in place, may slip and cause the stack to buckle and fall; if some specimens have large irregular parts, the pressure may not be equally applied; these weights are impossible to use if artificial drying is attempted. Others prefer to strap the press together. The straps are placed a few inches in from the ends and around the press. By pulling the straps, tight pressure is applied to the pile of specimens. After the drying proceeds for a time the straps will become loose, because of loss of moisture from the plants. These should be tightened enough to take up the extra space between the driers. Care should be taken not to apply much pressure after the plants are thoroughly dried; otherwise much breakage of the more delicate parts will likely occur. The strap press is the most satisfactory form to carry into the field.

A clamp press is very convenient when large numbers of specimens are to be taken and dried at a single time. The same slat press is used as in the other methods. Pressure is easily applied by means of the tail or crank nuts. These can be obtained at hardware stores dealing in farmers' supplies. They are commonly used on endgate rods of truck beds. There is some danger of applying too much pressure, causing crushing of specimens. Apply just enough pressure to hold the pile of specimens solidly together. A little experience will teach one how much pressure may be applied without danger.

The drying process may be allowed to take place at ordinary prevailing temperatures. The driers between the specimens must be changed (moist blotters exchanged for dry ones) every day or so for at least the first week and over a longer period if the specimens are succulent or the atmosphere is moist. Too often this uninteresting task is neglected, and as a result the specimens mold. Probably 90 per cent of the specimens collected by amateurs are lost in this way. When the blotters, paper folders, and specimens feel dry to the touch, the plants may be removed safely.

Much time may be saved and the collector freed of a tiresome task by drying over a source of artificial heat. The simplest method is to place the press filled with specimens edgewise on a framework over a heater. The frame is wrapped with a sheet of canvas to direct currents of hot air up through the ventilators between the blotters. A more satisfactory structure than a framework support and canvas is a rectangular flue box made of galvanized iron sheets, with dimensions of about 16 by 30 by 36 in. This arrangement reduces the fire hazard. The metal sheets may be fastened by stove bolts to four 36-in. angle-iron posts, with a 6-in. space left at the bottom for the source of heat. This enables one to take the box apart and pack it compactly for traveling. A $\frac{5}{8}$-in. flange made by bending the upper and lower edges of the sheet iron at right angles gives the box more strength.

Several sources of heat have proved satisfactory. For long trips when the collector is camping in the field, an ordinary gasoline camp stove serves very well. If this is not available two ordinary no. 2 kerosene lanterns may be used successfully. An open wood fire is not very satisfactory since it is difficult to regulate the heat. A still better arrangement for the laboratory or home is a gas hot plate. If gas is not available, electric heaters of various styles may be used. These have an advantage over all others in that there is less danger of fire. An electric heater of the concave reflector type, hot plate, or toaster may be used. A special electric heater may be made easily from two heater cones such as are used in the above concave reflector heaters. These can be obtained from electric supply stores for about 50 cents each. Two ordinary wall or ceiling light sockets are attached to an asbestos-covered board. The heater cones are inserted just as light bulbs are. Heater cones may be replaced with 100- to 150-watt light bulbs if desired. If bulbs are used, four to six may be necessary, hooked up in series to give sufficient heat for rapid drying. A heating unit made of one or two infrared heat-lamp bulbs makes an even better heat source. The light bulb and infrared heat-lamp units are the most fireproof of all artificial heat sources. However, fires have been caused by them.

When an artificial-heat source is used in drying, no change of blotters is necessary and the specimens may be thoroughly dried in 8 to 20 hr., depending upon the type of specimen and the amount of heat available. With a gas hot plate thorough drying may be obtained in 8 to 10 hr. for the average specimen. Care should be taken not to use too high temperatures, as discoloring of specimens and scorching of driers may occur. In all cases where heaters are used, pressure should not be removed permanently from the pack until it has cooled down to air temperature. If the hot specimens are exposed to cool air, they will absorb sufficient moisture in a short time from the atmosphere to cause them to curl. If left in the press and allowed to cool under pressure, the moisture is absorbed evenly and no curling occurs. Much better color is retained in specimens dried rapidly than by the slow method of ordinary air temperature.

In instances where but a few specimens are collected and must be dried hurriedly, an electric flatiron (such as used for laundry purposes) may be used as the source of heat and pressure applied by hand during the pressing-drying process. The specimen is placed between three to four blotters (newspapers may be substituted) and "ironed" for about 20 min. or until thoroughly dried. Fine specimens are quite possible by this method.

After drying, the specimens should be mounted on standard herbarium sheets (11½ by 16½ in.). A good grade of white paper treated to prevent yellowing with age is preferable. This paper may be obtained from botanical supply companies. If the specimens are small, enough may be placed on a sheet to fill it, but do not crowd. This is often advantageous for purposes of comparison. The range of fluctuation (nonheritable variation) is very great in many species. A series of these variations make a collection more valuable. A series of specimens ranging from seedlings to flowering and fruiting stages are valuable in determination of many species. Most seedlings are quite unlike the more mature plant. Flowering stalks and other parts near the inflorescence may vary greatly from the ordinary vegetative portions. Rosettes and basal leaves often exhibit important diagnostic characters. Occasionally these are not present when the plant is flowering or fruiting. Collect all these parts with each specimen whenever possible.

Unusual variations in an individual of a given species should always be collected. These may prove of great interest as time goes by. When collecting dioecious plants, both staminate and carpellate specimens should be obtained, and in monoecious forms branches with both kinds of flowers are necessary.

It is not practical to collect entire specimens when they range over 18 to 24 in. in height. Bending of stems at an angle, not a curve, is permissible as many times as is necessary to get the specimen to fit a herbarium sheet. To keep the bulk at a minimum the "angled" stems should not overlap. Prevent overlapping of leaves as far as possible. Some should be turned upside down to show underside characters. Flowers always should be placed on top of leaves or by themselves. Connections between parasitic plants and their hosts should never be severed. For large herbaceous and woody plants only a small portion can be satisfactorily mounted on a herbarium sheet. Select only portions showing important characteristics. Thick, succulent plants such as most of the *Crassula* are improved by treating in boiling salt water for 30 to 60 sec. before pressing. Flowers of these forms should not be immersed in the hot water. Such treatment helps to retain the leaves and normal green color. For cactus species the thicker ones should be split longitudinally and the mucilaginous inner parts scooped out and the "shells" dried as usual. Plants should be placed in the driers in such a way as to give the pressed specimen as nearly a normal appearance as possible. Thorny specimens may be placed between boards and pressed down with considerable weight. This prevents tearing of folders and driers.

In some plants, such as hemlock and spruce, leaves shatter from stems soon after specimens are pressed and dried. This can be prevented by first preserving the specimens in the following solution for about 10 days or until the leaves show a normal green color:

Glycerin	100 cc.
Grain alcohol (50 per cent)	100 cc.
Formalin (commercial)	5 cc.
Glacial acetic acid	5 cc.
Copper sulfate	1 lump, size of match head

Soon after the specimens are placed in this solution a yellowish-green color appears in the leaves. However, after a week to 10 days a more or less normal green color appears which is permanent. The specimens are then carefully rinsed in water, placed between driers, and pressed in the usual way. Leaves and green color are retained by this treatment.

Dried specimens should be poisoned before attaching to the herbarium sheets. This may be done very satisfactorily with 70 per cent grain alcohol saturated with mercuric chloride. If the pure grain alcohol is not available, rubbing alcohol may be substituted. The poison solution is applied with a paint brush. Spraying is dangerous since the operator may inhale some of the mist. The alcohol will evaporate readily and leave a slight deposit of mercuric chloride. Any insect pest eating this will be killed. Paradichlorobenzene (dichloricide of the druggists) crystals also may be used successfully to destroy and prevent entrance of insects if the collection is kept in a tight case. However, it evaporates rather rapidly, so has to be replaced frequently.

Specimens must be attached to a herbarium sheet in some way. Gluing is resorted to by some. Glue may be "painted" directly on the undersurface of the specimen, then carefully laid and gently pressed in position on the herbarium sheet. Another procedure is to "paint" the glue on a glass plate (piece of window glass), then lay the specimen in it. If removed immediately enough glue adheres to the plant to stick it to the mounting sheet. Cellulose acetate dissolved in acetone may be substituted for the glue. It dries more rapidly (3 to 5 min.) than glue and does not discolor specimens nor the mounting paper. Gluing of any type prevents easy removal of the specimen from the sheet. For this reason many collectors prefer to use gummed tape of some description. The transparent gummed tape used in book repair presents a neat appearance and will last a long time. A cloth tape has a longer life. Wherever large stems are bent over to fit on a sheet, extra reinforcement is necessary to hold them in place. In any instance the specimen should be placed on a sheet in such a way as to give it as normal an appearance as possible.

A permanent label should be attached to the herbarium sheet. This is placed in the lower right-hand corner. This should contain the scientific name of the plant, common name or names, notes concerning the habitat, location (town, county, state), date of collection, and the collector's name. None of these should be neglected if one intends to build up a standard collection. Each sheet should be placed in a genus cover. This consists of heavy manila folder paper cut and folded once to the dimensions of 11½ by 17 in. In large collections, specimens of a single species are kept in separate folders. Not more than the species of a single genus should be placed in a single folder. In large collections, these folders are numbered in the lower left-hand corner along with the generic and specific names. Specimen numbers are also given on the herbarium sheets in many herbaria. A catalogue and notes of the whole collection may then be kept conveniently. The specimens may be stored successfully in carefully constructed homemade cases or in cabinets obtainable from botanical supply houses.

Specimens which are to be used frequently for classwork should be mounted more sturdily than on a herbarium sheet. The Riker or other special mounts sold by biological supply houses are more or less ideal for this purpose. However, in most instances these are rather expensive. An inexpensive mount may be made as follows: Secure a heavy piece of cardboard of the desired dimensions of the mount to be made. This will serve as a back. Place a layer of absorbent cotton on the upper side of the cardboard. On this place the pressed specimen. Cover the specimen with cellophane, celluloid, or glass (thin glass used by photographers is preferable). Fasten the transparent cover to the cardboard by means of gummed tape. A wooden mount (Fig. 12.13) may be made of strips especially manufactured and supplied by the A. I. Root Company, Medina, Ohio. These are ready cut and grooved for folding into rectangular frames. The grooves where the strips are to be bent must be moistened with water for 2 to 3 min. before folding. A few drops of glue, two glass covers (old photographic negatives are ideal), absorbent cotton to fill the mount, and some binding tape for fastening all parts together are all the necessary materials. The largest size (5 by 7 in.) may be finished for 25 to 30 cents each. Specimens may be mounted on both the upper and lower surfaces if desired.

Moss and Liverwort Herbaria. Mosses and liverworts usually are not pressed, but preserved dry as they are collected. They may be stored in envelopes or folders made from 8½- by 11-in. sheets of paper. The collector's data are placed on the outside. Average specimens of a hundred or more species may be kept in a single shoe box or similar container. Insects do not infest the Bryophytes nearly to the extent that they do seed plants. When collecting these forms, sporophytes should be included whenever possible. Most critical characters for identification are found in the sporophytes. Dried mosses and the "leafy" liverworts will regain almost normal appearance when soaked in water for 3 to 4 min. A moss gametophyte with sporophyte attached in some of the larger species such as *Polytrichum, Catharinea, Mnium, Dicranum,* and *Funaria* make excellent material for demonstrating alternation of generations. They may be mounted easily and effectively in any of the special demonstration mounts described above. If the plants are unisexual, archegonial and antheridial plants should be collected and appear with the sporophyte-bearing gametophyte. Archegonia and antheridia can be dissected from dry material after soaking. The same is true for species bearing gemmae. A few genera such as *Pogonatum, Buxbaumia,* etc., have persistent protonema. A piece of soil along with mature gametophytes and sporophytes should be collected. The feltlike protonema of *Pogonatum* will retain its green color for a long time after drying. If slightly pressed while drying it makes fine demonstration material for such groups.

Fungi Herbaria

Slime Molds. These primitive fungi may be collected and dried successfully in their fruiting forms. They are delicate organisms, requiring considerable protection. Pieces of wood or other substrate to which they are attached should be carefully removed and glued in cardboard boxes. Key characters are based largely upon dried material. Collectors data should accompany these the same as for any other organism.

Fungi Causing Plant Diseases. Many forms pathogenic for plants may be successfully dried and kept for long periods. Such collections are of great value because of the economic importance of this group. If the diseases appear on leaves, these organs should be pressed. If the infections occur on stems, roots, or small dry fruits, they may be dried without pressing. Fleshy fruits should be kept in preservative. A few common examples of disease-causing forms which may be successfully dried are as follows: black stem rust of wheat, loose smut of oat and wheat, bunt smut of wheat, corn smut, apple scab, downy mildew of grape, powdery mildew of lilac and willow, bean rust, corn rust, white-pine blister rust, chestnut blight, white blister on mustards, and most potato and tomato diseases.

Fleshy Fungi. Many taxonomists prefer dried specimens of mushrooms, including "toadstools" and the hard and leathery forms causing wood decay, to liquid-preserved forms because spore color is often better maintained. The drying may be carefully done near a source of heat. The specimens are then stored in boxes.

Lichens. Usually lichens are so closely associated with the substrate upon which they are growing that they are difficult to remove from the foreign material. Ordinarily a piece of the substrate, bark, wood, leaf, stone, or soil is taken with the specimen. Specimens with reproductive bodies should be selected if possible. The collection may be stored in paper folders or in boxes.

Algal Collections

The fresh-water algae are not preserved very successfully as dried specimens. Exceptions to this rule are such genera as *Tribonema, Oedogonium, Cladophora,* and *Pithophora.* Many marine forms make excellent specimens when dried. Place them in a shallow pan of water and float the specimens on to a sheet of mounting paper. As the paper is slowly lifted the various parts may be spread out in as nearly a normal position as possible. Carefully drain off excess water and cover the specimen with a piece of cheesecloth. Place the specimen sheet between driers as for seed plants. A series of these may be piled together and dried at the same time. Some pressure is applied to the stack while drying in order to flatten out the specimen sheets. After they are thoroughly dry the cheesecloth may be removed and the specimen adheres to the mounting paper. They may be stored then as for herbarium sheets of ferns or seed plants. A collection of marine algae (seaweeds) is of particular value to the inland teacher.

Leaves and Leaf Prints

Preparation of Leaf Skeletons. A knowledge of the vascular system of leaves is important in understanding food and water relationships of such organs. Leaf skeletons of some forms can be made easily. They are valuable in illustrating such vascular systems both macroscopically and microscopically. Leaves of English ivy and the creeping rubber plant (*Ficus pumila*) are particularly suitable in the preparation of skeletons. English ivy is a widely used, hardy perennial evergreen vine. The creeping rubber plant is hardy only in the Southern states but is commonly grown in greenhouses and conservatories. Select soft-textured small to medium-sized leaves. Dry them in an oven or over a hot-air register. When they are dry place them in a jar of water, set in a warm dark place, and allow decay to take place for 4 to 6 weeks. To insure the presence of rotting bacteria, add a tablespoonful of decaying organic matter. To speed up growth of the bacteria add a teaspoonful of a garden fertilizer and about the same amount of sugar to each gallon of water.

After this treatment pour off the solution and with fresh water carefully rinse the leaves to remove disagreeable odors and loosen decayed portions. The remainder of the work has to be done with individual leaves. Place a leaf on a piece of window glass. Direct a small slowly flowing stream of water on the leaf and peel away remaining strips of epidermis. The stream of water will remove most of the decayed mesophyll. Some spots may have to be lightly brushed with a camel's-hair brush. If carefully done nothing but the vascular system will remain. The skeleton may be gently floated to another glass plate where it is allowed to dry. After drying it may be loosened from the drying plate with a razor blade or penknife and mounted. The leaves may be mounted between two blank lantern slides, the edges being bound with lantern-slide binder or other tape. The skeleton may be projected on a screen just as the subject of any ordinary lantern slide. Such mounts are serviceable also for macroscopic observations. If microscope slide mounts are desired, a small square or disk may be cut out of a skeleton, stained in safranin or Bismarck brown and mounted in balsam, using the same general technic as for a stem or root section.

Leaf Prints. An interesting collection of leaf prints may be made from leaves of trees, shrubs, and even herbaceous plants. The following methods are recommended.

Printer's Ink Method. Obtain a small can of printer's ink from a print shop. Dilute a small portion of this with boiled linseed oil until it will brush out as paint. Coat the leaf surface with ink, placing the painted surface next to a newspaper or on mimeograph paper. Place another paper on top and press with a flatiron (used for laundry purposes) or a photographic squeege roller. This will remove the excess ink. Transfer the leaf to the sheet which is to be saved. Locate on paper so that the transferred print will make a balanced page. Mimeograph paper is best, since it will absorb the ink readily. Cover the leaf as before and press. Several trials will probably be necessary to get the leaf characters transferred properly. Too much or too little ink must be avoided for the best work. Labels are best typewritten since fountain-pen ink will run on the softer qualities of mimeograph paper.

Cabon-paper Prints. Place the leaf to be printed on a piece of newspaper. Lay a piece of carbon paper such as is used in typewriting, with the carbon surface next to the leaf. Cover with another piece of newspaper. Press it thoroughly with a hot electric flatiron such as is used in laundry work. Remove the leaf and place the carboned surface next to the sheet which is to receive the print. Place a newspaper on top and carefully press again with the hot electric iron. Some practice will soon enable one to make good prints.

Blueprints of Leaves. Obtain a photographic printing frame. Cut a piece of blueprint paper to fit the frame. Place the leaf to be printed next to the glass and cover with the blueprint paper, coated surface next to the leaf. The above procedure must be carried on in a darkened room. Then expose to bright light for 3 to 4 min. Return the frame to the dark room, remove the exposed paper and rinse in cold water. Dry the print thoroughly between blotters. Mount the print just as a photograph.

Plaster Casts of Leaves. Obtain a shallow cardboard box somewhat larger than the leaf to be cast. Prepare enough plaster of paris to make a plaque of the desired thickness. Mix the plaster of paris with enough water to make it the consistency of cream. Do not stir. Place the leaf in a central position in the box and pour the plaster of paris over it. Place some sort of hanger in the end opposite the tip of the leaf. Allow to stand for 24 hr. or longer. After setting remove from the box and carefully tear the leaf away. The leaf impression may be painted with water colors.

Specimens of Autumn-leaf Coloration. Obtain moist specimens of various colored leaves. Pour some powdered resin on a newspaper. Place a hot electric flatiron in the resin until it melts. Pass the iron over the leaf. This will give the leaf a varnishlike coat of resin. Such treatment will preserve the colors for some time. The flatiron may be cleaned by rubbing with newspaper while it is still hot or by scraping with a safety-razor blade.

REFERENCES

Vertebrates—General

1. Benton, A. H., and W. E. Werner: *Principles of Field Biology and Ecology,* McGraw-Hill Book Company, Inc., New York, 1958. An excellent coverage of the basic principles of field biology.

2. Berrill, N. J.: *Origin of Vertebrates,* Oxford University Press, New York, 1955.

3. Jordan, A. T.: "Field Trip in Biology," *Texas Outlook,* **25**:43, August, 1941.

4. Pratt, H. S.: *Manual of Land and Freshwater Vertebrates,* McGraw-Hill Book Company, Inc., Blakiston Division, New York, 1935.

5. Worden, A. N.: *The Care and Management of Laboratory Animals,* The Williams & Wilkins Company, Baltimore, 1948.

Mammals

6. American Museum of Natural History: *Capture and Preservation of Small Animals for Study,* Guide Leaflet 61.

7. Anthony, H. E.: *Mammals of America,* Garden City Books, New York, 1942.

8. Baynes, E. H.: "Mankind's Best Friend, the Dog," *Nat. Geograph. Mag.,* **35**:185–280, March, 1919.

9. Booth, E. S.: *How to Know the Mammals,* William C. Brown Company, Dubuque, Iowa, 1950.

10. Burt, W. H., and R. P. Grossenheider: *Field Guide to the Mammals,* Houghton Mifflin Company, Boston, 1952.

11. Cahalane, V. H.: *Mammals of North America,* The Macmillan Company, New York, 1957.

12. Comstock, Anna Botsford: *The Pet Book,* Comstock Publishing Associates, Inc., Ithaca, N.Y., 1930.

13. Lloyd, Freeman: "Man's Oldest Ally, the Dog," *Natl. Geograph. Mag.,* **69**:247–274, February, 1936. Excellent illustrations.

14. Lloyd, Freeman: "Field Dogs in Action," *Natl. Geograph. Mag.,* **71**:85–108, January, 1937. Excellent illustrations.

15. Moore, C. B.: *Ways of Mammals,* The Ronald Press Company, New York, 1953.

16. Nelson, E. W.: "The Larger North American Mammals," *Natl. Geograph. Mag.,* **30**:385–412, November, 1916.

17. Palmer, E. L.: *Palmer's Fieldbook of Mammals,* E. P. Dutton & Company, New York, 1957.

18. Scott, W. B.: *History of Land Mammals in the Western Hemisphere,* The Macmillan Company, New York, 1938. Classification, evolutionary history.

19. Yerkes, Robert M., and Ada W. Yerkes: *The Great Apes,* Yale University Press, New Haven, Conn., 1929. Studies on gibbon, orangutan, chimpanzee, gorilla; structure, habits, distribution, intelligence, etc. Extremely readable with excellent illustrations.

Birds

20. Allen, R. P.: *On the Trail of Vanishing Birds,* McGraw-Hill Book Company, Inc., New York, 1957.
21. American Audubon Society: Audubon Bird Cards, National Association of Audubon Societies, New York. These cards have a variety of uses in teaching.
22. Barton, R.: *How to Watch Birds,* McGraw-Hill Book Company, Inc., New York, 1955.
23. Brand, A. R.: Bird Song Foundation. "American Bird Song Records," Cornell University Press, Ithaca, N.Y. 2 vols., two 12-inch 33⅓ rpm records. Descriptive circular on request.
24. Campbell, B.: *Bird Watching for Beginners,* Penguin Books, Inc., Baltimore, Md., 1952.
25. Chapman, F. M.: *Handbook of Birds of Eastern North America,* Appleton-Century-Crofts, Inc., New York, 1932. A standard work on birds.
26. Fisher, J., and R. M. Lockley: *Sea Birds,* Houghton-Mifflin Company, Boston, 1954.
27. Headstrom, R.: *Birds' Nests: A Field Guide,* Ives Washburn, Inc., New York, 1949.
28. Lockley, R. M.: *Bird Ringing,* John de Graff, Inc., New York, 1953. A good book on bird banding.
29. *National Geographic Magazine,* 1932 to 1937. Nearly every volume has one or more articles on birds. Colored plates and descriptions. Also bound separately in two volumes. Excellent and inexpensive.
30. National Geographic Society: *The Book of Birds,* 3d ed., Washington, D.C., 1927.
31. Pearson, T. Gilbert: *Birds of America,* Garden City Publishing Company, Garden City, N.Y., 1936. Includes everything concerning birds and bird life and habits. Plates by Louis A. Fuertes excellent, with many supplementary photographs.
32. Peterson, R. T.: *Field Guide to the Birds,* rev. ed., Houghton-Mifflin Company, Boston, 1947.
33. Vogt, William: *Audubon's the Birds of America,* The Macmillan Company, New York, 1937. Contains 500 beautifully prepared color plates and a concise descriptive text.

Reptiles and Amphibia

34. Cochran, Doris M.: *Frogs and Toads, Natl. Geograph. Mag.,* **61**:629–654, May, 1932. Good illustrations and interesting reading.
35. Ditmars, R. L.: *Reptiles of the World,* The Macmillan Company, New York, 1935.
36. Kauffeld, C.: *Snakes and Snake Hunting,* Doubleday & Company, Inc., Garden City, N.Y., 1957.
37. New York W.P.A. Writers: *Reptiles and Amphibians,* Albert Whitman & Co., Chicago, 1939.
38. Pope, C. H.: *Reptile World,* Alfred A. Knopf, Inc., New York, 1955.
39. Wright, Anna A., and Albert H. Wright: *Handbook of Frogs and Toads,* Comstock Publishing Associates, Inc., Ithaca, N.Y., 1933. Composed of descriptions and excellent photographic illustrations.
40. Zim, H. S., and H. M. Smith: *Reptiles and Amphibians,* Simon and Shuster, Inc., New York, 1953.

Fishes

41. DuFresne, F.: *Alaska's Animals and Fishes,* Binfords & Mort, Portland, Ore., 1955.

42. Eddy, S.: *How to Know the Freshwater Fishes,* William C. Brown Company, Dubuque, Iowa, 1957.

43. Fremling, C.: "New Biological Frontier; Your Favorite Lake," *Am. Biol. Teacher,* **16**:48–49, February, 1954.

44. Hausman, L. A.: *Beginner's Guide to Fresh-water Life,* G. P. Putnam's Sons, New York, 1950.

45. Jordan, D. S.: *American Food and Game Fishes,* Doubleday & Company, Inc., New York, 1937.

46. Mellen, I. M.: *Wonder World of Fishes,* Dodd, Mead and Company, New York, 1951.

47. National Geographic Society: *The Book of Fishes,* Washington, D.C., 1924. Beautifully illustrated in colors.

48. Pels, G. J.: *Care of Water Pets,* Thomas Y. Crowell Company, New York, 1955. Includes finding, feeding, and breeding of pets and setting up aquarium.

49. Schultz, L. P., and E. M. Stern: *Ways of Fishes,* D. Van Nostrand Company, Inc., Princeton, N.J., 1948.

50. Smith, Hugh M.: "Goldfish and Their Cultivation in America," *Natl. Geograph. Mag.,* **46**:375–400, October, 1924. Good illustrations and descriptions.

51. Trautman, Milton B.: *The Fishes of Ohio,* The Ohio State University Press, Columbus, Ohio, 1957.

Invertebrates—Other Than Arthropods

52. Bullough, W. S.: *Practical Zoological Illustrations—Invertebrates,* St. Martins Press, Inc., New York, 1950.

53. General Biological Supply House: *Rearing Protozoan Cultures.* 8200 South Hoyne Ave., Chicago, Ill. This second edition of the protozoan booklet offers detailed and dependable directions for culturing and rearing the commonly studied laboratory protozoans, such as amoeba, paramecium, euglena, and others.

54. Jahn, T. L.: *How to Know the Protozoa,* William C. Brown Company, Dubuque, Iowa, 1949.

55. Kirby, H.: *Materials and Methods in the Study of Protozoa,* University of California Press, Berkeley, Calif., 1950.

56. Kudo, Richard R.: *Handbook of Protozoology,* Charles C Thomas, Publisher, Springfield, Ill., 1954. Advanced character. Reference work.

57. Needham, J. G., et al.: *Culture Methods for Invertebrate Animals,* Comstock Publishing Associates, Inc., Ithaca, N.Y., 1937.

58. Needham, J. G.: *The Life of Inland Waters,* Comstock Publishing Associates, Inc., Ithaca, N.Y., 1937.

59. Pelczar, M. J., and R. D. Reid: *Microbiology,* McGraw-Hill Book Company, Inc., New York, 1958.

60. Pennak, R. W.: *Fresh-water Invertebrates of the United States,* The Ronald Press Company, New York, 1953.

61. Pratt, H. S.: *Manual of the Common Invertebrate Animals Exclusive of Insects,* McGraw-Hill Book Company, Inc., New York, 1953.

62. Sonneborn, T. M.: "Protozoa in the General Biology or Zoology Course," *Am. Biol. Teacher,* **17**:187–190, October, 1955.

63. Woodruff, H. B.: "Microorganisms in Everyday Life," *Am. Biol. Teacher,* **18**:153–155, April, 1956.

Arthropods

64. Alexander, R., and D. J. Borror: "Songs of Insects," Cornell University Press, Ithaca, N.Y. One 33⅓ rpm 12-inch record. Descriptive circular on request.

65. Borror, D. J., and D. M. DeLong: *Introduction to Study of Insects,* Holt, Rinehart and Winston, Inc., New York, 1954.

66. Comstock, J. H.: *How to Know the Butterflies.* Comstock Publishing Associates, Inc., Ithaca, N.Y. 1936. 150 species and varieties described. 312 illustrations and 49 text figures.

67. Comstock, J. H.: *The Spider Book,* Doubleday & Company, Garden City, N.Y., 1944. Revised by Gertsch.

68. Curran, C. H.: *Insects in Your Life,* Sheridan House, Inc., New York, 1951.

69. Ewing, Henry E.: "Afield with the Spiders," *Natl. Geograph. Mag.,* **64**:163–211, August, 1933.

70. Harman, I.: *Collecting Butterflies and Moths,* John de Graff, Inc., New York, 1950.

71. Hercules Powder Co.: *Handbook of the Insect World,* Wilmington, Del., 1956. Pictures and description of important insects, named to order.

72. Herrick, Glenn W.: *Insect Enemies of Shade Trees,* Comstock Publishing Associates, Inc., Ithaca, N.Y., 1935.

73. Holland, W. J.: *The Butterfly Book,* Doubleday & Company, Garden City, N.Y., 1942.

74. Jaques, H. E.: *How to Know the Insects,* William C. Brown Company, Dubuque, Iowa, 1941. A good section on the collection and preservation of insects.

75. Lutz, F. E.: *Field Book of Insects,* 3d rev. ed., G. P. Putnam's Sons, New York, 1935.

76. Needham, J. G.: *Culture Methods for Invertebrate Animals,* Comstock Publishing Associates, Inc., Ithaca, N.Y., 1937.

77. Peairs, L. M., and R. H. Davidson: *Insect Pests of Farm, Garden and Orchard,* 5th ed., John Wiley & Sons, Inc., New York, 1956.

78. Pieper, M. B.: "Preparation of Insect Mounts," *Am. Biol. Teacher,* **16**:69, March, 1954.

79. Sandars, E.: *Insect Book for the Pocket,* Oxford University Press, New York, 1946.

80. Snyder, Thomas E.: *Our Enemy the Termite.* Comstock Publishing Associates, Inc., Ithaca, N.Y., 1935.

81. Stefferud, Alfred (ed.): *Insects, The Yearbook of Agriculture,* 1952, U.S. Department of Agriculture. For sale by Superintendent of Documents, Washington, 25, D.C.

82. Swain, R. B.: *Insect Guide,* Doubleday & Company, Inc., Garden City, N.Y., 1948.

83. Williams, C. B.: "Butterfly Travelers," *Natl. Geograph. Mag.,* **71**:568–585, May, 1937.

Ferns and Seed Plants

84. Baerg, Harry: *How to Know the Western Trees,* William C. Brown Company, Dubuque, Iowa, 1955.

85. Bailey, V. L., and H. Edwards: *Guide to the Flowering Plants and Ferns of the Western National Parks,* University of Notre Dame Press, Notre Dame, Ind., 1955.

86. Beaty, J. Y.: *Luther Burbank: Plant Magician,* Julian Messner, Inc., New York, 1943.

87. Beaty, J. Y.: *Plant Breeding for Everyone,* Charles T. Branford Company, Newton Centre, Mass., 1954.

88. Benson, Lyman: *Plant Classification,* D. C. Heath & Company, Boston, Mass., 1957.

89. Blackburn, B. C.: *Trees and Shrubs in Eastern North America,* Oxford University Press, New York, 1952.

90. Bowers, N. A.: *Cone-bearing Trees of the Pacific Coast,* Pacific Books, Palo Alto, Calif., 1942.

91. Braun, E. Lucy: *The Woody Plants of Ohio,* The Ohio State University Press, Columbus, Ohio, 1961.

92. Brooks, F. T.: *Plant Diseases,* 2d ed., Oxford University Press, New York, 1953. Illustrated.

93. Bucholtz, K. P. et al.: "Weeds of the North Central States," *Univ. Ill. Agr. Exp. Sta., North Central Regional Publ.* 36, *Circ.* 718, 1954.

94. Canada Department of Resources and Development, Forestry Branch: "Native Trees of Canada," Canada Department of Research and Development, *Bull.* 61, 4th ed., 1949.

95. Cobb, Boughton: *A Field Guide to the Ferns and Their Related Families,* Houghton Mifflin Company, Boston, Mass., 1956.

96. Core, Earl L.: *Plant Taxonomy,* Prentice-Hall, Inc., Englewood Cliffs, N.J., 1955.

97. Dudley, R. H.: *Our American Trees,* Thomas Y. Crowell Company, New York, 1956. Illustrated.

98. Durand, H.: *Field Book of Common Ferns,* G. P. Putnam's Sons, New York, 1949. Illustrated.

99. Felt, E. P.: *Plant Galls and Gall Makers,* Comstock Publishing Associates, Inc., Ithaca, N.Y., 1940. 2,000 varieties of plant galls in North America.

100. Fernald, M. L.: *Gray's Manual of Botany,* 8th ed., American Book Company, New York, 1950.

101. Fischer, H. F., and G. F. Harshbarger: *Flower Family Album,* University of Minnesota Press, Minneapolis, Minn., 1941. Illustrated.

102. Free, M.: *Plant Propagation in Pictures,* Doubleday & Company, Inc., Garden City, N.Y., 1957.

103. Frye, T. C.: *Ferns of the Northwest,* Binfords & Mort, Portland, Ore., 1934.

104. Fuller, H. J., and Oswald Tippo: *College Botany,* Holt, Rinehart and Winston, New York, 1955.

105. Gleason, H. A.: *The New Britton and Brown Illustrated Flora of the Northeastern United States and Adjacent Canada,* New York Botanical Garden, N.Y., 1952.

106. Gilkey, H. M.: *Handbook of Northwest Flowering Plants,* 2d ed., Binford & Mort, Portland, Ore., 1951. Illustrated.

107. Gottscho, S. H.: *Wildflowers: How to Know and Enjoy Them,* Dodd, Mead & Company, New York, 1951. Illustrated.

108. Graf, Alfred Byrd: *"Exotica" Pictorial Cyclopedia of Indoor Plants,* 2d ed., Julius Roehrs Co., Rutherford, N.J., 1959. This is a fabulous contribution with over 4,000 photographic illustrations, descriptions, origin and care of exotic ornamental plants. It provides pictorial identification of most plants used as ornamentals.

109. Graves, A. H.: *Illustrated Guide to Trees and Shrubs,* Harper & Brothers, New York, 1956. Includes a "Winter Key" plus 300 drawings.

110. Green, C. H.: *Trees of the South,* University of North Carolina Press, Chapel Hill, N.C., 1939.

111. Hadfield, M.: *Everyman's Wild Flowers and Trees,* British Book Centre, New York, 1956. Illustrated. Seed plants of Great Britain.

112. Hadfield, M.: *British Trees,* British Book Centre, New York, 1957.

113. Harlow, W. M.: *Trees of the Eastern United States and Canada,* McGraw-Hill Book Company, Inc., New York, 1942.

114. Harrar, E. S., and J. G. Harrar: *Guide to Southern Trees,* McGraw-Hill Book Company, Inc., New York, 1946.

115. Hitchcock, A. S.: *Manual of the Grasses of the United States,* U.S. Department of Agriculture, Miscellaneous Publication 200, 1935.

116. Hottes, A. C.: *Book of Trees,* 3d ed., Dodd, Mead & Company, New York, 1952. Illustrated.

117. Jaeger, E. C.: *Desert Wild Flowers,* Stanford University Press, Stanford, Calif., 1940.

118. Jaques, H. E.: *How to Know the Trees,* rev. ed., William C. Brown Company, Dubuque, Iowa, 1946.

119. Johnson, M. P., and M. Free: *Concise Encyclopedia of Favorite Flowers,* Doubleday & Company, Inc., Garden City, N.Y. 1953. Illustrated.

120. Johnston, E. C. F.: *Macmillan Wild Flower Book,* The Macmillan Company, New York, 1954. 425 flowers pictured and 500 described.

121. Lane, F. C.: *Story of Trees,* Doubleday & Company, Inc., Garden City, N.Y., 1952. Illustrated.

122. Matthews, F. A.: *Field Book of American Wild Flowers,* rev. ed., Norman Taylor (ed.), G. P. Putnam's Sons, New York, 1955.

123. Marx, D. S.: *Learn the Trees from Leaf Prints,* Botanic Publishing Co., Cincinnati, Ohio, 1945.

124. Moldenke, Harold N.: *American Wild Flowers,* D. Van Nostrand Company, Inc., Princeton, N.J., 1949. How to know and appreciate our wild flowers. Illustrated with 88 photographs in full color and 67 in gravure.

125. Muenscher, W. C.: *Poisonous Plants of the United States,* rev. ed., The Macmillan Company, New York, 1939. Illustrated.

126. Muenscher, W. C.: *Aquatic Plants of the United States,* Comstock Publishing Associates, Inc., Ithaca, N.Y., 1944.

127. Palmer, E. L.: *Wooded Laboratories,* Cornell Rural School Leaflet, vol. 44, no. 4, Spring, 1951.

128. Preston, R. J., Jr.: *Rocky Mountain Trees,* Iowa State College Press, Ames, Iowa, 1940.

129. Rickett, H. W.: *Wild Flowers of America,* Crown Publishers, Inc., New York, 1953. Four hundred species in color, from paintings by Mary Vaux Walcott and Dorothy Falcon Platt. Edited with an introduction and detailed descriptions by Dr. H. W. Rickett of the New York Botanical Garden.

130. Rogers, M.: *First Book of Tree Identification,* Random House, Inc., New York, 1951. Illustrated. A book of Canadian trees.

131. Rowe, W. H.: *Trees and Shrubs,* Penguin Books, Inc., Baltimore, Md., 1944.

132. Shaw, E. E., and M. Dorwood: "Selection and Care of Plants in the Classroom," *Outdoors Illustrated,* vol. 2, no. 5, November–December, 1950.

133. United States Department of Agriculture: *Trees: Yearbook of Agriculture.* Washington, D.C., 1949.

134. Wells, B. W.: *The Natural Gardens of North Carolina,* University of North Carolina Press, Chapel Hill, N.C., 1932.

135. Wherry, E. T.: *Guide to Eastern Ferns,* 2d ed., Science Press, Lancaster, Pa., 1942.

Liverworts and Mosses

136. Bodenberg, E. T.: *Mosses: A New Approach to the Identification of Common Species,* Burgess Publication Company, Minneapolis, 1954.

137. Conard, H. S.: *How to Know the Mosses,* William C. Brown Company, Dubuque, Iowa, 1944.

138. Conard, H. S.: *How to Know the Mosses and Liverworts,* William C. Brown Company, Dubuque, Iowa, 1956.

139. Grout, A. J.: *Mosses with a Hand Lens,* 4th ed., published by the author, Staten Island, N.Y., 1947.

140. Jennings, O. E.: *Manual of the Mosses of Western Pennsylvania and Adjacent Regions,* University of Notre Dame Press, Notre Dame, Ind., 2d ed., 1951.

141. Richards, P. W.: *Mosses,* Penguin Books, Inc., Baltimore, Md., 1950.

142. Sterling, D.: *Story of Mosses, Ferns and Mushrooms,* Doubleday & Company, Inc., Garden City, N. Y., 1955.

143. Watson, E. V.: *British Mosses and Liverworts,* Cambridge University Press, New York, 1955.

Algae

144. Bold, H. C.: *Morphology of Plants,* Harper & Brothers, New York, 1957.

145. Fogg, C. E.: *Metabolism of Algae,* John Wiley & Sons, Inc., New York, 1953.

146. Fritsch, F. E.: *Structure and Reproduction of the Algae,* Cambridge University Press, New York, vol. 1, 1935; vol. 2, 1945.

147. Prescott, G. W.: *How to Know the Freshwater Algae,* H. E. Jaques (ed.), William C. Brown Company, Dubuque, Iowa, 1954.

148. Pringsheim, E. G.: *Pure Cultures of Algae,* Cambridge University Press, New York, 1946.

149. Smith, G. M.: *The Fresh-Water Algae of the United States,* 2d ed., McGraw-Hill Book Company, Inc., New York, 1950. An excellent reference book with keys and illustrations. Technical.

150. Tiffany, L. H.: *Algae, the Grass of Many Waters,* 2d ed., Charles C Thomas, Publisher, Springfield, Ill., 1958.

Fungi

151. Barnett, H. L.: *Illustrated Genera of Imperfect Fungi,* Burgess Publishing Company, Minneapolis, 1955.

152. Christensen, C. M.: *Common Edible Mushrooms,* University of Minnesota Press, Minneapolis, 1943. Illustrated.

153. Christensen, C. M.: *Common Fleshy Fungi,* Burgess Publishing Company, Minneapolis, 1955.

154. Funder, S.: *Practical Mycology Manual for Identification of Fungi,* Hafner Publishing Company, New York, 1953.

155. Gwynne-Vaughan, H., and B. Barnes: *Structure and Development of the Fungi,* 2d ed., Cambridge University Press, New York, 1937.

156. Henrici, A. T.: *Molds, Yeasts and Actinomycetes,* 2d ed., John Wiley & Sons, Inc., New York, 1947.

157. Krieger, L. C. C.: *The Mushroom Handbook,* The Macmillan Company, New York, 1947.

158. Nearing, G. G.: *The Lichen Book,* published by the author, Ridgewood, N.J., 1947.

159. Ramsbottom, J.: *Mushrooms and Toadstools,* The Macmillan Company, New York, 1953.

160. Smith, A. H.: *Puffballs and Their Allies in Michigan,* University of Michigan Press, Ann Arbor, Mich., 1951. Illustrated.

161. Stefferud, Alfred: *Plant Diseases,* The Yearbook of Agriculture, U.S. Department of Agriculture, Washington, D.C., 1953. For sale by the Superintendent of Documents, Washington 25, D.C.

162. Thomas, W. S.: *Field Book of Common Mushrooms,* new rev. ed., G. P. Putnam's Sons, New York, 1948.

163. Wolf, F. A., and F. T. Wolf: *Fungi,* John Wiley & Sons, Inc., New York, 1947. 2 vols.

Bacteria

164. Birkeland, Jorgen: *Microbiology and Man,* Appleton-Century-Crofts, Inc., New York, 1949.

165. Clifton, C. E.: *Introduction to the Bacteria,* 2d ed., McGraw-Hill Book Company, Inc., New York, 1958.

166. Rahn, Otto: *Microbes of Merit,* The Jacques Cattell Press, Lancaster, Pa., 1945.

167. Sarles, W. B., et al.: *Microbiology: General and Applied,* 2d ed., Harper & Brothers, New York, 1956.

168. Stanier, R. Y., et al.: *Microbial World,* Prentice-Hall, Inc., Englewood Cliffs, N.J., 1957.

169. Thomas, S. J., and T. H. Grainger: *Bacteria,* McGraw-Hill Book Company, Inc., New York, 1952. Illustrated.

170. Waksman, Gelman A.: *Microbial Antagonisms and Antibiotic Substances,* The Commonwealth Fund, New York, 1945.

Marine

171. Berrill, N. J.: *Living Tide,* Dodd, Mead & Company, New York, 1951. Illustrated.

172. Chapman, V. J.: *Sea Weeds and Their Uses,* Pitman Publishing Corporation, New York, 1950.

173. Dawson, E. Y.: *How to Know the Seaweeds,* William C. Brown Company, Dubuque, Iowa, 1956.

174. Conger, P. S.: *Lesson of the Diatoms, Am. Biol. Teacher,* **18**:187–193, October, 1956.

175. Flattely, F. W., and C. L. Walton: *Biology of the Seashore,* The Macmillan Company, New York, 1922.

176. Guberlet, M. L.: *Seaweeds at Ebb Tide,* University of Washington Press, Seattle, Washington, 1956. Illustrated.

177. Hausman, L. A.: *Beginner's Guide to Seashore Life,* G. P. Putnam's Sons, New York, 1949.

178. Hylander, C. J.: *Sea and Shore,* The Macmillan Company, New York, 1950. Illustrated. Recommended for grades 7 to 9.

179. MacGinitie, G. E., and Nettie MacGinitie: *Natural History of Marine Animals,* McGraw-Hill Book Company, Inc., New York, 1949.

180. Miner, R. W.: *Field Book of Seashore Life,* G. P. Putnam's Sons, New York, 1950. Illustrated.

181. Miner, R. W.: "Marauders of the Sea," *Natl. Geograph. Mag.,* **68**:185–207, August, 1935.

182. Miner, R. W.: "Denizens of Our Warm Atlantic Waters," *Natl. Geograph. Mag.,* **71**:199–219, February, 1937.

183. Morris, P. A.: *Field Guide to the Shells of Our Atlantic and Gulf Coasts,* rev. ed., Houghton-Mifflin Company, Boston, 1951.

184. Rogers, J. E.: *Shell Book,* rev. ed., Charles T. Branford Co., Newton Centre, Mass., 1951.

185. Stephenson, E. M.: *Naturalist on the Seashore,* The Macmillan Company, New York, 1951. A book about marine biology of Great Britain.

Fossils

186. Cassanova, R.: *Illustrated Guide to Fossil Collecting,* Naturegraph Company, San Martin, Calif., 1957. Illustrated.

187. Raymond, P. E.: *Prehistoric Life,* Harvard University Press, Cambridge, Mass., 1939. Illustrated.

188. Senet, A.: *Man in Search of His Ancestors,* McGraw-Hill Book Company, Inc., New York, 1955.

189. Simpson, G. G.: *Life of the Past,* Yale University Press, New Haven, Conn., 1953.

190. Sternberg, C. H.: *Life of a Fossil Hunter,* C. H. Sternberg, San Diego, Calif., 1931.

Photography

191. American Forestry Association, 919 17th St., N.W., Washington 6, D.C. Charts and Pamphlets on forest education.

192. Bond, F.: *Better Color Movies,* 2d ed., Camera Craft Publishing Co., San Francisco, Calif., 1955.

193. Charles, Brother H.: "Make Your Own Color Slides," *Am. Biol. Teacher,* **12**:62–64, March, 1950.

194. Feininger, A.: *Successful Color Photography,* Prentice-Hall, Inc., Englewood Cliffs, N.J., 1954.

195. Stevens, G. W.: *Microphotography,* John Wiley & Sons, Inc., New York, 1957.

General Reading

196. Anderson, Edgar: *Plants, Man and Life,* Little, Brown & Company, Boston, Mass., 1952.

197. Barker, W.: *Familiar Animals of America,* Harper & Brothers, New York, 1956.

198. Blaydes, Glenn W.: "The Romance of Domesticated Plants," *Ohio J. Sci.,* **53**:193–215, 1953; also reprinted in *Smithsonian Repts.* for 1954, pp. 317–336. Deals with the origin of domesticated plants, genetic variation in seeds, vegetative multiplication, hybridization and somatic mutations, with 41 photographic illustrations (2 in color).

199. Breland, O. P.: *Animal Facts and Fallacies,* Harper & Brothers, New York, 1948.

200. Briggs, J., and K. F. Weaver: "How Old Is It?" *Natl. Geograph. Mag.,* **114**:234–255, August, 1958. Deals with the discovery and application of the radiocarbon (carbon 14) method of dating organic remains.

201. Camp, W. H., V. R. Boswell, and J. R. Magness: *The World in Your Garden,* National Geographic Society, Washington, D.C., 1957. Deals with the origin of domesticated horticultural plants. Should be in every school library.

202. Carson Rachel L.: *"The Sea Around Us,"* A Mentor book by Oxford University Press, New York, 1951.

203. DeKruif, Paul Henry: *Microbe Hunters,* Harcourt Brace & Company, New York, 1926. Deals with lives and scientific achievements of Pasteur, Koch, Bruce, Ross, Reed, and others.

204. DeKruif, Paul Henry: *Hunger Fighters,* Harcourt, Brace & Company, New York, 1928.

205. DeKruif, Paul Henry: *Men Against Death,* Harcourt, Brace & Company, New York, 1936.

206. Dodson, Edward O.: *A Textbook of Evolution,* W. B. Saunders Company, Philadelphia, 1952.

207. Gillespie, W. H.: *Edible Wild Plants of West Virginia,* Scholar's Library, New York, 1951.

208. Hoshaw, R. W., and R. M. Harris: *Survey and Use of the Plant Kingdom,* Burgess Publishing Company, Minneapolis, 1957.

209. Jaques, H. E.: *Living Things; How to Know Them,* William C. Brown Company, Dubuque, Iowa, 1946.

210. Martin, A. C., et al.: *American Wildlife and Plants,* McGraw-Hill Book Company, Inc., New York, 1951. Illustrated.

211. Medsger, O. P.: *Edible Wild Plants,* The Macmillan Company, New York, 1939. Illustrated.

212. Mohler, C. W.: "Bringing Wildlife to the Classroom," *Audubon Mag.,* **54**:308–311, September, 1952.

213. Murie, O.: *Field Guide to Animal Tracks,* Houghton-Mifflin Company, Boston, 1954.

214. Needham, J. G., and R. R. Needham: *A Guide to the Study of Fresh-Water Biology,* 3d ed., Comstock Publishing Associates, Inc., Ithaca, N.Y., 1935.

215. Platt, Rutherford: *The Woods of Time,* Dodd, Mead & Company, New York, 1957.

216. Schmidt, K. P.: *Homes and Habits of Wild Animals,* M. A. Donohue & Company, Chicago, 1934.

217. *Scientific American:* Contains articles written by specialists in all areas of science, in language understandable to the laymen. A means of keeping up to date on many new developments in science. Should be available in every school library.

218. U.S. Government Publications: national parks, forest service, geological survey, etc. Get price list 35 (Geography and Explorations) from the Superintendent of Documents, Washington, D.C.

219. Wessel, J. P.: "Laboratory Studies in Animal Ecology," *School Sci. and Math.,* **32**:371–381, 1932.

CHAPTER 13

⚜ Laboratory Aids and Substitutes ⚜

Since one of the major problems of a great many teachers of biological subjects is the finding of sufficient materials and equipment for the laboratory, it becomes important that limited funds be spent wisely, that inexpensive substitutes be provided for more expensive apparatus, and that use be made, wherever possible, of common and easily obtained teaching aids.

Throughout the chapters of this book there occur numerous suggestions of this character appropriate to the subjects of those chapters. A number of additional suggestions are given here which have more general usefulness. It is by no means intended that this be an exhaustive list, as almost any experienced teacher could add something, but rather that it act as an example for inexperienced teachers and for those who are not accustomed to improvising to meet their daily needs.

ADHESIVES

Acetic acid placed between two celluloid surfaces will cause them to become cemented together. This enables one to make useful pieces of apparatus from celluloid. Plastic cements can be had in tubes at small cost.

Rubber cement, obtainable at five-and-ten-cent stores, gasoline stations, and stationery supply companies, is very useful in mounting photographs, small charts, etc. It does not cause wrinkling, and the mounted object can be readily removed later without tearing.

Parafilm is very useful in mounting or reinforcing large charts, maps, photographs, etc., which are to be folded and used extensively. It comes in rolled sheets 25 in. long and 20 in. wide, also 150 ft. by 20 in. The parafilm sheet is placed between a chart and the mounting cloth, then pressed with a moderately hot iron. A circular telling of its uses is provided with each roll. It is on sale at bookstores, draftsmen's and artists' supply concerns.

Aquarium Cement

Putty	5 parts
Red lead	1 part
Litharge	1 part

Mix to the proper consistency for glazing by the use of boiled linseed oil and a few drops of drier. A sufficient amount of lampblack is added to change the color from red to slate. Mix the above ingredients with enough of the linseed oil to form a stiff paste. Support the pieces of glass so that cement may be pressed firmly into all corners and smooth with a putty knife. Be certain that no air spaces remain. Allow the cement to become thoroughly dry before placing water in the aquarium. After drying rinse the aquarium thoroughly before placing the permanent water supply in it.

Wax for Sealing Glassware

Powdered resin .... 15 parts
Beeswax .... 35 parts
Petroleum jelly .... 50 parts

Melt the beeswax and petroleum jelly and mix. Gradually add the resin while stirring.

APPARATUS ACCESSORIES

Automatic Siphon. Sometimes it is necessary to keep water running into an aquarium or culture jar. If the aquarium has no drain pipe the result would be that the water would reach the top and run over. To avoid this use the device shown in Fig. 13.1. Whenever the water in the aquarium reaches the height of the leveling

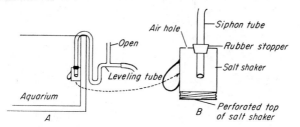
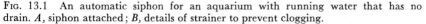

Fɪɢ. 13.1   An automatic siphon for an aquarium with running water that has no drain. *A,* siphon attached; *B,* details of strainer to prevent clogging.

tube, the siphon principle operates and drains off part of the water. A wire cap placed over the outlet will keep small organisms from escaping, or a can, as shown in Fig. 13.1, will prevent the outlet from clogging with plants. Several small holes must be made in the cup bottom as shown in the figure. Always remember that the flow of water into the vessel must not exceed the amount which the siphon can remove. The U-shaped bend in the siphon must be filled with water at the start.

Carbon Dioxide Generator. Where tanks of carbon dioxide are not to be had, it is convenient to be able to produce your own supply whenever needed. The usual bottle type of generator that is found in any general chemistry laboratory is quite satisfactory for this purpose.

Materials. Any kind of bottle with a wide mouth, such as a pickle, olive, or mayonnaise bottle, or the usual 250- to 500-cc. laboratory bottle; cork or rubber stopper to fit the bottle; a piece of glass tubing of small bore (about ¼-in. bore); if possible a small funnel or thistle tube; some acid (hydrochloric is probably best although sulfuric, nitric, or even strong vinegar will do); some lime compound, such as finely broken marble, limestone, bicarbonate of soda (baking soda); the vinegar can be used only with the baking soda and even then the stronger acids are to be preferred.

The small pieces of marble or limestone or the baking soda (about 1 tablespoonful) is placed in the wide-mouthed bottle and about 50 to 75 cc. of water added. The stopper, with its connections, is put in place. The tube is connected with the vessel that is to be filled with carbon dioxide. The acid is added last, a little at a time. If no funnel or thistle tube is obtainable, the acid can be poured through the mouth of the bottle and the stopper inserted quickly. Some of the carbon dioxide is lost in this way, but that is unimportant. When bicarbonate of soda is used, the carbon dioxide is generated very rapidly and the generation does not last long. The marble gives a slower, steadier generation but is not so readily obtained. The carbon dioxide passes out through the tube and may be collected or used as needed. Care must be taken when a funnel is used to see that the end of the funnel is below the level of the water in the generator. Do not collect the carbon dioxide which is generated first as it will be diluted with air. Clear the generator by allowing it to run a while before collecting.

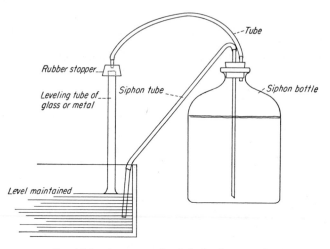

FIG. 13.2   A constant-level device for aquaria.

Constant-water-level Device. There are times when it is a great convenience to have the water in an aquarium or culture jar remain at an approximately constant level, or when (as during a vacation period) it would be inconvenient to replenish water in some container for a week or more. The device diagramed in Fig. 13.2 is one way of assuring that such a situation is taken care of. The leveling tube may be of glass or metal but must be not less than ½ in. in its inside diameter. If it is flared at the open end, this is an added assurance that it will spill its water when the level goes below that desired. All connections must be airtight. Rubber stoppers are best since they are less likely to allow air leaks in the system. The siphon bottle must be slightly higher than the aquarium.

Equipment from a Dump. When it comes to raw materials that are free and from which much useful laboratory equipment can be made, it is hard to beat a common town dump. What one will find in a dump will vary with the location and the chief source of debris, and it will vary in the same dump from one week to another. On one visit to such a dump the following items were collected:

Wallboard. This was the soft spongy kind about ½ in. thick. Much of it was warped and torn, but pieces containing 1 sq. ft. were easily obtained. These were taken to the laboratory and used as inside bottoms of small boxes such as cigar boxes. The boxes were lined with white paper and used for insect collections. The soft fibrous wallboard is excellent for holding the pinned insects. It has fine insulating properties and may be used for lining incubators or temperature-control boxes of any kind.

Flower Pots. There were several sizes.

Bottles. A variety of these is seldom missing from a dump. There were the usual apothecary's dispensing bottles with the volumes marked both in liquid ounces and in cubic centimeters. After cleaning they may be used as containers for supplies or as measuring devices, substituting for expensive graduated cylinders and flasks.

Jars. There were glass jars of many shapes and sizes: quart jars, pint jars, and many smaller jars such as are used for cheese and jam, wide-mouthed jars and narrow-mouthed jars, and jars with and without caps. If cleaned and sorted into sizes, they may be stored on shelves or in boxes and kept as containers for preserved specimens, collecting apparatus, killing jars, experiments, and demonstrations.

Bricks. These included pressed bricks, common bricks, fire-clay bricks, and glazed tiles. These may be used for weights in pressing plant specimens, supports for apparatus, ornaments for aquaria and terraria, and fire brick wherever exposure to high temperatures is desired.

Glass. Windowpanes were almost always broken, but sometimes large enough pieces were found from which quite usable sections could be cut. They are needed in aquaria, terraria, glass animal cages, pocket gardens, culture-jar covers, and the like.

Wire. This was apparently wire from bales of straw or hay.

Woven Wire of Several Meshes. There was window screen, $\frac{1}{4}$-in.-mesh woven wire, and 1-in.-mesh chicken wire. This material is exactly what one needs for the construction of cages, partitions in aquaria and terraria, screening sand and soil, and protecting plants.

Tinned Cans. It is surprising how many of these can be found in good condition. Some were of the baking-powder-can type with smooth edges and a lid; others had screw caps, and there was one large oil can that would hold 3 gal. It was nearly new, soiled only with oil which could be removed readily with soap and water, and fitted with a screw cap.

Wood. There were many kinds of wood. Some of it was in the form of old 2 by 4 and 2 by 6 planks. These were usually broken or decayed at the ends, but there were several feet of good solid wood in each piece. There were parts of packing boxes and crating that was nearly new. For those much-wanted cages, flower boxes, flats, and shelves these were all very useful.

Nails. From the boxes and crating wood it was not hard to reclaim a number of sizes of nails that had not rusted.

Keg. A very substantial keg was found, but it was not made for holding liquids. If it had been it could have been sawed in two across the middle and two tubs would have resulted which might have done very well as aquaria.

Sheet Metal. This dump, like most others, had several kinds of sheet metal: old tin roofing, corrugated sheet iron, and used flat sheets. Most of these were rusted, twisted, and torn, but with tin shears it was possible to cut out sections as large as 2 ft. square that were still very usable. One seldom needs so large a piece in a classroom.

Marble. The badly broken top of a dismantled washbowl as such did not furnish a piece large enough for any laboratory use, but when crushed into fine particles and stored in one of the empty bottles it stood ready on the shelf for the day when a carbon dioxide generator was to be set up for a physiological demonstration.

Strap Iron. From a heavy piece of sheet metal several strips of strap iron were unscrewed, the rust was rubbed off and when bent at right angles and painted, the strips made the supports that were needed for two window shelves.

Dishes. A dump is the graveyard of old dishes. Most of them are of no use, but an occasional saucer that lost its cup may be saved and may prove a better background for small specimens than glass. A room with an assortment of such containers may not be so pleasing in appearance as one equipped with stender dishes or crystallization dishes, but they save money and are just as useful.

Wax. In a cardboard carton was discovered a dozen bricklike packages. When unwrapped they were found to be cakes of beeswax. These were taken back to the school building. One of the girls went to a five-and-ten-cent store and bought three cake pans 9 by 14 in., pebbled and heavily tinned. The wax was melted and poured into the pans to a depth of $\frac{1}{2}$ in. The result was three very fine dissecting pans at a saving of at least $1 per pan.

There is no lack of volunteers who will consider it a privilege to hunt the dumps. It is fun.

Faucet Suction Pump. Wherever running water is available in a laboratory or schoolroom, a small pump for producing a flow of air or for evacuating bottles, as in the respiration apparatus shown in Fig. 19.4, is a great convenience. Excellent metal pumps that fasten directly to the water faucet may be purchased from supply

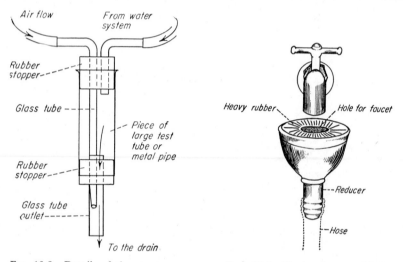

FIG. 13.3 Details of the construction of a simple faucet suction
pump.

FIG. 13.4 Device for attaching a
hose to an unthreaded faucet.

companies. One may be made in the laboratory from such materials as are shown in Fig. 13.3. In using this pump, it must be remembered that it will not stand the full pressure of the water system and, therefore, the water should be turned on slowly until the flow of air is started. Too strong a water flow may cause it to come apart at the connections.

Hose Adapter for Faucet. For sink faucets not equipped with connections for attaching hose and rubber tubing of various sizes, an adapter may be purchased from plumbing supply stores, hardware stores, and five-and-ten-cent stores. These come in various styles and sizes. Figure 13.4 illustrates a common type.

Pump for Reagent Bottles. For some reagents it is occasionally desirable to pump out the liquid instead of pouring. The pump consists of two glass tubes passed through a stopper. One of the tubes is long, reaching to the bottom of the reagent bottle, with the outer end bent at an angle convenient for delivery of the liquid. The shorter tube extends only through the stopper and does not contact the liquid.

A rubber tube is placed on the outer end of the short tube. The operator blows into the short tube, and liquid comes out the other. An atomizer bulb may be used as the source of air pressure. This is better than sucking as it eliminates the possibility of chemicals being drawn into the mouth.

Sterilizers. A sterilizer of some description is almost indispensable about a biological laboratory. Autoclaves are too expensive for many schools. The double-boiler type is the simplest one which is serviceable for test tubes, petri dishes, and small amounts of culture media. Water is placed in the lower part, and the objects or materials to be sterilized are placed in the upper section. Boiling for 1 hr. or more is usually necessary. If a double boiler is not available, a metal bucket with a lid may be used. An inner container is made of heavy wire screen (hardware cloth) to fit the bucket. This should be suspended 2 to 3 in. above the bottom to keep tubes, dishes, or culture media out of the boiling water. When pathogenic organisms are involved, one should not risk the use of these sterilizers. But for many ordinary bacterial cultures, molds, protozoa, etc., they are satisfactory.

An inexpensive commercial steam cooker is more effective and more rapid than the above types. More steam pressure and higher temperatures are possible with it. These are obtainable at hardware stores.

High-pressure cookers such as are often used in home canning, with screw clamp lid, pressure gage, and safety valve, are very good. Most of them are set for 15 lb. steam pressure. This is just right for efficient sterilizing. Many of the commercial forms are of exactly the same construction as the more expensive ones sold by scientific supply companies. They are very efficient and may be used in situations where pathogenic organisms are involved.

COLLECTING APPARATUS

Coffee Can and Fruit Jar Cage and Strainer. Small cages which can be quickly constructed are a necessity in any biological laboratory where living animals are studied. One which answers the purpose for many insects and other small animals may be made from pound-size coffee cans of several of the vacuum-packed brands of coffee. After the lid is cut away, an inner tin collar is found. This should be removed with a pair of wire pliers. Place a piece of cheesecloth over the mouth of the can and clamp it in place with the tin collar, reversing the collar from the way it was inserted originally. This gives a rounded edge to the collar, inserts easily, and prevents cutting of the cloth. In case of gnawing animals, a wire screen may be substituted for cheesecloth, but it has to be soldered to the collar. A sheet of cellophane may be used as the cover if light and transparency are desired. Such a can (with cheesecloth or screen wire) may be used as an emergency strainer or sieve, if desired.

An ordinary fruit jar with a Kerr or Crown screw cap makes a very satisfactory cage for many purposes. The caps come in two parts—the metal disk lid and the threaded ring. Only the ring is used for the cages. Cheesecloth, muslin, or screen wire is fitted over the jar mouth and the ring screwed in place to hold it. The Kerr jars and wide-mouthed Ball jars are more suitable for many purposes than the ordinary Mason jar because of the wide mouth. (See Chap. 12 for numerous suggestions of other collecting apparatus.)

Dip Net. Fish and tadpoles should not be caught in the hand. A small dip net is indispensable to the aquarium. Tea strainers with demountable frame and handle may be had in various sizes. If the wire gauze is cut from its metal rim and a small, thin sack substituted for the wire the rim may be replaced in the handle and frame, making a splendid net (Fig. 12.15).

ELECTRICAL DEVICES

Heating Devices. Electric heating devices may be built very simply. Several of the concave reflector types of electric heaters on the market have replaceable cone units. These cones are sold separately for replacements and often can be obtained at stores for 25 to 35 cents. If porcelain electric-light sockets are fastened to a base covered with asbestos board, asbestos cement, or other heat-resistance substance, and these cones screwed into the sockets, an effective heater results. Figure 13.5 shows details of such a heater. Larger heaters may be constructed by using a series of cones and a larger block can. Do not use a can with soldered seams as it may heat enough to melt the solder. If an ordinary electric flatiron is available it may be inverted, supported in some way, and the flat surface used for heating purposes. Also inexpensive electric flatiron heating units are sold for repairs. One of these inverted and fastened to a heat-resisting base and then covered with an iron plate works satisfactorily. The two pole connections are allowed to project at one side, and an ordinary electric flatiron cord is used to make the current connection. An ordinary tin pan or tin sheet is not satisfactory for covering the heating unit since it warps badly upon heating and soon burns out. Resistance wire for replacements may be obtained in a coil which contains about 18 ft. of wire. From this, plus a few odds and ends about the laboratory, heaters may be built to suit individual needs. A rod type of tumbler heater, sometimes used to heat milk for babies, may be obtained inexpensively; heaters of various other types are also available.

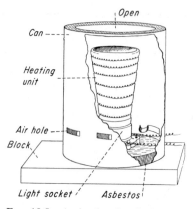

FIG. 13.5   A simple electrical heating device.

Microscope Lights. An ordinary ceiling type of socket and bulb fastened to a wooden base and properly wired serves very well as a microscope light. A shade for the bulb may be made from a tin can or, better, from sheet aluminum (an excellent reflecting material).

Reversing Switch. In experimental work it is often desirable to be able to reverse or alternate the direction of flow of current from a battery. Any commercial two-way switch can be converted into a reversing switch with two short pieces of copper wire arranged as shown in the diagram (Fig. 13.6). Where the wires cross over

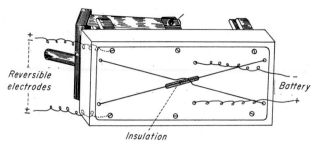

FIG. 13.6   Method of wiring a double-throw switch to make reversible electrodes.

they must be carefully insulated to avoid short-circuiting. It is also a good plan to have the porcelain block of the switch screwed to a board or table top.

Thermostats are useful in connection with construction of certain electrical apparatus. Several inexpensive ones are available at hardware stores, electrical supply shops, mail-order houses, etc. A gas-filled one, wafer type, used in the construction of certain incubators, is very inexpensive. A very good one of the bimetallic bar type is a little more expensive but more reliable.

SUBSTITUTES FOR STANDARD LABORATORY GLASSWARE

Very few of the occasions for using standard glassware in the laboratory really require this glassware specifically. Nearly always some very common substitute could be used quite as well. It must be remembered, however, that these substitutes will not stand heating over a flame or electric heater.

Aquaria. An aquarium is an aquatic habitat for organisms and does not imply that it must be a rectangular vessel with plate-glass sides. Try using most of the containers mentioned below as substitutes for culture jars and battery jars. In addition to these the following make satisfactory aquaria: fish bowls, porcelain-coated pans, earthenware crocks, a small barrel or keg sawed in half, wooden tubs, an old hot-water tank cut in two lengthwise.

Beakers. Use water tumblers, jelly glasses, and mayonnaise jars. (Do not heat.)

Wide-mouthed Bottles. Cheese jars and mayonnaise jars, olive and pickle bottles do very well as substitutes.

Finger-bowl Culture Dishes. A very satisfactory substitute may be obtained in the form of covered butter dishes. In some of these there is a glass lid which fits into a depressed groove making a level top. Usually these dishes may be stacked the same as the finger-bowl type of culture dish.

Culture Jars and Battery Jars. The larger pickle jars which can be found at grocery stores or junk and secondhand dealers; half-gallon, quart, and pint fruit jars; tumblers and cheese jars are suitable for most purposes.

Museum and Specimen Jars. Plain round or square fruit jars in clear glass, pickle jars in gallon and half-gallon sizes, and sealed tubes are satisfactory substitutes.

Syracuse Watch Glass. Coasters or caster cups which may be bought at any five-and-ten-cent store are almost identical with Syracuse watch glasses.

HECTOGRAPH

A Simple Duplicating Device (Hectograph). There are many occasions when a teacher needs to have a number of copies of examination questions, diagrams, or directions, but feels that to copy them by hand or on a typewriter would be too much work. For such occasions a hectograph is recommended. It is very easy to make from the following formula.

Water	6 oz.
Glycerin	6 oz.
Sheet gelatin	1½ oz.
Carbolic acid	10 drops

Soak the gelatin in the water until soft. Heat in a double boiler until dissolved. Heat the glycerin and pour it slowly into the gelatin. When thoroughly mixed, pour into a shallow pan of a size somewhat larger than the paper to be used and let stand until cool. If bubbles arise while hot, skim them off with a card. It should not be used for 2 days. Ink for writing with a pen can be bought from bookstores. Ribbons for typing with hectograph ink may be purchased, and duplicating paper of hectograph ink can be had and used exactly like carbon paper. The second copy is used to make the impression on the gelatin.

Wet the gelatin surface uniformly with a soft sponge. Wipe off excess water. Lay the copy upon the gelatin, inked surface down. Roll with a small hand roller or rub uniformly with the fingers over the entire sheet. Peel the paper from the gelatin, beginning at one end. Lay a plain sheet of paper on the hectograph, roll, and remove. It will be a duplicate of the original. One hundred or more copies may sometimes be made in this way.

MEASURING DEVICES

Centimeter Rules. While centimeter rules are very cheap, they are not yet in common use. The teacher sometimes finds a situation in which it would be advantageous to have each student supplied with one. These may be produced at a fraction of a cent each in the following manner:

1. Take a sheet of millimeter-ruled graph paper and cut it into narrow strips.

2. Fasten these on narrow strips of thin wood or heavy cardboard with rubber cement. Ordinary library paste may be used, but it tends to cause the paper to stretch and does not fasten so permanently as the rubber cement.

3. By using a sheet of ⅛-in.-ruled graph paper, a similar strip may be fastened parallel to the millimeter strip and a comparative inch-metric scale is established.

4. Mark with black India ink to indicate the number intervals.

5. If sprayed with shellac or very thin paraffin, the rules will be waterproof and last a long time.

Metric- and inch-ruled graph paper may be bought by the foot or yard. If two strips one metric- and one inch-ruled are cemented together and mounted on a narrow flat board a comparative millimeter-inch scale may be made of any desired length. This can be hung at a convenient place on the classroom wall where it acts as a useful reference table. Such a long rule should have the accuracy of its paper checked at intervals of about 6 in. (Inches times 25.4 equals millimeters.)

Gram-Ounce Spring Balance. A small letter scale weighing with considerable accuracy can be purchased at five-and-ten-cent stores. These little platform scales usually read up to 12 oz., but since each ounce is equal to 28.3 g. it is impossible to weigh small amounts in grams directly because of the small size of the divisions on the scale. Thus 12 oz. would require 339 subdivisions. Such a platform scale may be converted into a 10- or 15-g. beam scale with but little difficulty. It will weigh to ½ g. with accuracy sufficient for most school purposes, as in the making of a 10 per cent solution of some salt.

Most of the details of the transformation are apparent from Fig. 13.7. They consist of (a) the metal fulcrum which must be rigid and firmly fastened to the side of the scales. (b) The pivot is a needle, or a fine nail with sharp points filed on each end. The ends are seated in small depressions in the fulcrum which act as bearings. One of the pinion wheels removed from an old alarm clock may be used instead of the needle or nail. (c) To this pivot is soldered or fastened a beam. The material of the beam may be almost anything, provided that it is lightweight and rigid. A small aluminum tube would be ideal. If there is too much difficulty in finding something rigid and yet light in weight, it is quite possible to use heavier material, extending the beam beyond the fulcrum in the opposite direction and counterbalancing it as is shown by the dotted lines of the diagram. (d) The weighing pan is made from the aluminum lid of a cold-cream or ointment jar. The beam and pan are made to contact the platform of the scale by a pin or fine nail. If this pin is hinged where it fastens to the beam it is better. (e) The gram scale is made by gluing a strip of paper along the front of the apparatus. Where the marker now rests may be designated as zero. Measure accurately 5, 10, or 15 cc. of water and pour it into the weighing pan. The marker will descend toward the bottom of the scale. Mark this point as being the weight of the water. Since water (pure) weighs 1 g. per cubic centimeter, the number of cubic centimeters of water is registered as grams of weight. If this is 15 the space between 0 and 15 may be divided into 15 equal divisions, or smaller amounts of water could be used and the points marked off. If the original ounce marks are not covered, the scale will still weigh in ounces by lifting the beam and placing the material to be weighed directly upon the platform.

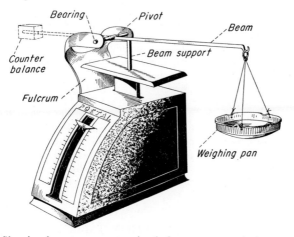

FIG. 13.7   Showing how to convert a simple letter ounce scale into a gram scale.

The number of gram divisions possible on such a scale is governed by the length of the pan arm of the beam. One must decide this on the basis of the choice between quantity weighable at one time and accuracy of weight, since the larger the divisions, the more accurate the weighing.

Manometers. To measure the amount of reduction in pressure produced in a closed container, construct the following mercury column (Fig. 13.8):

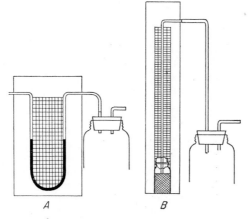

FIG. 13.8   Two types of mercury manometers that may be useful in experiments.

1. Place 75 cc. of clean mercury in a narrow bottle.

2. Place 95 cm. of 1-mm. glass capillary tube into the mercury through the neck of the bottle. Close the bottle with cotton to keep out dust.

3. Support the capillary tube on a board.

4. Bend the upper end of the tube and attach to a heavy-walled gum tube.

5. When connected as shown in Fig. 13.8B, the amount of reduction in pressure within the container is registered by the height of the column of mercury in the tube. This is measured on the millimeter scale, which may be made from graph paper.

For measuring increase in pressure within a container it is necessary to have a U tube containing mercury as shown in Fig. 13.8A. The two columns of mercury are equal if open at both ends. When pressure is increased (or decreased) the levels differ. The total difference is a measure of the amount of pressure change.

Measuring Bottle. Sometimes it is not possible to have a graduated cylinder or other means of measuring liquids, especially in cubic centimeters (milliliters). Wherever a high degree of accuracy is not required, an ordinary medicine bottle will serve the purpose. The average size is 4 liquid ounces. Such bottles usually are calibrated in ounces and cubic centimeters. For further calibrations on the bottle, a strip of graph paper may be glued on the surface so that there is an even number of lines running between the ounce and cubic centimeter marks. This will enable one to measure in fractions. A coat of hot paraffin over the paper will waterproof, acid-proof, and alcohol-proof it. If only ounce measures are desired an infant's milk bottle will serve the purpose. Usually it is calibrated to half ounces. Eight-ounce bottles are the usual size and are very inexpensive at five-and-ten-cent stores.

TRANSFORMATION TABLES

Measures of Length

English			Metric
1	foot	= 30.48	centimeters
1	inch	= 2.54	centimeters
39.37	inches	= 1	meter
0.39	inch	= 1	centimeter
0.039	inch	= 1	millimeter
3.9	inches	= 1	decimeter

Measures of Capacity

1 quart (dry)	= 1.1	liters
1 quart (liquid)	= 0.94	liter
1 ounce (fluid)	= 28.3	cc. (milliliters)
1 dram (fluid)	= 3.5	cc. (milliliters)

Measures of Weights

1	grain	= 0.06	gram
1	dram (av.)	= 1.77	grams
1	dram (ap.)	= 3.8	grams
1	ounce (av.)	= 28.3	grams
1	ounce (ap.)	= 31.1	grams
1	pound (av.)	= 453.5	grams
1	pound (ap.)	= 373.2	grams
2.2	pounds (av.)	= 1	kilogram

Measures of Temperatures

$+60°$C. $= 140.0°$F.
$55°$C. $= 131.0°$F.
$50°$C. $= 122.0°$F.
$45°$C. $= 113.0°$F.
$40°$C. $= 104.0°$F.
$35°$C. $=\ \ 95.0°$F.
$30°$C. $=\ \ 86.0°$F.
$25°$C. $=\ \ 77.0°$F.
$20°$C. $=\ \ 68.0°$F.
$15°$C. $=\ \ 59.0°$F.
$10°$C. $=\ \ 50.0°$F.
$5°$C. $=\ \ 41.0°$F.
$0°$C. $=\ \ 32.0°$F.
$-5°$C. $=\ \ 23.0°$F.

Temperature Conversion Formulas

To convert centigrade to Fahrenheit, substitute the number of centigrade degrees for n in the formula

$$\frac{9n°C.}{5} + 32$$

To convert Fahrenheit to centigrade, substitute the number of Fahrenheit degrees for n in the formula

$$\frac{5(n°F. - 32)}{9}$$

MICROSCOPE MAGNIFICATIONS

OCULAR	OBJECTIVE LENS	MAGNIFICATION
10×	3.5 × (30 mm.)	35 diameters
10×	10 × (16 mm.)	100 diameters
10×	43 × (4 mm.)	430 diameters
10×	97 × (1.8 mm.) oil immersion	970 diameters

RELATIVE HUMIDITY TABLE

Sometimes it is desirable to be able to maintain a constant relative humidity within a jar or apparatus. Supersaturated solutions of certain salts will give definite atmospheric humidities in the air that passes slowly through them or in the air which stands above them. Thus, if a battery jar is filled to one-fourth full with one of the following solutions and covered with a plate of glass, the air above the solution will gradually come to the per cent of relative humidity given for that solution.

SUPERSATURATED SOLUTION	RELATIVE HUMIDITY AT 25 TO 30°C.
Calcium chloride ($CaCl_2$)	26 per cent
Sodium hydroxide (NaOH)	31 per cent
Copper nitrate ($Cu(NO_3)_2$)	45 per cent
Sodium chloride (NaCl)	73 per cent
Potassium sulfate (K_2SO_4)	90 per cent
Concentrated sulfuric acid (c.p.)	0 per cent
Distilled water	100 per cent

FREEZING MIXTURES

If common salt (NaCl) or calcium chloride ($CaCl_2$) is mixed with snow or finely cracked ice, a temperature well below freezing of water will be produced. The absorption of heat by evaporating ether will freeze water. A simple apparatus for doing this is illustrated in Fig. 13.9. It is too expensive to use on a large scale, and it should be done under a hood and away from a flame.

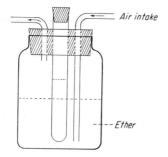

Fig. 13.9 Apparatus for producing low temperatures by evaporating ether.

MOUNTS AND DISPLAYS

Embedding in Plastics. Beautiful and permanent mounts of biological specimens can be made by embedding them in polyester resins. The process is not something for every student to do as laboratory work but a project for one or more capable students. A little practice is necessary to ensure success and to avoid wasting of material. Many producers of these resins also sell equipment for doing the work. While such equipment as power saws, sanders, and electric ovens are convenient, they are not necessities. It is suggested that simple handwork be done, at least until the procedure is mastered. A basic list of equipment would consist of power drill with buffer attachments; sander, oscillating type; sandpaper, various degrees of fineness; pumice, fine and powder; buffer wheel; wax compound.

Directions for embedding are usually furnished by the supplier of the resin, giving step-by-step instructions. Listed below are the names and addresses of supply sources. A letter to any one of them from a teacher would bring some literature on their products. Pittsburgh Paint and Glass Company, Gateway Center, Pittsburgh, Penn.; Allied Chemical and Dye Corporation, 40 Rector St., New York, N.Y.; General Biological Supply House, 8200 South Hoyne Ave., Chicago, Ill.; Ward's Natural Science Establishment, 3000 Ridge Road, E., Rochester, N.Y.; Natcol Laboratories, Redlands, Calif.

A project of this character has many desirable effects. It involves the use of biological specimens, an appreciation of their physical characteristics, the use of the hands in manipulations, a sense of the artistic, and a satisfaction that comes from producing something that can be seen and handled when finished. It produces useful material for laboratory work of other students and a basis for a permanent collection. This project may also be done at home because of the time involved. It might also become a fascinating hobby.

Lantern Slides. Schools possessing a projection lantern need not find it useless because of a lack of money necessary for buying slides. There are several ways of producing very good lantern slides that have considerable teaching value. Cut some thin clear glass into pieces the size of lantern slides (3¼ by 4 in.). These should be kept as stock. Old sensitive plates that are spoiled or are no longer wanted make excellent slide material if thoroughly cleaned. Diagrams can be made with India ink directly on the slide. India inks come in a variety of colors, but for most purposes black is best. The glass plates may be laid upon a printed diagram or picture and a tracing made upon the glass. If ink does not adhere readily to the glass, the plate may be coated with a very thin adhesive. The best procedure is to develop a lantern slide without exposure. The emulsion becomes clear and takes ink easily. For glass without emulsion, a thin coat of gelatin may be added by dipping the plate in a dilute solution of table gelatin dissolved in hot water, to which has been added a pinch of sodium benzoate or a drop of carbolic acid. Let the treated slide stand on edge in a warm place so that as much gelatin as possible will run off the glass. Very thin collodion (see footnote, p. 332) may be used in a similar manner. Another coating may be made by dissolving egg white in cold water and skimming off the scum at the surface. Do not beat the egg. This preparation also needs a preservative such as sodium salicylate or thymol (about 2 per cent). Temporary slides may be constructed in this manner, washed off, and used over again. If the slide is to be kept and used again, it should be built up with a second piece of glass, as shown in Fig. 13.10B. The diagram goes between the two pieces of glass for

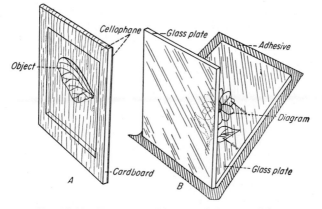

FIG. 13.10   Two types of homemade lantern slides.

protection, and these are bound together with gummed paper or adhesive tape. Another useful and still less expensive type of slide may be made as shown in Fig. 13.10A. A piece of heavy cardboard is cut to form a frame. Sheet cellophane is fastened over one side of the frame, and some partly translucent object, such as an insect wing, is stuck to it. Then the cellophane is wrapped around to cover the other side of the frame and sealed. The object is within the two sheets of cellophane, and the lantern throws a good shadow image on the screen.

Microscope Slide Box. To keep expensive microscope slides from resting upon each other and sticking together, they need to be filed in a slide box. Boxes are inexpensive, but a substitute can be made at almost no cost whatever. Remove the paper from one side of a corrugated paper carton and glue strips of the corrugated portion inside a narrow shallow box, such as a thread box. The corrugations make grooves which hold the slides (see Fig. 13.11).

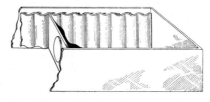

FIG. 13.11   Showing how to make a microscope slide box without cost.

Museum Demonstration Mounts. Usually much can be done about a laboratory to improve the appearance of demonstration specimens. For demonstrations of small animals or plants which will fit into a test tube, the tube may be filled with preservative, sealed with a cork, and dipped in collodion to make the seal more permanent. Wooden blocks may be prepared with a hole drilled partly through the block and of such a size that the mouth end of the test tube will fit into it. The tube may be cemented in place with hot sealing wax, or left removable. A label may be placed on the tube or block. Larger specimens which require jars as containers are improved by fastening them with silk thread or catgut to a glass plate, then setting them in the container and surrounding them with preservative. Small specimens, such as many of the mosses and liverworts, may be dried enough to remove surface liquid, then cemented to a good-grade card with collodion. Various macroscopic parts may be labeled on the card with India ink. After the collodion and ink are dry, place in a vial or small bottle, fill with preservative, and seal.

Terrarium (Wardian case). This is a most useful structure in a biological laboratory. Commercially made ones are expensive, prohibiting their purchase by many. Anyone who can make a fairly good wooden box and cut glass (or have it cut) can easily prepare such a case. In most laboratories and greenhouses the humidity is so low that many plants cannot be grown successfully. However, with a case of this type, humidity can be maintained at a high percentage even in a very dry laboratory. It is very useful for growing many ferns, liverworts, some mosses, *Selaginellas,* and for starting seedlings, cuttings, etc. One containing a 2- to 3-in. layer of sifted pine duff (decayed litter from a pine forest) makes an excellent place to grow fern prothallia and numerous other delicate plants. Terraria may be used for demonstrating typical plants of a bog, swamp, woods, desert, etc. They are useful also for caging numerous small animals under more or less natural conditions.

A good-sized terrarium for the above purposes may be made as follows: Construct a wooden box 14½ by 18¼ in. with a depth of 3½ in. (inside dimensions). To make the box more permanent, coat it with asphaltum paint. Cut four pieces of window glass of such dimensions that they will fit on edge inside the box as shown in Fig. 12.33. The glass sides and ends should have a depth of about 16 in. Set the panes of glass on edge against the box walls. Brace them at the bottom by nailing a strip of wood to the box bottom, with the strips pressing tightly against each pane. Screws may be used instead of the strips by partly driving them into the bottom, allowing the heads to brace the glass walls. Support the corners above the box with four galvanized iron strips 1½ by 14 in., bent at right angles lengthwise through the center, forming four angle irons. Each of these is slit ½ in. at one end along the bend, and the two pieces formed by the cut are bent at right angles to the angle irons. A hole is punched or drilled in each of these to receive a nail or screw to fasten them on top of the wooden box corners. The opposite ends of the angle irons are slit along the bend for a distance of about 1 in. It is best to remove a ⅛-in. strip of metal in making the slit. Fasten the perforated ends to corners of the box with screws or nails as shown in Fig. 12.33. Fit the angle irons tightly against the glass corners. With pliers bend the opposite slit ends down over the adjoining panes. This locks the corners at the top and adds greatly to the strength of the case. A large pane of glass should be used as a cover for the terrarium. The metal corners raise the lid slightly, which is beneficial for ventilation. The dimensions of the case may be varied to suit materials at hand for its construction or for the specific needs of the laboratory.

TOOLS

Dissecting Needles. Various sizes of dissecting needles are made by driving needles or steel pins into wooden handles ranging in sizes from match sticks up to those the size of a pencil. To do this, place the needle in a vise or hold it in a pair of pliers and pound the handle onto the needle. Another type of handle may be made of glass by warming a piece of glass tube and placing one end in melted sealing wax to a depth of 1 in. or more. Place the finger over the other end of the tube and lift it from the wax cup. While the wax in the tube is soft, thrust a needle into it to a depth of 1 in. Hold it until the wax has hardened enough to keep its place.

Dissecting Pan. From a five-and-ten-cent store get a rectangular cake pan about 1 in. deep. Melt over a slow fire equal quantities of beeswax and paraffin. Pour this into the cake pan to a depth not to exceed ⅜ in. When the wax has frozen the dissecting pan is ready for use. This will cost less than half the price asked by supply houses.

Drills. Often one finds that the right size of drill is not in the tool collection. One can be made quickly and easily from a wire nail. Cut off the head. Flatten the pointed end with a hammer to the width necessary. File or grind a sharp bevel on each edge. Placed in a brace this serves as an emergency drill for wood and soft metal.

A drill for glass may be made by breaking the end from a three-cornered file. This leaves a sharp, ragged edge. This may be straightened up on a small emery wheel to give it bite. Place the handle end of the file in a brace and proceed as with an ordinary drill. The glass must be on a very even surface and less pressure is applied than for wood or metal. Too much pressure is sure to cause breakage. After the drill has started through the surface, progress is more rapid. Some patience is required at first. A few trials should be made first on worthless pieces of glass to determine the proper amount of pressure.

Hole Cutter. For drilling holes in cork or rubber stoppers, vegetables, or any soft substance, a set of standard cork borers is very convenient but not always available. Small drills, gimlets, and apple corers can usually be had at any five-and-ten-cent store and will serve satisfactorily as substitutes for the more expensive equipment. The edge of a small piece of metal pipe may be ground at one end or filed so as to make a sharp cutting edge. This will make a good hole cutter for corks, etc. A cork should be placed tightly in the neck of a bottle before being drilled with a bit or gimlet to prevent the hole from being irregular.

Scalpels. Safety-razor blades (single-edge type with a back) with a part of the blade broken out serve as dissecting knives for various purposes. The pieces broken out may also be made into serviceable instruments by soldering them onto handles. Very small ones may be made by heating the tip of a dissecting needle, flattening the point out with a hammer, and tempering by plunging into cold water while very hot. A suitable edge is then prepared by filing or grinding. These are very useful in cleaning fern prothallia, moss rhizoids, etc.

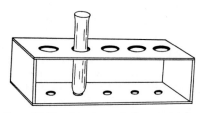

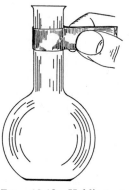

Fig. 13.12 An inexpensive test-tube rack.

Fig. 13.13 Holding a hot tube or flask with a folded, heavy, paper strip.

Section Razor. A discarded old-style straight-edge razor often makes a good razor for freehand sections. Safety-razor blades with one edge and a back, such as the Gem, are inexpensive and serviceable. Also, there is a section razor on the market which is very good. It is of metal construction, has a blade similar to a Gem safety-razor blade but is longer and with a more durable edge. Extra blades may be purchased. The razor has something of the appearance of the old-style straight edge.

Test-tube Rack. A test-tube rack is a necessity whenever test tubes are used. Make one from small strips of thin wood or a shallow box. Bore holes in one side slightly larger than the tubes; in the other side bore holes of half that diameter. A cardboard box may be used and square holes cut with a knife.

Test-tube or Flask Holder. To avoid burning the fingers when heating test tubes or flasks, fold a square of paper into a strip and wrap it about the tube or neck (Fig. 13.13).

WATERPROOFING

Asphaltum is useful in waterproofing many surfaces where a black paint is not objectionable. It may be used on metal, wood, and concrete. In concrete tanks there is a slow diffusion of calcareous materials into the water. Sometimes this is objectionable in growing cultures of plants and animals. Coating the surface with asphaltum paint reduces this difficulty to a minimum. Containers coated with asphaltum should be dried thoroughly before using, then washed with numerous changes of water to remove all traces of oils or other substances released by the paint.

Collodion or cellulose acetate is a useful substance for waterproofing and sealing corks in bottles and waterproofing labels. Dilute solutions (about 6 per cent) should be used. Fit the cork tightly in the bottle. Dip the cork, submerging a portion of the bottle neck, in the sealing compound and allow it to dry. This will occur more rapidly in a current of air or near a source of heat, such as an electric light. If properly done, a thin membrane of collodion will cover the cork and extend down on the glass of the bottle. If desired, this membrane may be increased in thickness by repeatedly dipping and drying. This method is particularly useful for vials or other small bottles containing liquids which are to be shipped or stored for long periods. The collodion or cellulose acetate seal will prevent the loosening of corks and resulting leakage. Several kinds of liquid plastics can be obtained and painted over surfaces like varnish.

Paraffin is a very useful material about most laboratories. Corks may be waterproofed and made airtight by boiling them for half an hour or longer in paraffin. This procedure is often necessary for corks used in wide-mouthed bottles where air is to be forced through a system as in the respiration apparatus (see Fig. 19.4). Screw-cap metal lids may be dipped into paraffin to prevent rust and to assist in sealing. Occasionally in experimental work it is desirable to waterproof clay flower pots. This may be done by dipping the pots in melted paraffin, or the paraffin may be painted on with a paint brush. At times it is necessary to waterproof table tops, labels, fabrics, etc. Melted paraffin is useful in treating such surfaces. If the surface is large and difficulty is experienced in keeping the paraffin melted, it may be dissolved in gasoline at the rate of about 1 lb. to the gallon. The paraffin should be melted and then poured into the gasoline. Never mix the hot paraffin with the gasoline in a room where there is a flame or other open fire. The gasoline vapor ignites readily. The gasoline solution of paraffin may be applied to surfaces the same as paint. When the gasoline evaporates a layer of paraffin remains. Table tops may be paraffined in another way which may be more convenient than the above methods. Scatter some paraffin shavings or powder over the surface to be treated. With a hot electric flatiron melt the paraffin and hasten the penetration by "ironing" the surface repeatedly for several minutes. It is possible to force a large amount of paraffin into a wooden table top by such means. When thoroughly done the table top is not only waterproofed but is also nearly acidproof. This treatment is not recommended for desks.

Silicones, certain polymeric compounds of silicon which have remarkable properties of elasticity, protective covering, insulation, and waterproofing may be obtained in liquid form and applied over surfaces or impregnated into cloth to protect and render them watertight.

Shellac is used widely as a waterproofing material. It is soluble in alcohol. Clear, or white, shellac should be used for waterproofing labels, and where the appearance of the grain of wood is to be retained.

Petroleum jelly is useful in rendering cork stoppers leakproof and even airtight. For corks used in bottles containing liquids, such as preservative on specimens, drop the corks into melted petroleum jelly and keep hot for 20 min. Remove the corks and stand them on a newspaper until the petroleum jelly cools. This treatment usually prevents bottles from losing liquid contents over a long period of time.

SOURCES OF BIOLOGICAL SUPPLIES

Biological Supply Companies

California Botanical Materials Company, 787 Melville Ave., Palo Alto, Calif. Microscope slides and preserved botanical materials. Many Pacific Coast species are offered along with others.

California Insectaries, Inc., 1612 W. Glenoaks Blvd., Glendale, Calif.

Cambosco Scientific Company, 37 Antwerp St., Brighton Station 35, Boston, Mass. Biological materials, collecting supplies, etc.

Carolina Biological Supply Company, Elon College, N.C. Living and preserved biological materials.

Chicago Apparatus Company, 1735 N. Ashland Ave., Chicago, Ill. Biological materials, microscope slides, general laboratory apparatus and reagents.

Denoyer-Geppert Company, 5235 Ravenswood Ave., Chicago 40, Ill. Preserved biological materials, microscope slides, charts, models, and general laboratory equipment.

General Biological Supply House (Turtox), 8200 South Hoyne Ave., Chicago, Ill. Living and preserved biological materials, microscope slides, general laboratory supplies.

Hazen, J. M., Alburg, Vt. Living frogs.

Marine Biological Laboratories, Supply Dept., Woods Hole, Mass. Living and preserved biological materials. Many marine species are offered.

New York Scientific Supply Company, Inc., 28 West 30th St., New York 1, N.Y. Preserved biological materials, microscope slides, etc.

Oregon Biological Supply Company, 1806 S. E. Holgate Blvd., Portland, Ore. Biological materials.

Southern Biological Supply Company, 517 Decatur St., New Orleans, La. Living and preserved biological materials, microscope slides, etc.

South-Western Biological Supply Company, 415 Tyler Ave., Dallas, Tex. Living and preserved biological materials, microscope slides, etc.

Triarch Botanical Products, Ripon, Wis. Living and preserved botanical materials, microscope slides, etc.

Ward's Natural Science Establishment, Inc., 3000 Ridge Road, Rochester, N.Y.

Preserved biological materials, microscope slides, skeletons, insect collections, fossils, etc.

W. M. Welch Manufacturing Company, 1515 Sedgwick St., Chicago, Ill. Preserved biological materials, microscope slides, and general laboratory equipment.

General Laboratory Supplies

American Museum of Natural History, 77th St. and Central Park West, New York 24, N.Y. Lantern slides, photographs, pamphlets, etc.

Bausch & Lomb Optical Company, Rochester, N.Y. Microscopes and other optical equipment, microtomes, etc.

Carolina Biological Supply, Elon College, Ohio, N.C.

Central Scientific Company, 1700 Irving Park Blvd., Chicago, Ill. Laboratory apparatus.

DeVry. Q. R. S. DeVry Corporation, 4829 Kedzie Ave., Chicago, Ill. Projection apparatus, motion-picture film, etc.

Eastman Kodak Company, Rochester, N.Y. Projection apparatus, cameras, motion pictures, chemicals, etc.

Eimer and Amend, 933 Greenwich Ave., New York 11, N.Y. Laboratory apparatus and reagents.

Fisher Scientific Company, 709–719 Forbes St., Pittsburgh, Pa. Laboratory appliances.

Harshaw Scientific Co., 1945 East 97th St., Cleveland 6, Ohio.

Kewaunee Manufacturing Company, Kewaunee, Wis. Laboratory furniture.

American Optical Company, Buffalo 15, N.Y. Microscopes and other optical equipment, microtomes, etc.

Thomas. Arthur H. Thomas Company, Vine Street at 3d, Philadelphia 5, Pa. Laboratory apparatus and reagents.

REFERENCES

1. Alexandra, Sister Mary: "How to Equip Your Science Laboratory and Prepare for a Science Fair," *Catholic School J.*, **55**:348, December, 1955.

2. Berg, Clifford O.: "Technique for Projecting Images of Living Animals, etc.," *Trans. Am. Microscop. Soc.*, **67**(4):384–387; plate 1, October, 1948.

3. Chiscon, J. A.: "Cut-out Life Cycles," *School Sci. and Math.*, **55**:741–742, December, 1955.

4. Davis, H. M.: *Scientific Instruments You Can Make*, Science Service, Inc., Washington, D.C., 1954.

5. Duke, H. E.: "Providing and Adapting Apparatus and Equipment for Teaching Biology," *Am. Biol. Teacher*, **13**:128–131, October, 1951.

6. Gray, E.: "Model Making for Biology," *School Sci. and Math.*, **43**:828–836, December, 1943.

7. Johnson, K. C., and T. J. Kerwan: "Current Practices in the Use of Greenhouses as Part of the Biology Program in High Schools," *Sci. Educ.*, **36**:85–89, March, 1952.

8. Lister, H.: *Aids to Zoology*, 5th ed., The Williams and Wilkins Company, Baltimore. In preparation.

9. Lynde, C. J.: *Science Experiences with Inexpensive Equipment*, 2d ed., D. Van Nostrand Company, Inc., Princeton, N.J., 1950.

10. Needham, J. G.: *Culture Methods for Invertebrate Animals*, Comstock Publishing Associates, Inc., Ithaca, N. Y., 1937.

11. Parkhurst, J. L., Jr.: "Inexpensive Exhibits for Biology Teachers," *Am. Biol. Teacher*, **18**:193–195, 1956.

12. Richardson, J. S., and G. P. Cahoon: *Methods and Materials for Teaching General and Physical Science,* McGraw-Hill Book Company, Inc., New York, 1951.

13. Scott, L.: "Use of Liquid Rubber in Making Plaster Models for Science Classes," *Am. Biol. Teacher,* **17**:226–228, November, 1955.

14. Stork, H. E.: "Use of Experiments in Biology Teaching," *Am. Biol. Teacher,* **13**:80–83, April, 1951.

15. Woolever, J. D.: "Using Maps as a Teaching Aid in Biology," *Am. Biol. Teacher,* **18**:91–92, February, 1956.

16. Yothers, L. R.: "Identification Aid When Dissecting Frogs," *School Sci. and Math.,* **47**:421–423, May, 1947.

CHAPTER 14

---⊰ Preparations for the Microscope ⊱---

This chapter is not intended to be a complete treatise on microtechnic. In most instances only the simpler methods which do not require the use of expensive apparatus such as microtomes have been included. Procedures for representative forms have been selected and discussed, expecting that they may be applied to similar tissues which may be more available than the ones specifically mentioned. Many of the methods dealing with plant tissues may be applied to animal tissues as well, and vice versa. At the end of the chapter some standard references are given for the benefit of those who wish to pursue more intricate methods than are given here.

Use of the Microscope. Learning to use a fine compound microscope is a privilege which no intelligent person should be denied. With such an instrument, a vast new world is made available for him to explore. For many, it has meant the initiation of a lifetime career.

Magnification. One of the first problems occurring to the beginner is the power or extent of the magnification resulting from use of any particular lens system. This may be readily explained if a standard microscope is available. The eyepiece (ocular) will bear a number such as 10× or 12×. Also, the objectives are marked as to the power of their particular lens systems such as 45× for the high power. If a 10× ocular is used in combination with the 45× objective, the magnifying power of this combination is 10 times 45, or 450. That is, *any one dimension* will be magnified 450 times. The magnification is properly expressed as diameters, and not areas. For example, the 10× ocular lens system would make a line appear to be 10 times longer than without magnification. Two sides of a square would be magnified 10 times along one side and 10 times along the other; therefore the included area would be 100 times as great. However, it would give an erroneous idea to state that for this reason such a lens system has the power of 100. This has happened in the advertising of some cheap substandard microscopes.

Measuring with the Microscope. Microscopic measurements are as important for the proper visualization and understanding of microscopic objects as macroscopic measurements are in our daily lives. The dimensions of vegetative or somatic cells of various tissues, nuclei, chromosomes, plastids, spores, pollen grains, and cells of unicellular organisms are a few examples of microscopic structures commonly measured by the biologist.

To make measurements with a microscope an *ocular micrometer* [1] (eyepiece micrometer or scale) is necessary. The ocular micrometer is a glass disk with an engraved scale of, usually, 50 accurately spaced divisions. These divisions are

[1] The ocular micrometer disk and the stage micrometer are available from the following: American Optical Company, Buffalo 15, N.Y.; Bausch & Lomb Optical Company, Rochester, N.Y.

usually ruled in tenths of a millimeter, but this ruling is magnified by the lens of the ocular. Since these spaces do not have a known standard value, they must be calibrated for each ocular and objective combination. To make this calibration a *stage micrometer* is necessary. The stage micrometer consists of a microscope slide bearing an engraved scale of known values, usually ruled in tenths and hundredths of a millimeter.

To calibrate the ocular micrometer, place the ruled disk, ruled side down, in the ocular. This is done by unscrewing the upper lens mounting (eye lens) of the ocular and resting the disk on the metal diaphragm within the tube of the ocular. Place the stage micrometer on the stage of the microscope. Locate the rulings with the medium power. Turn on the high power, if the high-power objective and ocular system are to be calibrated, and focus until the ruled lines appear sharply. Adjust the ocular micrometer by turning the ocular so that the ruled scale coincides with the scale of the stage micrometer. Move the stage-micrometer slide so that both the large (0.1 mm.) divisions and the smaller divisions (0.01 mm.) are visible. Adjust until the first line (to the left) of the ocular-micrometer scale exactly coincides with a larger division line and the other end of the ocular micrometer scale is superimposed on the smaller (0.01 mm.) divisions of the stage micrometer.

As an example, using a 10× ocular and a 45× objective, the 50 divisions of the ocular micrometer cover or equal one large space and six small spaces of the stage-micrometer scale. Since a large space of the stage micrometer equals 0.1 mm. and the small spaces 0.01 mm., the 50 spaces of the ocular micrometer equal 0.16 mm. Therefore, one ocular micrometer division equals 0.16 divided by 50, or 0.0032 mm. Since 1 mm. equals 1,000 microns (μ is the Greek symbol for the initial letter of the Greek word meaning micron), and one division of the ocular micrometer scale equals 0.0032 mm., 1,000 times 0.0032 equals 3.2 μ, or the value of a small division of the ocular micrometer. In other words, each small division of the ocular micrometer has a value of 3.2 μ when using a 10× ocular and 45× objective combination. This does not mean that another microscope with this same lens system (10× ocular and 45× objective) would have exactly the same calibration value (3.2 μ). Slight variations in the manufacture cause individual differences. In other words each lens system must be calibrated as described above, if they are to be used in making microscopic measurements. The calibration value should be written in India ink or typed on a gummed slide label and applied to the base of the microscope for easy reference. The stage micrometer is of no further use as long as the same lens system is used.

As a specific example, suppose that the length of the long axis of a cell is desired. Place the slide bearing the cell on the stage of the microscope, and adjust the focus sharply. Arrange the ocular micrometer so that the scale is superimposed on the cell, in the same way as one would use a ruler, and determine the length in terms of small divisions of the ocular micrometer. Suppose that the length of the cell equals two and one half small divisions of the ocular micrometer. Then 2½ times 3.2 equals 8 μ, the length of the cell.

Mounting Media for Temporary Preparations. As is known by everyone who has had a little experience examining objects with a microscope, water is a satisfactory mounting medium for almost numberless structures. One only has to examine an object surrounded by air and then reexamine it mounted in water to appreciate the value of proper mounting media. The increased visibility in water over that of air is due to the fact that the refractive indexes of water and glass lenses are more nearly the same than air and glass. It becomes the almost ideal material for mounting purposes when a living organism, or living tissue, is to be examined. Water has some defects or objectionable characteristics, however. It evaporates readily from under a cover glass. This may be prevented temporarily by sealing the edges of the cover glass with petroleum jelly or other material impervious to water. The water is soon relieved of its oxygen supply, causing a living tissue or organism to be suffocated. Cell parts of some tissues have about the same refractive index as water and hence are invisible through the microscope. Some structures have surfaces which cannot be "wet" easily because of surface tensions. Often a layer of air exists about such structures and prevents clear visibility. This is somewhat true of bread mold. If some alcohol is added to the water, better mounts may be had, but the organism is killed. However, for most purposes this does not matter.

Mineral oil (the pharmaceutical product Nujol is very good) is useful for studying living tissues. It is not toxic and is especially valuable in cyclosis (cytoplasmic movement) studies. A piece of onion epidermis mounted in it will remain alive and in active condition for at least 3 days. Visibility of cell parts is better in it than in water.

Protoplasmic Movement (cyclosis). One of the most exciting things, and an experience remembered by nearly all who ever use a microscope, is the movement of cytoplasm visible in several organisms. One of the finest objects for use in demonstrating such movement is a leaf from *Elodea* (*Philotria,* or *Anacharis,* water thyme). Select a leaf from near the growing tip. Carefully remove it from the stem and place it in a drop of water on a slide. Cover with a clean cover glass and examine with the medium power of a microscope. The usually rectangular (in two dimensions) cells are readily apparent as well as several chloroplasts in each cell. If the leaf is in good condition, a slight movement may be noticed. The high-power objective will immediately reveal more. The chloroplasts do not move about individually but are carried by the moving cytoplasm. The movement appears to be speeded up, owing to the higher magnification. Nuclei also may be observed. By focusing up and down one can determine that the cytoplasm lines the cell wall and that a vacuole is located in the central part. This movement may be observed in *Vallisneria* (eel grass); in the long internodal cells of *Chara* and *Nitella* (stoneworts); the epidermis from the concave surface of the fleshy scale leaves of an onion; the hairs on pumpkin, squash, cucumber, and tomato stems; and the stamen hairs of *Tradescantia* (spiderwort), pickerel weed, water hyacinth; etc. Pollen from *Impatiens sultanii,* a common ornamental house and garden plant, known to florists as Sultana or Sultana Daily Bloomer and Touch-Me-Not, placed in a drop of tap water on a microscope slide may germinate in 5 to 10 min. The pollen tube filled with protoplasm usually shows movement of the cytoplasm. *Agrostis alba* (redtop grass) seedlings are unusually fine for this demonstration. Seeds sown on a water surface and kept in a warm room will germinate and be large enough to use within 3 days. Mount a whole seedling in a drop of water and cover with a cover glass. Movement is very prominent in the root hairs and in cells of the primary root. In several of the above-named plants chloroplasts will not be seen but cytoplasmic granules are visible. It will pay to examine many such structures if time and material are available. When using elodea, if movement is not readily found, expose the plants to an electric light for an hour before use. Also gradually warm the water to about room temperature. The movement may be stimulated by placing a copper wire or penny in the water surrounding the plants for a time before using. The addition of a drop of thiamin chloride (vitamin B_1) solution to the elodea leaf mount may speed up the cytoplasmic movement. The light exposure is usually effective. Chloroplasts are quite prominent in the moving cytoplasm of elodea.

Preparations for Demonstrating Mitosis, or Ordinary Cell Division. Cells are the units of structure of all living organisms. Each cell, at least when it is young, is composed of protoplasm (the living system), and ordinarily the unit of protoplasm is enclosed by a cell wall. In turn, the protoplasm of a cell (protoplast) is composed of cytoplasm and, usually, a single nucleus. The cell, as presented here, is unique to the biological world. The protoplasm is the only thing that is alive. Another characteristic, unique to living organisms, is that young cells reproduce (duplicate) by ordinary cell divisions, with the resulting two cells being genetically identical. This ordinary cell division is known as *mitosis*. The zygotes (fertilized eggs) of mammals and seed plants (gymnosperms and angiosperms) divide mitotically, resulting in all the somatic or vegetative cells continuing to be diploid and genetically alike, unless a cytological accident (aberration or mutation) occurs. The roots, stems, and leaves of a given variety of sweet potato may be used in the vegetative propagation of the same variety. What inference may be correctly drawn as to the cytological mechanism involved? See Chap. 21 for further facts and application. Mitosis, or ordinary cell division, is a basic process in understanding growth in any organism.

Warmke's Root-tip Smear Method for Chromosomes in Various Phases of Mitosis. Root tips of the common onion (*Allium cepa*) have long been used for demonstrating the various phases of mitosis.

The chromosomes are relatively large and the diploid number is 16. Dry onions purchased from a vegetable market may be used as a source of root tips. Use pint fruit jars which have been coated with black paint or wrapped with black paper or aluminum foil to exclude light. Fill the jars with tap water. Select onion bulbs which are slightly larger than the diameter of jar mouth. The root end of the onion bulb should just come in contact with the water surface. If the jars are set in a room at about 70°F., a crop of root tips should appear within a week to 10 days. For a maximum number of mitotic division figures the root tips should be taken from roots which are about one-fourth inch in length. Use a sharp safety razor, single-edge blade, to cut off the root tips ⅛ in. or slightly less in length. The meristematic tissue is quite limited as to volume and is located just back of the root cap. The harvesting should be done at about 12:00 noon, since there is evidence of a rhythm in the mitotic divisions of onion during a 24-hr. period, with the maxima for the number of cells actively dividing occurring at 12:00 noon and again about midnight. The procedure after harvesting the root tips is as follows:

1. Fix (kill) the root tips in a solution composed of 1 part glacial acetic acid and 3 parts absolute alcohol, for 12 hr. or more.

2. Transfer the fixed root tips to a solution consisting of 95 per cent alcohol (ethyl) and 1 part concentrated hydrochloric acid for 5 to 10 min.

3. Then transfer the root tips to Carnoy's solution for 5 min. or longer. Carnoy's solution is composed of 3 parts chloroform, 2 parts absolute alcohol, and 1 part glacial acetic acid.

4. Cut a small piece (0.5 mm. or less) from a treated root tip and place it on a clean slide in a drop of iron acetocarmine.

5. Press directly on the piece of root with a small flat scalpel. The cells should separate and float free in the stain. The iron is introduced from the scalpel.

6. Place a cover slip on the drop of stain and apply gentle pressure.

7. Heat carefully by passing the slide three to four times through the flame of an alcohol lamp. This heating increases contrast between the chromosomes and cytoplasm.

8. The slide should now be ready for examination. If it is desirable to keep the preparation for several hours or days, seal the edges of the cover glass as soon as they are dry. The sealing may be done with the paraffin and gum mastic mixture, petroleum jelly, Canada balsam, spar varnish, or Duco cement.

9. If an unusually good slide preparation results, it may be desirable to make the slide permanent. This may be done by the procedure outlined following the discussion and methods suggested for meiosis.

Preparations for Demonstrating Meiosis, Including the Reduction Division. In *meiosis* in contrast to mitosis, homologous chromosomes pair (synapse) at the metaphase stage and do not duplicate. The duplication occurs during the *second* division of meiosis. The chromosome number is reduced by half. In other words, meiosis which occurs in diploid cells results in the formation of haploid cells. An independent recombination of chromosomes results at the time of fertilization. This is the fundamental structural basis which enables hybrid segregation to occur. The meiotic divisions occur but once in a given sexual life cycle, whereas mitosis may occur a billion times before another reduction division may occur. The position of the meiotic divisions in the sexual life cycle varies somewhat in the great groups of living organisms. In nearly 100 per cent of the sexual animals, meiosis occurs immediately preceding the formation of gametes (sexual cells; sperms and eggs). In the Bryophytes (mosses and liverworts), Pteridophytes (ferns and fern allies), Gymnosperms (conifers), and Angiosperms (higher seed plants), meiosis occurs immediately preceding the formation of spores (including the microspores and megaspores). In many of the algae and fungi, meiosis occurs during the first two divisions of the zygote, as germination starts.

The common Easter lily (*Lilium longiflorum*, Croft, Ace, Georgia, and Estate are common varieties) is ordinarily good material for demonstrating meiosis in the young anthers. If the bulbs can be planted 75 to 80 days before being needed in the laboratory, and kept at 60°F. at night and 70°F. during the day, flower buds of the right size should be available for demonstrating the meiotic divisions. When the buds are approximately one-fourth to one-third grown, they are usually at about the right state for such work. One must remember that one phase of the meiotic division passes rapidly to another when the plants are under good growing conditions.

A native spring-flowering plant the purple flowering wake-robin (*Trillium erectum*) is excellent for the study of meiosis in the anthers. The short stout rhizomes of this plant will likely have flower buds with anthers containing sporogenous tissues (microspore mother cells or microsporocytes) about August first. By careful and slight dissection, the tip of the young bud at the apical end of the rhizome may be exposed. Snip off a piece of an anther tip, crush it and stain with the simplified acetocarmine method given below. If the microspore mother cells are still inactive, place the rhizomes in moist peat in a container, which can be covered with a glass plate and kept under good growing conditions. Examine the bud once or twice daily until meiosis is discovered. When in the state desired, store the container, with the rhizomes covered by moist peat, in a refrigerator at a temperature somewhat above freezing, until the material is needed for class use, perhaps several weeks later.

Tuberlike rhizomes of *Trillium erectum* may be purchased from Gardens of the Blue Ridge, E. C. Robbins, Nurseryman, Ashford, McDowell County, N.C.

Procedure for Using the Iron Acetocarmine Method for Staining Sporogenous Tissue

1. With a sharp razor, cut off a small piece of a lily anther from a young bud. Place it in a drop of iron acetocarmine and crush with a flattened or spear-point needle.

2. Cover the mount with a cover glass. Place the slide between blotters (filter paper will do). With the left index finger hold the blotters and left end of the slide tightly against the table. With the right index finger give a smearing stroke over the cover glass from left to right. This should separate the cells and chromosomes. Remove the blotter and pass the slide through an alcohol flame until small bubbles appear evenly distributed over the mount. The heating removes most of

the color from the cytoplasm and concentrates stain in the chromosomes. Seal the cover to the slide.

3. The slide is ready for examination. If desirable to keep it for several hours or days, seal the edges of the cover glass as soon as they are dry. The sealing may be done with petroleum jelly, paraffin and gum mastic mixture, Canada balsam, valspar, Duco, etc.

4. If overstaining occurs, run acetic acid under the cover glass and warm slightly.

Permanent Acetocarmine Preparations

1. Obtain young anthers (lily is excellent) in various stages of development.

2. Crush an anther on a clean slide and spread the contents over a small area.

3. Place the slide in a petri dish or some other convenient container and cover the slide with the following solution:

Solution *A*

Distilled water .... 86.5 cc.
Glacial acetic acid 12   cc.
Chromic acid (saturated solution) .... 1.5 cc.

Solution *B*

Distilled water .... 50 cc.
Formalin (commercial strength) .... 50 cc.

Mix equal quantities of solutions *A* and *B* just before using. Pour the solution carefully into the dish. Do not dash it on the anther smear. Allow the slide to remain in this solution for 2 hr.

4. Wash in tap water for about 3 min. Make several changes of the water. Remove anther-wall debris with forceps or a dissecting needle.

5. Stain approximately 5 min. in 1 per cent aqueous crystal violet which has been boiled and filtered.

6. Rinse in water.

7. Dehydrate in 30 and 50 per cent alcohols for about 3 min. each.

8. Treat for 30 sec. with a solution of 100 cc. of 80 per cent ethyl alcohol to which has been added 1 g. of iodine and 1 g. of potassium iodide.

9. Dehydrate by passing through 95 per cent and absolute alcohol.

10. Clear in oil of wintergreen or oil of cloves.

11. Rinse in xylene.

12. Mount in Canada balsam and apply a cover glass.

If preparations are too dark, either destain in 95 per cent alcohol or reduce the time of staining. Some fine preparations of reduction division, mitosis, and, consequently, chromosomes are possible with this method.

Bacteria. *Temporary Mounts.* Allow some grass or weeds to decay in water which is kept at a temperature of 70 to 80°F. for 1 week. The liquid will be teeming with organisms by that time. Place a drop on a slide and examine with a 4-mm. lens. See that the lenses are thoroughly clean as well as the cover glass. The light should be carefully adjusted to get best results. Dead flies or bees allowed to decay in water for 2 to 3 days will also produce bacteria in abundance, many of which are very large. Rod, sphere, and spiral forms are usually found in abundance from such cultures.

India-ink Preparations. Place a drop of India ink on a clean cover glass. With a toothpick collect scrapings from the teeth near gum margins. Place this material in the India ink and allow it to dry. After drying dehydrate in 100 per cent alcohol for 1 min., clear in xylene for 2 min., and place the cover glass, ink-covered surface down, in a drop of balsam on a slide. Allow the mount to dry. Observe with a 4-mm. lens or, better, with an oil-immersion lens, if available. Spiral forms are usually found in abundance in such preparations.

Gram's Stain

1. Thoroughly clean a cover glass with ether or by scouring with powdered pumice.

2. Place a loop of water (with a loop needle) on the clean cover glass.

3. With a sterile transfer needle touch a pure culture of the bacteria desired and touch it to the drop of water. Do not stir with the needle.

4. Pass the needle through a flame several times to sterilize it. After cooling, spread the culture drop by means of the side of the sterilized needle.

5. Allow the film produced to become air-dry.

6. Fix the bacteria by passing the cover glass through a flame three times at 1-sec. intervals. Hold the cover glass with a pair of forceps during this process.

7. Stain 3 to 4 min. with Gram's aniline gentian violet.

8. Rinse by carefully flowing water over the cover glass, then stain in Lugol's iodine for 1 min.

9. Rinse with 95 per cent alcohol for about 30 sec. or until the excess stain is removed.

10. Rinse with water, and stain with safranin (1 per cent aqueous) for about 1 min.

11. Rinse with water and allow to become air-dry. Dehydrate by passing through 100 per cent alcohol. Air-dry the smear and invert the cover glass in a drop of balsam on a slide. Some bacteria stain blue (Gram positive), while others lose the blue but stain red in the safranine (Gram negative). This method is used often to differentiate between organisms.

Loeffler's Methylene Blue

1–6. Prepare a film of the desired bacteria on a cover glass as directed in steps from 1 to 6, under Gram's stain.

7. Stain the preparation with Loeffler's methylene blue for 2 to 3 min. The time will vary with the kind of organism and its age.

8. Rinse with water by carefully flowing it over the cover glass. Air-dry the preparation and complete the dehydration by passing it through 100 per cent alcohol. Air-dry the dehydrated smear and invert it in a drop of Canada balsam on a slide.

Spores and Pollen Grains. *Collection of Spores and Pollen Grains.* Spores of numerous forms may be observed readily in a drop of water, formalin–acetic acid–alcohol (F.A.A.) fixative, or glycerin. Spores of numerous fungi, algae, mosses, liverworts, ferns, club mosses, horsetails (*Equisetums*), *Selaginellas,* and pollen grains of all the higher plants, some of which are available to everyone, make very interesting preparations. A collection of pollen from various plants is of importance in botanical studies for purposes of comparison. They are of direct economic importance to beekeepers and in the study of hay fever (allergy). The following schedule will give satisfactory results for numerous spores and pollen grains.

1. Smear a slide with gelatin fixative.

2. Sprinkle pollen over the gelatin surface. Be careful not to concentrate it too much.

3. Kill and fix the pollen, flooding the smear with a few drops of 5 per cent formalin. Allow the slide to air-dry for 3 to 4 hr.

4. Hydrate in the following alcohol series: 95, 70, 50, 30 per cent to distilled water at intervals of about 2 min. each.

5. Transfer to 4 per cent aqueous solution of iron alum for 5 min.

6. Rinse with five to six changes of distilled water.

7. Stain for 1 hr. in 0.5 per cent aqueous hematoxylin.

8. Rinse in distilled water.

9. Destain with 2 per cent aqueous iron alum for 5 to 7 min. or until a grayish color appears in the grains.

10. Rinse in distilled water with five to six changes.

11. Intensify with alkaline tap water or with 50 per cent saturated solution of lithium carbonate for 2 to 5 min. A dark-blue color should be produced if destaining did not continue too long in step 9.

12. Rinse in distilled water.

13. Stain in phenol-Bismarck brown for about 5 min.

14. Rinse in distilled water.

15. Dehydrate in 30, 50, 70, 95, and 100 per cent alcohols.

16. Clear in oil of wintergreen or oil of cloves.

17. Transfer to xylene for 2 min.

18. Mount in Canada balsam.

Fern Spore Dispersal. Scrape off a cluster of sporangia which are just mature. Examine in a drop of water by means of a microscope to see that the sporangia are still closed and contain spores. Place a drop of glycerin on one side of the cover glass and a piece of filter paper in contact with the water on the opposite side of the cover. This will draw the water out and the glycerin under. Allow the mount to stand for about 2 min., then examine with the microscope. If the sporangia are mature, they will soon begin to break open, beginning at the lip cells and tearing through the thin wall cells to the annulus, which curves outward. This movement pushes the spores out of the broken sporangium. Glycerin is a dehydrating agent. Dehydration of the annulus and its resulting movement cause the breaking of the sporangium wall. Essentially the same thing happens in nature when the ripened sporangia dry out.

Permanent Preparations of Pollen Tubes

1. Apply a very small drop of Mayer's egg-albumin fixative to a clean slide. With a clean finger tip, smear it as thin as possible over the slide area to receive the mount.

2. Sprinkle some pollen from newly opened flowers of lily or petunia. Do not get the pollen grains too thick.

3. Set the slide in a moist chamber where it will be in a temperature of about 80°F.

4. Examine with a microscope every hour or so for pollen tubes (usually germination occurs within 2 to 5 hr.).

5. When the pollen tubes are found to be present, fix the mount by a few drops of absolute alcohol, decanting it gently after 2 to 3 min. Allow the preparation to air-dry just until the surface appears dry. Prolonged drying will cause plasmolysis of the tubes.

6. Stain in fast green for 10 to 20 sec.

7. Rinse in 95 and 100 per cent alcohols.

8. Clear in a few drops of oil of wintergreen or oil of cloves.

9. Rinse in xylene.

10. Mount in Canada balsam and apply a cover glass.

If phenol-Bismarck brown is desired as a stain the procedure is as follows:

1–5. Proceed as in above directions.

6. Hydrate pollen tubes by dipping in the following alcohol series at 3-min. intervals: 95, 70, 50, 30, and, finally, distilled water.

7. Stain in phenol-Bismarck brown for about 5 min.

8. Rinse in distilled water.

9. Dehydrate in 30, 50, 70, 95, and 100 per cent alcohols at 3-min. intervals.

10. Clear in oil of wintergreen or oil of cloves for 5 min.

11. Rinse in xylene.

12. Mount in Canada balsam and apply a cover glass.

Delafield's hematoxylin also gives very satisfactory results. The procedure is as follows:

1–5. Proceed as in above directions.

6. Hydrate to 50 per cent alcohol.

7. Dilute stock Delafield's hematoxylin about one-third with distilled water and stain the preparation for about 1 min.

8. Rinse in alkaline tap water.

9. Dehydrate in 50, 70, 95, and 100 per cent alcohols.

10. Clear and mount as above.

Stored Foods. *Temporary Preparations.* Starch grains may be examined easily in a drop of water by means of a microscope. Scrape off a small amount of the starchy portion of any structure and mount in water or very dilute iodine. The diluted iodine will give a bluish color to the grains. Potato tuber, *Canna* rhizomes, grains of wheat, corn, oat, barley, rye, rice, etc., give interesting types. Scrapings from the endosperm of castor beans placed in iodine (same as used for starch test) show light-brown protein crystals surrounded by other protein material. Observation of this must be made with a high-power objective (4-mm. lens). Cubical protein crystals may be observed in cells of a potato tuber. They are found most abundantly in cells near the cork layer (peel). In most tubers they are not found abundantly. Poorly developed tubers seem to be the best types in which to locate them in considerable abundance. Thin freehand sections of coconut endosperm, corn cotyledon, castor-bean endosperm, Brazil nut, etc., will show fine oil globules if stained for 15 to 30 min. in Scharlach R (Sudan III), then transferred to a drop of glycerin for observation. The oil droplets stain from pink to a red color.

Permanent Preparations of Tissues Containing Fats. Coconut endosperm, castor bean, Brazil nut, tissues containing cutin, etc., are excellent for study of fat storage and fatty substances.

1. Section tissues in fresh condition. Place in 70 per cent alcohol or 7 per cent formalin for 10 to 20 min.

2. Rinse and treat with 4 per cent iron alum solution for 15 to 20 min.

3. Rinse in distilled water with about six changes.

4. Stain in 0.5 per cent hematoxylin until the cell walls are clearly differentiated.

5. Rinse in tap water. If overstained, destain in 2 per cent iron alum solution. Rinse carefully after this procedure in alkaline tap water.

6. Stain in Scharlach R (Sudan III) for 30 min. or overnight.

7. Rinse thoroughly in 70 per cent alcohol or 10 per cent glycerin in 70 per cent alcohol.

8. Pass through the following glycerin series (made up in 70 per cent alcohol) at 5-min. intervals: 10, 25, 50, 80, and 100 per cent.

9. Mount in glycerin jelly (see page 293).

Leaf Epidermis. *Temporary Mounts.* Select a plant from which epidermal layers peel readily, such as wandering Jew (*Tradescantia zebrina, Zebrina pendula*); ghost plant (*Graptopetalum weinbergii*); *Echeveria weinbergii*, a common succulent grown in homes; plantain (*Plantago major*), a common lawn weed; Boston fern; head lettuce, etc. If the *Tradescantia* is selected, allow the leaves to wilt 8 to 10 hr. before attempting to peel. Much larger strips usually are available under such conditions. Any of these mounted in water makes excellent temporary preparations.

Permanent Preparations

1. Strip off the epidermal layers, keeping the leaf submerged in water during the process. This helps to prevent rolling of the tissue.

2. Transfer the strips to absolute alcohol for fixation for 10 min.

3. Transfer at 3-min. intervals through the following alcohol series: 95, 70, 50, and 30 per cent, then into distilled water.

4. Stain in phenol–Bismarck brown for 3 to 5 min.

5. Rinse in distilled water to remove excess stain.

6. Dehydrate by passing the tissue through the following alcohol series at 3-min. intervals: 30, 50, 95, and 100 per cent.

7. Clear in oil of wintergreen or clove oil. This step may be dispensed with if these reagents are not available. Clearing results are better if one of these oils is used.

8. Cut the strips into about ⅛-in. squares. This can be done easily with a sharp safety-razor blade.

9. Rinse in xylene (xylol). If step 7 is not followed the pieces should remain in the xylene for 2 to 3 min.

10. With a camel's-hair brush transfer the pieces to a drop of Canada balsam on a clean slide.

11. Examine under a microscope and see that the outer surface of the tissue is turned up.

12. Cover with a clean cover glass and allow to dry.

It is possible to prepare an interesting series of such mounts showing presence or absence of stomata on certain surfaces, comparison of numbers of stomata of the same plant species growing in various situations, comparison of plants of various ecological situations, various plant families, etc.

Preparation of Silicious Epidermal Mounts from Equisetum (horsetail, scouring rush)

1. Split stem into strips about 3 to 4 mm. wide.

2. Cut transversely to about 6- to 8-mm. lengths.

3. Soak pieces in concentrated sulfuric acid for 15 to 20 min., swirling gently toward the end to loosen the decomposing tissue.

4. Decant the acid carefully.

5. Rinse thoroughly with water.

6. Dehydrate in 80, 95, and 100 per cent alcohols.

7. Clear in zylene for 2 to 3 min.

8. Mount in Canada balsam and cover with cover glass. If bubbles are present, warm over a hot plate, being careful that the balsam does not get hot enough to bubble.

Such amounts show the epidermal layer in skeleton outline, with the stomata and guard cells nicely displayed. *Equisetum praealtum* and other plants of this general type serve satisfactorily for such preparations.

Maceration of Tissues

1. Cut longitudinal pieces of roots or stems into pieces about 1 mm. in thickness. Drop these into a solution of equal parts of 10 per cent nitric acid and 10 per cent chromic acid (Jeffery's maceration solution). Use the solution immediately after it is made.

2. Let the material stand for 24 to 48 hr. and examine. If the pieces fall apart by teasing with a dissecting needle, they are ready to be removed.

3. Filter out by means of filter paper in a funnel.

4. Wash thoroughly with tap water by pouring it into the filter until no sign of the acids remains. The residue may be stored in 50 or 70 per cent alcohol until needed for mounting.

5. The residue is made up of tissue elements. It is excellent material for studying cell forms. A small quantity may be mounted in glycerin and studied immediately as temporary mounts. Or it may be stained and mounted permanently.

6. Staining is done in the filter the same as washing. Dehydration is also accomplished by pouring alcohol over the residue in the filter. Clearing with xylene may be done in the same way, or the residue may be transferred to a small dish of xylene. With a dry camel's-hair brush transfer small bits to the Canada balsam on a slide. Cover and dry as usual.

Glycerin Preparations. Glycerin is a favorable mounting medium for many objects. It does not evaporate and has a favorable refractive index for many tissues. Algologists often keep their slide collections in the form of glycerin mounts. A small mass of the desired alga is transferred from the preservative to a slide and covered with a cover glass. Glycerin is run under the cover glass and gradually replaces the other preservative. These mounts are serviceable for occasional examinations. If the glycerin spreads out from under the cover glass more glycerin may be added, the mount still remaining usable. This loss can be prevented by sealing the mount with paraffin, gum mastic, asphaltum cement, Duco, or other sealing mixtures. Bryologists often make collections of moss and liverwort parts as glycerin mounts. The parts are placed on a slide in a drop of half water and half glycerin. The slide is held over a flame until penetration takes place. Some require more heating than others. Remove bubbles by pressure on the cover glass. Clean off excess glycerin and seal. Such mounts will often retain a living appearance for many weeks. A collection of such mounts may be retained in suitable form for many years if seals are repaired when broken and lost glycerin is replaced.

Venetian Turpentine Method (Venice turpentine). By means of this method excellent preparations of algae, filamentous fungi, pollen tubes, fern gametophytes (prothallia), moss protonemata, etc., may be made. Beginners often fail with this method because of not following directions carefully. Low concentrations of Venetian turpentine absorb moisture rapidly. If this occurs the preparations are spoiled. The following schedule will give good results if followed carefully:

1. Fix plant material in F.A.A. solution. Leave in this solution for 24 hr. or longer.

2. Transfer to 70 per cent alcohol, rinsing with two or three changes.

3. Complete the dehydration by transferring to 10 per cent glycerin made up with 70 per cent alcohol. Cover the container with cheesecloth to keep out dust particles and allow to concentrate by evaporation to concentrated glycerin.

4. Rinse with 95 per cent alcohol until the glycerin is removed.

5. Stain with phloxine or fast green. The time for the phloxine will range from 10 min. to overnight. Usually it does not overstain seriously. The fast green usually stains sufficiently in 30 to 60 sec.

6. Rinse in 95 per cent alcohol to remove excess stain.

7. Rinse three to four times with 100 per cent alcohol.

8. Transfer to 10 per cent Venetian turpentine. The stock turpentine is diluted to approximately 10 per cent with absolute alcohol. It is difficult to measure accurately because of its viscous nature, and the mixing procedure is necessarily rapid to prevent absorption of moisture as much as possible. Keep the 10 per cent stock in a ground-glass stoppered bottle.

9. As soon as the material is transferred to the 10 per cent Venetian turpentine, set it in an anhydrous calcium chloride desiccator. Close and seal the desiccator immediately. If a regular desiccator is not available one may be made from a battery jar or other glass container which can be sealed airtight with petroleum jelly between the lid and jar. Place about 1 lb. of anhydrous calcium chloride in the

bottom. Cover this with a metal screen ("hardware cloth" will serve). The container with specimens in the Venetian turpentine is set on the screen and left open. Be sure to seal the desiccator airtight with petroleum jelly or other medium. Allow the specimens to remain in the desiccator until the turpentine is of the consistency of glycerin, or thicker. By this time the turpentine is not very sensitive to moisture.

10. Drive moisture off a slide by holding over a flame for 2 to 3 sec. With a needle or forceps quickly lift a specimen with a drop of the Venetian turpentine adhering and place it on the heated area of the slide. Arrange the specimens with a dissecting needle. Pass a cover glass through a flame once or twice to remove hygroscopic moisture and cover the specimen. The Venetian turpentine is used as the mounting medium instead of Canada balsam. It drys more slowly than balsam. Excess turpentine on the slide may be removed after drying first by scraping with a safety-razor blade and followed by a cloth "wet" with absolute alcohol.

The Glycerin-jelly Method. Glycerin jelly is not so permanent as Canada balsam or Venetian turpentine but has the advantages of being quicker and does not necessitate complete desiccation of tissues. For some tissues there seems to be no other substitute. The refractive index is different from that of Canada balsam and Venetian turpentine. Consequently some structures can be seen more clearly when mounted in it than in other media. For tissues in which it is desirable to retain fat compounds, glycerin jelly is the usual mounting medium recommended. The higher grades of alcohol, xylene, ether, chloroform, etc., are used in other technics to remove fats. The following general procedure and one detailed schedule for a tissue containing fat will give a fair idea as to use of this method:

1. Fix in proper solution for the given material for 24 to 48 hr.

2. Remove the fixative by washing in water.

3. Stain as desired. Stain combinations containing safranine usually are not satisfactory since safranine will diffuse slowly from the tissue into the glycerin jelly.

4. Transfer to 10 per cent glycerin made up in water.

5. Allow the glycerin to concentrate in a dish covered with cheesecloth to prevent entrance of dust.

6. After glycerin is concentrated, transfer to pure glycerin, then to melted glycerin jelly. This is done best at a temperature of 60 to 65°C. Remove as much of the pure glycerin as possible before transferring to the glycerin jelly. This may be done by lifting the tissue on a small camel's-hair brush and touching the underside of the brush to filter paper. Too much glycerin carried over will prevent proper hardening of the glycerin jelly.

7. Let the tissues stand in the melted glycerin jelly for 10 to 20 min. before mounting.

8. Arrange to have slides, cover glasses, forceps, brush, and glycerin jelly at the same temperature if possible. This helps to prevent formation of air bubbles in the mounts. Circular cover glasses are preferred since the completed mount must be sealed if the mount is to last. Mounts covered with circular covers are more easily and neatly sealed than squares or rectangles.

9. Place a piece of the tissue in a drop of melted glycerin jelly on a slide and cover with a cover glass. If bubbles develop the larger ones may be teased out with a dissecting needle.

10. Allow the mount to cool. The glycerin jelly will harden within a few minutes when exposed to a cool atmosphere. Any excess may be removed with a safety-razor blade, followed by rubbing with a cloth wet in hot water.

11. Allow the mount to cure for about 1 week. Then seal edges of cover glass to slide with Canada balsam, Duco, asphaltum, gold size, or other sealing compound. The seal should consist of at least two coats of any of these sealing com-

pounds. Allow each to dry thoroughly after each application and before another is applied. A slide turntable is very serviceable in this procedure, but is not absolutely necessary.

Permanent Preparations with Green-colored Chloroplasts. By employing F.A.A. solution with copper sulfate as a fixative, it is possible to fix and "stain" certain plant materials sufficiently by this one procedure. The chloroplast color closely approaches the normal green of chlorophyll. Satisfactory results have been obtained with moss protonemata, fern gametophytes, *Selaginella* sporophylls, and numerous algae. The procedure is as follows:

1. Fix in F.A.A. solution which has been saturated with copper sulfate. A copper wire instead of copper sulfate placed in the F.A.A. along with the specimens also gives very satisfactory results. Leave specimens in the fixative until a normal green color appears, which usually results in 3 to 4 days.

2. Rinse the specimens in 70 per cent alcohol and transfer to 10 per cent glycerin made up with 70 per cent alcohol.

3. Cover the dish containing the glycerin and specimens with cheesecloth to keep out dust. Leave the dish at room temperature and allow the glycerin to concentrate by evaporation.

4. When the glycerin is concentrated, mount the specimens in glycerin jelly. Materials prepared in the above manner cannot be mounted in Canada balsam or Venetian turpentine since the higher alcohols remove too much of the green color.

Fibers. Textile fibers may be mounted easily in water containing a little blue fountain-pen ink (methylene blue), red ink (eosin), or safranine. Fibers from wool cloth, cotton, silk, rayon, linen, etc., make instructive preparations. They are of particular value to those interested in home economics. Such preparations may be made in permanent form with little difficulty. Permanent stains should be used rather than temporary ones such as methylene blue and eosin. Safranine, aniline blue, fast green, any of the hematoxylin dyes, Bismarck brown, etc., are suggestions of stains that will serve satisfactorily. The lower percentages of alcohols may be dispensed with in dehydration. After staining, fibers may be transferred through 95 and 100 per cent alcohols with two changes in the absolute alcohol (100 per cent), cleared in oil of wintergreen, oil of cloves, or cedarwood oil (this may be dispensed with if the oils are not available), transfered to xylene for about 2 min. (about 5 min. if the oils are dispensed with), and into Canada balsam as usual. Such preparations, if properly made, are valuable in teaching beginning students depths of focus of microscope. A good preparation for this may be made by crossing two or three fibers stained differently. Determining which is above and which below helps the beginner to learn to use a microscope and indicates to the instructor the student's ability with this instrument.

Freehand Sections. *Fresh Tissues.* Even though a laboratory may be equipped with expensive microtomes it is of value to know how to make presentable freehand sections of tissues. It is a simple and timesaving method to use when sections do not need to be cut accurately or be of exactly the same thickness. Many tissues can be studied successfully from carefully made freehand sections. Safety-razor blades or the ordinary razor may be used. Whichever is used, a sharp blade is a necessity. For fresh tissues the blade should be kept flooded with water, flooding before each stroke. For preserved tissues wet the knife in the preservative, and also transfer sections to this solution. Make all transfers with a small camel's-hair brush. Hold the tissues in the left hand. With the razor in the right hand make a long oblique stroke through the tissue from left to right toward the operator's body. If sections are to be used in the preparation of permanent mounts, they should be transferred to F.A.A. solution or other recommended fixative. The sections should be carefully examined and worthless ones discarded. Usually considerable practice is necessary before a large percentage of the sections is satisfactory. It is not always necessary to get complete cross sections of the organ or tissue being studied. Often small slivers are valuable. For delicate tissues it is often necessary to clamp the material between two blocks of cork, pith (elderberry, corn, sunflower, etc.), pieces of carrot, or potato. Zoologists often use blocks of liver which have been hardened in 10 per cent formalin. Leaves, stems, and roots also may be encased in paraffin by dipping single pieces or bundles of pieces, depending upon size, in paraffin which has been cooled to almost congealing point. Successive dippings will soon build up a heavy layer of paraffin about the tissues. The tissues may be successfully supported for cutting in this manner. The paraffin will separate readily from the tissues when floated on the water.

Paraffin Infiltrated and Embedded Tissues. Soft tissues such as root tips, stamens, ovularies (ovaries), herbaceous stems, and many leaves cut more satisfactorily when infiltrated and embedded in paraffin. The following schedule gives satisfactory results:

1. Fix the fresh tissues in F.A.A. for about 3 days. Pieces may be left indefinitely in this solution if desired.

2. Transfer to the following alcohol series at 3-hr. intervals—they may be left longer in each if necessary—70, 80, 95, and 100 per cent. Change two or three times in the 100 per cent alcohol.

3. From the absolute alcohol transfer through the following xylene series: 25, 50, 75, and 100 per cent at intervals of about 4 hr. each. The xylene series is made up by diluting xylene with absolute alcohol. Make two changes in the pure xylene.

4. Add a block of paraffin, the volume of which is approximately equal to the xylene volume. Allow this to stand at room temperature for 2 or 3 days. Some of the paraffin should remain undissolved. If not, add more paraffin.

5. The xylene now must be removed, chiefly by evaporation. Place the container near some heat source which will just keep the paraffin melted. Do not get it too hot. A glass platform suspended over an electric-light bulb and adjusted properly will give the right amount of heat. After the xylene has nearly disappeared, as detected by odor or taste, decant the paraffin and replace with fresh melted paraffin. Two such changes should remove all the remaining xylene.

6. The specimens now are ready to embed. Prepare paper boxes or small dishes for this purpose. Pour melted paraffin into the container and transfer the tissues to it. Arrange the pieces so that blocks of paraffin may be cut out containing a single specimen. Slowly submerge the container in a pan of cold water. As soon as a thin film of congealed paraffin forms over the surface, the dish may be completely submerged. Allow it to remain in the cold water until the paraffin is thoroughly congealed. The blocks then may be removed from the containers and cut immediately or stored indefinitely.

7. Blocks of paraffin containing individual specimens are cut from the large piece. Support these in a clamp or small vise and make freehand sections. Use a very sharp razor for sectioning and make the sections as thin as possible.

8. Place a small drop of egg-albumen fixative, about the amount carried on the end of a match stem, on a clean slide. With a clean finger smear the drop over the slide until the smear appears dry. Place a drop of water on the smear. Transfer a section or sections to it. Warm the slide enough to smooth out the sections but do not allow them to melt. Decant the water and lay the slide away to dry for 24 hr. or longer.

9. Remove the paraffin by placing the slide in xylene for about 10 min. The xylene may be kept in a glass tumbler and may be used over for many slides.

10. Rinse with absolute alcohol and treat as for other freehand sections.

Preparation of Dried Wood for Sectioning. With a saw and sharp knife cut wood into blocks of a size convenient to handle. Trim the end to be sectioned to size of the desired section. In cutting the block one must have in mind the type of section to be made, transverse (cross section), radial longitudinal (made in a plane parallel to the vascular rays), or tangential longitudinal (made in a plane at right angles to the rays). Drop the blocks in water and boil for 10 min. Transfer them quickly to cold water and leave until cool. Plunge them quickly into boiling water, as before. Repeat the cold-water process. Often they will sink this time. If not, repeat the process until sinking occurs. After sinking boil again and plunge the blocks into glycerin. Allow the blocks to remain in the glycerin for 3 to 4 days or until needed. This softens most woods sufficiently for sectioning. Before staining, carefully wash glycerin out of the sections with 50 per cent alcohol or water. Stain as for stems or roots.

Sectioning and Staining of Leaf Tissues

1. Cut inch-long strips of the desired leaf such as privet, lilac, blue myrtle, or a dozen or more such lengths of pine needles. Tie them in bundles and dip in melted paraffin which is just about ready to congeal. Repeat the dipping several times until a considerable thickness of paraffin is built up about the leaf pieces. Cool the paraffin in cold water. Section freehand with a sharp razor blade or on a microtome.

2. Drop the sections into F.A.A. and let stand for 10 to 20 min. or until ready to use.

3. Rinse in 70 per cent alcohol and stain in safranine Y for 30 to 60 min.

4. Rinse off excess safranine in 70 per cent alcohol and pass the sections through 80 and 95 per cent alcohols.

5. Stain in fast green for 30 sec., rinse in 95 and 100 per cent alcohols.

6. Clear in oil of wintergreen or oil of cloves.

7. Rinse in xylene and transfer to Canada balsam.

8. Cover with a cover glass, dry, and clean.

Stem and Root Sections. *Safranine-fast Green*

1. Make fresh sections either freehand or with a microtome.

2. Transfer to 70 per cent alcohol for about 10 min. For herbaceous structures where plasmolysis occurs use F.A.A.

3. Transfer to 50 per cent alcohol for 3 min.

4. Stain for 1 to 2 hr. in safranine.

5. Rinse in 50 per cent alcohol.

6. Dehydrate in 70 per cent for 3 min.

7. Stain in fast green for 20 to 60 sec.

8. Decant the stain quickly and rinse in 95 per cent and absolute alcohols.

9. Clear in oil of wintergreen or oil of cloves for 3 min.

10. Rinse in xylene.

11. Mount in Canada balsam and cover with a cover glass.

Iron alum–hematoxylin–phenol–Bismarck brown

1. Transfer fresh sections to 70 per cent alcohol or F.A.A. solution for 10 min.

2. Hydrate in 50 and 30 per cent alcohols.

3. Transfer to distilled water.

4. Place sections in 4 per cent iron alum solution for 10 min.

5. Wash with six changes of distilled water for about 20 min.

6. Stain in 0.5 per cent aqueous hematoxylin about 1 min. This will vary for various species.

7. Rinse in distilled water.

8. Destain in 2 per cent iron alum until a grayish-blue color results.

9. Wash in six changes of distilled water for about 20 min.

10. Intensify hematoxylin with alkaline tap water or distilled water with 1 per cent sodium bicarbonate added. The rapidity of intensification will vary with the

amount of destaining done in step 8. A blue-black color will result in lignified walls, nuclei, and especially in middle lamellae.

11. Rinse carefully in distilled water.

12. Stain for 1 to 5 min. in phenol–Bismarck brown. The time varies with different tissues and different species.

13. Rinse in distilled water.

14. Dehydrate in 30, 50, 70, 95, and 100 per cent alcohols.

15. Clear in oil of wintergreen or oil of cloves.

16. Rinse in xylene.

17. Mount in Canada balsam and cover with cover glass.

Chemical Test for Common Materials Found in Tissues. *Fats, Oils, Suberin, and Cutin.* Saturate 70 per cent alcohol with Scharlach R (Sudan III) and filter the solution. When tissues containing fats, oils, suberin of cork cells, and cutin (cuticle) are treated in this solution for half an hour or longer a pink to red color appears. When these fatty substances are not present in abundance, it is best to transfer the treated sections to glycerin and observe them by means of a microscope.

Lignin. Lignin is characteristically present in the cell walls of mature wood. Its presence may be tested for by placing a tissue in 5 per cent phloroglucin for about 3 min., then treating with 25 per cent hydrochloric acid for 1 to 3 min. A pinkish red to deep red color is produced if lignin is present.

Cellulose. Treat material with chlorzinc iodide for a minute or so and follow with 70 per cent sulfuric acid. A blue color is produced if cellulose is present.

Starch. Apply iodine solution to tissue. Do not heat. If starch is present a blue-black color is produced. For most practical purposes this test is satisfactory. However, narceine produces blue crystals when present; saponarin in solution in some cell saps and amyloid, a membrane material, give a blue reaction when treated with iodine. Amylodextrin (red starch) gives a red reaction with iodine. It can be produced when ordinary starch is heated, and is found in the endosperm of sweet, waxy, and waxy-sweet varieties of corn.

Sugar (Glucose). *Fehling's test* (see Chap. 17).

Tannin. Make a water extract of tissue to be tested. Add some ferric chloride. A black color indicates tannin. Tissue dipped directly into the iron solution will give the test.

Protozoa. *Temporary Preparations.* Large forms of protozoa such as paramecium, large amoeba, opalina, etc., are best observed in a drop of their culture medium without a cover glass. Care must be taken to avoid attempts at using an objective as high powered as 4 mm. because its focal distance will bring it within the top of the liquid. In the study of such living organisms there is a use of the microscope which is frequently overlooked. An amoeba, for example, has practically no color and as seen with light transmitted from a mirror it seems to have but two dimensions. If a dark field is produced by completely closing the diaphragm under the stage and a strong light placed so that it shines down upon the specimens from above, the amoebae immediately assume a third dimension (depth) and are transformed into snow-white objects. They are beautiful but opaque, which means that for internal structure it is necessary to use the transmitted light.

Many protozoa, especially the ciliates, which are most abundant, can be lightly stained with neutral red by placing a little of this nontoxic dye in a drop of culture. Forms like paramecium absorb it, staining heavily such structures as food vacuoles and food particles. Sometimes it brings out clearly the cilia, which usually are difficult to see. The stain does not kill the animals, and they continue to swim about actively. Methylene blue can be used in like manner for some organisms.

Permanent Mounts. Kill some of a highly concentrated culture of protozoa. Transfer a drop of material containing numerous individuals to a microscope slide which has been previously smeared with albumen fixative. Allow this to evaporate without heating until just a film of moist fixative remains. The protozoa will adhere to this and the slide may be run into the stain (hematoxylin-eosin) and then into 35, 50, 70, 95 per cent and absolute alcohols and then into xylene. Two minutes in each alcohol is sufficient. As the xylene dries add the Canada balsam and cover with a cover glass.

Sponges. Some of the small sponges known as calcareous sponges (such as *Scypha*) have skeletons composed of needlelike spicules. If such a sponge is placed in a small porcelain dish or beaker with a little hot solution of caustic soda or caustic potash (NaOH or KOH) the organic matter will be dissolved, leaving a small residue of spicules looking like splinters of glass. These may be examined in a drop of water, or they may be dried and then stuck to a microscope slide on which has first been placed a thin smear of balsam. No cover glass is needed.

If very small bits of common bath sponge are dipped into cedarwood oil or xylene, then touched to a piece of paper to remove excess oil, and laid on a drop of balsam, they will sink into the balsam with but few air bubbles. They may be covered with a cover glass and dried. The natural brown color of the spongin skeletal material is readily visible without staining.

Uncovered Mounts of Dried Objects. Some small organisms, or their skeletal parts, are seen to advantage when mounted whole. If the form is angular or aborescent it may be difficult to mount under a cover glass. Such things as fish scales, the skeletons of bryozoa, sponges, the hard parts of insects, such as the whole head of a fly, and the like, may be cleaned and mounted on a microscope slide by placing the object upon a small thin drop of Canada balsam and setting it aside to dry. These things are large and too opaque for transmitted light and must be examined under a reflected beam. They also require low magnification with which a dark-field background gives a binocular effect which is often a decided advantage.

Compound Eyes of Insects. The compound eye of an insect such as a fly, dragonfly, or grasshopper is large enough so that it can be partly peeled and the outer layer showing facets removed. Cut through the eye surface with a safety-razor blade and try to get the outer surface to loosen over a small area. If this does not seem to work, try making a very thin slice, the edges of which will be thin enough to see clearly with a microscope. Such a preparation can be made permanent in the same manner as given for hair, feathers, and scales.

Whole Mounts of Small Insects, Mites, Ticks, Etc. Many animal forms do not require staining for serviceable mounts. Thoroughly dehydrate each specimen in an alcohol series, clear in oil of wintergreen or oil of cloves, allow to stand a few minutes in xylene and mount in Canada balsam. A very interesting collection can be prepared in this way. Parts dissected from large forms may be prepared similarly—mouth parts of a honeybee, wings, legs, stinger, etc.; eye of a housefly, wings, legs, mouth parts, portion of abdomen, etc.; scales from moth and butterfly wings, antennae, eggs of smaller forms, etc.

Glochidia of Common Mussels. When adult clams or mussels are collected and opened or preserved to be used later, one should always examine the gills carefully. If these seem to be thick and swollen it is reasonably certain that they are filled with the larvae (glochidia) of the clam. If a portion of the gill is torn open, tiny glochidia will be set free like minute grains of sand. When seen under the microscope they are found to have the same bivalve form as the adult clam. The glochidia may be dehydrated in an alcohol series (50, 75, 95, 100 per cent), transferred to xylene, and mounted in Canada balsam. No staining is necessary but alum carmine or hematoxylin may be used.

Tapeworms. These parasitic worms are frequently found in dogs, cats, and rats and may be obtained in large numbers at times from slaughterhouses where they are taken from pigs and sheep. To remove them from a fresh intestine without breaking the worms and losing the most interesting part, the scolex, pass a quantity of very warm salt water through the intestine. This usually causes the worms to relax their hold and to pass out. They may be killed in the relaxed condition by placing in water and slowly heating to about 60°C. They may be fixed in cold corrosive sublimate (bichloride of mercury) 7 per cent or formalin 6 per cent. Tapeworms may be preserved entire and used in wet mounts as needed, but the internal structures are best made visible as follows:

1. Cut the worm into small pieces of one or two complete proglottids, according to size. The mature proglottids are best. Place in a dish and wash to remove the fixative or preservative.

2. Carefully remove the scoleces with a few adjacent proglottids. Keep these in a separate dish.

3. Stain in either Delafield's hematoxylin or alum carmine. The staining time will have to be watched carefully and varied with the size of the part. If staining is done in a shallow glass dish, such as a watch glass, it may be placed upon the microscope stage and the degree of staining watched. If the small and large parts are kept separate they can be stained uniformly.

4. Dehydrate the scoleces and proglottids separately in an alcohol series up to 90 or 95 per cent, clear in oil of wintergreen and mount directly in Canada balsam. The proglottids should be mounted separately from the scoleces because of the differences in thickness.

Skin Cells (epithelium). If a frog or mud puppy is placed in a pan or jar containing 1 in. of water and allowed to stand for several hours, the water becomes cloudy with thin flakes and strings of the epidermis or outer layer of skin. Lift a small piece of this material out and place in a large drop of water on a microscope slide. If manipulated with pin points it can be made to float out into a sheet, stain with fountain-pen ink for several minutes and then cover with a cover glass and examine. The regular pavementlike cells with straight sides and definite nuclei make excellent illustrations of cell structure.

The unused pieces of skin should be placed in 5 per cent formalin to which has been added 10 per cent glycerin. It can thus be kept and used at any time. Similar material can be obtained from the membrane of the human mouth. Use a very dull knife or a sharp-edged paddle (a toothpick will do) and scrape the inside of the cheeks. Wash the mucus so obtained in a drop of water or smear it on a dry slide. Stain with fountain-pen ink (methylene blue or neutral red) and mount in water. Cover with a cover glass and examine the entire field carefully with high power (4-mm. lens). Small groups or isolated cells should appear here and there. This is an attractive demonstration for elementary students, as it shows the cellular character of their own bodies.

The epithelium cells of many animals possess small hairlike projections called *cilia*. In most forms the ciliated cells are restricted to certain regions of the body. In man the trachea and some other internal organs are lined with such cells. For demonstrating to a class it is desirable that the tissue be obtained while it is still alive in order that the waving action of the cilia may be seen. Such tissue can be procured from the trachea of any freshly killed mammal or from the throat cavity of a frog. The latter is probably the most convenient source.

As soon as the frog has been pithed, split the jaws at the corners of the mouth until the throat cavity is clearly exposed. Turn the lower jaw and throat back so as to expose the dorsal surface of the throat. Wash away any blood that may be present. Place some very small pieces of wood about the size of a pinhead, or any other small objects, on the posterior portion of the dorsal surface of the throat. Watch these for a few minutes and they will be seen to move slowly toward the mouth, or anterior region. This is accomplished by the ciliary action. Next place the frog under a microscope so that this region can be focused upon, and if a strong light can be arranged to shine down upon the surface of the membrane the wavelike movements of the cilia are quite visible.

Blood Cells. Temporary preparations of blood are best for elementary use. White cells can be obtained from pimples or other infections that are "coming to a head." Pus from a very recently festered source is best. Place a small droplet of blood on a slide. Prepare a very thin film from the blood by dragging the edge of a cover glass through the droplet (see Chap. 18). Place a drop of fountain-pen ink diluted with water on the blood smear. This will stain the cells slightly. Even without the staining, the red cells will appear to have lost their red color. The irregular cells, often containing more than one nucleus, are white cells.

Prepare a thin blood smear and allow it to dry in air. Add enough of Wright's stain to cover the smear completely and allow it to stand about 1 min. Dilute this drop of stain by adding slowly, one drop at a time, an equal amount of distilled water. Let this stand about 3 min. and wash in water. Dry between two pieces of filter paper. Mount in thin balsam. This staining helps bring out the white cells and the nuclei.

Hair, Feathers, Scales, Etc. The hard, dry outgrowths of animals such as hair, wool, feather, and scales can be observed dry or in water, but permanent mounts are made without difficulty. Take the hair, feather barbs, or small fish scales and place them in cedarwood oil or xylene for a few minutes. Lift them out, draining off excess oil, and immediately lay them on a drop of Canada balsam on a microscope slide. Cover with a cover glass and set aside to dry.

Striated Muscle. Excellent preparations of ordinary striated muscle can be made even by a student. Place ¼-in. cubes of the leg muscles of a frog (small pieces of beef or any other vertebrate will do) in 6 per cent formalin for 24 hr. or longer. The material can be kept indefinitely in this preservative. From one of these pieces remove a small shred no bigger than a heavy thread. With two pins tear and fray this shred in a large drop of water. Cover with a cover glass and examine under high power (4-mm. lens). It is important that the direction and intensity of light be carefully adjusted in order to emphasize the striations. The more finely divided the tissue is the better the preparation will be. A little ink from a fountain pen placed in the drop of water may be found to stain the fibers and increase the visibility of striations. This does not show nuclei unless Delafield's hematoxylin is used as the stain.

Preparation of Reagents

Fixing Agents. *Formalin–acetic acid–alcohol* (*F.A.A.*). This is one of the simplest and most usable fixatives or preservatives for simpler plant and animal preparations. It is advantageous for the following reasons: materials are easily procured; it is a rapid penetrator; it will fix large volumes of tissue as compared to volume of liquid; it keeps indefinitely; tissue fixed in it does not have to be washed in water before dehydration and may be transferred directly to 70 per cent alcohol (ethyl or grain); tissues may be kept in it indefinitely without injury; and it is a very satisfactory preservative for museum specimens. Two formulas are in common use as follows:

Alcohol (ethyl or grain) 50 per cent .... 90 cc.
Formalin (commercial) .... 5 cc.
Glacial acetic acid .... 5 cc.

Alcohol (ethyl or grain) 70 per cent .... 85 cc.
Formalin (commercial) .... 10 cc.
Glacial acetic acid .... 5 cc.

Other variations of the above formulas are occasionally used.

Transeau's Algal Preservative. This is an excellent fixative for most blue-green and green algae. The formula is as follows:

Water .... 6 parts
Alcohol (ethyl) .... 3 parts
Formalin (commercial) .... 1 part

The addition of glycerin equaling about 5 per cent of the total volume will prevent complete drying out of specimens when the liquid evaporates because of an unsatisfactory stopper.

Absolute Alcohol. This is occasionally used alone as a fixative. If not available locally, it may be easily prepared from stock 95 per cent alcohol (ethyl) as follows: In a crystallizing dish heat some powdered copper sulfate to drive off the water of crystallization. When this process is complete the powder is of a dirty white color instead of blue. Pour this into the alcohol (roughly 1 part copper sulfate to 10 parts alcohol), shake, and allow to stand in a tightly closed container for 3 or 4 hr. or at least until all the copper has settled out. Decant the clear liquid into a clean dry bottle and keep tightly stoppered. Absolute alcohol will absorb moisture from the air if left exposed. It is wise to test a sample of the alcohol before removing all of it from the copper to see if it is water free. This may be done readily in two ways: (1) by placing about 5 cc. of the alcohol in a test tube and adding two or three drops of xylene (xylol). If much water is still present a milky color will appear. (2) A more sensitive test is made by potassium permanganate. Drop three to four crystals in 5 cc. of the alcohol. If water is present a purple color will appear.

Acetic Alcohol

Glacial acetic acid .... 1 part
Absolute alcohol .... 2 to 3 parts

Stains. *Belling's Iron, Acetocarmine.* Dilute glacial acetic acid to 45 per cent with distilled water. Heat to boiling point and add 0.5 g. of carmine to each 100 ml. Certified carmine (NCa_2) has given particularly good results. Continue the heating in a reflex condenser or stoppered bottle for 30 min. or more. Cool the solution and filter. A good stain does not always result. One continues to make stain until a product is obtained which stains satisfactorily. A good stain properly used results in darkly stained chromosomes and nearly colorless cytoplasm. Once obtained, a good stain remains good for years.

Alum Carmine

Carmine .... 1 g.
Ammonia alum (2.5 per cent aqueous solution) ...... 100 cc.

Boil for 20 min. and filter after cooling.

Delafield's Hematoxylin. Saturate 100 cc. of distilled water with ammonia alum (aluminum ammonium sulfate) and filter. Dissolve 1 g. of hematoxylin crystals in 6 cc. of absolute alcohol. Add the hematoxylin solution drop by drop to the ammonia alum solution. Place in a beaker, covering with cheesecloth, in a well-lighted situation for 15 days. Then add 25 cc. of methyl alcohol and the same amount of glycerin. The solution should have a dark bluish-purple color. It is ready for use after filtering. If not contaminated this dye will remain in good condition for a year or more.

Fast Green F C F

Fast green crystals .... 0.2 g.
Alcohol (ethyl), 95 or 100 per cent 100   cc.

Gram's Aniline Gentian Violet. Dissolve 2.5 g. of crystal violet (gentian violet) in 12 cc. of 95 per cent alcohol. Add 100 cc. of aniline water. The aniline water is prepared by saturating water with aniline oil. Pour the oil in distilled water, shake it vigorously, allow it to stand overnight, then filter.

Hematoxylin (Aqueous)

Hematoxylin crystals .... 0.2 g.

Heat 100 cc. of distilled water to boiling, remove from flame and add the dye when boiling stops. It is ready for use as soon as the solution cools.

Loeffler's Methylene Blue

Saturated solution of methylene blue in 95 per cent alcohol ....   9 cc.
Aqueous solution of sodium hydroxide, 1 part NaOH to 10,000 parts of distilled water ....   30 cc.

Lugol's Iodine Solution

Iodine ....   1 g.
Potassium iodide ....   2 g.
Distilled water .... 300 cc.

Neutral Red. A 5 per cent solution in distilled water is approximately a saturated solution. However, a much more dilute solution is commonly used, especially in vital staining. It is not toxic to living cells.

Phenol–Bismarck Brown Y or G (Aniline Brown)

Bismarck Brown Y ....   1 g.
Distilled water .... 100 cc.
Phenol (carbolic acid) ....   5 g.

If concentrated liquid phenol is available instead of crystalline form, use 5 cc. Allow the above mixture to stand for 2 to 3 hr. or longer, then filter.

Phloxine

Phloxine crystals ....   1 g.
Alcohol (ethyl) 90 per cent .... 100 cc.

Safranine Y

Safranine Y crystals ....   1 g.
Alcohol (50 per cent) .... 100 cc.

Sudan III (Scharlach R). Saturate 70 per cent grain alcohol with the Sudan III and filter.

Wright's Stain. This blood stain can be obtained from drug and supply companies. This stain is rather difficult to prepare.

Other Reagents. *Acid Cleaner*

Sulfuric acid (commercial) .... 400 cc.
Potassium or sodium bicarbonate, enough to make a saturated solution.

This reagent may be used over several times for cleaning glassware. When a greenish color develops, it has lost its cleaning properties.

Glycerin Jelly

Gelatin, best grade	10	g.
Distilled water	30	cc.
Glycerin	26	cc.
Phenol (carbolic acid)	0.05	g.

Allow the gelatin to stand in the water for 2 to 3 hr. or until very soft. Then add the glycerin and phenol. Warm in a water bath (double-boiler arrangement) until all the gelatin melts. Stir while heating. While the mixture is still warm filter through fine-meshed cheesecloth.

Mayer's Albumen Fixative

Egg albumen (the thicker portion may be discarded)	25	cc.
Glycerin	25	cc.
Phenol (carbolic acid) crystals	0.5	g.

Filter through linen or fine cheesecloth.

Jeffrey's Maceration Solution

A. Nitric acid (10 per cent in water)	100	cc.
B. Chromic acid (10 per cent in water)	100	cc.

Solutions A and B are to be mixed just before using for macerating stems, roots, and leaves.

Phloroglucin. Use a 2 to 5 per cent solution in distilled water or 70 per cent alcohol. The commercial material is rather expensive. A very satisfactory evasion of cost is to make your own extract. Fill a 500 cc. beaker three-fourths full of stems and bark from the wild black cherry (*Prunus serotina*). Cover with distilled water and boil for an hour. Filter and use the aqueous solution the same as commercial material. Some alcohol may be added to preserve the solution

Chlorzinc Iodide

Potassium iodide	50	g.
Iodine	0.5	g.
Distilled water	140	cc.

Mix the above first, then add 300 g. of zinc chloride.

Zinc chloride	25	g.
Potassium iodide	8	g.
Iodine	1.5	g.
Distilled water	8.5	cc.

Iodine for Starch Test

Iodine	0.3	g.
Potassium iodide	1.5	g.
Distilled water	100	cc.

Cellulose Acetate

Cellulose acetate (dry)	12	g.
Acetone	100	cc.

If cellulose acetate (dry) is not in stock, old photographic negatives may be substituted. Clean the emulsion from the negatives by washing in hot baking-soda water. The cellulose acetate solution has many uses about a laboratory. It is serviceable in repairing broken glassware. Broken edges may be cemented together with it. When stoppered vials are dipped in it and allowed to dry, the corks are held in place and waterproofed. It is serviceable also for fastening pieces of plant tissues to blocks for sectioning.

Quick, Easy Way to Label Slides. Prepare a very dilute solution of Canada balsam, diluting with xylene. With the solution paint the end of slide to be labeled. Allow to dry slightly. Write directly in the undried balsam with India ink. Another coat may be given after the ink dries. The balsam should be dilute enough to dry within a few minutes after application. This also proves useful in the preparation of lantern-slide diagrams.

Paraffin–Gum Mastic Sealing Mixture. Heat equal parts of paraffin and gum mastic. Thoroughly stir the mixture. Allow the mass to cool. It may be applied to edges of a cover glass by means of a heated wire. It is convenient to have a ½-in. length of the wire at one end bent at right angles. This end is heated and placed in the paraffin–gum mastic. Enough adheres to the wire to be carried to the edges of the cover glass. It will solidify upon cooling.

REFERENCES

1. Baker, J. B.: *Cytological Technique,* 2d ed., John Wiley & Sons, Inc., New York, 1946.

2. Beiser, A.: *Guide to the Microscope,* E. P. Dutton & Co., Inc., New York, 1957.

3. Belling, John: *The Use of the Microscope,* McGraw-Hill Book Company, Inc., New York, 1930.

4. Berg, Clifford O.: "Technique for Projecting Images of Living Animals, etc.," *Trans. Am. Microscop. Soc.,* **67**(4):384–387, plate 1, October, 1948.

5. Bourne, G. H.: *Aids to Histology,* The Williams & Wilkins Company, Baltimore, 1960.

6. Cole, W. V.: "Preparation of Microscopical Sections for Biological Laboratories," *Am. Biol. Teacher,* **13**:5–10, January, 1951.

7. Corrington, J. D.: *Exploring with Your Microscope,* McGraw-Hill Book Company, Inc., New York, 1957.

8. Gage, Simon Henry: *The Microscope,* 16th ed., Comstock Publishing Associates, Inc., Ithaca, N.Y., 1936.

9. Gray, Peter: *Handbook of Basic Microtechnique,* 2d ed., McGraw-Hill Book Company, Inc., New York, 1958.

10. Guyer, Michael F.: *Animal Micrology,* University of Chicago Press, Chicago, 1936.

11. Headstrom, B. R.: *Adventures with a Microscope,* J. B. Lippincott Company, Philadelphia, 1941.

12. Johansen, D. A.: *Plant Microtechnique,* McGraw-Hill Book Company, Inc., New York, 1940.

13. Larson, E. A.: "Revealed by the Microscope," *Am. Biol. Teacher,* **14**:205–208, December, 1952. Together with a key to some common fresh-water invertebrates.

14. Munoz, Frank F., and Harry A. Charipper: *The Microscope and Its Use,* Chemical Publishing Company, Inc., New York, 1943.

15. Sass, John E.: *Botanical Microtechnique,* 2d ed., The Iowa State College Press, Ames, Iowa, 1951.

CHAPTER 15

--ᵈ{ Photosynthesis }ᵉ--

Twenty million kilocalories (kcal) of light (radiant) energy is received daily by each area of 40,000 sq. ft. (slightly less than an acre) of earth surface. Most of this light energy is quickly dissipated in various ways, with only a relatively small amount (in terms of tenths of 1 per cent) being trapped (absorbed) by *green* plants, and is transformed into potential (chemical) energy, accumulating in sugar made in these plants. Each person, on the average, uses about 3,000 kcal from food every day and 146,000 kcal from coal, gas, oil, gasoline, etc., or a total of about 150,000 kcal of energy per day.

Photosynthesis is the process by which green (chlorophyll-bearing) plants absorb some of this light energy, causing carbon dioxide and water to combine chemically, forming eventually a simple (hexose) *sugar* such as glucose, and oxygen is set free. This may be expressed in a condensed form as follows: water + carbon dioxide, when in green plant cells and exposed to light, form sugar + free oxygen. If the words representing the materials are converted into chemical symbols, a balanced equation results which is more meaningful, as follows:

$$6H_2O + 6CO_2 \xrightarrow[\text{chlorophyll in plant cells}]{674 \text{ kcal light energy}} C_6H_{12}O_6 + 6O_2$$

The understanding may be enhanced by rewriting the equation in quantitative terms of gram molecular weights, as follows:

$$108 \text{ g. } H_2O + 264 \text{ g. } CO_2 \xrightarrow[\text{chlorophyll in plant cells}]{674 \text{ kcal light energy}} 180 \text{ g. } C_6H_{12}O_6 + 192 \text{ g. } O_2$$

When 180 g. of sugar is oxidized (burned) in a laboratory crucible or in cells of the human body, 674 kcal. of chemical energy from the sugar is converted to heat energy. This heat energy can be measured experimentally.

Perhaps this may be illustrated more effectively by common personal activities in which the potential or stored (chemical) energy resulting from the photosynthetic process is released and used by man. In the autumn one may rake up the plant trash which has accumulated from the lawn and garden and dispose of it by burning. Although the fire is of short duration, a considerable amount of heat energy is released. This heat energy was converted from the light energy which was absorbed by the garden and lawn plants during the past summer. Warmth from a wood fire is converted sunlight energy which fell on the tree during many growing seasons, ranging perhaps from 20 to 100 years or more. Homes heated by the combustion of coal are kept warm by the stored energy from light energy trapped by the photosynthetic process in a carboniferous forest some 300 million years ago. The energy a person obtains from eating table sugar (sucrose) is converted light energy which was stored in either sugar-cane or sugar-beet plants during one growing season. The starch found in abundance in most bread and potatoes when digested becomes sugar. This sugar may then be oxidized (respired), the released energy having been stored during one growing season from wheat and potato plants.

All the more complex carbohydrates are synthesized entirely from the simple or hexose sugars such as glucose. Some of the more common ones are starch, cellulose, pectin, lignin, inulin, and complex sugars such as sucrose (table sugar). All fats, their intermediates the fatty acids and glycerin, and all fat derivatives are synthesized from sugar in both plant and animal cells. Proteins are composed of about 85 per cent sugar. The remaining 15 per cent is made up of nitrates, sulfates, and occasionally phosphates. These salts of nitrogen, sulfur, and phosphorus ordinarily come from the soil. It should be evident from this that sugar is involved in the synthesis of all organic material.

So far, only sugar as a product of the photosynthetic process has been considered. However, the equation presented previously, representing the over-all photosynthetic process, indicates that with every 180 g. of sugar made 192 g. of oxygen is released from the green plant. The earth's atmosphere (air) contains approximately 20 per cent oxygen. The respiration (biological oxidation) of all living organisms, with very few exceptions, is dependent upon this supply of free oxygen. If the supply of oxygen is not constantly available, the organism dies of suffocation. In addition, all other oxidation processes, mostly free oxygen from the atmosphere, are used as in the burning of coal, oil, and gas. Photosynthesis is the process in nature which is of great importance in maintaining a rather constant supply of oxygen in the atmosphere. From what has been said here and from other available information, one must necessarily conclude that photosynthesis is one of the most important biological processes occurring in nature. Yet, when in 1942 a national survey was made of biology courses in the secondary schools as to subject content, only 13 out of 1,086 replies claimed some attention given to the process of photosynthesis. The following demonstrations are suggested in an effort to overcome this serious situation.

STARCH IN PLANT TISSUES

Botanists and biochemists have more or less agreed that a simple sugar is the product of photosynthesis. However, chemical tests to demonstrate this with absolute certainty are somewhat difficult. The presence of starch, which is usually synthesized immediately from glucose, ordinarily is taken to indicate that photosynthesis is occurring, or has taken place very recently. The following demonstrations have been prepared upon this basis.

A Test for Starch. Starch is soon present after photosynthesis occurs in leaf and stem tissues. Starch may be produced in the chlorophyll-bearing tissues, or the glucose may be translocated from the chlorenchyma to chlorophyll-free tissues of the plant and there synthesized into starch. Starch is a common storage product in numerous tissues of green plants.

Materials. Cornstarch; wheat flour; white potato; water; air-slaked lime; iodine solution; [1] piece of ordinary muslin; piece of paper toweling; notebook paper; four test tubes.

Add a few drops of iodine to a test tube of water. Note the amber color. Mix some lime in a test tube of water. Add a few drops of iodine. Shake and note the yellowish-amber color. Mix a small amount of cornstarch in water. Add a few drops of iodine. Note the blue-black color which indicates the presence of starch. Add a few drops of iodine to a fresh slice of potato. Note the color change. Place a few drops of iodine on the muslin, paper toweling, and notebook paper. Watch for color changes.

A blue-black color indicates the presence of starch. The amber, or ordinary diluted iodine color, indicates an absence of starch. However, if the starch is present only in minute quantities, the blue-black color may not be apparent to the unaided eye but can be seen with a microscope. Such examination is often useful when studying leaf, stem, and root tissues.

If a starch paste is made of the cornstarch or wheat flour before testing, the paste must be cooled to room temperature. At high temperature the iodized starch (the blue-black compound) is not formed. The starch test also may be successfully applied to plant tissues preserved in formalin or alcoholic solutions.

Manufacture of Starch in the Chlorenchyma. Variegated leaves and certain others have tissues which do not bear chlorophyll. The iodine test applied to such tissues usually shows an absence of starch.

Materials. A yellow coleus (elm, maple, geranium, or other available green leaf); several variegated leaves of the Trailing Queen coleus; iodine solution; grain alcohol; source of heat—electric hot plate is best. The yellow coleus of florists is also sold as Golden Bedder coleus. It is easily grown and serves splendidly for this purpose. The Trailing Queen coleus is a very common variety with small leaves showing white, red, green, and purple areas. If 95 per cent grain alcohol is not available, ordinary medicated or rubbing alcohol may be used successfully.

Heat some water to the boiling point. Drop a yellow coleus leaf into the hot water and allow to remain for 2 to 3 min. Transfer the killed leaf to grain alcohol. Results will be greatly hastened if the alcohol is heated. It is dangerous to heat the alcohol over an open flame since the alcoholic vapor may become ignited. For this reason it is highly preferable to use an electric hot plate. Note the disappearance of the chlorophyll from the leaf tissues. When the leaf is white, dip in cool water to rinse off and displace the alcohol. Spread the leaf out on a glass plate or other flat surface and cover with iodine. Repeat this procedure with variegated coleus leaves. When the yellow coleus leaf is placed in hot water, note that the chlorophyll is not removed, indicating that chlorophyll is not water soluble. Chlorophyll is present throughout the entire leaf and in the living organ is masked by the xanthophyll. When the hot-water-treated leaf is placed in alcohol, the chlorophyll is

[1] Formula for iodine solution used in the starch test:

Iodine (crystals)	0.3 g.
Potassium iodide	1.5 g.
Water	100 cc.

Tincture of iodine also may be used. In addition it is also valuable as an antiseptic. A formula for it is as follows:

Iodine	20 g.
Potassium iodide	7 g.
Grain alcohol (95 per cent)	100 cc.

dissolved and diffuses out into the solution. When the decolorized leaf is placed in iodine solution, a blue-black color appears in all chlorophyll-bearing tissues, indicating the presence of starch.

When the variegated coleus leaf with its yellow, red, purple, and green areas is placed in hot water, the red (anthocyanin) and purple (anthocyanin) pigments are dissolved out. The purple pigment masks chlorenchyma, but no chlorophyll-bearing tissue is found in the yellow and red areas. After chlorophyll is removed from the green areas (chlorenchyma) and iodine is applied, the presence of starch is demonstrated readily in the chlorenchyma, none appearing in tissue which formerly was colored yellow and red. This indicates that chlorenchyma is necessary before starch can be manufactured and that chlorophyll is essential before the process can occur.

Do Red-leafed Plants Have Chlorenchyma? If available, treat a bright red leaf of blood leaf (*Iresine*) in hot water. The red pigment is removed readily with boiling water. The treated leaf is bright green. While the leaf was living, the chlorophyll was masked by the anthocyanin. Starch can be demonstrated throughout the leaf after the chlorophyll is removed.

The Necessity of Light in Starch Manufacture. Many thousands of dollars are invested in greenhouses throughout the colder part of the world. This is to make it possible to cultivate plants out of season and for tropical plants to be had in northern regions. Glass houses must be used for this purpose since light is necessary before photosynthesis can occur.

Materials. A coleus plant which has been kept in a dark room or light-tight box for 2 to 3 days; another coleus plant which has been kept in sunlight or under electric light for a day or so; water; grain alcohol; iodine; source of heat.

Test a leaf from each plant for starch. No starch is present in the leaf which was kept in darkness, while starch is found in the leaf which has been exposed to light. Chlorophyll is present in both, and environmental conditions were the same except for light. Therefore, light must be necessary in the process of photosynthesis.

The same phenomenon may be demonstrated readily by covering a single leaf on a coleus plant with black paper or aluminum foil. In the paper or aluminum foil cut out the word "starch" or some geometrical figure such as a star. Carefully cover the leaf with the paper or aluminum foil, holding it in place with ordinary wire paper clips. The only part of the leaf exposed to light is the area directly opposite the opening made in the paper or aluminum foil. Allow the plant to remain in sunlight for 2 days. An uncovered leaf, when given the iodine test, will show starch throughout. The covered leaf shows starch only in the exposed areas.

Disappearance of Starch from Green Leaves. When green plants are kept in the dark of poorly lighted places, they eventually die. Death is due to starvation since photosynthesis cannot occur in the absence of sufficient light.

Materials. A coleus plant which has been in sunlight for at least a day; light-tight box; materials for starch test.

Test a leaf for starch. Then keep the plant in the dark for 2 to 3 days and test another leaf for starch. The first leaf shows the presence of starch in the plant. The second leaf from the plant, after being in darkness, should show no starch. Disappearance of the starch under such conditions is due usually to digestion and translocation of the resulting sugar to the stems or roots. This sugar may be oxidized in the process of respiration, or it may be recondensed into starch.

CARBON DIOXIDE IN RELATION TO PHOTOSYNTHESIS

Necessity of Carbon Dioxide in Photosynthesis. Glucose, the product of photosynthesis, is a carbon compound. The carbon is derived from carbon dioxide used in the process of photosynthesis. Coal is a fossilized plant product and has a high percentage of carbon in its composition. This carbon also came originally from carbon dioxide used in this process.

Materials. Three coleus plants which have been kept in the dark until starch free; a bell jar (battery jar, aquarium, or other glass container which can be sealed airtight); materials for starch test; petroleum jelly; carbon dioxide generator; wooden box as shown in Fig. 15.1.

Place one of the starch-free plants under a bell jar and with it a glass container with about 250 cc. of 20 per cent aqueous potassium or sodium hydroxide. Seal the bell jar to a glass plate with petroleum jelly to make it airtight. The potassium or sodium hydroxide solution will remove any carbon dioxide from the enclosed atmosphere under the bell jar. Place a second starch-free coleus plant under a bell jar, sealing it to a box through which a gas inlet is passed to the inside of the jar; allow the third plant to remain uncovered. Place all three plants side by side in the sunlight. Allow carbon dioxide from the generator to enter the bell jar on the box for 15 sec. every 5 or 6 hr. After 2 days make the starch test on leaves from all three plants. If starch is found in the uncovered plant and also in the covered plant, to the atmosphere of which was added carbon dioxide, and not found in the other covered plant which received no carbon dioxide, the inference that carbon dioxide is necessary in the process of photosynthesis becomes apparent.

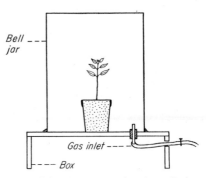

FIG. 15.1   Apparatus for introducing extra carbon dioxide to the atmosphere of a plant.

Rate of Photosynthesis as Affected by Addition of Small Amounts of Carbon Dioxide. From the above experiment it was apparent that an absence of carbon dioxide prevented the process of photosynthesis. It should be remembered that if carbon dioxide is increased to 8 per cent of the atmosphere about a plant it becomes toxic for many species.

Materials. A quart or ½-gal. fruit jar with several elodea or *Vallisneria* plants rooted in sand and submerged in water. These should stand for a week or two to become well established. A carbon dioxide generator (see Chap. 13) is also useful.

Place the jar aquarium in bright sunlight and watch for chains of bubbles arising from the leaves. As will be shown in another experiment, the gas of these bubbles contains oxygen. Count the number of bubbles which escape per minute. Then add some carbon dioxide (a dozen or so bubbles) from the generator. If this apparatus is not available, blow through a glass tube into the water. Make a recount of the gas bubbles escaping from the leaves. An increase in the number of bubbles escaping per minute indicates roughly an increase in the rate of photosynthesis. When manure is added to soil about growing plants, there may be a sudden increase in growth which cannot be accounted for by the addition of available minerals. The increase in available carbon dioxide will explain the increased growth rate under such conditions.

LEAF STRUCTURE IN RELATION TO PHOTOSYNTHESIS

Leaf Structure and Its Relation to the Entrance of Carbon Dioxide. Since carbon dioxide is a gas, it must enter the leaf through cell walls or openings by the process of diffusion. To get an idea of its path of movement into and through the leaf tissues, it is necessary to know something of general leaf structure.

Materials. A permanent microscope slide of a cross section of some leaf such as privet or lilac is desirable for study. If not available, satisfactory cross (transverse) sections may be made with a sharp safety-razor blade and the hand microtome described in Chap. 18. Dip a small bundle of leaf pieces in melted paraffin, cool, and dip again. Continue the dipping process until a block of paraffin is built up about the leaf pieces sufficiently thick to hold them together while cutting. Place this block in the microtome and section as thin as possible. Place the leaf sections in water. The paraffin will separate from the tissues. Mount the sections in a drop of water and examine under medium- and high-power objectives of a microscope.

The epidermal layers of many leaves may be peeled off without difficulty from the chlorenchyma. For this purpose common plantain, a weed in most lawns, leaflets of the Boston fern, head lettuce, patience dock, wandering Jew (*Tradescantia zebrina, Zebrina pendula*), English daisy, broad-leafed sedums, and many others will give satisfactory results. Wilting of the leaves often makes the stripping process easier. This is particularly true of the wandering Jew. This plant wilts slowly, however; so it is usually necessary to cut off a few branches and leave them exposed to dry air for a day or so. To remove the epidermal layers, wrap a leaf about the forefinger of the left hand and with forceps, a knife, or thumbnail of the right hand, gouge into the leaf and strip the tissue in a plane parallel to the leaf surface. A little practice will soon enable one to obtain epidermal pieces free of the chlorenchyma and sufficiently large to demonstrate its structure under a microscope. Mount the strips in a drop of water and examine with the medium- and high-power lenses. Compare the upper and lower portions of the epidermal layer. The wandering Jew has no stomata in the upper surface. The Boston fern has them in both the upper and lower surfaces. Ordinary epidermal cells do not have chloroplasts. However, the Boston fern and some varieties of head lettuce do have a few chloroplasts in these cells.

Escape of Gases through Stomata. Certain experiments dealing with photosynthesis indicate that carbon dioxide is necessary before photosynthesis can occur and that the gas enters through the epidermal surface containing stomata. Further proof as to the relation of stomata to gaseous diffusion may be illustrated by the following experiment.

Materials. A thick leaf of some species such as *Bryophyllum* or one of the broad-leafed sedums (live-forever); beaker; water; source of heat.

Drop the leaf in water near the boiling point. Note the bubbles arising from points rather regularly distributed over the epidermis. These bubble streams correspond to the location of the stomata. Heating causes the cool gas in the intercellular air spaces of the leaf to expand and escape through the stomatal openings. In some delicate organs such as elodea leaves, fern gametophytes (prothallia) and moss protonemata, moss scales (so-called leaves) and algae, the carbon dioxide diffuses through cell walls. There are no stomata in such structures.

Entrance of Carbon Dioxide through Stomata. In most plants carbon dioxide enters the leaves through the stomata. The entrance of carbon dioxide through these openings can be demonstrated easily if a plant is selected which has stomata only on one surface.

Materials. A coleus plant which has been kept in darkness until no starch is present in the leaves; petroleum jelly; materials for starch test.

The stomata of coleus are located on the lower surface of the leaves. With petroleum jelly cover one-half of the lower surface of one to several leaves on the plant. The petroleum jelly will seal the stomata on the covered area. Set the plant in sunlight for one to several hours. After the light exposure remove one of the treated leaves and boil in water for a minute or so to remove the petroleum jelly. Then remove the chlorophyll in hot alcohol and test for starch. The half of the leaf which was coated with petroleum jelly should show no starch, while the other half gives a good starch test.

The Release of Oxygen in Photosynthesis. If water plants are kept in a balanced aquarium, the water does not have to be changed and the fish will survive. If no green plants are present, the water must be changed at regular intervals or the fish die of suffocation. Bubbles of gas are often seen escaping from the aquatic plants.

Materials. Battery jar (or wide-mouthed gallon pickle jar), elodea or eel grass (*Vallisneria*); sand; water; funnel which will fit inverted in the jar; three or four stones to hold funnel up from the bottom; test tube; 4- to 5-in. splinter of some soft wood.

Place an inch of sand in a jar. Wash with running water until water in the container remains clear. Plant four or five elodea or eel-grass plants in the sand. Allow to stand for a week or two to become established. Place stones in the bottom near the jar wall. Invert the funnel (wide mouth down) over the plants and support on the stones. Some prefer to dispense with the sand, using a bundle of about six elodea (*Anacharis*) cuttings which are 4 to 6 in. in length, placed with cut ends up, under the inverted glass funnel. Fill the test tube with water and invert it over the stem end of the funnel, being careful to allow no air to enter. Set the apparatus in the bright light of a window or close to a desk light provided with a 100- to 150-watt light bulb. Leave the apparatus in the bright light until water in the inverted test tube is half displaced by a gas which arises as bubbles from the leaves or the cut ends of the elodea stems. When the elodea plants are working satisfactorily, chains of gas bubbles will rise from the plants. While the students are closely observing these, cut off the light supply by lowering the window blind or turn off the electric light. The bubbles will soon *stop* rising. As soon as this has happened, turn the bright light on again and chains of gas bubbles will soon reappear. To the attentive students it will be obvious that this demonstration illustrates the necessity of light as the source of energy in this process.

Lift the test tube vertically and seal with a thumb, immediately after it is raised above the water level in the battery jar. Ignite a splinter of soft wood in a flame. Allow it to burn for a few seconds, extinguish

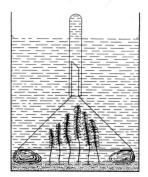

Fig. 15.2   Apparatus for collecting oxygen from water plants in which photosynthesis is occurring.

the flame and insert the glowing end in the gas in the test tube. A burst of flame or brighter glow indicates that the gas contains oxygen. Figure 15.2 illustrates the apparatus.

LEAF PIGMENTS

Extraction and Separation of Leaf Pigment. The green pigment chlorophyll is the commonest leaf-coloring material. As pointed out in some of the above experiments, its presence is necessary before photosynthesis can occur. Some leaves also contain yellow (xanthophyll), orange (carotene), and red (anthocyanin) pigments which can be seen in the living leaves. These colors are often prominent in the autumn in leaves which were bright green during the summer. Even green leaves may contain all these pigments besides the chlorophyll, and especially xanthophyll and carotene. However, their concentration is dilute as compared to the chlorophyll, so may not show up except in extractions.

Materials. Green leaves of spinach, wood nettle (*Urtica gracilis*), star cucumber (*Sicyos angulatus*), tree tobacco (*Nicotiana glauca*). If these forms are not available many other green leaves may be used more or less successfully. Grain alcohol (95 per cent); petroleum ether or benzol; test tubes, bottles, or cylinders to contain the solutions; electric hot plate. Living spinach can be purchased in any season at a grocery store. The *Urtica* and *Sicyos* are widely distributed weeds found growing along stream banks and other moist places. The tree tobacco has been introduced from South America and has escaped in California and Texas. It is occasionally grown in greenhouses. Whenever good material is found for the chlorophyll extract, the leaves may be dried, crumbled, and the powder stored in sealed fruit jars for use whenever needed. Leaf powder 4 years old has given good results. This enables the teacher to have good material during seasons when the living plants are difficult to obtain. If the pure grain alcohol is not available, ordinary medicated rubbing alcohol will serve satisfactorily for most purposes. This also is much less expensive. The label should be examined to see that the solution contains 70 per cent alcohol. If a separation of the carotenoids (xanthophyll and carotene) is to be attempted with this solution, use approximately one part chlorophyll extract to one part petroleum ether, or benzol. The separation is not quite so rapid and clear-cut but will demonstrate the pigments fairly well.

Place the living green leaves or leaf powder in sufficient alcohol to cover the material. Heat the mixture on an electric hot plate, hot-air register, or in a hot-water bath. An open flame is dangerous since the alcoholic vapor will ignite if it comes in contact with a flame. When the leaves appear more or less colorless and the solution is a dark-green color, the extraction is sufficiently complete. Filter or strain out all the leaf pieces. Place in a slender glass cylinder (bottle will do) and hold between a strong light and the observer. Note the bright-green color by this transmitted light. Then observe by reflected light (light and observer on same side of container). Note the red color. This property is known as fluorescence.

Take about 50 cc. of the chlorophyll extract and dilute it to 82 per cent with distilled water. Add an equal volume of petroleum ether or benzol. Shake the mixture and allow to stand for a few minutes. Note that the liquid separates into a green upper layer and yellow lower layer. The green solution contains two pigments, chlorophyll *A* and chlorophyll *B*. The yellow part contains carotene and xanthophyll.

Relation of Light to the Formation of Chlorophyll. In most species chlorophyll does not develop in the absence of light.

Materials. Corn, oat, or wheat grains; soil; box or flower pot; dark box.

Plant a few grains of the type available. Keep the soil moist and in the dark box in a warm (about 70°F.) room for 10 to 14 days. Note the color of the seedlings. Then set the seedlings in a light situation and watch for chlorophyll formation. A check test may be run along with the above by germinating and keeping the seedlings in a light place. The inference is obvious that light is necessary for chlorophyll formation in the above species. A green pigment may be formed in the absence of light in pine seedlings, pumpkin, grapefruit, and a few others.

REFERENCES

1. Benson, A. A.: "Photosynthesis: First Reactions," *J. Chem. Educ.,* **31**:484–487, September, 1954.

2. Blaydes, Glenn W., and L. V. Domm: "The Effectiveness of Our Schools in the Teaching of Biological Sciences," *Sci. Teacher,* **15**:57–58, April, 1948.

3. Bonner, J., and A. W. Galston: *Principles of Plant Physiology,* W. H. Freeman and Company, San Francisco, Calif., 1952.

4. Bower, F. O.: *Botany of the Living Plant,* 4th ed., St. Martin's Press, Inc., New York, 1947.

5. Conant, J. B., and A. H. Blatt: *Fundamentals of Organic Chemistry,* The Macmillan Company, New York, 1950. For students concerned with biology, agriculture, etc.

6. Cummins, G. B., et al.: *Laboratory Problems in Plant Science,* Burgess Publishing Company, Minneapolis, 1948.

7. Curtis, O. F., and D. G. Clark: *Introduction to Plant Physiology,* McGraw-Hill Book Company, Inc., New York, 1950.

8. Dushane, G., and D. Regnery: *Experiments in General Biology,* W. H. Freeman and Company, San Francisco, Calif., 1940.

9. Eames, A. J., and L. H. MacDaniels: *An Introduction to Plant Anatomy,* 2d ed., McGraw-Hill Book Company, Inc., New York, 1947.

10. Fuller, Harry J., and Oswald Tippo: *College Botany,* Holt, Rinehart and Winston, Inc., New York, 1955. Useful for all plant processes and survey of the plant kingdom.

11. Harer, E. L., and C. G. Remley: *Fundamental Activities in Biology,* Republic Book Co., Flushing 68, N.Y., 1960.

12. Hill, R., and C. D. Whittingham: *Photosynthesis,* John Wiley & Sons, Inc., New York, 1955.

13. Levitt, J.: *Plant Physiology,* Prentice-Hall, Inc., Englewood Cliffs, N.J., 1954.

14. Loomis, W. E.: "Importance of Photosynthesis in Biology Teaching," *Am. Biol. Teacher,* **13**:64–65, March, 1951.

15. Meyer, B. S., and D. B. Anderson: *Plant Physiology,* 2d ed., D. Van Nostrand Company, Inc., Princeton, N.J., 1954.

16. Newman, B. J., and E. Thoma: "Aids in Demonstrating Evolution of Oxygen during Photosynthesis," *Am. Biol. Teacher,* **14**:3–5, January, 1952.

17. Popham, R. A.: *Developmental Plant Anatomy,* Long's College Book Company, Columbus, Ohio, 1952.

18. Robbins, W. W., T. E. Weier, and C. R. Stocking: *Botany, An Introductory Course to Plant Science,* 2d ed., John Wiley & Sons, Inc., New York, 1957. Useful for all plant processes and survey of the plant kingdom.

19. Shortess, G. S., and G. W. Howe: *Laboratory Directions for the First Course in Biology,* G. P. Putnam's Sons, New York, 1956.

20. Sinnott, E. W., and K. S. Wilson: *Botany: Principles and Problems,* 5th ed., McGraw-Hill Book Company, Inc., New York, 1955. Useful for the study of structure, processes, and survey of the plant kingdom.

21. Thomson, J. A.: *Biology for Everyman,* E. J. Holmyard (ed.), E. P. Dutton & Co., Inc., 1935.

22. Tiffany, L. H.: *Study of Plants,* Harper & Brothers, New York, 1946.

23. Transeau, E. N., H. C. Sampson, and L. H. Tiffany: *Textbook of Botany,* rev. ed., Harper & Brothers, New York, 1953. Useful for study of processes, ecology, and survey of the plant kingdom.

24. Weatherwax, Paul: *Botany,* 3d ed., W. B. Saunders Company, Philadelphia, 1956. The discussion on photosynthesis and other food syntheses is recommended for beginning students.

25. Whaley, W. G., et al.: *Principles of Biology,* Harper & Brothers, New York, 1954.

CHAPTER 16

⊸ Digestion, Nutrition, and Growth ⊱

The life of any organism is the life of all the cells that make up that organism. The protoplasm of each cell is a living unit. This is demonstrated by the fact that parts of organisms may be kept alive in culture long after that organism as an individual has died. The functioning of ciliated cells that have been removed from a frog's throat as described in Chap. 14, Preparations for the Microscope, is an illustration. Also tissues have been removed from embryos and placed in sterile culture media where they live and grow for many years beyond the normal life of the species of animal from which they were obtained. The activities of this protoplasm in its living state require that energy be supplied regularly to the cells and that additional materials be added from which growth takes place. This material is food.

Most of the foods used by living things are in forms which do not diffuse, or pass through membranes. Since the protoplasm of nearly all cells is completely enclosed in some sort of membrane, it is evident that something must first occur to these insoluble food substances before they or their energy is available to the living cell for its activities. Most organisms produce substances which they secrete and which, when they come into contact with these nondiffusing foods, so modify the chemical composition of the food that it is changed from a nondiffusing (nonsoluble) into a diffusing (soluble) state. This process is digestion. Thus the foods pass through the membranes surrounding the living protoplasm, supplying energy in some cases and materials of growth in others.

CARBOHYDRATE FOODS AND ENZYMES IN ANIMALS

Both plants and animals make use of carbohydrates which are one of the principal classes of food substances. Some of these (sugars) are readily diffusible through most membranes but others (starches), which plants frequently store and which animals regularly use, are not diffusible. Demonstrations of these characteristics and of how these substances are digested should be given to or done by the student.

Sugar. For the making of a collodion bag, or any other diffusion setup, see Chap. 17, Diffusion. Use the bag to show that sugar (glucose) will diffuse and test with Fehling's solution as proof.

Starch. Since starch is a nondiffusing carbohydrate, a demonstration should be given which shows this, plus a demonstration of how it may be converted into sugar, which does diffuse.

314

Materials. Boiled cornstarch; test tubes; small beakers or cups; Fehling's solution (see Chap. 17), collodion; saliva or amylopsin; iodine (aqueous solution).

Make several collodion bags in a large test tube (see Chap. 17). In one of these bags place a quantity of boiled starch. Suspend this in a beaker, tumbler, or cup of water. With another part of the boiled starch mix about a tablespoonful of fresh saliva or some amylopsin which can be purchased dry and dissolved in water. Place this mixture in a second collodion bag and suspend it in a similar glass of water. Let these stand for several hours or overnight. Make a check test for starch with iodine. Make a test for sugar using Fehling's solution as a check. Next remove some of the water from the tumbler containing the bag of starch solution without the enzyme. Make a test for starch to show that the starch has not diffused through the membrane. Also test for sugar. If the starch solution was freshly made there should be no sugar test. Then test the water from the tumbler surrounding the bag of starch to which the enzyme was added. It should be negative for starch and positive for sugar. This shows the nondiffusing character of starch, the converting action of the enzyme, and the diffusing character of sugar.

EXTRACTION OF ENZYMES

Proof of the Presence of Enzymes in Animals. That enzymes are present in tissues of the body and especially in glandular tissues can be shown easily in the following manner.

Materials. Six test tubes or large vials; iodine (aqueous solution); Fehling's solution; living rat, guinea pig, rabbit, frog, or fish.

Remove from a freshly killed mouse, rat, guinea pig, rabbit, or other mammal the pancreas, which lies in the mesentery between the stomach, liver, and small intestine. Remove also about 1 in. of the small intestine near the stomach and a piece of muscle from the leg or body wall. A goldfish or a grass frog can be used if a mammal is not available. It is more difficult to locate the pancreas in very small forms, but the intestine can always be found. Chop these materials into bits, using care not to get them mixed in any way. Macerate the tissues in separate containers and add a few cubic centimeters of water. Let these stand for 20 min. or longer to extract any enzyme present. Pour off the liquid from each extract and add it to 10 cc. of starch in a test tube. After 3 min. test each tube of starch with one drop of iodine. Use a check tube of untreated starch and iodine for comparison. There is usually enough enzyme in a pancreas or small intestine to give a clear negative iodine test. Muscle and some other tissues may give a pinkish or purple color, showing some enzyme effect. Subsequent boiling with Fehling's solution may demonstrate the presence of sugar.

STRUCTURES AND MOVEMENTS OF THE DIGESTIVE TRACT

Demonstration by Dissection. In spite of the fact that the student probably knows more about his own internal anatomy than about many other biological facts, it is surprising how many errors exist concerning position and relation of parts. An examination of the gross internal structures of some small animal can do much to correct this.

Materials. If possible, have a frog or small mammal for each two students; scissors; paper; and pencil. A frog seems less like a pet than do mammals. Its structures are nearly enough like that of mammals and man to be very satisfactory.

Let each pair of students open completely the ventral body wall of a preserved frog and locate each part and name it. Diagrams are useful for this. The regions

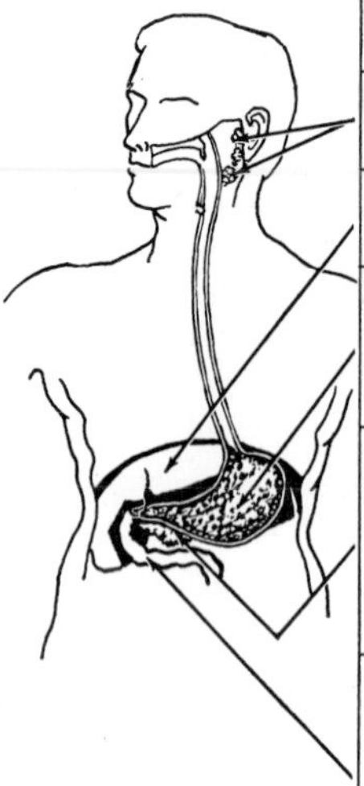

DIGESTIVE JUICES AND GLANDS

JUICE	PRO- DUCED BY	ACTIVE SUBSTANCE OR ENZYME	FOOD ACTED UPON	PRODUCT FORMED
Saliva	Salivary glands	Ptyalin	Starches	Double sugar
Bile	Liver	Bile salts (not enzymes)	Fats	Emulsified fats
Gastric juice	Glands in stomach wall	Pepsin	Proteins	Proteoses and peptones
		HCl (not an enzyme)		
Pancreatic juice	Pancreas	Amylopsin	Starches	Simple sugar
		Trypsin	Proteins	Amino acids
		Steapsin	Fats	Fatty acids and glycerol
Intestinal juice	Glands in wall of intestine	Erepsin	Proteins	Amino acids
		Maltase	Malt sugar	Simple sugar
		Lactase	Milk sugar	Simple sugar
		Invertase	Cane sugar	Simple sugar

FIG. 16.1

where enzymes are secreted should be clearly worked out in connection with a study of digestion. See Fig. 16.1 and chart.

Peristaltic Movement of the Digestive Tract. The action of nonstriated (involuntary) muscle as well as the method of propelling food along the digestive tract can be shown in most small laboratory animals.

Materials. Living frog, rat, or rabbit; scissors.

Cut open the pithed frog or etherized mammal and watch the surface of the stomach and intestine for several minutes. Usually slow wavelike movements of the constricting tract walls can be seen to travel along the stomach or intestine. If no movement is apparent after careful observation, try scratching the surface with a sharp pencil or other instrument. Sometimes a few drops of warm water poured on the tract will cause the movement to begin. Application of an electric shock from a battery or weak induction coil is another method of inducing movement. Do not continue the stimulation for more than a second at a time. If the animal has been fed previous to the observation so that there is food in the stomach and intestine, peristalsis is more likely to be going on. It is quite possible to force-feed a frog. One person can do it, but it is much easier for one person to hold the frog and pry open its mouth with a flat instrument while a second person places small pieces of lean meat (¼ by ¼ by ½ in.) in a pair of forceps and thrusts it part way down the frog's throat. Four or five such pieces is enough.

RELATION OF FOOD TO GROWTH IN ANIMALS

Growth of Fly Larvae. A simple, rapid demonstration of the relation of protein, carbohydrates, and fats to growth and development can be done either as a class project or, better, by two careful students. It should be done in early autumn or late spring in order to obtain blowflies (those whose larvae feed on spoiled meat) for the test.

Materials. Three large test tubes or small wide-mouthed jars; small amount of nutrient agar (as used for bacteria); 5 g. of lean beef; 0.5 g. of suet (beef fat).

Prepare the agar medium according to directions and pour about 4 to 5 cc. into each of the three test tubes (if jars are used cover the bottoms to depth of not over ¼ in.). Chop the lean beef very fine and mix it into the agar of two of the three tubes before it cools and sets. Divide the suet into three equal parts and drop one part into each of the three tubes. Plug the tubes (or jars) with rolled wads of cotton. The plugs should fit rather tightly to prevent the escape of maggots. If these agar preparations are placed in a refrigerator, they can be kept for some time. By baiting with a piece of meat out of doors in warm weather, flies will lay eggs and when these have hatched (after 8 to 24 hr.) the young maggots should be carefully counted into groups of about 20 or 30 each. Use one egg mass, if possible, to avoid difference in species. Place one half of the young larvae in the tube of agar without lean meat and the other half in one of the tubes with lean meat. Plug and leave in a warm place for several days, examining them once per day. In 5 to 7 days the larvae with lean meat (protein) will be fully grown and should be taken out and placed in a jar with scraps of paper where they will pupate. Those in the agar without protein will be quite small but still alive.

At this time divide the retarded larvae into groups and add one group to the second tube containing lean beef and leave the other group in the tube without lean beef. Watch the growth rates of these two groups. The protein-fed flies finish their growth and metamorphosis while those with protein deficiency remain alive but do not mature. This is a good illustration of the energy-yielding and growth values of food types.

IMPORTANCE OF VITAMINS

The importance of vitamins in diet has become a matter of general knowledge and concern. An understanding of their importance and effects is a vital part of the student's training in biology, physiology, hygiene, or domestic science. A great deal of commercial propaganda has been based upon the fact of their importance without much regard for the accuracy or mode of application. It therefore becomes important that the student be able to judge such encroachments upon scientific usage. The only way to arrive at a proper appreciation of these effects is through a well-planned and well-executed test as shown in a feeding experiment. There are no simple chemical tests that are satisfactory. Anyhow, the primary interest for the general student lies in the effect of the presence or absence of these substances. Consequently, the following feeding experiment is suggested to demonstrate in a striking manner the importance of vitamins in diet. While there is some inconvenience attached to preparing cages and a place to keep the animals, any extra effort put forth by the teacher or pupils in doing this is well repaid.

Vitamin C Deficiency. This is the easiest effect to produce in a short time. Vitamin C is known as the antiscorbutic vitamin since its presence prevents the development of the condition known as scurvy. It can best be brought about under laboratory conditions in guinea pigs. Rats cannot be used for this.

Materials. Young guinea pigs (about half grown) weighing as near 300 g. as possible; enough cages to keep the experimental and control animals separate (the best arrangement is to keep each animal in a separate cage but this is not absolutely necessary); food as listed below; scales; record sheets.

Be sure that the guinea pigs are young and healthy and of as near the same weight and age as possible. Keep a weight record each day from the beginning. Mark each pig (or cage) and do not allow the animals to become mixed up at any time. Keep the cages clean and supplied with fresh water at all times. The animals must not be handled or played with by students. Feed each pig 20 g. of the food mixture daily, always removing any uneaten portions of the food remaining from the day before. It is suggested that the ideal experiment would be to use the sprouted peas in addition to the mixture for the feeding of the control animals since this would add nothing new in the type of food used. It further shows that while dry peas do not possess vitamin C the same peas sprouted do possess it. If, however, the sprouting is considered too much trouble, cabbage, orange juice, or tomato juice may be used instead of the sprouted peas. Daily records of the feeding and the weights must be kept and any significant changes noted on the dates when they occur.

The following diet is prepared in quantities sufficient for 2 days at a time or, if a good refrigerator is available for storage, it may be prepared for a week at a time.

Rolled oats	300 g.
Wheat bran	270 g.
Dry peas (finely ground)	300 g.
Fresh butter (melted over hot water and thoroughly mixed with the grain)	27 g.
Common salt (NaCl)	3 g.

The above diet is deficient in vitamin C content. If in addition to it the check pigs are fed sprouted peas (20 g. per day), or an equivalent amount of green cabbage, or tomato juice, or orange juice, the vitamin C content is added and the animals get along nicely. One experiment run according to the above directions, using cabbage as the source of vitamin C with three control guinea pigs and three experimental guinea pigs, gave the following results:

1. Changes in weight. At first the weight fluctuated up and down slightly with a net gain for all. As the test progressed the experimentals reached a point where they lost weight rapidly and consistently while the controls did not show this marked drop. The graphs in Figs. 16.2 and 16.3 show this difference.

2. Changes in appearance and behavior. At the end of 2 weeks one animal lacking vitamin C in its diet showed signs of listlessness and an indisposition to jump about when disturbed. Its coat soon became roughened and its eyes dull. From this time on it lost weight rapidly, and at the end of 3 weeks the condition was so far advanced that it was unable to eat cabbage and, consequently, died. A second experimental animal followed a few days behind the first with these same symptoms and the third had begun to show them when the experiment was stopped and the experimental animals were allowed to recover from their deficiency by the addition of the vitamin to their diet. The control pigs with only cabbage added to their diet never showed any of the signs in appearance or behavior described for the experimental ones.

Vitamin B₁ Deficiency. A good diet that is deficient in vitamin B_1 is given below. All materials for setting up the experiment are the same as in the vitamin C deficiency experiment above except that half-grown rats are used instead of guinea pigs. The deficient diet is as follows:

White flour	150 g.
Butter	30 g.
Dried beef	15 g.
Common salt (NaCl)	3 g.
Slaked lime	3 g.
Starch	99 g.

This makes 300 g., which should last six rats a number of days. Always feed just a little more than will be eaten each day. Keep plenty of fresh water present at all times. Clean the cages and feeding dishes regularly. Weigh the animals each day (or every 2 days). Note the first indications of B_1 deficiency. Plot a curve for the experimental animals and the controls. To the above diet add any one of the following: ground wheat 10 g., or 30 g. of middlings or wheat bran, or 5 g. of bakers' yeast, to be fed to the control animals. Any one of these additions will supply vitamin B_1. When the animals that are fed vitamin B_1-deficient diet have shown definite signs of the deficiency, start feeding them an addition of the wheat or bran or yeast to restore them to normal and keep a complete record.

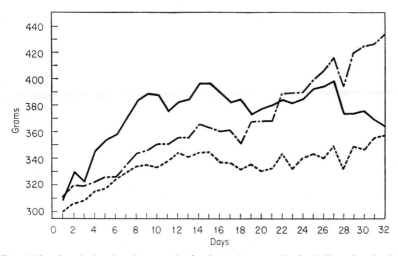

Fɪɢ. 16.2   Graph showing the growth of guinea pigs on a diet including vitamin C.

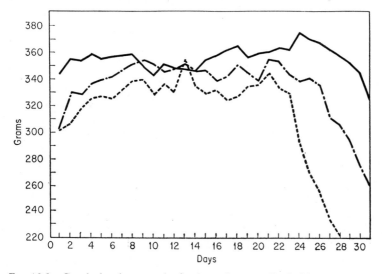

Fɪɢ. 16.3   Graph showing growth of guinea pigs on a diet lacking vitamin C.

Vitamin A Deficiency. Using rats as in the experiment above feed the following diet:

Wheat	114 g.
Dried beef (or lean meat)	30 g.
Starch	150 g.
Common salt	3 g.
Slaked lime	3 g.

This diet is deficient in vitamin A. To this diet add 30 g. of fresh butter for feeding the control animals. It may take 5 to 7 weeks to get results in vitamin A deficiency tests.

Other Vitamin Deficiencies and Diets. Anyone interested in further experimental work with diets and deficiencies is referred to the numerous articles and books upon the subject that are available in almost all libraries. See the bibliography at the end of this chapter.

Calcium Deficiency. Another very interesting and instructive feeding experiment is as follows: Select four or six young rats about 25 days old. Use half for controls. To the experimental animals feed the following diet:

Flour	129 g.
Dried beef	51 g.
Butter	18 g.
Lard	18 g.
Dried potatoes	36 g.
Sugar	45 g.
Common salt (NaCl)	3 g.

To the diet of the control animals add bone meal, about 30 g. The above diet is fairly well balanced in most respects, and there is little evidence externally for some time except weakness in the limbs and some effect upon stature. As soon as you are certain that the experimental animals have a marked defect, select the one which is most noticeably deficient and one of the controls which has had additional bone meal and appears normal, and kill both animals. Have two students thoroughly clean the skeletons and assemble the bones in an approximate position for comparison (see Chap. 12). Compare the skeletal weights of the two. The most marked results of this test are, of course, in the skeleton.

Three- or five-day-old chicks may be used instead of rats for the above experiment. Prepare their diet by grinding finely all ingredients and thoroughly mixing them. Feed just what will be eaten and keep the excess in a refrigerator or prepare fresh every second day. It must be remembered that the deficiency in this experiment is one of mineral elements and not of vitamins.

CARBOHYDRATE FOODS AND ENZYMES IN PLANTS

Starch, Digestion, and Extraction of Diastase. Foods in plants are digested in fundamentally the same way as in animals. In both cases enzymes are the chemical substances, secreted by the organism, which bring about the breakdown of complex stored foods into simpler molecules which are immediately available for use in respiration. Diastase is the enzyme responsible for the digestion of starch in plants. It is found in germinating seeds as well as in vegetative parts. That secreted in germinating seeds is the most active. Diastase can be extracted in pure form, and is sold commercially. However, an impure extract can be made readily which works satisfactorily to demonstrate starch digestion, details of which are given below.

Materials. Germinating corn, barley, castor beans, or other seeds which may be available (corn is very satisfactory); food chopper or mortar and pestle; water; funnel; filter paper; three test tubes; iodine for starch test; 2 or 3 g. of cornstarch, wheat flour, or potato starch; source of heat.

Grind the germinating corn in the food chopper. Cover the ground mass with water and allow to stand for ½ hr. Filter the mass, saving the more or less clear liquid which passes through the filter. This contains the diastase. In the meantime prepare a dilute starch paste in a beaker by adding a small amount of starch (such a quantity as may be conveniently picked up on the tip of an ordinary scalpel or penknife) to about 30 cc. of water. Boil the mixture for a few minutes and allow to cool to room temperature. Place 5 to 10 cc. of the starch paste in a test tube and test for starch with the iodine. In another test tube place a similar volume of starch paste and add 2 to 3 cc. of the enzyme extract. Test for starch immediately. In the third test tube add the same quantity of starch paste and enzyme extract. Allow this tube to stand for 5 to 20 min., then test for starch. If the enzyme is present in good condition, no starch will appear by the iodine test, indicating that the starch has disappeared. That it has been changed to sugar can be shown by Fehling's test. The optimum temperature for the action of corn diastase is 56 to 57°C. However, good results may be obtained at room temperature.

The corrosive action of diastase on starch grains can be observed easily by scraping off some starch from a germinating corn grain, mounting in water, and observing with a microscope. The same action can be demonstrated by mounting some untreated starch grains in a drop of the diastase extract, allowing to stand for 15 to 20 min., then observing microscopically.

The fungi excrete enzymes which, upon coming in contact with the proper substrate, will bring about digestion outside the hyphae. The products of this digestion, glucose, fatty acids, glycerin, and amino acids, being soluble may diffuse into the hyphae, supplying them with the required food. A result of this action can be observed in a bread-mold culture growing on bread. After the mold has been growing on the bread for 3 or 4 days, the color and texture of the bread changes. The same process can be observed in decaying fruits, wood, etc. Diastase is found abundantly in the downy mildew (*Aspergillus oryzae*) from which it is extracted commercially. This commercial extract is used in medicine and laboratory digestion experiments. A certain downy mildew (*Penicillium*) enzyme is used as a clearing agent in the manufacture of cider.

Sugar Digestion by Sucrase. Sucrose (cane sugar) which occurs in many plants, and is particularly abundant in sugar cane and sugar beet, must be changed to a simpler sugar before it is available in respiration. The enzyme sucrase is the digestive substance which brings about digestion of this nonreducing sugar. Sucrase occurs abundantly in yeast. Extracts can be made readily from commercial yeasts such as Yeast Foam and Fleischmann's yeast.

Materials. One-fourth package of yeast; 1 g. of cane sugar (sucrose); funnel; filter paper; tap water; Benedict's solution; source of heat; mortar and pestle or other means of grinding; four bottles, test tubes, or beakers.

Prepare a fine powder of the dry yeast in a mortar. Add this to about 30 cc. of water and allow it to stand for 15 to 30 min., then filter. The filtrate contains the sucrase extract. If moist yeast is used, place the yeast mass in 30 cc. of water and stir until a fine suspension is formed. Filter and save the filtrate. Prepare about 50 cc. of 2 per cent sucrose in water. To 15 cc. of this add 5 to 10 cc. of the sucrase extract and keep it at room temperature or somewhat higher for 30 to 60 min. Then add about 5 cc. of Fehling's or Benedict's solution and heat. If reducing sugar (glucose) is present, a yellow to brick-red color (precipitate) will appear upon boiling. Check tests also may be run on the sucrose solution without the sucrase extract, on the sucrase extract, and on sucrose solution to which has been added some boiled sucrase extract. Compare the results in the sucrose plus sucrase test with the checks. The sucrose plus Benedict's solution may show a slight yellowish tinge while hot but usually clears up to a blue color. The sucrase extract may show a little precipitate. The sucrose plus boiled sucrase extract usually shows no precipitate. High temperature destroys the enzyme. The sucrose plus sucrase extract will show much more precipitate than any of the checks. The presence of a reducing sugar after the enzyme treatment indicates that the sucrose has been digested.

PROTEIN FOOD IN PLANTS

Demonstration of Protease. Proteins are essential foods in plants as well as animals. Proteins must be changed into amino acids before they are available in the respiratory and assimilation processes. The presence of protease in plant tissues brings about this digestion. The protease bromelin is found abundantly in fresh or frozen pineapple juice. It may be tested as follows:

Materials. About 30 cc. of fresh or frozen pineapple juice (canned material is of no use); hard-boiled egg; source of heat; two test tubes or bottles with stoppers; a few drops of toluol; sharp razor blade.

Prepare two or three cubes of cooked egg white (largely protein) about 2 mm. square by cutting with a sharp razor blade. Drop these in a test tube containing about 15 cc. of the fresh pineapple juice. Pour the same quantity of juice in another tube and boil. After cooling add the same number of egg white cubes to it. Add 2 or 3 drops of toluol as a preservative to each tube. Stopper both, shake the contents, and label. Set in a warm place, preferably an oven with a temperature of 30 to 38°C. Allow the tests to stand for about 2 days and examine. The one with the unheated pineapple juice should show some corrosion of the cubes. The tube with boiled juice should show no action on the egg albumen.

If pineapples or the frozen juice is not obtainable, a commercial extract Papain can be obtained from chemical supply companies. It is an extract of the tropical papaw (*Carica papaya*) and is very active. Make up a saturated solution of this and use the same as the pineapple juice.

EFFECT OF CERTAIN MINERAL SALT DEFICIENCIES UPON PLANT GROWTH

Demonstration of Various Deficiencies. It is a well-known fact that certain mineral salts are essential in the normal growth of plants. The wide use of fertilizers is a practical application of this knowledge. Primitive peoples accidentally discovered the value of fertilizers. They applied the discovery even though they knew nothing of the actual mineral nutrients, some developing superstitions concerning them. The following experiment, if carefully carried out, will show the value of a complete cultural solution and the effect of lack of any of the essentials. The time required to carry it out successfully is about 40 days.

Materials. Chemicals necessary are as follows:

Magnesium sulfate (anhydrous) ($MgSO_4$), with distilled water added to make volume of 100 cc. .... 12 g.

Calcium nitrate [$Ca(NO_3)_2$] with distilled water added to make volume of 100 cc. .... 16.4 g.

Potassium dihydrogen phosphate (KH_2PO_4) with distilled water added to make volume of 100 cc. .... 13.6 g.

Ferric tartrate, 0.2 per cent .... 100 cc.

Manganese chloride, 0.2 per cent .... 100 cc.

The above materials represent the essential elements for a complete cultural medium. Solutions deficient in each of the mineral elements are made from the following substitutes:

Sodium sulfate (Na_2SO_4), with distilled water added to make
volume of 100 cc. .... 14.2 g.
Magnesium chloride (anhydrous) ($MgCl_2$), with distilled water
added to make volume of 100 cc. .... 9.5 g.
Sodium nitrate ($NaNO_3$), with distilled water added to make
volume of 100 cc. .... 8.5 g.
Calcium chloride ($CaCl_2$), with distilled water added to make
volume of 100 cc. .... 11.1 g.
Sodium dihydrogen phosphate (anhydrous) (NaH_2PO_4), with
distilled water added to make volume of 100 cc. .... 12 g.
Potassium chloride (KCl), with distilled water added to make
volume up to 100 cc. .... 7.4 g.

If the above stock chemicals are not anhydrous, that is, if the compounds contain water of hydration, the weights must be modified as follows: magnesium sulfate 24.6 g., magnesium chloride 19.3 g., and sodium dihydrogen phosphate 13.8 g. In making all solutions be certain to add distilled water to the chemical making the volume up to 100 cc.

Eleven bottles (100 cc. or larger) to contain stock solutions of the above chemicals; scale for weighing chemicals; graduated cylinder or similar device for measuring solutions; seven glazed or paraffined flower pots (4 in.); bag of pure silica or quartz sand, obtainable from building supply companies; tomato or pea seeds; distilled water for watering; labels.

Carefully clean the flower pots and rinse with distilled water. Fill each with sand to within about 1 in. of the top. To each pot transplant six seedlings, which have been grown from seeds placed in moist soil or peat, just at the time they show the first true leaves developing above the cotyledons. After they are well established, thin to three seedlings. To make up a complete mineral nutrient use the following amounts of the various solutions given above:

$MgSO_4$ .... 7.2 cc.
$Ca(NO_3)_2$ .... 4.8 cc.
KH_2PO_4 .... 7.2 cc.
Ferric tartrate, 0.2 per cent .... 2 cc.
Manganese chloride, 0.2 per cent .... 2 cc.

Mix the above and add enough distilled water to make 1 liter. This is the complete cultural solution.

Use 7.2 cc. of Na_2SO_4 to replace $MgSO_4$, for deficiency of Mg.
Use 7.2 cc. of $MgCl_2$ to replace $MgSO_4$, for deficiency of SO_4.
Use 9.6 cc. of $NaNO_3$ to replace $Ca(NO_3)_2$, for deficiency of Ca.
Use 4.8 cc. of $CaCl_2$ to replace $Ca(NO_3)_2$, for deficiency of NO_3.
Use 7.2 cc. of NaH_2PO_4 to replace KH_2PO_4, for deficiency of K.
Use 7.2 cc. of KCl to replace KH_2PO_4, for deficiency of PO_4.

Label each of the seven pots to show what is to be received. Place the pots in a well-lighted situation at room temperature. At the beginning water each thoroughly with its proper mineral nutrient solution, using equal volumes on all seven. Application of these solutions should be made every 2 or 3 weeks. During intervening periods apply distilled water to each in equal volume. Watch the plants from day to day and take note of differences—color, size, development of roots, stem, and leaves. After 30 to 40 days take final notes. Weight of tops and root systems may be obtained if desired. Record all data in tabular form.

This experiment requires considerable labor, but lends itself nicely as a student project. It is of particular interest and value in agricultural communities. If time is available, reading references may be assigned on the role of mineral elements in plants, fertilizers suitable for various crops (particularly those of local interest), etc.

Growth of Clover Plants in Relation to Nitrogen-fixing Bacteria. An immediately available nitrogen supply is important in the rapid growth of most plants. It seems to be particularly true of leguminous plants which commonly bear bacterial nodules on the roots.

Materials. A few red clover seeds; two clay flower pots filled with soil; sheet of sandpaper; 1 cc. of bichloride of mercury (2 parts to 1,000 parts of water) or 70 per cent alcohol; bake oven for heating soil to a high temperature; bacterial culture for red clover—obtainable from seed supply companies.

Heat the two pots of soil to 160°C., or near that, for 1 hr. Sterilize the seed coats with bichloride of mercury or 70 per cent alcohol. After the seed coats are covered with the antiseptic, allow them to dry for a minute, then rinse thoroughly in sterile water. Dry the seeds and scarify by rubbing between two pieces of sandpaper. Divide the seeds into equal lots. Inoculate one lot with a commercial culture of nitrogen-fixing bacteria. If this is not available, obtain soil from about the roots of a clover plant which shows well-developed nodules. Sift this over the seeds to be inoculated. Plant the two groups of seeds. Water alike and keep side by side at about room temperature. Compare growth of the seedlings. Before starting, see that the soil is alkaline by testing a suspension in distilled water with litmus paper. If it is acid, mix a little powdered limestone in it.

EFFECT OF ANTISEPTICS AND OTHER TREATMENTS UPON THE GROWTH OF BACTERIA

A Series of Demonstrations. Control of the growth of bacteria is one of the most important problems of modern civilization. The prevention and cure of diseases depend upon it. Commercial and home canning and preserving of food products, pasteurization of milk, purification of water supplies, etc., are impossible without such knowledge. The principles used in the above processes may be illustrated easily by using nutrient agar (Chap. 12) and sterile petri plates. Other nutrient materials may be used if desired. In communities where there is direct interest in the canning and preserving of foods, the actual vegetables, fruits, and meats may be canned and preserved under varying conditions by members of a class. Such experiments also give students ample opportunity for testing the values and claims for commercial antiseptics often so highly advertised.

Materials. Nutrient agar 300 cc.: 24 petri dishes or test tubes; living culture of some common bacterium; transfer needle; gas or alcohol flame; means of sterilizing petri dishes and nutrient agar (Chap. 12); moist chamber; desiccator (see Chap. 20); refrigerator—necessary only for culture to be kept at low temperature; about 10 cc. of 2 per cent phenol (carbolic acid); 10 cc. bichloride of mercury (1 g. per 1,000 cc. of water); 5 to 10 cc. of tincture of iodine; 10 cc. of 70 per cent grain alcohol; 10 cc. of 95 per cent grain alcohol; 10 cc. of each of the following concentrations of salt (sodium chloride): 5 per cent, 20 per cent, and saturated solution; samples of available commercially advertised antiseptics.

Prepare and sterilize nutrient agar as directed in Chap. 12. Also sterilize petri dishes in the same way; this is probably more satisfactorily done in an oven for an hour at 165°C. (dry, hot air sterilization). Allow the agar as well as dishes to cool. Do not open the dishes until agar is ready to be poured into them. Remove the cotton plug from the flask or tube containing the sterile agar, carefully lift the petri dish lid, holding it directly over the bottom, and pour in the agar. Replace the cover immediately and allow the agar to set. Repeat this immediately for all the dishes to be used. After the agar has congealed, inoculate the plates by dipping the sterile transfer needle into the living culture and streaking it across the agar in each plate. Label each plate to indicate treatment to be received. Place one plate in a refrigerator at 0°C. and another in an oven at 60 to 70°C. for 30 to 60 min. Place one plate with lid off in direct sunlight for ½ hr. (sunlight which passes through window glass is practically free of ultraviolet rays—the rays which are destructive to bacteria), one in subdued light, and another in darkness. In another series place a culture in a moist chamber, one under room conditions, and another in a desiccator —all at approximately the same temperature. Flood a plate culture with 2 per cent phenol, others with bichloride of mercury, tincture of iodine, 70 per cent alcohol, 95 per cent alcohol, the three salt solutions, and others with commercial antiseptics. After flooding the cultures with the above materials, drain off the excess, replace the lids, and set in a warm, dark situation. When the cultures are about 48 hr. old, final observations may be made. Ask the students to make applications to practical situations based upon the conclusions drawn from these observations.

Suggested Projects. Various projects may be assigned following this experiment. A few suggestions are as follows:

1. Inspection trip to a packing house. Learn about the smoking of meats, salting, drying, canning, refrigeration, etc.

2. Trip to a pasteurizing plant. Learn about different methods of pasteurizing. The students may pasteurize milk in test tubes in the laboratory. One way is to hold the temperature at 63°C. for 20 to 30 min. Compare the keeping qualities of the treated milk with untreated.

3. Inspection trip to one or more of the following: canneries, health laboratories, tanneries, vaccine and serum laboratories, water-supply systems, sewage-disposal plant, cheese factory, hospitals, veterinary clinics.

4. Collection of advertisements of various commercial antiseptics from magazines. Test out claims made by such.

5. Collection of material dealing with the tubercular testing of cattle.

6. Reading references and reports on serums and vaccines.

Other projects will suggest themselves to a teacher.

REGION OF ELONGATION IN ROOTS AND STEMS

Definite Growing Regions. Elongation of roots and stems is restricted to definite zones. This can be illustrated easily by the following experiments.

Materials. Germinating lima-bean seeds with hypocotyl about 1 in. long; vigorously growing wandering Jew (*Tradescantia zebrina*) plant, either in water or soil; sweet pea, garden pea, castor bean, or other convenient seedlings which have become well established in the soil and having one to three nodes above the hypocotyl; India ink; moist chamber (quart fruit jar); a stiff horsehair, wheat beard, or filament from light bulb (steel pen will do)—these are to be used in marking the stems and roots with India ink lines. Some injury may be caused by the pen. The horsehair, wheat beard, or tungsten filament work satisfactorily.

On the lima-bean hypocotyl mark off fine lines with India ink 1 to 1½ mm. apart, from tip up to the point of rupture in the seed coat. Allow the ink to dry. Suspend the bean in a moist chamber. A hooked pin may be inserted into the seed coat, a string tied about the pinhead is attached to the jar cap, or the cap screwed down on it, suspending the bean over a water surface in the moist chamber. After 24 to

48 hr. remove the bean and examine the marks for distances apart. This will definitely show that elongation occurs just back of the tip, a centimeter or more, but not entirely to the point of attachment to the remainder of the seed. In instances of the sweet pea, garden pea, castor bean, sunflower, etc. (dicotyledonous plants), place India ink marks similar to those for the roots, but extending from the tip of the seedling back three or four nodes. Place the plant in a suitable environment for growth. Observe the marks for distances apart after a period of 48 to 60 hr. Here again the region of elongation is just back of the tip and often extends throughout about 2½ cm. of the stem.

In the wandering Jew (monocotyledonous plant) a different situation is soon apparent. Mark the stems in the same way, over a distance including three or four internodes. Make observations after about 72 hr. Note that the elongation occurred in regions just above each node. This is characteristic of many monocotyledonous plants.

Regions of Expansion in Leaf Blades. Expansion of leaves after buds open is one of the most noticeable phenomena of plants in the spring and early summer. This enlargement is localized chiefly in the lower portion of a leaf rather than at the apex. The following experiment will demonstrate this characteristic.

Materials. A vigorously growing young plant (tobacco is very satisfactory, but many others may be used successfully); India ink; stiff hair (wheat beard, tungsten filament from old light bulb, or pen); and a ruler.

Select a leaf large enough to handle conveniently. Mark it off into ⅛-in. squares, being careful not to injure the leaf. Replace the plant to good growing conditions and observe the marked leaf after a week or 10 days. The larger squares in the basal portion indicate the location of greatest enlargement.

PRODUCTION OF ROOT HAIRS

Location of Root Hairs. Root hairs are characteristically found a short distance back of the region of elongation of roots. They are of importance in the absorption of water and minerals. They are very delicate extensions of epidermal cells, so are easily destroyed when a plant is removed from soil or exposed to dry conditions. The following experiments suggest ways of producing them successfully for laboratory observations as well as good types of seeds to use, migration of the root-hair zone, growth under varying conditions, etc.

Materials. Seeds or grains of radish, cabbage, redtop (cultivated grass), corn, barley, rye, or oats; bichloride of mercury (2 parts in 1,000 parts of water) is useful in sterilizing seed-coat surfaces—other antiseptics may be used; enough petri dishes for each two students—other closed containers may be used if petri dishes are not available; filter paper.

Dip the seeds or grains in the antiseptic. Remove and allow them to stand for a minute or so. Rinse in sterile water. Place a piece of filter paper in the bottom of each petri dish and moisten. Place a few seeds or grains in each dish. Cover the dish and set in a warm (about room temperature) situation. Within 2 to 3 days roots with root hairs will be found. Note the relation of the root-hair zone to the region of elongation and root tip. Recall here the experiment above in this chapter dealing with the region of elongation in the lima bean. Seedlings with small roots such as the redtop are excellent for study by means of a microscope. If small roots are mounted in water and observed, often the epidermal cells from which the root hairs arise can be seen clearly. Usually moving protoplasm can be detected.

Migration of Root-hair Zone. Ordinarily root hairs live but a few days. From the above experiments it will have been noted that the root-hair zone is just back of the region of elongation. The shortest and youngest root hairs are nearest the elongating region and the longest are farther away. Roots ordinarily are capable of producing root hairs only in the region of differentiation which is located just back of the elongating portion. While a root is growing the root-hair zone migrates toward the tip as new root hairs develop and old ones die. The following demonstration will illustrate this characteristic.

Materials. Ordinary tumbler (water glass) or glass funnel; filter paper; sand; corn grains.

Line the inside of a tumbler or funnel with filter paper. Fill the container with sand, soil, or peat. Place soaked corn grains about 1 in. apart between the paper and glass and about 1 in. below the mouth of the container. Moisten the sand and set the container in a warm place. If the seeds were soaked before starting, roots will develop in 2 to 4 days. As they grow, mark on the glass the position of the root-hair zone at various intervals. *Cercis* (red bud), *Gymnocladus* (Kentucky coffee tree), *Gleditsia* (honey locust), and some others have thick-walled root hairs which live as long as the epidermal cells. They may remain for several months. If these plants are available such observations may be made. Honey-locust seeds germinate readily if a notch is filed through the seed coat. Seedlings may be allowed to develop in the laboratory for such observations if desired.

Effects of Moisture on Root-hair Development. Environment and heredity control root-hair development. Moisture, temperature, oxygen, mineral supply, kind of plant, etc., are probably the more important factors in such growth. Some plants fail to produce root hairs under one set of conditions, but may produce them under others, while in some cases root-hair production does not occur under any circumstances. Saturated soil often suppresses root-hair development; *Acorus calamus* (sweet flag) and elodea do not produce them in water and *Lemna* and *Spirodela* (duckweeds) do not produce them under any conditions.

Materials. Four quart fruit jars or glass cylinders; enough cheesecloth to tie over mouths of the jars; four handfuls of sand; elodea, duckweeds, and sweet flag plants growing in water of an aquarium; corn and wheat grains.

Fill two of the jars about one-third full of water and fill the other two completely. Tie cheesecloth over the openings. Cause the cloth to sag somewhat and place soaked corn grains on two of the cloths, one partly filled with water and the other full. Put soaked wheat grains on the other two. Cover all four plantings with a handful of sand to keep the grains moist. Place all in a warm light situation and observe development. Both corn and wheat roots will produce an abundance of root hairs in the moist atmosphere. When corn roots grow in water no root hairs develop. Wheat occasionally produces poorly developed hairs when growing in water.

EFFECT OF LENGTH OF DAY

Growth and Reproduction. Length of the daylight period has a very definite effect upon the development of many plants. Certain of our native and cultivated plants bloom early in the spring and others in the autumn, both during periods of short-day lengths. Such plants are known as "short-day plants." Others come into bloom only during long-day periods and are known as "long-day plants." There is an important third class known as "everbloomers," such as the everbearing strawberries. This phenomenon is known as *photoperiodism*. Practical application of these facts now are being made by many florists. A demonstration of photoperiodism is comparatively simple.

Materials. Source of electric light current; 200-watt light bulb; chrysanthemum or poinsettia rooted cuttings; radish seedlings (Scarlet Globe is very satisfactory); moth mullein rosettes and wild prickly lettuce rosettes well established in pots.

The chrysanthemum and poinsettia are short-day plants, usually coming into flower in late autumn for the chrysanthemum and late November and December for the poinsettia. These may be forced into flowering out of season by giving them a 7- to 8-hr. day instead of the normally longer light period. This may be done by keeping the plants in a dark room or box and exposing them for about 8 hr. to normal daylight. Three to four weeks is required for the development of flowers. Duplicate plants must be kept as checks in the normal light condition. If the experiment is to take place during the normal short-day period, duplicate plants must be kept in a 14-hr. light period. This may be done by use of a 200-watt bulb which is lighted either in the morning or evening of the short days. Place the light about 2 ft. above the plants. If not convenient for someone to turn off the light at the proper time, an alarm clock may be rigged up to cut off the current when desired. Usually plants kept in the long-light condition will remain in the vegetative state while those in the short light come into flower.

For long-day plants prepare two pots of each of the following: radishes, three or four plants to each pot; moth mullein, one rosette to each pot, and the same for prickly lettuce. The moth mullein and prickly lettuce are common weeds which can be transplanted readily. After the plants are established place one of each type in 14-hr. light and keep the other in short-light condition (7- to 8-hr. period is best). Plants kept in the long light will soon begin to develop long stems and may come into flower, while those in short light remain in the rosette state.

BREAKING OF DORMANCY OF BUDS

Importance and Ways of Breaking Dormancy. Many plants, especially of the temperate regions, become dormant during certain periods in the year. Before buds of such plants will develop satisfactorily certain physiological changes may take place during "rest periods," as, for example, in potato tubers, with no radical change in temperature. Others require periods of low temperature. Breaking of dormancy assumes considerable economic significance. In some instances it is of importance in the distribution of plants in nature as well as limiting the use of certain plants in various regions.

Materials. After the following woody plants have been exposed to freezing temperatures for a few weeks collect a branch of lilac (select a forked branch); pear stem with several fruit spurs; Japanese quince (*Cydonia* or *Chaenomeles*); forsythia (golden bells); pussy willow; papaw; oak; etc. Also obtain three or four tubers of "new potatoes," and the same number and variety, if possible, of tubers which have been stored for 4 or 5 months.

After branches of the woody plants have been cut off and placed in water, cut off a segment an inch or two in length from the cut end while it is submerged in water. This removes air-plugged vessels which may prevent further entrance of water into the stems. For the forked branch of lilac, prepare a small opening in a windowpane so that one branch may be exposed to out-of-doors conditions. With cardboard or other insulating material seal the opening about the exposed stem to prevent lowering of the temperature inside the window. If the room temperature remains at about 70°F. the flower and leaf buds will open, developing flowers and leaves in 3 to 4 weeks, while those exposed to the outside temperatures remain dormant. The other woody stem specimens may be kept in water at about room temperature (70°F.) and their development watched. Some will develop very rapidly while others, such as the oak and papaw, are slow. To make the experiment more complete it is well to collect the same type of branches before they have been exposed to low temperatures in the fall. Collect data on them and compare with results on those after the low-temperature exposure. If an electric refrigerator is available, the low-temperature exposure may be made artificially. Such exposure should be made for a period of 2 weeks at near freezing temperatures. A student may be willing to do this in his home. As for the potato tubers, plant the two sets in the same kind of soil, water them, and keep them at the same room temperature. Watch for sprouting and compare results from the two sets. See Chap. 22, under seed dormancy, for methods of breaking dormancy in certain seeds.

Considerable work has been done on breaking dormancy of buds by means of chemical treatments. Under ordinary laboratory conditions results are often not very satisfactory. However, they may be of interest to try. Several papers may be obtained at low cost from the Boyce Thompson Laboratory for Botanical Research, Yonkers, N.Y. Also see F. E. Denny and Ernst N. Stanton, Localization of Response of Woody Tissues to Chemical Treatments That Break Dormancy, *Am. J. Bot.*, **15**:337–344, 1928; and F. E. Denny, *Am. J. Bot.*, **13**:386–396, 1926; **15**:327–336, 1928.

REFERENCES

1. Abrahams, H. J.: "Science Lecture in the High School Assembly," *School Sci. and Math.*, **50**:545–551, October, 1950. Lecture on enzymes.

2. Best, C. H., and N. B. Taylor: *Human Body, Its Anatomy and Physiology*, Holt, Rinehart and Winston, Inc., New York, 1956.

3. Frampton, H., and T. Reed: "Transparent Working Model of the Human Digestive System," *Sci. Teacher*, **19**:69–70, March, 1952.

4. Fuller, H. J., and O. Tippo: *College Botany*, Holt, Rinehart and Winston, Inc., New York, 1955.

5. Gabriel, M., and S. Fogel: *Great Experiments in Biology*, Prentice-Hall, Inc., Englewood Cliffs, N.J., 1955.

6. Greulach, V. A.: "Photoperiodism: The Remarkable Influence of Length-of-day on Plant Processes," *School Sci. and Math.*, **33**:707–720, 1933.

7. Keliher, A. V.: *Life and Growth*, Appleton-Century-Crofts, Inc., New York, 1941.

8. Lesser, M. S.: "Digestion-Absorption Sequence," *Sci. Teacher*, **19**:90, March, 1952.

9. Meyer, B. S., D. B. Anderson, and C. A. Swanson: *Laboratory Plant Physiology*, 3d ed., D. Van Nostrand Company, Inc., Princeton, N.J., 1957. An excellent laboratory manual with detailed descriptions of many physiological experiments.

10. Meyer, B. S., and D. B. Anderson: *Plant Physiology*, 2d ed., D. Van Nostrand Company, Inc., Princeton, N.J., 1954.

11. Robbins, W. W., T. E. Weier, and C. R. Stocking: *Botany, An Introduction to Plant Science*, 2d ed., John Wiley & Sons, Inc., New York, 1957.

12. Sinnott, E. W., and K. S. Wilson: *Botany: Principles and Problems*, 5th ed., McGraw-Hill Book Company, Inc., New York, 1955.

13. Vance, B. B., and D. F. Miller: *Biology for You*, J. B. Lippincott Company, Philadelphia, 1958.

14. Wilson, C. L., and W. E. Loomis: *Botany*, 2d ed., The Dryden Press, Inc. (combined with Holt, Rinehart and Winston, Inc.), New York, 1957.

15. Yocum, L. E.: *Plant Growth*, The Ronald Press Company, New York, 1945.

CHAPTER 17

·-·◄ Diffusion ►·-·

The physical process of diffusion in its various forms is of vast importance in the lives of plants and animals. Without diffusion neither the materials of growth nor energy-yielding foods could enter cells, the products of physiological processes could not be eliminated, and the condition called "life" could not be maintained. Specific examples, applications, and means of demonstrating this fundamental process, designed to assist the student to a clearer understanding, are suggested below.

DIFFUSION WITHOUT MEMBRANES

Showing the Movement of Molecules in Gas. It is possible to show that the molecules of one volatile substance may, by their own movements, become scattered among the molecules of another substance, the spread always taking place in a direction from the region of higher concentration of the diffusing substance.

Materials. Bottle containing any highly volatile substance such as ammonia, acetic acid, oil of peppermint or oil of wintergreen, perfume.

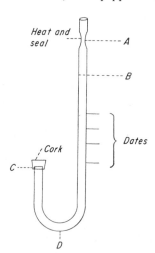

FIG. 17.1 J tube to show slow diffusion.

The teacher should, without explanation, open the container early in the class period or pour a small amount into a dish. The nearest students should be able to detect the odor sooner than those farther away. Neither the teacher nor the students should overlook the possible complication due to air currents, which are almost certain to exist in a classroom, and the fact that individuals differ in their ability to detect odors.

Showing the Movement of Molecules in Liquid. When a soluble substance is placed in a liquid, the molecules of the solid move away from the solid and disperse among the molecules of the liquid. If a simple apparatus is prepared, the direction and rate of the diffusion may be guided and observed.

Materials. A 2-ft. piece of glass tubing; a stopper; crystals of some colored soluble solid, such as potassium permanganate or copper sulfate.

Heat and bend the glass tube into the form of a J (see Fig. 17.1). Heat and draw out a portion near the long end of the J tube as shown at *A*. When the tube is cool place the curved portion in a vessel of water and suck in water to fill the tube to the point *B*, about 2 in. below *A*. Hold this level by placing the finger over the open end *C*. Reheat *A* and draw out until

330

the tube is sealed. Add a few crystals of the soluble substance through C. These will collect in the crook at D. (The water will not run out after sealing at A.) Place a stopper over C to prevent evaporation. The tube must be kept in an upright position after the crystals have been added and should be fastened securely to the wall and not disturbed. The colored substance will diffuse slowly up the long end of the J tube and may be marked at intervals as suggested on the diagram. This may be watched for days or weeks.

If a tube of larger diameter ($\frac{1}{2}$ in. or more) is used and not bent into a J, the crystals may be placed in the bottom and water added very carefully with a long slender tube. This will show diffusion, but there is usually some convection, causing roiling.

DIFFUSION THROUGH MEMBRANES

The living system, or protoplasm, of plants and animals is usually separated from the environment by some sort of limiting or restraining material called a "membrane." These membranes ordinarily must be permeable to such substances as are used for food by these organisms and to such waste products as are produced within the cells. In most instances, however, these membranes may permit certain substances to pass through and prevent others from doing so, or they may allow rapid diffusion of some substances and very slow diffusion of others. Such membranes are said to be *differentially permeable* (also *selectively permeable or semipermeable*).

Liquids as Simple, Differentially Permeable Membranes. It is easy to demonstrate that the interfaces of liquids may act as differentially permeable membranes. This illustrates somewhat the physical phenomena involved in a living organism when substances diffuse from cell to cell or from the vacuoles of plant cells into the protoplasms of the same cell.

Materials. Test tube (or other cylindrical glass tube, vial or bottle; a 50-cc. burette is ideal); 20 cc. of chloroform; 0.5 cc. of water faintly colored with methylene blue (blue ink or eosin is satisfactory); 20 cc. of ether; cork to fit the tube; pipette (medicine dropper or a small bore glass tube will do).

First, place the chloroform in the test tube. With the pipette allow the colored water to flow gently onto the surface of the chloroform. In the same manner place the ether upon the surface of the water. Tightly stopper the tube and allow it to stand for a few minutes until the colored water forms a clear-cut layer between the ether and the chloroform. Mark the level of the water on the tube with India ink, wax pencil, or gummed label.

Set the demonstration where it will not be disturbed and observe over a period of several days or longer. Within a few days it will be noted that the water level is higher than the original mark. The water layer is more permeable to ether than to chloroform.

Diffusion of Carbon Dioxide through a Rubber Membrane. When water diffuses through cell membranes, any resulting pressure within the retaining membrane is known as *osmotic* pressure. The release of this pressure results in wilting in plants.

Materials. Two toy rubber balloons (new ones should be used); two glass jars which can be tightly sealed; a simple carbon dioxide generator (see Chap. 13) or tank of carbon dioxide.

Open the balloons so that they will be filled with ordinary air but not inflated under pressure. Twist the necks and tie tightly so that they will be airtight. Drop or suspend one of them in one of the jars and seal the jar. The balloon is now surrounded with air. Fill the other jar with water and displace the water with carbon dioxide from the generator or tank. Drop the other balloon into the atmosphere of carbon dioxide and quickly seal the jar.

Observe the two jars after a few hours or overnight. Ordinarily the balloon in the carbon dioxide atmosphere becomes inflated. The pressure resulting in the balloon is osmotic pressure. The balloon in the atmosphere of air does not become inflated since the rubber is not readily permeable to air. If two basketballs are inflated to the same pressure and at the same time, one from a person's lungs and the other from a pump, the one filled from the pump retains its pressure much longer than the one filled from the lungs because of the loss of the carbon dioxide. If a leaf of lettuce is placed upon the laboratory table for an hour or two it usually wilts. If this leaf is then placed in water it may regain its turgidity. The phenomenon of osmotic pressure is responsible for the turgidity of many such plant tissues.

Demonstration of Osmosis. In the cells of plants the rapid diffusion of water becomes the most important factor in the development of osmotic pressure. The direction of diffusion is altered from time to time by changes in the concentration of sugar, minerals, and other substances in solution in the cell sap. Such materials act as diluting substances in the water. The life processes depend directly or indirectly upon this phenomenon.

Materials. Twenty cubic centimeters of 2 to 4 per cent collodion;[1] a large test tube (a 50-cc. flask or wide-mouthed bottle will do); 50 cc. of a concentrated sugar solution (corn sirup or glucose); 18 to 30-in. piece of small-bore glass tubing; water; glass container that will hold about a quart.

FIG. 17.2 Method of making a collodion bag for the demonstration of diffusion.

See that the test tube is clean and dry. Pour some of the collodion into the tube. Tilt the tube sufficiently for the collodion to extend from the bottom of the tube to its top, and rotate until the entire inner surface becomes coated with collodion. Pour out excess collodion and continue to rotate the tube, blowing into it occasionally until the collodion appears dry. The tube is then lined with a fairly tough membrane. After 1 hr. carefully loosen the membrane from around the mouth of the tube. Pull this loosened portion aside and allow cold water to run into the space between the tube wall and the collodion membrane (see Fig. 17.2). This will loosen it entirely from the tube wall, and it may be lifted out with the fingers. Fill the bag with water to test for leaks. If the bag is not to be used immediately, it may be kept in good condition by filling it with water and then submerging it in a vessel of water. This prevents excessive drying and hardening. When it is to be used fill it three-fourths full of sugar solution, twist the mouth tightly, and tie. If any sugar solution was spilled on the outside of the bag wash it off first. Suspend the bag to the depth of the sugar solution in a vessel of water. If a piece of glass tube is available, prepare another bag exactly as the first except that the tubing should be inserted into the open end of the bag and tied. Suspend this bag as the other and support the tubing in some way.

Observe what happens in both bags after half an hour or more. The bag without the tubing becomes distended and tight (turgid). The pressure distending the bag is osmotic pressure. If this bag is filled too full at the start and left in the water too long, it may burst. This sometimes happens to plant cells, as for example tomato fruits during wet seasons. The liquid rises in the glass tubing, relieving pressure in the other bag. Test the water surrounding the bags for sugar. A good sugar test may

[1] Collodion solution can be had from a drugstore or may be made up by dissolving collodion cotton (pyroxylin) in equal parts of ether and absolute alcohol.

be made with Fehling's solution [2] or Benedict's solution.[3] A series of several such bags containing different concentrations of the sugar solution will, when tested, give an interesting set of results that are roughly quantitative to the eye.

The following questions may be used for discussion: Which moves the more rapidly, the sugar from the bag or the water into the bag? The movement of which material results in osmotic pressure? How long will the water continue to move into the bag? What applications can you make of these principles to plants and animals? How would you demonstrate the above principles with plant or animal material instead of collodion bags?

If one does not wish to prepare collodion bags for demonstrations of osmosis, cellulose dialyzer tubing is available. The tubing is sold in 100-ft. rolls, with a flat width of 1⅝ in. and diameter of 1⅛ in. when inflated, by The Arthur H. Thomas Company, Philadelphia, Pa. It is relatively inexpensive and is very convenient to use. Pieces of the desired length are cut off and the ends tied tightly with cotton twine. Also, ordinary wrapping or packaging cellophane may be converted into good differentially permeable membranes for demonstrating osmosis. Packaging cellophane has a waterproof film on each surface, which must be removed before it is suitable for this purpose. This may be done by placing pieces of the cellophane in 95 per cent ethyl (grain) alcohol for about 3 min. After this treatment, transfer to water and usually the film may be wiped off with the fingers. With this treatment the cellophane becomes a membrane which is permeable to water. Isopropyl alcohol may be substituted for the ethyl alcohol, but requires more time (*Turtox News,* August, 1958).

The Use of Living Plant Tissues. The physical process of diffusion through non-living membranes has been demonstrated in several ways. The same phenomenon can be demonstrated readily with certain living tissues.

Materials. Two medium-sized carrots or white potatoes; piece of small-bore glass tubing 18 in. or more in length; cork borer or small-bladed knife; sugar or sirup; heavy rubber band or ¼-in. tape; small glass vessels, such as tumblers, jars, or bottles; small cork perforated to hold tube.

Slice off top of carrot to give a flat surface. With a 15-mm. cork borer cut a cylindrical plug in the center of the cut end of the carrot parallel to the long axis. This plug can be removed readily with a corkscrew or may be carefully cut out with a knife. With a knife shape the cut end of the carrot like the neck of a bottle (see Fig. 17.3), making the neck about 15 mm. high. This neck need be no more than about 3 mm. thick. Fill the cavity of this carrot about one-half to three-fourths full of granulated sugar or concentrated sirup. Fit the glass tube into the cork tightly so that there will be no leaks (it must hold liquids). Insert this cork with

[2] Fehling's solution is made by mixing parts *A* and *B* each time just before it is used. The *A* and *B* solutions are made as follows: Solution *A*: 17.3 g. copper sulfate made up to 250 cc. with distilled water. Solution *B*: 86.5 g. sodium potassium tartrate (Rochelle salts) to 125 cc. distilled water, 25 g. sodium hydroxide to 125 cc. distilled water. When parts *A* and *B* are mixed and added to a sugar solution and the mixture is heated, a reddish-brown (or yellow) precipitate (cuprous oxide) is produced. The quantity of precipitate will increase with any increase in the concentration of the sugar solution.

[3] Benedict's solution is made as follows: Add 173 g. of sodium citrate and 100 g. of anhydrous sodium carbonate to 600 cc. of distilled water and heat until the chemicals are dissolved. Filter this solution. Add 17.3 g. of copper sulfate to 150 cc. of distilled water. After the copper sulfate has dissolved, slowly add this solution to the sodium citrate and sodium carbonate solution, with constant stirring. Add enough distilled water to bring the whole solution up to 1 liter. When this solution is mixed with a sugar solution and heated, a brick-red color develops. When no sugar is present, the solution remains blue upon heating.

its tube into the neck of the carrot bottle. Seal it by means of the rubber band or tape, cutting the rubber band, if it is used, and tying as you would a string. A string or narrow rubber band will cut through the soft plant tissue. If the cavity is too full, the sirup will rise into the tube. Mark this level. Suspend the carrot in a container of water. Watch for a slow rise of the sugar solution in the glass tube.

A simpler arrangement is as follows. Cut both ends off a carrot, or white potato, so that the cut surfaces are parallel to each other. With a cork borer or a small-bladed knife make a pit in one of these surfaces. This forms the vegetable into a sort of "cup." Half fill the cavity with dry sugar or heavy sirup. Set this "cup" in a pan or dish of water (see Fig. 17.4). If the potato is used, peel the portion which

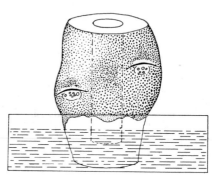

Fig. 17.3 Ap-
paratus for dem-
onstrating os-
mosis, using a
carrot with its
living cell mem-
branes.

Fig. 17.4   Potato tuber cup for demonstrating osmosis.

is to be submerged in water. If the air temperature is high in the laboratory rapid bacterial action can be prevented by the addition of a few crystals of phenol (carbolic acid), or drops if the liquid is at hand, to both the sugar solution and water. Within a few hours the sugar will be dissolved and the "cup" will be filled with liquid. When the sirup is used, the volume of the liquid also will increase.

Diffusion into a Desiccated Frog. The following makes an excellent problem for the entire class or for a small group of students. Besides illustrating diffusion through animal membranes, this experiment shows the method of absorption of water by a frog (which is said not to drink water by mouth).

Materials. Two living frogs; two jars or cans to be used as containers for the frogs; scales for weighing the frogs.

Weigh each frog in a can or jar, subtracting the weight of the can so as to have the exact weight of the frogs alone. Place each frog in a container and add 1 in. of water to one of the cans, keeping the other perfectly dry. Do not feed either frog for 24 hr., and then get the exact weight of each frog again. Record all weights. If there is any change in either frog, find out how much (figure the loss in per cent). This may be continued another 24 hr. if desired. Then add 1 in. of water to the frog container which has been dry and let stand overnight. Weigh each frog as before. Record what has happened. If accurate records of each weight and the percentage of loss and gain are recorded, this little problem represents a good elementary experience for the student in the making of observations, the recording of data, and the interpretation of that data; in other words, an introduction to the scientific method of procedure. The teacher should supervise the work to ensure exactness.

The Frog-skin Boot. Will water diffuse into the body of a frog when it is in water? (This demonstration may be used independently or as a continuation of the preceding one on loss of weight of a frog by drying.)

Materials. One recently killed frog; sirup or sugar solution; piece of small-bore glass tubing; tumbler, can, or beaker; short piece of string.

Cut the skin around the frog's leg just below the hip. Peel this skin down toward the knee and then toward the ankle just as in removing a stocking. Stop at the ankle. Cut the foot off, leaving it inside the skin, since it is impossible to remove the skin from the foot without tearing it. Into the boot which you have made pour some concentrated sirup or sugar and water. Tie the top of the boot around the end of a glass tube, so that it will not leak, by winding the string around several times before tying. Submerge the boot in a can or glass of water up to the level of the string, but not above it. If the sirup stands up in the glass tube, mark the level and observe the rise of level after several hours or longer. (If this experiment is considered in relation to the one on the drying and absorption of water by the frog, it has a direct bearing upon the explanation.)

The Digestive Tract and Other Visceral Membranes. Most of the thin sheet tissues of an animal can be used as diffusion membranes if stretched across a thistle tube and tightly tied. The mesentery, if free from holes, the stomach and intestine, or the urinary bladder serve satisfactorily.

A good illustration of diffusion approximating absorption of digested food into the blood stream is very illuminating and may be made easily by using the intestinal tract of any small vertebrate, such as a frog, mouse or rat, guinea pig, fair-sized fish, or a piece of chicken intestine.

Materials. Any small vertebrate such as suggested above; tumbler, beaker, or small can; string; sugar solution; starch suspension (in water); iodine (tincture or aqueous solution); Fehling's solution.

Remove the stomach and intestine entire and intact. Clean out the intestinal contents and flush with water by inserting a medicine dropper into one end. Fill as nearly as possible with the sugar solution. Tie both ends of the tract tightly after filling and suspend in a tumbler of water in such a manner as to leave both tied ends above the water level (see Fig. 17.5). If any of the sugar solution was spilled on the outside of the tract, be sure to wash it off before the preparation is suspended in the water. Test the water in the tumbler immediately for sugar. Note results. Test the water again after several hours or overnight. If the tumbler did not have too much water in it to begin with, there should be a good sugar test this time.

FIG. 17.5   Portion of a digestive tract filled with sirup or honey to demonstrate diffusion.

Make a similar setup or use the same one later, using starch and water in the place of sugar and water. Test the surrounding water for starch immediately and after several hours. Test for sugar after several hours or overnight. If sugar should be found in the water, it will make a very interesting question for class discussion. (If enough enzymes were present in the tract to convert some of the starch to sugar, it might be found in the tumbler. This may not happen.)

CHANGING THE PERMEABILITY OF CELL MEMBRANES

Many substances are retained within a cell because the limiting membrane (protoplasmic membrane) is little or not at all permeable to those substances. This condition of permeability is essential to the life processes going on within the organism.

The Common Garden Beet. Permeability of membranes may be increased by certain treatments. This can be demonstrated easily by using cubes of the common garden beet. The red color of the beet is due to the presence of a pigment (anthocyanin) which is in solution in the cell sap. Ordinarily the cell membranes are not permeable to this pigment. However, by treatment with anesthetics, toxic substances such as sodium and calcium chloride, or by low and high temperatures, the permeability is greatly increased and the anthocyanin readily diffuses out.

Materials. An ordinary garden beet which has not been exposed to frost or freezing temperatures; 10 test tubes or any other glass containers; ether, chloroform, sodium chloride (table salt), calcium chloride; a freezing mixture of ice and salt (3 parts cracked ice to 1 part of salt) or a refrigerator which will give temperatures of 0 and 10°C.; an alcohol burner or other source of heat; gummed labels; thermometer; ordinary chemical scale (see Fig. 13.7).

Cut ten ¼-in. cubes from the beet. Rinse these in water at room temperature until all traces of the red pigment which escapes from the injured cells have been removed. If the pigment continues to diffuse out after a few rinses, try another beet, as the first one has been frosted or injured. Place a cube in each of the 10 test tubes. Label each tube, giving the treatment (substance used, etc.) to which it is to be subjected. Treat one cube with ether, a second with chloroform, a third with 10 per cent salt, a fourth with 10 per cent calcium chloride. Allow all four to stand 10 to 15 min., decant the liquids and replace them with ordinary water. Set these aside and after a few minutes observe what happens. Cover a fifth untreated cube with water and keep at room temperature. This is to be used as a check against the other nine. Cover the remaining cubes with water and subject one of each to one of the following temperatures: 0, 10, 40, and 60°C., and boiling temperature. The cubes to be treated at 0 and 10°C. should be exposed to the low temperatures for 20 to 30 min.; a few minutes is sufficient for the others. Observe each of the 10 tubes for the appearance of traces of anthocyanin in the surrounding water.

Turgidity of Plant Tissues. Many plant tissues are rigid because of supporting or mechanical tissues. Others are rigid because of high osmotic pressure within the cells.

Materials. Carrot (potato tuber, beet, radish, parsnip, cucumber, or other succulent organ may be used); container for water; a strong sodium chloride (salt) solution; concentrated sugar solution (corn sirup is very satisfactory); burner or other source of heat.

Peel the carrot and cut out a piece approximately 2 in. long, ½ in. wide, and ½ in. thick. Note that the piece cannot be bent much without breaking. Place in a container and cover with either the salt or sugar solution (or one piece in each kind of solution). Allow these to stand for 15 to 20 min. If permitted to stand too long, death may occur. Try bending the pieces after this treatment. Note that the treated tissue is much more flexible than the fresh carrot. Rinse off the solution from the pieces and place them in water for 30 min. Try the flexibility again. Note that the pieces have regained most of their original turgidity. Heat a similar piece of carrot in boiling water for 3 to 4 min. The carrot tissue becomes very flexible. Transfer to cool water for half an hour or more and test again. Turgidity of the boiled carrot is not regained since the tissues are dead and the membranes are more permeable.

PLASMOLYSIS

Demonstration of Water Loss from Cells. Excessive loss of water from the vacuole of a plant cell results in a pulling away of the cytoplasm from the cell wall. When in this condition the cell is said to be plasmolyzed. Ordinarily, if the cell remains plasmolyzed for long, death occurs. The red corpuscles of animal blood show plasmolysis readily, but the cell membrane draws in with the shrinking of the cytoplasm, resulting in a withering or crinkling of the surface.

Materials. Living *Spirogyra* (some other filamentous algae will also serve), or the leaves of elodea, leaf epidermis of purple wandering Jew (*Tradescantia*), etc.; small drop of blood; small amount of concentrated salt or sugar solution; microscope slide and cover glass; water; compound microscope.

Mount a few filaments of the *Spirogyra* in a drop of water on the slide, cover with the cover glass and examine with the microscope. Note that the chloroplast is in a definite spiral form, lying more or less against the inner surface of the wall. Occasionally the nucleus may be seen as if suspended near the center of the cell by strands of cytoplasm. Place a drop or two of the sugar (or salt) solution along one edge of the cover glass. At the opposite edge of the cover glass, place a piece of blotter or filter paper in contact with the water under the cover glass. This will draw out the water from under the cover glass, and it will be replaced by the sugar solution. Watch this preparation for effects upon the plant cells. After the changes have been noted, remove the filaments and place in water again. If the cells have not been killed, they will regain their original appearance. A similar demonstration may be made using blood cells instead of *Spirogyra*. The corpuscles, however, should be placed in the drop of sugar or salt solution at once before adding the cover glass, since drawing out the water with the blotter will also remove them. The concentrating of the cell contents and consequent shrinking of the cytoplasm is a demonstration of plasmolysis.

IMBIBITION

Effects of Absorption of Water. Imbibition is the diffusion of a liquid into a solid, resulting in the swelling of the solid. Particles of colloidal material in the gel state usually have an affinity for water. This affinity is often so great that water is absorbed from the environment even against enormous pressures.

Materials. Sheet of dry gelatin; dry bean seeds; castor-bean seeds; two thoroughly dried blocks of wood; one C-shaped screw clamp; ruler; a few date seeds; scales or balance (see Fig. 13.7).

Place a piece of dry gelatin in water for 20 min. Count out 25 beans. Measure and mark a few of these. Weigh the beans dry, soak them in water overnight, and reweigh. Subtract the first weight from the second to get the amount of water imbibed. Also measure the marked beans again. Remove the seed coat from a castor bean. Note that the coat is hard and brittle. Keep the seeds moist and warm for a few days, and then try removing a seed coat. Compare with the dry bean. Try cutting a slice from a dry date seed. Soak in water for about 5 days and try cutting again. Measure the dry blocks of wood. Place the screw clamp on one tight enough to hold in place, but not tight enough to dent it. Soak both blocks in water overnight. The blocks may be weighed before and after soaking. Tulip-tree wood is excellent for this purpose. Compare the soaked gelatin with the dry sheet as to thickness, tensile strength, transparency, weight, etc. Compare the weight and size of the soaked beans with that of the dry. Note the rupture of the seed coats. Compare the dry and wet measurements of the wood blocks.

EFFECTS OF MOLECULAR MOVEMENT

Brownian Movement. The molecules of all substances are in a state of motion. The force which causes diffusion is this molecular movement. These moving molecules collide with each other as well as with the molecules of other substances with which they come in contact. Molecules are too small to be seen with the highest powered microscope, but impacts of these moving molecules with small, but visible, particles of other substances may cause those particles to move, and this movement may be detected under magnification. The peculiar vibrating movement of these tiny particles is known as *Brownian movement*.

Materials. Compound microscope with a high-power objective (4 mm.); microscope slide and cover glass; water and a small quantity of some finely divided substance which is not soluble in water: chalk dust, wall plaster, air-slaked lime, carmine (a red dye), lampblack, vermiculite, plaster of paris or gypsum (calcium sulfate), pumice, graphite (lubricating powder), calcium carbonate, and wheat flour. Any of these materials may be improved by grinding with a mortar and pestle.

Place an amount of graphite, or any of the other substances selected, which can be scooped up on a dime in 25 cc. of water. To aid in the dispersal, add a few granules of a laundry detergent. Shake thoroughly and let stand for a few minutes. With a medicine dropper place a drop of the suspended material on a microscope slide. Cover with a cover glass and examine with the high-power objective of a microscope.

Look for a vibratory movement of the small particles of the substance in the water. They do not move across the field of view from one side to the other but, instead, they move back and forth in minute paths. Remember that the movement of such particles is *not* the result of the activity of *its own* molecules but the bombardment of these particles by the molecules of water which are moving more rapidly than the molecules of the solid.

The attenuated apices of the desmid *Closterium* contain gypsum particles which almost invariably show Brownian movement. See Chap. 12 for a description of *Closterium*.

REFERENCES

1. Boyle, W. S.: *Principles and Practice in Plant Cytology,* Burgess Publishing Company, Minneapolis, 1953.

2. Brooks, S. C., and M. M. Brooks: *Permeability of Living Cells,* J. W. Edwards, Publisher, Inc., Ann Arbor, Mich., 1951.

3. Gabriel, M. L., and S. Fogel: *Great Experiments in Biology,* Prentice-Hall, Inc., Englewood Cliffs, N.J., 1955.

4. Miller, E. V.: *Within the Living Plant,* McGraw-Hill Book Company, Inc., New York, 1953.

5. Parker, J. B., and J. J. Clarke: *Laboratory Exercises in Animal Biology,* 4th ed., The C. V. Mosby Company, St. Louis, 1955.

6. Rogers, C. G.: *Laboratory Outlines in Comparative Physiology,* McGraw-Hill Book Company, Inc., New York, 1938.

7. Transeau, E. N., H. C. Sampson, and L. H. Tiffany: *Textbook of Botany,* rev. ed., Harper & Brothers, New York, 1953.

8. Wilson, Carl L., and Walter Loomis: *Botany,* 2d ed., The Dryden Press, Inc. (combined with Holt, Rinehart and Winston, Inc.), New York, 1957.

CHAPTER 18

--⊰ Circulation ⊱--

Circulation, in the usual sense of the term, is a function which is peculiar to animals but not common to all of them. It usually involves the passing of a fluid called the "blood" through tubes called "blood vessels" (veins, arteries, and capillaries) or spaces called "sinuses." It is true that there is the passage of water through plants and the movement of cytoplasm within cells, but these are not comparable to true circulation in most cases and will be considered under other headings.

BLOOD

Structure of Blood. Long before a child enters school he is aware of the presence of blood in his own body and the bodies of other animals. He has cut his skin and seen the red fluid seep from the wound. He has seen the formation of a clot and scab, and he may have learned that the blood contains something known as "corpuscles." All this may safely be assumed; therefore, it becomes our duty in biology teaching to make sure that he sees and understands of what the blood is composed.

Materials. Half pint or pint of fresh blood; fork or small straight stick; test tube or vial; some small dishes or a bowl about the size of a soup bowl; microscope and a glass slide, cover glass; pint or quart jar with cap; normal salt solution (0.9 per cent NaCl).

Blood Cells. Make a microscope preparation of blood to show corpuscles. Place a droplet of blood upon a slide. Bring the edge of a cover glass or another slide into contact with this drop and drag it across the slide. This will seem to wipe off the blood, but it is merely because the blood is spread so thinly. Lay the cover glass upon the smear and examine under high power for the red corpuscles (see Fig. 18.1). The blood cells will appear to have lost their red color. Occasionally an irregular cell will appear. It may have more than one nuclear body. These are white cells. If a small amount of fresh pus can be obtained, as from a pimple, smear it and examine. Pus is mostly white blood corpuscles. It makes a splendid contrast with the red cell smear. A drop of fountain-pen ink in a little water may be poured over the smear before the cover glass is added. This will stain the cells slightly. They must be smeared thinly over the slide. A drop of Wright's stain is better, if available. Pus from a very recently festered source is best. If it is old the cells will have disintegrated.

Plasma and Fibrin. Fresh blood may be obtained at any packing house or slaughterhouse. It must be collected as it emerges from the animal. The butcher will usually permit a vein to be opened and a glass tube inserted if you ask. Collect the fresh blood in the pint or quart jar, nearly filling it. Screw the cap on tightly to keep out the air. The blood may clot on the upper surface, but the lower portions will keep for a short time. If some of the fresh portion of blood is poured into a bowl and whipped very slowly with a fork or small stick, the clotting will continue with the formation of strings of material (fibrin) which will also contain most of the corpuscles. If some of the blood is allowed to stand in a vessel for several hours the clot will form, leaving a clear or straw-colored liquid, the plasma or serum.

Such questions as: "What causes clotting and the value of it?" "What is hemophilia and what can be done about it?" may be discussed or reported by students.

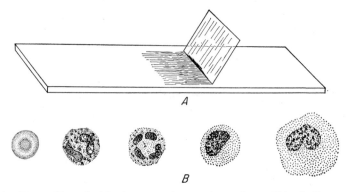

FIG. 18.1   The making of a blood smear: *A*, smearing a drop of blood; *B*, appearance of blood cells that may be seen.

The Flow of Blood. The fact that the blood flows or is pumped about in the blood vessels is well known to the student, but few, if any, ever have seen it flowing normally within these tubes. Indirectly the beating of the heart and pulse are evidences of blood flow and should be studied as well as other phenomena of circulation.

Circulation in the Tail of a Fish or Tadpole. Materials. A goldfish (almost any other fish will do); a fish or frog board (see Fig. 18.2); thumbtacks or pins; piece of cloth about 4 by 12 in., or small cloth tobacco sack with drawstring; microscope; small grass frog.

Saturate the piece of cloth with water and wrap it loosely around the body of a small fish. Spread the tail fin over the hole in the board and fasten it with thumbtacks. Then fasten the cloth to the board in the same manner. Pour a little water on the head end of the wrapped fish. Examine the tail under a microscope and you will easily see the blood vessels running along the rays of the tail fin and capillaries running between larger vessels. Keep the spread tail wet at all times. This may require dropping a little water on it every few minutes. If the fish is not used more than 20 min. and is kept wet, it may be returned to the aquarium and will be in good condition. A tadpole may be used exactly as the fish for the above demonstration.

Circulation in the Web of a Frog's Foot. If a grass frog is substituted for the fish, it may be placed in a tobacco sack or wrapped just as the fish, with its foot spread over the hole (see Fig. 18.2). This offers one of the finest obtainable demonstrations of circulating blood.

Circulation in the Internal Organs of a Frog. Lungs. If the life of the frog can be sacrificed, the body may be opened and circulation within the organs observed. Pith the frog by destroying its brain (Fig. 18.3). With dissecting scissors remove the ventral wall of the body exposing stomach, intestines, and lungs. If the lungs are inflated with air they should be placed under the microscope at once and their surface examined. The saclike character of the lungs, their thin walls, and the complete network of minute capillaries show beautifully when the lungs are well inflated and demonstrate vividly how the blood stream comes into intimate relation with the air inhaled into the lungs. The lungs can be forcibly inflated by inserting a small glass tube through the mouth and glottis and forcing air through this into the lungs. It is difficult to keep them inflated.

Stomach and Mesentery. The surface of the stomach frequently shows very clearly the flow of blood in the blood vessels if a good light can be directed upon it from above. Some of these vessels, with the aid of a microscope, can be seen to turn down into the stomach wall and disappear in the tissues. The thin transparent membrane (mesentery) stretching between intestines and other organs is full of blood vessels. If properly spread out beneath the microscope, the circulation may be readily observed.

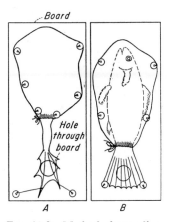

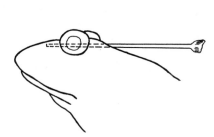

Fig. 18.2   Method of spreading a frog's foot web *A,* and a fish tail fin *B* to show circulation of blood.

Fig. 18.3   Method of destroying a frog's brain by pithing.

Circulation in the Chick Embryo and Fish Fry. The preparation of a chick embryo and its blood vessels has been described in Chap. 22. Use may be made of this for circulation. If fish eggs are available at any time and can be hatched, be sure to see the newly emerged fry with yolk sac. They are nearly transparent, and beautiful circulation demonstrations can be made from them. The beating heart and gill circulation may be seen.

Circulation in a Rabbit Ear. Materials. A young rabbit; scissors, razor blade; microscope.

From the thinnest portion of the ear of a young rabbit clip away the hair with scissors. Then shave this area with a safety razor after softening the hair with soap and water. Be careful not to cut the skin. Place the rabbit near the stage of the microscope, hold it firmly and bend the ear over the stage so as to be able to focus a strong light from the mirror through the shaved spot. If the ear is thin, the light bright, and care used in focusing, the circulation shows plainly. It is a little less convenient to use than fish or frog because the rabbit may move and require constant attention, but does very well if a rabbit is more easily obtained.

Circulation in the Earthworm. Materials. Large earthworms (night crawlers); a dozen common pins; wax-bottomed pan or a soft pine board; hand lens or low-power microscope; grain alcohol; shallow pan or dish; fine-pointed scissors.

Place a large worm in the shallow pan or dish and pour in enough water to about cover the worm. Add enough alcohol to make the solution 2 or 3 per cent. Stir thoroughly and in a few minutes add the same amount of alcohol again, making 5 or 6 per cent. After several minutes the alcohol will have anesthetized the worm and it will become almost inactive. Watch carefully to avoid killing the worm. Remove it from the alcohol and wash in fresh water. Lay the worm on the wax-bottomed pan or board. Pin it tightly, as shown in Fig. 18.4. Very carefully cut through the middorsal line of the worm, making certain to cut only as deep as the body wall. Pin this out, as shown in Fig. 18.4, and it will disclose the dorsal blood vessel and the five pairs of beating hearts. This is a striking illustration of circulation in an invertebrate. It is possible to make the dissection without anesthetizing the worm, but it writhes violently and the dissection is difficult. Watch a large

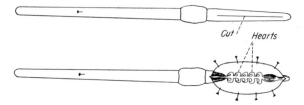

FIG. 18.4   Method of dissecting and spreading an earthworm to expose the hearts.

worm as it lies or crawls upon a table. Along its middorsal line the blood vessel can be seen plainly and the direction of flow (posterior to anterior) will be discovered.

CIRCULATORY ORGANS

Structure of Vessels. *Cross Sections.* To show the structure of vessels, preserve pieces of blood vessels (vein and artery) in formalin and cut very thin rings from them with a razor so that the make-up of these tubes may be seen and compared. If the piece to be sectioned is dipped into warm paraffin (barely melted) and withdrawn immediately and cooled, then dipped again and again in like manner, a paraffin block will be formed which can be fitted into the hand microtome (Fig. 18.5) and much thinner sections cut from it. An examination of the sections cut from a vein compared with those cut from an artery shows the difference in their structure. Another method is to push a piece of pith into a blood vessel so as to fill the cavity and then surround the vessel with more pith. Fasten this in the microtome and section.

Structure of the Heart and Valves. *Dissection.* Have a student visit a butcher who kills his own meat and arrange to secure a heart from a pig or calf with the blood vessels attached. It is usually difficult to make the butcher understand that you do not wish the heart dressed as for market, but insist upon it. Such a heart will make a very satisfactory specimen for dissection. Things to be noted are the difference in the size of the two sides of the heart, which can usually be seen before dissection; the coronary artery on the outer surface of the heart; the intimate relation of the vessels to the lungs (part of the lungs are likely to be attached); the difference in appearance between the auricles and ventricles. Have someone try gently to force a pencil or small rod of any kind through the vessels back into the heart. Some of them will admit the probe, others will not. The question of why this is true offers a good introduction to the study of the valves and their relation to the direction of blood flow. If a large vessel, such as the aorta, is carefully split lengthwise the semilunar valve will be disclosed, and if the probe is reinserted until it stops, the vessel can be slightly opened and the action of the valve actually seen (Fig. 18.6). The chambers of the heart should also be opened to give an idea of the difference in the walls of the chambers and to show the tricuspid and mitral valves.

The Heart Beat. The following experiment should not be omitted from any study of circulation because it is the one demonstration which will interest every student, and it offers an opportunity to introduce elementary students to controlled experimentation, to the scientific method of observation, and to the recording and interpretation of data.

Materials. A large frog or turtle with shell 5 to 7 in. in length; pan in which to place dissected animal; small saw for cutting shell if turtle is used; scissors for dissecting; thread; a lever as shown in Fig. 18.7.

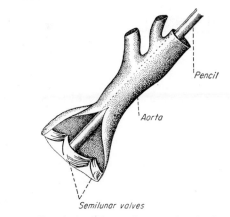

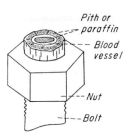

Fɪɢ. 18.5   Homemade hand microtome to be used with a razor blade.

Fɪɢ. 18.6   The semilunar valves in the aorta.

Pith a frog and expose its heart through the ventral surface of its body. If a turtle is used etherize it, as it will be necessary to saw the lower shell (plastron) loose on each side. When it has been carefully removed the heart will be exposed. In all dissections it is best to avoid cutting large blood vessels as the loss of much blood may cause the heart beat to stop.

If but a few students are to use the preparation they may assemble about the specimen to watch it. If the class is too large for this method the lever shown in Fig. 18.7 should be attached to the heart. This will serve to visualize the beating to the entire room. The lever may be made from any materials available such as the following: a base from any flat board; an L arm to the end of which is fastened a disk of smooth-surfaced cardboard on a nail or pin small enough to allow it to turn very freely. See Fig. 18.7*B* for details of arrangement of moving parts. The thread is attached to a hook made from a bent pin. This is fastened to the tip of the heart (Fig. 18.7*C*) and the string drawn taut so that any movement of the heart will lift the lever. The movements of the lever will be seen without difficulty anywhere in the room.

An Experiment on Rate of Beat. Have the class count the number of beats while one student keeps time with a watch. Get several ½-min. counts and let the class record in terms of beats per minute. Record the room temperature. Slowly pour over the heart and body some water which is about 40°C. (warm but not hot). Add enough of this to just cover the body and heart. Let the class count and record the rate of beating again. Drain the warm water off of the animal and replace it with cold water about 10°C. Count and record the beats again. Other intermediate temperatures may be used if desired. Do not fail to have the data recorded in table form and averaged or summarized. If several temperatures are used a graph can be drawn from the data.

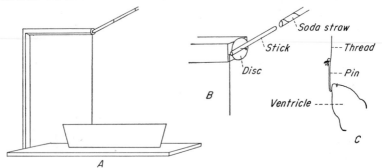

FIG. 18.7   Apparatus for demonstrating heart beat: *A,* complete setup; *B,* detail of lever arm; *C,* hook to attach to ventricle.

A discussion should follow which should bring out the relation of rate of beat to temperature. This opens the way for a discussion of whether other activities such as arm- and leg-muscle contraction, etc., are similarly affected. If one or two capable students care to work this out as a project it should be allowed, and they could demonstrate it with leg muscle of a frog for the class at the proper time.

REFERENCES

1. Berger, Henry I.: *Blood, Clinical and Laboratory Diagnosis,* Battle & Company Chemical Corporation, St. Louis, Mo., 1934. Complete study of blood; methods of preparation for blood counts; discussion of blood diseases.

2. Best, C. H., and N. B. Taylor: *Human Body, Its Anatomy and Physiology,* Holt, Rinehart and Winston, Inc., New York, 1956.

3. Gregg, D. E.: *Coronary Circulation in Health and Disease,* Lea & Febiger, Philadelphia, 1950. Illustrated.

4. Harvey, W.: *Motion of the Heart and Blood,* E. P. Dutton & Co., Inc., New York, 1960.

5. Hintz, M. A.: "Hematology," *Am. Biol. Teacher,* **16**:7–9, October, 1954.

6. Lutz, B. R.: *Living Blood Vessels,* Boston University Press, Boston, 1952.

7. Marshall, A. M.: *Frog: An Introduction to Anatomy, Histology and Embryology,* St. Martin's Press, Inc., New York, 1957.

8. Mitchell, P. H.: *Textbook of General Physiology,* 5th ed., McGraw-Hill Book Company, Inc., New York, 1956.

9. Race, R. R., and R. Sanger: *Blood Groups in Man,* 2d ed., Charles C Thomas, Publisher, Springfield, Ill., 1955. Illustrated.

10. Rogers, C. G.: *Laboratory Outlines in Comparative Physiology,* McGraw-Hill Book Company, Inc., New York, 1938.

11. Sanders, J. M.: "Demonstrating Circulation in a Frog," *Am. Biol. Teacher,* **12**:31, February, 1950.

12. Vance, B. B., and D. F. Miller: *Biology for You,* J. B. Lippincott Company, Philadelphia, 1958.

13. Wiggers, C. J.: *Circulatory Dynamics,* Grune & Stratton, Inc., New York, 1952. Illustrated.

CHAPTER 19

⊸⊰ Respiration ⊱⊸

One of the outstanding differences between matter in the living and in the dead states is in the continuous chemical change that is taking place within the living system. These changes frequently result in the transformation of relatively complex compounds into simpler compounds. The commonest reactions of this type involve the addition of oxygen or the oxidation of materials within the cells. This is respiration. One of the results of respiration is the release or transfer of energy. As far as is known, this process occurs in all living cells and it is one of the fundamental processes of plant and animal life. The oxidation in this instance is slow when compared to the combustion of a piece of coal or wood. However, the underlying principle is exactly the same. The resulting products in both cases are ordinarily identical. By means of certain tests these products can be detected and measured.

OXIDATION AND ITS RESULTS

Test for Carbon Dioxide. Lime Carbonate. If the carbon dioxide generator described in Chap. 13 is put into operation and a little of this gas allowed to bubble through a test tube or glass of limewater [1] the carbon dioxide will unite with the lime, forming a carbonate of lime which is not soluble in water. The carbonate is white in color and therefore the limewater becomes milky. This is the usual simple test for the presence of carbon dioxide in air or gases.

Water as a Product of Oxidation. Condensation of Water over a Flame. Light a gas burner, alcohol burner, or candle. Hold a cold plate of glass or smooth metal about 6 to 10 in. above the flame and a deposit of moisture resembling dew will form on the surface. Be sure that the collecting plate is cold. It should be placed in a refrigerator or outside a window on a cold day to get best results. The water will disappear again if the plate becomes warm. How can you show that the water is a product of the combustion or oxidation and not moisture from the air? The part of the plate held over the flame becomes much wetter than the rest.

Oxidation. Ignition of Match Heads. The student is likely to be familiar with burning and rusting as examples of oxidation. The teacher also should see that the idea of the formation of new products (commonly carbon dioxide and water) is the frequent result of oxidation. A demonstration which will impress upon the student's mind the relation of the volume of oxygen consumed to the volume of material oxidized may be of value. The following simple setup can serve several purposes.

Materials. A small jar of any kind that has a cork or close fitting lid and does not

[1] Limewater is made by placing ordinary slaked lime in water, mixing thoroughly, and allowing it to stand until the excess lime has settled out. The clear liquid is drained or siphoned off and until used kept in tightly corked bottles so as to prevent absorption of carbon dioxide from the air.

345

hold more than ½ pt.; cork small enough to pass into the jar through the mouth; six ordinary matches; piece of wire or small metal rod; thermometer.

FIG. 19.1   Apparatus to show relation of volume of oxygen consumed to volume of material oxidized.

Sharpen the matches and stick them into the small cork in a straight row in such a manner that each match head is about ¼ in. from the one next to it (Fig. 19.1). Place the cork and its matches in the bottom of the jar. Take the temperature within the jar and record it. Heat the end of the wire. Thrust it into the jar and ignite the head of a match at one end of the row. Withdraw the wire and immediately close the jar tightly. The flaming match will ignite only one, or possibly two, more heads but these will be extinguished almost immediately, showing that even a match head cannot be ignited in the absence of oxygen. Take the temperature inside the bottle and compare with the original. This change in temperature indicates the transfer and transformation of energy from the material of the match heads to the heat of the air. The cork and matches should next be removed from the jar and placed upon the table. If the head at the other end of the row is now ignited the entire line will ignite and the sticks will burn as well.

Suggested questions which it should be possible for the class to answer: What caused the "suffocation" of the matches in the jar? What was the source of the heat (energy) in the jar which brought about the rise in temperature? Draw a parallel between the jar with its matches and a cell with its food supply.

OXYGEN CONSUMPTION AS AN INDICATOR OF RESPIRATION

Germinating Seeds. Place enough germinating seeds (corn, beans, peas, wheat, etc.) in a jar to fill it about one-third full. Close tightly and allow it to stand for several hours or overnight. Light a long slender stick, remove the stopper and quickly thrust the flaming stick into the jar. The flame is extinguished, showing the lack of oxygen. Repeat the test with another similar jar that has been sealed at the same time as the one with the germinating seeds but which had nothing in it except normal air. Compare the results and account for the difference. This idea of a check experiment should be impressed upon the students.

Measuring the Oxygen Absorbed. As shown by chemical equation for respiration in an experiment below (see Fig. 19.5), release of carbon dioxide by plants, free oxygen is necessary for most organisms to remain alive and grow. A rat or almost any other land animal will die of suffocation within a few minutes if submerged in water. The same is true for land plants excepting that a longer time is required. This is shown in another experiment below on the effects of insufficient oxygen. The amount of oxygen needed in the respiration of germinating seeds, opening flower buds, green leaves, etc., may be quantitatively measured as follows.

Materials. Germinating wheat grains; two 50-cc. graduated cylinders (test tubes or bottles may be substituted); two small pieces of cheesecloth or cotton; two shallow containers; 50 cc. of a saturated solution of potassium hydroxide or sodium hydroxide; 50 cc. of mercury (water may be used with the addition of three drops of hydrochloric acid which prevents carbon dioxide absorption).

Place about 15 cc. of germinating wheat grains in each cylinder. Press a piece of cheesecloth or cotton plug down on each mass of seeds to hold them in place. Invert one cylinder over the potassium hydroxide or sodium hydroxide and the other over mercury or acidulated water. Allow the experiment to continue for several hours. The cylinder over the potassium hydroxide or sodium hydroxide will show a rise of the liquid (see Fig. 19.2). The check apparatus over the mercury or acidulated water remains the same as at the start. Potassium hydroxide absorbs carbon dioxide while mercury or acidulated water does not. In the apparatus over the potassium hydroxide the carbon dioxide released by the germinating wheat is absorbed by the solution. The grains absorb oxygen, reducing the pressure within the cylinder and, consequently, the potassium hydroxide rises. The height of the column of liquid may be noted on the calibrations. The volume of this column of liquid is approximately equal to the volume of oxygen absorbed by the germinating grains since the experiment started. The volume may be determined in terms of cubic centimeters by removing the cylinder from the potassium hydroxide and filling with water. Then pour off (or remove with a pipette) the water down to the point reached by the

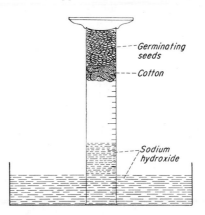

Fig. 19.2   Apparatus for measuring the oxygen absorbed by germinating seeds.

potassium hydroxide. The volume of the water removed is the same as the volume of oxygen absorbed. Note the check apparatus (see respiratory ratio or respiratory quotient). If fat-containing seeds were used what may happen to the mercury? This experiment may be repeated with small opening flower buds or green leaves. If the leaves are used the apparatus should be kept in the dark to prevent photosynthesis from occurring. Repeat, using several insects instead of seeds.

Effect of Insufficient Oxygen Supply. Flooding of land plants, earth fills around tree trunks, hardened, closely packed soil surrounding root systems, etc., may cause death of plants. Agricultural lands are drained, cultivated, and retaining walls are constructed about trees where fills are to be made in order to prevent loss of valuable plants. Several factors may be involved in such deaths, but a lack of adequate oxygen supply probably is the most important.

Materials. Four small potted plants (coleus plants are satisfactory) of the same age and size; a battery jar (a wide-mouthed gallon pickle jar may be used) or other glass container large enough in which to submerge one of the potted plants; light-proof box (shipping carton); bell jar (a wide-mouthed gallon pickle jar with lid may be substituted); 200 cc. of a saturated solution of potassium hydroxide or sodium hydroxide.

Submerge one of the plants in the battery jar filled with water. Place it in a warm (about 70°F.) light situation. Place a second plant in the dark box alongside the first. See that the soil is kept moist. Place a third plant under the bell jar which has a carbon dioxide–free atmosphere (see Chap. 15, Photosynthesis, for preparation). Keep this plant exposed to light along with the first. The fourth plant may be kept along with the other three as a check. Death of the submerged plant may occur within 10 days to 2 weeks. Death is due to suffocation because of an inadequate oxygen supply. Some student may suggest that the plant died of starvation due to reduced light in the water. To answer this, observation is made of the plant kept in the dark box. It will be found alive and in fairly good condition. Others may argue that there was a lack of carbon dioxide in the water and that this caused starvation. To answer this, the plant in the carbon dioxide–free atmosphere may be observed. It will be found in much better condition than the submerged plant. In addition, a starch test may be made on leaves of the submerged plant. The presence of starch indicates that the plant did not die of starvation.

The rate of diffusion of dissolved oxygen from water into tissues varies greatly in different plant species because of differences in tissue structure. The structures of aquatic plants are such that sufficient oxygen may diffuse into their tissues, allowing normal respiration to occur. Generally, for land plants, tissue structures are such that sufficient oxygen cannot diffuse into the cells when submerged, and death from suffocation results the same as may occur for land animals under the same conditions.

Germinating Seeds with and without Oxygen. In most living tissues free oxygen is necessary before respiration can occur. If respiration is prevented, growth cannot take place. In general, if seeds are placed deep in soil or water, sufficient oxygen is not available for their germination.

Materials. Freshly soaked seeds or grains such as wheat; two bottles with stoppers; string; two small pieces of mosquito netting; about 40 cc. of freshly made potassium pyrogallate (made by mixing equal volumes of a 6⅔ per cent pyrogallic acid solution and a 33⅓ per cent potassium hydroxide solution immediately before using).

Potassium
pyrogallate

FIG. 19.3 Apparatus for demonstrating the relation of oxygen to germination.

Divide the number of soaked seeds equally. Bag each group of seeds in the pieces of mosquito netting. Tie each bag securely with string, leaving one end of the string long. Moisten each bag of seeds with water. Suspend a bag of seeds in each bottle from the bottom of the cork. A pin will attach the string to the cork. Prepare the potassium pyrogallate, pour it into one bottle and stopper immediately. Pour an equal quantity of water into the other bottle and stopper with the bag of seeds suspended above the liquid (see Fig. 19.3). Allow the two bottles to stand for a few days and observe the wheat grains. The bottle with the potassium pyrogallate soon becomes oxygen free since this substance has a strong affinity for free oxygen. The other bottle still contains free oxygen since the water will dissolve but a small portion. The seeds germinate in the atmosphere containing oxygen; those in the oxygen-deficient atmosphere do not. Ordinary garden peas may be used to show a seed type which does not require free oxygen for germination. Soak and suspend these over the potassium pyrogallate as in the experiment above. This type of respiration is known as *intramolecular* or *anaerobic respiration*.

A Simple Respiration Apparatus. In the teaching of the subject of respiration it is most convenient to show the absorption of oxygen and release of carbon dioxide as evidence of the actual process of respiration having taken place within the organism. To do this a fairly simple apparatus can be constructed which will serve equally well for any kind of plant or animal material. This general usefulness of the setup makes it unusually valuable.

Materials. Three ½-pt. milk bottles (wide-mouthed bottles or small jars); stoppers to fit these bottles; one pint jar or bottle; some glass tubing to connect the bottles in a series; limewater; some large vessel such as a 5-gal. oil can, a carboy, or bottle; bucket. Instead of the last four items, which are used as a means of forcing air through the smaller vessels, an exhaust pump of any sort or an air-pressure line may be substituted (see Fig. 13.3). Figure 19.4 shows the general arrangement of these materials in assembling the apparatus. Two of the bottles are fitted with the stoppers and tubes and partly filled with limewater. These bottles are then connected with the pint jar which is used as the respiration chamber and in which is placed the plant material or the animal which is used in the experiment. This jar is also closely stoppered and connected with a third bottle of limewater. This series of three limewater bottles and a respiration chamber is next connected with a large carboy, or airtight can, which is filled with water and equipped with a siphon tube so that it can be drained.

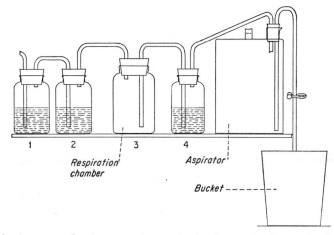

Fig. 19.4 Apparatus for demonstrating respiration in germinating seeds, flower buds, leaves, roots, and animals.

The method of operation is rather obvious. The living material is placed in the respiration chamber, and the stoppers and connections are all made airtight. If allowed to stand a while, there will be an accumulation of carbon dioxide in the respiration chamber. When ready to present to the class, the siphon is started by opening the pinchcock. If there is no water in the siphon, it will be necessary to suck on the end of the siphon tube to start. As the water flows out of the aspirator (large siphon bottle, or can), it produces a partial vacuum which causes a reduced pressure on the third limewater bottle. This in turn allows air to be forced from the respiration chamber through the limewater. If this air contains carbon dioxide, it will cause the limewater to become milky because of the formation of carbonate of lime. The withdrawal of air from the respiration chamber will allow air to flow into it from the other two limewater bottles and into these bottles from the free air of the room. The reason for using two limewater bottles at the intake end is to remove all carbon dioxide from the incoming air. Therefore the carbon dioxide in the air entering the third limewater bottle must have come from the organism within the respiration chamber. This should not be explained to the class as it makes a nice problem for them to figure out. When the siphon can or aspirator has emptied, it may be started over again by refilling the can with water.

If a water-faucet suction pump is available (Fig. 13.3) it may be attached instead of the aspirator (siphon can). If the air-pressure line is available, it may be attached to the intake end of the apparatus and the siphon omitted. Before operating the setup, be sure that all connecting tubes are arranged as shown in the diagram as regards the long and short ends of these tubes, or it will not work and limewater may be forced over into the respiration chamber.

The above experiment may be simplified satisfactorily for small plants. Germinate some oat, wheat, or corn grains in a wide-mouthed bottle. When the seedlings are growing rapidly, stopper the bottle and set it in the dark for 6 to

10 hr. Replace the stopper quickly with one which has a funnel and bent glass tubing inserted as in Fig. 19.5. Immerse the outlet end of the tube in a test tube containing limewater. Flood the seedlings by pouring water through the funnel until the bottle is nearly filled. This forces gases that have accumulated around the seedlings through the outlet tube into the limewater. If carbon dioxide is present, the limewater soon becomes milky.

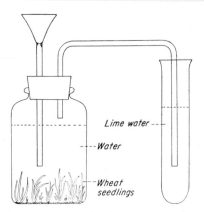

Lime water

Water

Wheat seedlings

Fig. 19.5 A simple apparatus for demonstrating the production of carbon dioxide by living organisms.

A yeast culture also may be used to demonstrate the release of carbon dioxide from microscopic plants. The culture may be prepared by inoculating (with commercial yeast) a 5 per cent glucose solution contained in a wide-mouthed bottle. Allow the culture to stand in a warm (75 to 80°F.) place for about 24 hr. or until it is growing vigorously as shown by the effervescence and cloudiness of the sugar solution. Seal the culture with a stopper which has a U-shaped bent glass tube, immersing the outlet end in a container with limewater. Enough carbon dioxide is generated to be forced out into the limewater after standing for an hour or so.

RELEASE OF CARBON DIOXIDE BY PLANTS AND ANIMALS

Release of Carbon Dioxide by Plants. Germinating Seeds. A simple sugar is produced in the photosynthetic process by a union of carbon dioxide and water in living cells in the presence of chlorophyll and sunlight. The chemical equation representing this process is a reversible one. The carbon, hydrogen, and oxygen of the glucose molecule come from the carbon dioxide and water. The energy is stored from the sunlight in this process. This stored (potential) energy in the glucose molecule is useless to organisms until it is released. The breaking down of such molecules within the organism is known as "respiration." It is an oxidation process. If the photosynthetic process is reversed, the products from the sugar molecule should be carbon dioxide, water, and released energy. The chemical equation indicating this reaction is as follows: $C_6H_{12}O_6$ (glucose) $+ O_2$ (oxygen) $\rightarrow 6CO_2$ (6 molecules of carbon dioxide) $+ 6H_2O$ (6 molecules of water) plus energy released (3.9 cal. per gram of glucose).

It can be seen from the above experiment (Germinating Seeds with and without Oxygen) that oxygen is required. In an experiment below, Transfer and Transformation of Energy by Plants, it is indicated that heat energy is released. The following experiments are designed to show qualitative tests for carbon dioxide released from living plant tissues.

Materials. Respiration apparatus as described and shown in Fig. 19.4; germinating seeds (wheat is very satisfactory); flower buds about ready to open; fresh green leaves; limewater; water.

Fill bottles 1, 2, and 4 about half full of limewater. Fill bottle 3 (which should be a ½ pint size or less) almost full of germinating seeds. Stopper the bottle tightly and let it stand for an hour or two. Then carefully and quickly unstopper and connect in the series as shown in the diagram (Fig. 19.4). See that all connections are gastight. Release a stream of water by means of the siphon from the aspirator.

The reduced pressure in the aspirator is instantly compensated by air from the bottle series. This soon results in a stream of air entering bottle 1 from the atmosphere. The limewater in bottles 1 and 2 removes the carbon dioxide from this air. By the time it enters bottle 3 it is carbon dioxide free. The carbon dioxide is converted into calcium carbonate in the limewater and appears as a white precipitate. After air passes from bottle 3 into the limewater of bottle 4 for a minute or so, a white precipitate appears abundantly. This indicates that germinating seeds produce carbon dioxide. Compare this with the results obtained when a frog is used instead of seeds, as in an experiment below (Small Terrestrial Animals).

By Other Plant Tissues. Instead of germinating seeds, opening flower buds, developing mushrooms, bacterial culture, mold culture, etc., may be used. Some fresh green leaves also will prove instructive. If green leaves are used the experiment should be run in the dark, or at least the respiration chamber containing the leaves should be covered with black paper or paint to prevent the entrance of light.

A Submerged Aquatic Plant. In most experiments land plants or portions of them are used in testing for carbon dioxide as an end product of respiration. It is equally simple to use a submerged aquatic plant in such demonstrations.

Materials. Two wide-mouthed bottles (about 250 cc.) or other similar containers; tap water; phenolphthalein in solution (0.5 g. in 100 cc. of 50 per cent grain alcohol, obtainable at drugstores); enough elodea plants to fill loosely one of the bottles.

Place about 200 cc. of tap water in each bottle. Add two or three drops of the phenolphthalein solution to each bottle, or just enough to give a definite pink color to the water, as in an experiment below (Aquatic Animals). Place the elodea plants in one bottle of treated water. Stopper both bottles and set them in a dark place for 30 to 60 min. Examine both bottles after this time for the pink color. It may be necessary to pour off water from about the plants into a third bottle and examine it carefully for disappearance of the pink color. Compare it with the check (bottle without elodea). Some of the carbon dioxide diffusing from an organism into water may dissolve and form carbonic acid. Such acid causes the disappearance of the pink color of the phenolphthalein. In other words, the disappearance of the pink color indicates indirectly that carbon dioxide was released by the elodea plants. If a pink color does not appear when the phenolphthalein is added, the water is acid. It may be made alkaline by the addition of ammonia or common baking soda.

Nongreen Plant Tissues. *Materials.* Same as in foregoing experiment, except that the entire root system of some plant such as beans, dandelion, pigweed, corn, tomato, *iris* rhizome, or sweet potato (fleshy root) is used instead of elodea. Same procedure as in foregoing experiment. Observe the solution for disappearance of the pink color after about 20 min.

Release of Carbon Dioxide by Animals. The Human Lungs. If a soda straw or piece of glass tubing is placed in the mouth and blown through so that the exhaled air passes into a small amount of limewater, the limewater will quickly become milky. This is a well-known test for carbon dioxide in the air from the lungs but offers an opportunity for the student to discuss the origin of the carbon dioxide and how it appears in the exhaled air.

Small Terrestrial Animals. In preceding experiments it was shown that various kinds of plant tissues released carbon dioxide in their activities. It may be shown with equal ease that the same thing occurs in animals. The same apparatus (Fig. 19.4) is used, and the sole change is to place an animal instead of plant material in the respiration chamber (jar 3). For this purpose any small animal serves quite well. A mouse or rat, a frog or toad, small kitten, various insects such as flies, beetles, or grasshoppers may be used with good results. If the animal is large in comparison with the size of the respiration jar, care must be taken not to leave the jar closed tightly very long or the animal may suffocate. This is especially true of warm-blooded animals.

Aquatic Animals. It is not usually demonstrated that aquatic animals release carbon dioxide into their environment similarly to air-breathing forms, though this has been proved and is generally accepted as a fact at least by analogy. To enclose fish in a jar of water and later to test the water with limewater may give a slight indication but it is not very striking for class use. The tests described here furnish demonstrations which are readily visible and sufficiently impressive for this purpose.

Materials. Four test tubes, or other small containers; 0.5 g. of phenolphthalein powder dissolved in 100 cc. of 50 per cent grain alcohol (drugstore); two small glass containers (large tumblers or small jars); small goldfish (about 3 in. long); soda straw or glass tube; a little baking soda dissolved in water and a little dilute acid such as hydrochloric (vinegar or lemon juice in water will do).

If drinking water is slightly alkaline in its chemical reaction and a few drops of phenolphthalein solution is added to 200 cc. of clear water from the tap or well, the color becomes deep pink. If no red color appears, it means of course that the water is slightly acid and should have a little solution of baking soda added to it one drop at a time until it is slightly pink (slightly alkaline). If the water is deep pink, add weak acid one drop at a time until the color is faintly pink. Stirred thoroughly, it should remain pink. Divide this water into two equal quantities and place each in similar vessels. Now add the goldfish to one of the containers and keep the other container for a check. Allow these to stand before the class for 15 to 40 min. The time that is required will depend upon the nearness of the water to neutrality for phenolphthalein and the relative amounts of water and fish. After the fish has breathed the water for some time, it will have added enough carbon dioxide to the water to make it acid in reaction, and this acidified condition will cause the pink color to disappear. The check dish will still be pink. In time it, too, will become clear due to absorption of carbon dioxide from the air. The fish may be removed and returned to its aquarium unharmed. Other aquatic animals, such as crayfish, insect larvae, tadpoles, newts, and even daphnia (water fleas) will give similar results. A large dragonfly nymph which breathes through its rectum can be placed in a test tube with head uppermost, and the pink color can be seen to fade in the bottom of the tube near the anus before it does in the upper part of the tube near the head. Blow the breath through a straw or tube into alkaline water containing phenolphthalein and the color will soon disappear.

RESPIRATION IS ACCOMPANIED BY A LOSS OF WEIGHT

Corn Grains. When food is completely oxidized, energy is released and carbon dioxide and water are produced. Some of the energy may be lost from the organism as heat, and eventually the carbon dioxide and water are eliminated. Obviously, this should cause a reduction in weight. It is common knowledge that an animal going without food for a considerable period of time shows a decided loss in weight. Excessive activity also increases the rate of weight loss. For instance, a football player will weigh several pounds less at the end of a game than before. One of the common methods of reducing overweight is by exercise. Exercise requires energy release, the release is brought about by oxidation (respiration) and the waste products are eliminated causing loss of weight.

Materials. Select two groups of corn grains, about 24 in each, of approximately equal weight; oven or some other heat source for drying grains and seedlings; chemical balance; quart fruit jar; lightproof box (an ordinary shipping carton is satisfactory).

Place one group of corn grains in an oven at about 100°C. and dry for 3 or 4 hr. At the end of this time carefully weigh the group immediately and record the weight. In the meantime soak the undried group in water overnight and then place them between moist pieces of paper in a moist chamber. A quart fruit jar will serve as a moist chamber. Perforate the lid with a nail to allow for exchange of gases. Place the moist chamber containing the grains in a warm (65 to 80°F.) lightproof box. The grains will germinate soon. Allow them to remain in the dark box for 2 weeks. At the end of this time carefully remove all parts of the seedlings and dry them in an oven at about 100°C. for 3 or 4 hr. At the end of the drying period carefully weigh the seedlings. Compare this weight with the weight of the first group of corn grains. If the experiment has been carried out carefully, the difference in weight is due to loss caused by respiration of the corn seedlings.

TRANSFER AND TRANSFORMATION OF ENERGY

Germinating Seeds. All viable seeds contain stored food. Before the embryo can develop further, energy must be released from the stored food supply. When the stored foods are digested and oxidized, energy is a product of the reaction. Some of this energy escapes in the form of heat and can be measured. The heating of freshly threshed grains or of poorly cured hay when piled in great heaps is a practical application of this phenomenon. The heating of poorly cured hay is due not only to the seeds and other living tissues present but largely to the many bacteria and fungi which grow vigorously under these conditions. It is thought that under certain conditions this heat may accumulate to such an extent that the combustion point is reached and a fire is the final result. This is commonly known as "spontaneous combustion."

Materials. Two ordinary thermos (vacuum) bottles of pint or quart size; cotton; two thermometers; germinating wheat grains (corn, oats, beans, mustard seeds, or any others which germinate readily may be used); bichloride of mercury solution, 1 part bichloride to 1,000 parts water; 50 cc. of 10 per cent formalin.

Measure out two equal quantities of the seeds (about 100 cc.). Moisten each quantity with the bichloride of mercury. Spread the seeds out immediately on sheets of paper and allow the seed surfaces to dry. Rinse the dry treated seeds in sterile (boiled) water. This treatment will kill most of the bacteria and molds. If the antiseptic is not at hand this step is not absolutely essential, although results will be more accurate if it is done. Place in separate containers, moisten the seeds with water, and allow them to germinate. When the sprouts are just beginning to appear, place equal quantities in each of the thermos bottles. Pour the formalin solution over the seeds in one bottle, insert a thermometer, suspending it in the bottle mouth with a tight cotton plug. The formalin will kill the seeds. Moisten the seeds in the other bottle with water, plug the bottle mouth with cotton through which insert the bulb of a similar thermometer. Record the temperature of the two thermos bottles immediately and also after a period of several hours and days, and compare results. The living germinating seeds usually produce a temperature which is several degrees higher than the dead seeds.

If the thermos bottles and thermometers are not at hand, a simpler set of apparatus will produce essentially the same results; however, the exact temperatures cannot be recorded. Obtain two wide-mouthed containers which can be tightly closed such as tin coffee cans with tight-fitting lids. Fill each can about three-fourths full of wheat grains which are starting to germinate. Treat one with 10 per cent formalin as above. Moisten the other can of wheat with water. Place a lid on each and allow to stand in a warm place (65 to 80°F.) overnight or for a day or so. At the end of this time, test the temperature by inserting the hands into the grain masses.

Oxidation of a Carbohydrate or Fat. The ratio of the volume of carbon dioxide released to the volume of oxygen used is known as the "respiratory quotient." When carbohydrates are being oxidized, the volume of oxygen consumed is about equal to the volume of carbon dioxide released, making the ratio 1. When a fat is being oxidized, the ratio is less than 1 since the volume of oxygen used is greater than the volume of carbon dioxide released. The difference is due to the fact that fats have less oxygen in proportion to the other atoms of the molecules than do the carbohydrates. The unsaturated condition is satisfied before actual decomposition occurs. Proteins are oxidized to a less extent than carbohydrates and fats.

Materials. Some starchy seed or grain such as wheat and a fat-bearing seed such as soybean; bichloride of mercury solution (1 part to 1,000 parts water); two bottles (100 to 200 cc.) with stoppers; two pieces of glass tubing bent into an S shape as shown in the diagram, Fig. 19.6; 20 cc. of mercury; cotton.

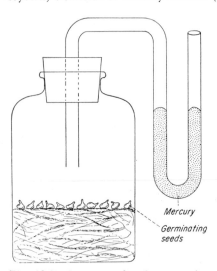

Select 2 or 3 doz. wheat grains and the same number of soybeans. Sterilize the grain and seed surfaces by dipping in the bichloride of mercury solution. Allow the coats to slightly dry and rinse in sterile water. Soak the grains and seeds in water overnight and keep in a closed moist chamber for two days. Bottles may be used for this. Germination will have started by this time. Place a piece of sterile moistened cotton on the bottom of the two bottles. In one place the wheat and in the other the soybeans. Mount the glass tubing in the stoppers. Place some mercury in the outside arms (see Fig. 19.6). Place the stoppers with glass tubing in the bottles. Be sure that they are sealed airtight. Allow these to stand 24 hr. and observe. Note that the mercury columns are equal when wheat is used, since the volume of oxygen consumed is equal to the volume of carbon dioxide produced. For the fatty seeds the mercury column nearest the seeds is higher than in the other arm. This is due to a greater volume of oxygen being used than the volume of carbon dioxide released.

Mercury

Germinating seeds

Fig. 19.6 Apparatus for demonstrating the respiratory ratio.

Cold-blooded Animals. Using the thermos bottles, rubber stopper or cork, and thermometer as in the preceding experiment, place a live frog in one bottle and a preserved one in the other. Note the difference in temperature between the two within 1 or 2 hr. Grasshoppers, flies, beetles, or honeybees may be substituted for the frog, using rather large numbers.

FERMENTATION

Formation of Alcohol and Acetic Acid. Alcoholic fermentation is of vast importance in the baking and alcohol industries. In the baking industry the carbon dioxide is used in making bread dough porous. The other product, grain alcohol, is of great importance as an industrial chemical and has a huge monetary value as a beverage. The process also occurs in some fruits and vegetables under certain conditions, causing spoilage. Acetic acid fermentation is also of great economic importance in the manufacture of vinegar and acetic acid.

Materials. A cake of dry or fresh bakers' yeast; 5 per cent sugar solution; two bottles (50 to 100 cc.); one stopper; short piece of glass tubing; piece of rubber tubing to fit the glass tube; limewater.

Place some of the yeast in a bottle three-fourths full of the sugar solution. Stopper and set in a warm place overnight. Note the bubbles rising from the solution. Insert the glass tube through the cork into the atmosphere above the yeast-sugar solution. To the outside end of the glass tube attach the rubber tubing and dip the other end in a bottle of limewater. After a few gas bubbles pass through the limewater, note what happens. The gas is identified readily as being carbon dioxide. Remove the stopper and glass tube and note the odor of the yeast-sugar mixture. You may be able to detect an alcoholic odor. Set the open bottle away for a week or 10 days and again test the odor. You may then detect the odor of vinegar due to the presence of acetic acid. Apple cider contains sugar and wild yeast. If it is kept in a warm situation for a few days fermentation proceeds rapidly. This takes place even when sealed and in the absence of air, indicating that *free* oxygen is not necessary in this process. However, oxygen is necessary and is *obtained from the sugar* when it is digested by the yeast enzyme. This type of respiration is known as *intramolecular respiration*. The completely fermented cider is called "hard" cider. It contains alcohol. If this solution is left exposed to air for a few weeks, vinegar results. The alcohol is changed to acetic acid (the sour principle of vinegar). Acetic acid–forming bacteria are responsible for this change. Enzymes produced by the bacteria act upon the alcohol. Free oxygen is necessary in this process. Experiments may be set up to demonstrate these points if desired. If this is done, be sure to start with cider which has *not* been heated or treated with a preservative such as benzoate of soda. Five or six weeks will be required before pure vinegar is produced.

THE MECHANICS OF BREATHING IN MAN

The relation of the ribs and muscles to the capacity of the chest cavity may be demonstrated by a simple framework with movable joints, such as is shown in Fig. 19.7, *A* and *B*. The relation of the diaphragm to the chest capacity and to the

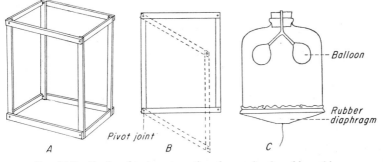

Fig. 19.7   Devices for demonstrating the mechanics of breathing.

inflation of the lungs is well illustrated by such an apparatus as that shown in Fig. 19.7*C*. The string may be attached to the rubber diaphragm by cementing a piece of rubber to the outside of the diaphragm with tire patch cement.

REFERENCES

1. Blackman, F. F.: *Analytic Studies in Plant Respiration,* Cambridge University Press, New York, 1954.

2. Fuller, Harry J., and Oswald Tippo: *College Botany,* Holt, Rinehart and Winston, Inc., New York, 1955.

3. James, W. O.: *Plant Respiration,* Oxford University Press, New York, 1953.

4. Meyer, B. S., and D. B. Anderson: *Plant Physiology,* 2d ed., D. Van Nostrand Company, Inc., Princeton, N.J., 1954.

5. Meyer, B. S., D. B. Anderson, and C. A. Swanson: *Laboratory Plant Physiology,* 3d ed., D. Van Nostrand Company, Inc., Princeton, N.J., 1957.

6. Mitchell, P. H.: *Textbook of General Physiology,* 5th ed., McGraw-Hill Book Company, Inc., New York, 1956.

7. Robbins, Wilfred W. T., Elliott Weier, and C. Ralph Stocking: *Botany, An Introduction to Plant Science,* 2d ed., John Wiley & Sons, Inc., New York, 1957.

8. Rogers, C. G.: *Laboratory Outlines in Comparative Physiology,* McGraw-Hill Book Company, Inc., New York, 1938.

9. Shull, A. F.: *Principles of Animal Biology,* 6th ed., McGraw-Hill Book Company, Inc., New York, 1946. Illustrated.

10. Stiles, W., and W. Leach: *Respiration in Plants,* 3d ed., John Wiley & Sons, Inc., New York, 1952.

11. Transeau, E. N., H. C. Sampson, and L. H. Tiffany: *Textbook of Botany,* rev. ed., Harper & Brothers, New York, 1953. Useful for study of all processes, ecology, and survey of the plant kingdom.

12. Weatherwax, Paul: *Botany,* 3d ed., W. B. Saunders Company, Philadelphia, 1956. Portion dealing with respiration is excellent.

13. Weisz, P. B.: *Laboratory Manual in the Science of Biology,* McGraw-Hill Book Company, Inc., New York, 1959.

14. Wilson, Carl L., and Walter E. Loomis: *Botany,* 2d ed., The Dryden Press, Inc. (combined with Holt, Rinehart and Winston, Inc., New York, 1957.

CHAPTER 20

⸺⸺ Water Relations of Plants ⸺⸺

The rate of evaporation of water from plant surfaces (transpiration) is a factor of utmost importance to the life of plants and their distribution. Plant tissues, on an average, are composed of about 80 per cent water. One of the raw materials used in the process of photosynthesis is water. Minerals necessary in protein synthesis must be in an aqueous solution. Sufficient water enables soft plant tissues to remain turgid and to function normally. Only a very small amount of the water absorbed is used in these latter processes. Most of it is lost by evaporation, and some in liquid form by gutation. The rate of transpiration varies greatly with change in the environment. Conditions which change the rate of evaporation also change the rate of transpiration. Certain desert areas may be made to yield large agricultural crops by irrigation, while parallel, unwatered areas yield nothing but desert plants. Other arid regions may be worthless even though irrigated because of high salt concentration in the soil. The high concentration of salts prevents the entrance of sufficient water in most plants even though the root systems may be submerged in it. Absorption of water must at least equal the loss; otherwise wilting occurs. If a deficiency continues long enough, death by desiccation will result. Absorption and loss of water may be demonstrated easily by several comparatively simple experiments.

Water-vapor Loss and the Process by Which It Occurs. Transpiration from plants can be demonstrated readily by the following experiment. The water is lost in the form of vapor which is not visible unless condensed on a cold surface. Transpiration is fundamentally an evaporation process under modified conditions in plant tissues.

Materials. Three bell jars (gallon pickle jars or battery jars may be used); a potted plant small enough to be covered by the bell jar; paraffin or other water-proofing material for the flower pot and soil surface; three glass plates (window glass may be used); petroleum jelly for sealing bell jars to glass plates; wet cloth or sponge.

Waterproof the outside of the flower pot with melted paraffin. Also cover the soil about the plant with melted paraffin which is just about ready to congeal. Be very careful not to injure the stem of the plant. Set the plant, in the waterproofed pot, on a glass plate and cover with a bell jar. Seal the jar to the plate with petroleum jelly. Under a second bell jar place the wet cloth, sponge, or an open container of water. Seal the jar to a plate. A third bell jar with nothing in it but ordinary air is sealed to another plate. Set all three bell jars in a moderately light, warm situation. After a few hours examine each. Condensed water vapor will be found on the jar containing the plant. Since the pot and soil were sealed, the water vapor had to come from the plant. Condensed water vapor will also be found on the jar covering the wet sponge, cloth, or container with water. The third, under ordinary conditions, will show no condensed water.

Water-holding Capacity of Leaves. Plants vary greatly in their water-retaining capacity. The presence of water-holding substances (colloids) and cutin in varying amounts is probably important in this variation. The distribution of a given species in nature may be determined by the amount of these materials present.

Materials. Leaves of several species of plants characteristic of a wide range of habitats such as elodea, eel grass, coleus, tomato, bean, rubber plant, wandering Jew, sedum, geranium, pine, etc.; piece of wallboard or other surface large enough to hold the leaves; pins or thumbtacks to fasten the leaves to the wallboard; watch or clock for recording wilting time.

Mount the leaves on the wallboard so they are 4 to 5 in. apart. Set the board so that all the leaves will be exposed to the same conditions. Keep a record of the time of wilting wherever possible. Also record the time for complete drying. This latter observation may require a period of several weeks.

How Water Rises in Stems. The problem of sap ascent in tall trees and vines has interested plant physiologists for a long time. The physical principles involved may be demonstrated by the following experiment and its modifications.

Materials. About 50 cc. of clean mercury; piece of glass tubing about 32 in. in length and about 5 mm. in diameter; a porous porcelain cup or cylinder (sold often as atmometer cups and obtainable from apparatus supply companies); rubber stopper to fit the cup, and perforated to fit the glass tubing; source of heat sufficient to boil water.

Boil the cup and 300 cc. of distilled water. The boiling is to drive off all air bubbles. Assemble the apparatus as shown in Fig. 20.1, and fill the system with the cooled boiled water. If hot water is poured into the system, bubbles result. Air bubbles must not be allowed to enter. Invert the apparatus in a cup of mercury, holding water in the system with a finger. Support the apparatus in an upright position in some convenient way. Allow the apparatus to stand and note the rise of mercury in the tube. The rise may be speeded up by directing a breeze from an electric fan on the clay cup. With an efficient apparatus atmospheric pressure will cause the mercury to rise 76 cm. or less, depending upon the altitude.

It is possible to get a column of mercury higher than 76 cm. in a modified and more carefully prepared apparatus. It has been recorded as high as 226.6 cm., or 150.6 cm. higher than can be explained by air pressure. In terms of water this would account for a rise of over 102 ft. This rise above 76 cm. may be explained by the fact that water and mercury are under tension after the column passes the point to which atmospheric pressure would force it. Water has great tensile strength. Ordinarily, to get the mercury to rise above 76 cm. it is necessary to modify the above apparatus. Complete details for carrying out the experiment are given by Meyer, Anderson and Swanson (see Ref. 7, Experiment 57, pages 54 to 56).

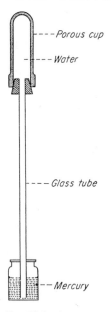

FIG. 20.1 Apparatus for demonstrating the rise of water in a stem.

The previous experiment demonstrated that a column of water and mercury may be raised by a purely physical system. No living cells are involved. The same principles may be demonstrated by incorporating living tissue in the above system. To do this use a branch of arborvitae or pine instead of the porous clay cup. The remainder of the apparatus is the same. Often the column of mercury cannot be raised to such a point as with the porous cup because of greater difficulty with air bubbles. A part of this difficulty may be removed by submerging the cut end of the branch, cutting off an inch or so under water, and attaching to the stopper and water-filled tube while submerged. This prevents air from clogging the tissues near the cut end of the branch.

A Simple Potometer for Measuring Transpiration. This potometer makes possible an easy method for measuring transpiration quantitatively under laboratory conditions. The effects of different environmental conditions upon water-vapor loss may be demonstrated readily by the same apparatus.

Materials. Two pieces of glass tubing, one 15-in. length and one 3-in. length, each with a bore of 2 mm. in diameter; T tube of about the same diameter; about 7 in. of rubber tubing which will fit tightly over the glass tubes; small funnel; pinchcock; metric ruler 30 cm. in length; two ring stands with clamps or other devices for supporting apparatus; gas or alcohol flame for bending glass tubing; cup or other container for water; living arborvitae or pine stem about 12 in. in length with leaves intact and freshly removed from a living tree.

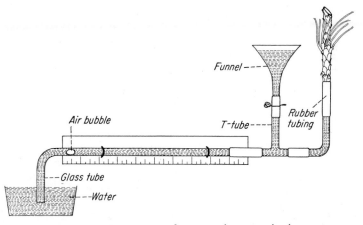

FIG. 20.2   A simple potometer for measuring transpiration rates.

Bend the longer piece of glass tubing at right angles, making a 3-in. arm. Bend the smaller piece at right angles at the center. Connect the two pieces by means of the T tube and pieces of rubber tubing (see Fig. 20.2). To the open end of the T tube fasten a short piece of rubber tubing which is closed by a pinchcock and then insert the funnel. Attach these connected tubes to the ruler with wire, string, or staples, as shown in Fig. 20.2. When procuring the branch, see that the cut end is submerged in water immediately after removal from the tree. Place the whole apparatus under water, including the stem, and release the pinchcock. While it is submerged, cut off about 2 in. from the cut end of the stem to remove any air plugs, and fasten the cut end of the branch to the glass-tube system by rubber tubing. See that no air remains in the tubing, especially about the cut end of the stem. Close the pinchcock. Remove the apparatus from the water, keeping the open end of the tube closed with a finger. Support the apparatus on the ring stand and submerge the open end of the tube in a container of water. Before this submergence, however, allow a bubble to enter. Fill the funnel with water. By opening the pinchcock slightly the bubble which is to act as a gage may be located at any desired point on the ruler. When it is located, close the pinchcock. As water vapor is lost from the leaves the bubble will move toward the stem, since water will be absorbed by the exposed stem tissues. Keep a record of the time taken for the bubble to move 2 cm. When this movement has occurred, it is obvious that a column of water 2 cm. long and 2 mm. in diameter has been absorbed by the stem. By a simple calculation the volume can be obtained, this volume representing the amount of water lost from the leaves in the time required by the bubble to move 2 cm. The rate of movement may be altered by placing the apparatus in shade, bright sunlight, strong air currents, etc. The "gage" bubble may be reset when desired by allowing water to enter from the funnel. As soon as the bubble reaches the desired point, the pinchcock must be closed.

Measuring Water-vapor Loss by the Cobalt Chloride Paper Method. The cobalt chloride paper method of measuring water-vapor loss is particularly suitable for field as well as laboratory measurements since a minimum of apparatus is required. It is also valuable because leaves and stems do not have to be removed and the plant does not have to be grown in a pot or under other abnormal conditions. The cobalt chloride paper is hygrometric and changes from a blue color when dry to pink when moist. The rate of color change indicates the relative rate of water-vapor loss.

Materials. Three grams of cobalt chloride c.p.; a few sheets of high-grade filter paper (Whatman no. 1 is satisfactory); transparent celluloid; box of gummed notebook reinforcements; box of small clamps (Dennison Card Holder, no. 42, is satisfactory); 1 lb. of anhydrous calcium chloride; six 100-cc. wide-mouthed bottles fitted with ground-glass stoppers or paraffined corks; small roll of absorbent cotton; leather punch or cork borer which will cut disks $\frac{15}{32}$ in. in diameter; pair of forceps.

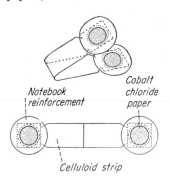

FIG. 20.3   Construction of cobalt chloride hygrometric paper clips for measuring water vapor loss from leaves.

Prepare 50 to 100 cc. of a 3 per cent aqueous solution of cobalt chloride. Wet a disk of the filter paper in this solution. Remove the excess liquid by pressing the treated paper between blotters or filter paper. Place in a low-temperature oven (about 40°C.) or some other source of heat for further drying. When paper is thoroughly dry, cut out as many disks as needed with the punch or cork borer. Cut out strips of celluloid $\frac{3}{8}$ by $1\frac{1}{2}$ in. Cut small notches on each side of the strip near each end as shown in Fig. 20.3.

Moisten two gummed notebook reinforcements and fasten them to each end so that the perforation is covered by the celluloid. Turn the strip over (side with reinforcements down). With forceps lay a disk of the cobalt chloride paper on the celluloid directly over the perforation of one of the reinforcements. Moisten another reinforcement about the outer edge, carefully lay it on top of the cobalt chloride paper, pressing projecting edges of the two reinforcements together and particularly in the notches. Repeat the procedure for the other end of the strip. Fold the strip along the short axis through the center in such a way that the exposed cobalt chloride paper surfaces may be clamped together and the celluloid-covered surfaces are on the outside. Figure 20.3 shows details of the structure. These cobalt chloride clips may be clamped to leaf surfaces with one of the paper disks exposed to the upper surface and one to the lower surface. Dennison card holders make convenient clamps for this purpose. Before a test is to be made the cobalt chloride paper must be desiccated. This is done by making small desiccators from 100-cc. wide-mouthed bottles. Fill a bottle half full of anhydrous calcium chloride. Cover it with a layer of cotton. Place the clips on the top of the cotton and stopper tightly. After 3 to 4 hr. the paper will be desiccated and appear blue. With forceps remove a clip quickly and clamp it to the leaf to be tested. Watch for the blue color to change to a light pink. The color change is due to absorption of water. Record the time for the color change. Compare the time for both the upper and lower surfaces. If there are no stomata on the upper surface the pink color may not appear for 30 min. or longer, depending on the temperature, while the lower surface with widely opened stomata may cause the color to change within 30 sec. This enables one to compare stomatal and cuticular water-vapor loss under the same conditions on a single leaf. Water-vapor loss from very young, mature, and old leaves may be compared in the same way, also different species of plants growing side by side.

It is possible to convert the above qualitative method in such a way that quantitative results can be obtained. This requires standardization of the paper. An analytical balance is necessary in this procedure. Also quite a little time is required. Meyer and Anderson (Ref. 6) give this procedure in detail.

The Benzene-infiltration Method of Studying Stomatal Movements. In general stomata close in darkness and open in light. In most species they reach their maximum opening during the early morning daylight period. Gradual closure starts soon after the maximum is reached, but complete closure usually does not occur until nightfall. Some species may have a few stomata open at night. Very young leaves usually have few if any open stomata at any time of day. The benzene-infiltration method offers a simple and easy way of demonstrating these movements in relation to light, periodicity, comparison of young and mature leaves, etc.

Materials. About 25 cc. of benzene; small camel's-hair brush; some living potted plants for testing.

Make preliminary tests on a well-watered plant which has been exposed to light for several hours. Lightly brush on some benzene and look for a translucent or water-soaked appearance. This translucence is due to penetration of tissues by the benzene through the stomata. If this occurs rapidly the stomata are wide open; if slowly and in patches, the stomata are partly closed. The translucence will appear within a few seconds after the application. If the stomata are found open, place the plant in a dark box. At intervals of 15 to 20 min., test other leaves on the plant and determine the time required for closure in darkness. Young and mature leaves may be tested and compared simultaneously. Tomato and monocotyledonous plants usually are not very satisfactory for this comparison. Periodicity studies are best carried on under field conditions.

Mechanism of Stomatal Movement. Increase of turgidity of guard cells causes stomata to open. Light plays an important part in this reaction since it decreases the acidity to such a point that an enzyme is activated, which in turn converts starch of the guard cells to sugar. The presence of this sugar causes an increase in turgor and results in opening of the stomata. Acidity increases at night. Sugar in the guard cells is condensed to starch which results in lowering of the osmotic pressure, allowing the guard cells to close the stomata. It is a comparatively easy matter to apply a sugar solution to guard cells surrounding opened stomata which will reduce their turgor and result in closure of the stomata.

Materials. About 25 cc. of a 35 per cent sucrose (cane sugar) solution; wandering Jew (*Zebrina pendula*) plant, Boston fern, plantain (*Plantago major*), or other plant showing large stomata and from which the epidermis is easily removed; slides; cover glasses; forceps; microscope.

Strip off two pieces of lower epidermis and mount on separate slides in a drop of water. Observe the stomata to see if they are widely opened. If not, make mounts until opened stomata are found. Add about two drops of the sugar solution to the edge of the cover glass of one of the mounts. Draw it under by applying a piece of filter paper or a blotter to the opposite edge. Observe by means of a microscope and note closing of the stomata. Compare with the tissue still in water. The treated piece may be remounted in water, placed in bright light, and the stomata will eventually open if the tissue was not left in the sugar solution too long.

Restoration of Turgidity to Wilted Leaves. Many plants may wilt for a short time without apparent injury. The turgidity is regained as soon as there is an available water supply if the wilted condition has not continued too long. If cut wilted stems are treated properly, the regain in turgidity may be so rapid that movements of the leaves may be detected by the eye. The rate of regain is determined largely by the treatment after wilting has occurred.

Materials. Pigweed (*Amaranthus retroflexus*) or tomato are very favorable plants. Cut three similar leafy branches and allow them to wilt; three containers with water; sharp razor blade.

Place one of the wilted plants in a container with water. With the razor blade cut 1 in. or so from the stem base of a second plant and immediately place the base of this branch in water. Submerge the cut end of the third plant in water and cut off about 2 in. from the base while under water. Observe the plants closely. The plant which was cut while the stem base was submerged usually regains its turgidity so rapidly that leaf movements may be seen. The one with part of the base removed in air and placed in water regains its turgor next, while the third requires a much longer period.

TISSUES INVOLVED IN MOVEMENT OF WATER THROUGH STEMS

In vascular plants xylem is the most important water-conducting tissue. This fact may be demonstrated easily by the following experiments.

Path and Rate of Water Conduction in Stems as Shown by Dyes. Aqueous solutions of dyes, which are absorbed by cell walls, are useful in demonstrating the tissues involved in water conduction, since these tissues are stained by the dye. The rate of conduction may be studied at the same time.

Materials. Potted sunflower plants which are about 10 to 12 in. in height (about 6 weeks old); if the sunflower is not available, coleus or sultana (*Impatiens sultanii*) of the florist, or other plant with a fairly transparent stem may be used; 5 cc. of a 2.5 per cent basic fuchsin solution made up in 95 per cent grain alcohol; dilute the fuchsin by adding 1 part of the dye to 100 parts of tap water. Allow the solution to stand overnight and filter. If this dye is not available, a 1 per cent methylene blue aqueous solution or 1 per cent eosin solution in water may be used. Red and green food-coloring dyes, obtainable at a food market, may be used if other dyes are not available. If a chemical balance is not available for weighing the dyes, good results have been obtained by roughly estimating the quantity of dye on the tip of a penknife blade; wide-mouthed container for the dye; sharp razor blade or scalpel.

Remove the plant from the soil by washing. Retain the upper 5 cm. of the root, cutting the lower part off while the whole root system is submerged in water. Quickly transfer the plant to the dye in the wide container. With the sharp razor blade cut off about 2 cm. of the remaining root system while submerged in the dye. Record the time. If available, place a bright light back of the stem. This will facilitate seeing the dye through tissues of the stem. Watch for the appearance of dye in the veins of the leaves. A rise of 10 cm. within 5 min. may be obtained. Because of the dark-red color, basic fuchsin gives excellent results. However, the other dyes mentioned may be used successfully. If the stems available are too opaque to see the stained tissues by transmitted light, the tissues may be cut into with a knife and the colored path exposed. Even willow branches without leaves may be used in this way. When no leaves are present, the ascent of the dye is much slower.

Path of Water Conduction as Shown by Sealing the Tissues. *Materials.* Two woody stems with approximately the same number of leaves and about ¼ in. in diameter (willow cuttings which have stood in water or moist sand long enough to develop a leaf system are satisfactory); two wide-mouthed bottles with 100 to 200 cc. capacity; paraffin; cotton for plugging the bottles; sharp knife or razor blade; graduated cylinder.

Remove all tissue external to the xylem for a distance of about 1 in. on each stem. Care should be taken that the xylem is not injured. Melt some paraffin and while plastic but not hot, seal one of the stems so that both xylem and phloem are sealed (see Fig. 20.4). Then with a sharp knife cut off, while submerged in water, ½ in. of the xylem from the base. This exposes the xylem tissue to water but not the phloem. The remaining stem should have the xylem completely sealed and the phloem exposed as shown in Fig. 20.4. Measure out equal volumes of water in each bottle; insert one of the stems in each. Plug the mouth of each bottle with cotton about the stems, and seal with plastic paraffin to prevent evaporation. Mark

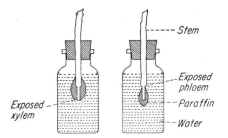

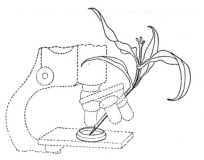

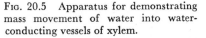

Fig. 20.4 Apparatus for demonstrating the path of water conduction in stems.

Fig. 20.5 Apparatus for demonstrating mass movement of water into water-conducting vessels of xylem.

the level of the water in the bottle. Set both in a situation where the transpiration rate is high. Compare the volumes of water in each bottle and watch for wilting of leaves. There should be no wilting of leaves on the stem which has xylem exposed, and the volume of water in the same bottle should be lowered. In the bottle with only the phloem exposed, the volume of water should not decrease and the leaves may wilt, indicating that water cannot travel to an appreciable extent in the phloem

Mass Movement of Water into Water-conducting Vessels. Ordinarily, the transpiration stream in a stem is under tension. In the water-conducting vessels this water moves by mass movement and not by diffusion. The following experiment permits direct observation of this mass movement as well as the fact that water is conducted through stems in elements of the xylem.

Materials. A bean, sunflower, or other convenient plant which has several living leaves intact; shallow dish such as a Syracuse watch glass; compound microscope with a low-power (40-mm.) objective lens (a medium-power—16-mm.—lens may be used if the lower power is not available); India ink; sharp razor blade.

Fill the watch glass about three-quarters full of water and place three to four drops of India ink in it. Set this over opening on the microscope stage. Cut the plant off near the base. Submerge the stem in water and cut off about a 2 in. piece from near the base in such a way that an oblique angle of about 15 to 30° is formed. Transfer the upper section of the stem with the leaves intact to the watch glass and submerge the cut portion in the diluted India ink. Support the stem in some con-venient way and focus on the water-conducting vessels (spiral, annular, or scalariform tracheae). Watch for currents of water entering these vessels carrying particles of carbon. Eventually the vessels are plugged with the carbon and appear as black streaks. Sometimes these streaks can be detected by the unaided eye. Figure 20.5 illustrates how this experiment may be assembled.

Length of Water-conducting Vessels in Stems. The length of open water-con-ducting vessels varies with different species of woody plants and also with position in the plant. In the main stem they are usually longer than in branches. In the main axis they become shorter as the tip is approached.

Materials. Stems of some woody species such as elm or grape; these pieces should be at least 3 ft. in length for the elm and from 10 to 20 ft. for the grape; short piece of rubber tubing; glass funnel; 200 to 500 cc. of mercury.

With a sharp knife cut off an inch length from one end of the stem to expose fresh tissues. Attach the funnel by means of the rubber tubing. In some convenient way, support the stem with the funnel uppermost in as nearly a vertical position as is practical, according to the length of the stem. Pour the mercury into the funnel. Set a glass container under the lower end of the stem. Cut a short segment from the lower end of the stem to expose fresh tissues. If no mercury globules appear after standing a few minutes, continue to remove segments about 1 in. in length until very small mercury globules appear. If only a few ends of open vessels are exposed, the mercury can be seen coming from the individual tracheae. By this means one can determine rather closely the length of open water-conducting vessels for the particular stem used.

GUTATION AND ROOT PRESSURE

Natural Gutation. Drops of water are often exuded from plants when the soil about their roots is moist and the surrounding atmosphere is very humid. Much of the so-called dew on plants early in the morning is gutated water.

Materials. Bell jar (gallon pickle jar may be used), or a glass case (Fig. 12.33); five or six seedlings of oats, wheat, corn, or young fern sporophytes which are rooted in a small pot of soil.

Thoroughly water the soil about the young plants. Cover them with the bell jar or enclose them in the glass case. Allow these to stand overnight or for several hours. Look for drops of water along the leaf edges and at the tip. If the glass case is used, see that there is a layer of moist sand, soil, or peat on the bottom. This will keep a humid atmosphere about the plant.

Redtop (*Agrostis alba*) seed, obtainable at seed stores, sown on a water surface in a tumbler or other glass container and kept in a warm room will develop into seedlings 1 in. or more in length within a week. If the mouth of the tumbler is covered for a few hours or overnight, droplets of gutated water will be found on the plants. This is a very simple and easy way of demonstrating gutation.

Forced Gutation. *Materials.* A tomato stem 8 to 12 in. in length with leaves intact; water pressure from a city water supply; gum tube of such size as to fit tightly on cut end of the tomato branch and of convenient length for reaching and attach-ing to the water faucet.

Prepare watertight connections between the tomato stem and the faucet by means of the hose. Turn the water on slowly and gradually increase the pressure. Within a few minutes water droplets are likely to appear along edges of the tomato leaflets. This result represents gutation brought about by artificial pressure.

Root Pressure. Active absorption results in the so-called root pressure. The exudation of water from cut stems of woody plants in the spring is a result of this pressure. It is particularly noticeable when grape vines are cut during this period. When pigweeds (*Amaranthus*) are cut off at the soil level, a wet spot of soil often appears surrounding the cut portion. This is caused by water exuding from the cut tissues.

Materials. A potted, vigorously growing plant of dahlia, *Bryophyllum*, tomato, or pigweed; piece of glass tubing about 1 ft. in length; short piece of gum tube.

With a sharp knife cut the top from the plant selected so that about 4 cm. of the stem remains above the soil. Connect the glass tube to cut end of the stem by means of the gum tube. The connections must be made watertight. Care must be taken not to injure the stem. It may be necessary to use grafting wax or some other sealing compound in making this connection. Support the glass tubing in an upright position in some convenient way. Add water to the glass tube until the water level is just visible above the connection with the gum tube. Saturate the soil about the roots. Place the setup in some convenient location and observe for a rise of the water column in the glass tube. Observations should be made at intervals over a period of 2 to 3 days.

ABSORPTION OF WATER BY ROOTS

Effect of Salt Concentration upon the Rate of Absorption. It is common knowledge that high salt concentrations kill plants. Fertilizer applied too heavily becomes destructive. Ordinary salt (sodium chloride) is occasionally used to destroy weeds, and is regularly used in the government program of barberry eradication. In some arid regions the soils contain such high concentrations of various salts that these lands are useless for irrigation purposes.

Materials. Calcium chloride, 35 g.; distilled water, 2,000 cc. (tap water may be used if the distilled water is not available); seven wide-mouthed bottles of 100 to 200 cc. capacity; cotton for plugging bottles; seven sunflower or tomato seedlings of as nearly equal size and development as possible.

Prepare a series of calcium chloride solutions such as 0.5, 1, 2, 3, 4, and 5 per cent. Place these in separate bottles and label accordingly. Fill the seventh bottle with distilled water. Carefully wash adhering soil from about the roots of the seedlings. Place a seedling in each bottle, plugging the bottle mouth about the seedling with cotton. Support the seedling by means of the cotton in such a way that the root system is completely submerged. Place the series of bottles in moderately diffuse light and observe over a period of 48 hr. If directions are properly followed, wilting of plants in the 2, 3, 4, and 5 per cent solutions is to be expected, and usually does not occur in the other concentrations.

REFERENCES

1. Crafts, A. S., et al.: *Water in the Physiology of Plants,* Chronica Botanica Co., Waltham, Mass., 1949.
2. DeBoer, J. H.: *Dynamical Character of Adsorption,* Oxford University Press, New York, 1953.
3. Follansbee, H.: "Secondary Root Demonstration," *Am. Biol. Teacher,* 16:19, October, 1954.
4. Haupt, A. W.: *Plant Morphology,* McGraw-Hill Book Company, Inc., New York, 1953. Illustrated.
5. Herrick, J. A.: "Root Hairs for Classroom Study," *Turtox News,* vol. 29, no. 1, January, 1951.
6. Meyer, B. S., and D. B. Anderson: *Plant Physiology,* 2d ed., D. Van Nostrand Company, Inc., Princeton, N.J., 1954.

7. Meyer, B. S., D. B. Anderson, and C. A. Swanson: *Laboratory Plant Physiology*, 3d ed., D. Van Nostrand Company, Inc., Princeton, N.J., 1957.

8. Moon, T. J., and P. B. Mann, and J. H. Otto: *Modern Biology*, Holt, Rinehart and Winston, Inc., New York, 1956. Illustrated. Frequently revised to bring information up to date.

9. Transeau, E. N., H. C. Sampson, and L. H. Tiffany: *Textbook of Botany*, rev. ed., Harper & Brothers, New York, 1953. Useful for study of processes, ecology, and survey of the plant kingdom.

CHAPTER 21

⟶⊷ The Behavior of Organisms ⊷⟵

One of the fundamental characteristics of all living things is the quality of irritability, or the capacity to respond to environmental change. These responses amount to the reactions, or behavior, noted in most animals but are also definitely shown in plants even when they are nonmotile. The phenomena of growth and development also are influenced by the forces of the environment. A great variety of experiments and demonstrations, especially of motile animals, is available for use and furnishes an extremely fascinating part of the study in the biological subjects. Those listed below should suggest many others to teachers and students. They form a good introduction to and illustrations for the study of the nervous system, behavior, ecology, psychology, heredity, and evolution.

It must be kept in mind that in these studies teleology is most certain to creep in and should always be guarded against. The practice of explaining behavior in terms of man's own reactions and mental states is contrary to clear thinking and not conducive to the production of a scientific attitude. For example, it is quite as wrong to say that a geranium grows toward a window "in order to get more light" as it would be to say that a moth flies into a flame "in order to singe its wings." Both are positive responses to light which in one case may be beneficial, in the other detrimental. If the real explanation is not clear or is too difficult for the student to understand, it should be recorded as observed fact and left at that for the time being. It is generally better teaching to use such demonstrations as the following in the form of problems to be solved by the class instead of illustrations of fact already learned.

THE BEHAVIOR OF ANIMALS

The following experiments show rather simple and clear-cut examples of animal reactions and can be done by students or teacher. How they can be made to fit into a particular course will have to be decided by the teacher, but, wherever possible, it is suggested that they be used as problems for discussion rather than as illustrations.

Protozoa

Paramecium. This is one of the easiest protozoans to obtain and keep alive at all times of year.

Materials. A culture of paramecium (pure if possible); medicine dropper or small glass tube; a few microscope slides; small amount of paraffin (or beeswax); 6 in. of glass tubing; dry cell (1½ volts); pieces of copper wire for battery leads; two test tubes or vials; corks; watch glass.

Response to Light. Place enough culture of paramecium in a small test tube or vial to nearly fill it. Cork tightly and place in a horizontal position. Cover one-half of the tube with dark paper or cloth or by inserting it into a paper tube. This must be opaque so as to exclude light. The cover must be loose enough to remove easily. After 20 to 30 min. carefully remove the cover without shaking the tube and note the distribution of organisms.

Response to Weak Acid. Warm a small piece of paraffin in water until it is soft enough to mold with the fingers. Make a layer of this on a microscope slide or piece of glass so that it is about 1½ in. long by ¼ in. wide by ⅛ in. thick. Cut or press out a middle portion of the wax so as to form a small narrow trough (see Fig. 21.1).

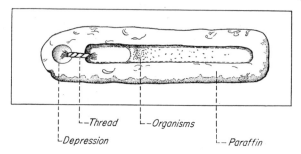

Fig. 21.1   Paraffin trough for demonstrating the responses of protozoa to chemicals and to electricity.

Make a small shallow depression in the wax near the end of the trough. Leading from this depression into the end of the trough place a short piece of thread forming a wick. With a medicine dropper add to the depression one drop of weak hydrochloric acid (one drop of concentrated acid to 10 cc. of water). It will soak through the wick into the culture. A second drop of acid may be necessary, depending upon the size of the trough. If no results are obtained, add a very small drop of acid directly to one end of the trough. The paramecia approach the acid but are unable to pass very far into it, thus forming a definite line across the trough as shown in the diagram, Fig. 21.1. Dilutions of acetic and other acids will do as well as hydrochloric acid.

Response to Carbon Dioxide. Make a small U tube from glass tubing. Nearly fill it with paramecium culture. Place a tube of air over one end and a tube of carbon dioxide over the other end. Let this stand for 30 min. to 2 hr. and note the change in distribution of paramecia. The solution of carbon dioxide in water forms a faintly acid condition which causes the organisms to concentrate there. The acidity is far less than in the acid-drop experiment described above.

Response to Food. If material from an active paramecium culture is poured into a flat glass dish such as a watch glass (or caster cup) or petri dish and allowed to stand 5 or 10 min. and is then examined under a microscope or strong hand lens, clusters of paramecia may be seen around the particles of decomposing food material or bits of bacterial scum.

Response to Electric Current. Use the small paraffin trough described above in Response to Weak Acid. Nearly fill the trough with paramecium culture. Place a wire lead from one pole of a 1½ to 3-volt dry cell in one end of the trough. Watch carefully what happens in the culture as the other electrode is applied to the opposite end of the trough. The animals quickly orient toward the negative pole and accumulate near it. If the poles are reversed, the response is repeated. This reversing may be accomplished by changing the position of the wires or by the use of a reversing switch (Fig. 13.6). With a good light and a dark background the results can be seen without a microscope.

Euglena. *Response to Light.* From a culture of active euglena take a large drop and place it in the middle of a microscope slide. Cover with a cover glass and place on a microscope stage. Set the microscope in a darkened room or shade well by setting up screens. Turn on an artificial light screened in such a manner that light may be reflected from the mirror of the microscope through the stage but so that no light will fall upon the slide from any other direction. A cardboard box as shown in Fig. 21.2 is very satisfactory for a schoolroom. Place beneath the slide containing the drop of euglena culture an opaque card with a slit 1/16 in. wide as shown in Fig. 21.3. Allow this to stand for 5 to 10 min. Open the screen or box and turn on

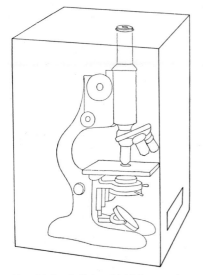

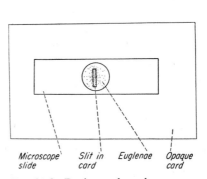

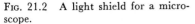

Microscope   Slit in   Euglenae   Opaque
slide   card   card

Fig. 21.2   A light shield for a microscope.

Fig. 21.3   Device to show the response of euglena to light.

light from above or carefully remove the card without disturbing the culture. Note the arrangement of the euglenae which has resulted from their positive reaction to light. If the culture has stood in complete darkness for several hours before the experiment, the reaction is faster and more marked. Pour 2 tablespoonfuls of active euglena culture into a flat dish. Cover one-half of the culture with an opaque object. Turn on a light directly (12 in.) above the dish. See that the screen darkens half the culture. After 10 min. remove the screen and notice that the euglenae have concentrated in the lighted half.

Coelenterates

Hydra. Except near the seashore about the only available coelenterate is hydra. These may be reared, found in ponds or lakes, or they may be purchased from supply houses. They are delicate and sensitive but interesting.

Materials. Small culture of hydra; watch glasses; a few water fleas (*Daphnia*) or very minute pieces of fresh beef.

Response to Contact. If a hydra is placed in a watch glass or other shallow dish of water, it may be set upon the microscope stage for examination. A microscope is not necessary, however, since the hydra is large enough to be seen easily without magnification. If undisturbed for several minutes, the hydra will elongate considerably. Carefully touch the tip of one tentacle with a pin point. Sometimes just the tentacle will shorten. If the stimulus was very strong, the entire animal responds quickly. When it has lengthened again, a touch on the body will produce contraction throughout the hydra.

Response to Food. Place a few daphnia or several tiny particles of lean meat near the tentacles. Drop them into the water with the least possible disturbance. If the hydra has not fed for 1 day or more previous to the time of the experiment, it may be seen to seize the food in its tentacles and to take it into the mouth and gastral cavity. If the food is alive and active like daphnia (water fleas) or very tiny worms, the hydra will sting it with its stinging cells (nematocysts). These can be seen under a microscope. Seashore bathers are sometimes rendered miserable by such stinging cells from jellyfish with which they may come in contact while in the water.

Worms

From this point on we will be dealing with animals that have bilateral symmetry and a definite differentiation into tissues such as nerves and muscles, which has not been true of the organisms mentioned above.

Common Flatworm, Planaria. *Materials.* Culture of planaria; small flat dish such as a watch glass or saucer; good dry cell 1½ volts; wire for leads from battery terminals; small piece of liver the size of a 25-cent piece.

Response to Food. Place three or four planaria in a saucer of fresh water. See that they are all near the edge of the water. Place the small piece of liver in the center of the dish and observe the behavior of the worms for several minutes. As soon as the juice from the liver has diffused to the worms, they should swim directly to the meat. Worms for the test should not have been fed for 2 days previously.

Response to Electric Current. Place a worm on a saucer or watch glass or on a piece of thoroughly wet filter paper. Place the leads from a dry cell so that the negative pole is about ¼ in. in front of the worm and the other, or positive pole, about ¼ in. behind the worm. Notice that the worm shortens violently and seems unable to continue locomotion. Now reverse the poles so that the positive pole is anterior and the negative pole is posterior to the planaria. Notice that it contracts but turns until the anterior end (head) is directed toward the negative pole. Place the electrodes about ½ in. from the sides of the worm, one pole on each side. The worm turns sideways with the head always toward the negative pole. Do not touch the worms with the terminals or continue a stimulating current for more than a few seconds, to avoid injuring the animal.

The Earthworm. *Materials.* Several living earthworms (night crawlers are best but not necessary); dry cell 1½ volts; wire leads for dry cell; aqua ammonia (or volatile acid); flashlight or other artificial light; a card or book to be used as a light screen; glass tube (½ in. or more inside diameter) about 12 to 18 in. long; corks to fit the end of the glass tube.

Response to Contact. Place a fresh worm on a sheet of damp paper when testing. Touch various places on its body with a pencil point or pin. Do not stick the pin into the surface. Note the negative responses. Touch a worm several times in rapid succession on the anterior end. The end retracts and the worm reverses its locomotion, crawling backward. If it does not do so, try light pressure with the end of the finger upon the anterior end of the worm. Turn a worm completely upon its dorsal surface (back). Notice that it readily assumes the normal position again.

Response to a Chemical. Start an earthworm crawling on a wet paper. Dip a match or toothpick in ammonia (acetic acid or hydrochloric acid will do) and bring the match to within 1 in. of the worm's head. Notice the sensitivity to chemicals of this sort. Do not touch the chemical to the worm. Try other regions of the body.

Response to Light. Place an active worm on a wet paper. Allow it to crawl a few inches in one direction. Keep the worm in a darkened room or shade it well from the light. Turn the beam of a flashlight or desk light on the anterior end as it crawls. Notice the sudden retraction from the lighted zone. If the worm is kept in complete darkness for 1 hr. before the experiment, it will react better.

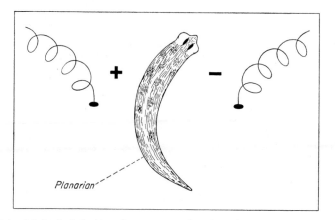

FIG. 21.4   Method of showing the responses of a planarian worm to direct current.

Response to Electric Current. Place an earthworm upon a piece of very wet paper, or in a glass dish with ⅛ in. of water over the bottom. Use two 1½-volt dry cells, connected in series so as to give 3 volts. Place the leads so that the positive pole is 1 in. from the anterior end of the worm, and the negative pole is 1 in. from the posterior end. The worm shortens. Reverse the direction of current. The worm lengthens. Place the poles on opposite sides of the worm an inch or two from its body. There is usually a turning of the anterior end toward the negative pole. Sometimes the posterior end responds in a similar fashion.

Place a worm in a glass tube the diameter of which is considerably greater than the diameter of the worm. Nearly fill the tube with water. Close each end of the tube with a cork through which has been passed a short piece of copper wire or a fine nail. Lay the tube on the table and apply the leads from dry cells (3 volts) to the terminals in the cork. Reverse the current. Notice the movement of the worm toward the negative pole.

Arthropods

Despite their high degree of specialization the arthropods are very mechanical in their behavior. This is especially true of the insects.

Dragonfly Nymph. These are large aquatic young insects that can be obtained from the mud at the bottom of ponds and quiet streams.

Materials. Dragonfly nymphs; small culture dish or pan; forceps; small worms or fresh pieces of earthworm or meat.

Response to Food. Use a nymph that has not eaten for 24 hr. Hold a small particle of food in the forceps and place it ½ in. before the head of the nymph. The nymph, if it has not been fed recently, will quickly snap at the food and devour it. Vision or chemical sense, or both, may function in the response. Examine the "lower lip" of the nymph to understand how it can reach out for food.

Blowfly Larvae. Any ordinary fly maggot may serve for most of the following reactions, but the bluebottle and greenbottle flies have been found to be best in most cases.

Materials. A dozen or more nearly full-grown maggots (always kept in a dark box when not used); table lamp that can be moved; large piece of cardboard or box such as a shoe box; flat pan such as a shallow cake pan; plate of heavy glass (windowpane); hot and cold water.

Response to Light Source. The response to light is best determined in a darkened room or by means of a box such as a shoe box. Prepare a light screen by cutting a hole ½ in. square in a card or in the end of a cardboard box (see Fig. 21.5). Place a fairly strong light (bright window with shade drawn low may be used) before the opening. This will throw through the hole a beam of light, which should fall along a shaded table top. Now place a maggot before the opening with its head (small end) away from the light. Notice its reaction and direction of crawl. Place it before the opening again with the head toward the light. It turns rapidly away. Cut a second opening in the side of the box (or erect a second screen) and place a light near it so that its beam falls on the table at right angles to the first one. Start a maggot as in the first test. When it reaches a point opposite the second light, turn on the second light and observe the change in the path of the maggot. The maggot swerves away from the second light. If a heated object be placed in the position of the second light so that heat rays instead of light rays fall across the path of the maggot, its course will swerve toward the source of heat.

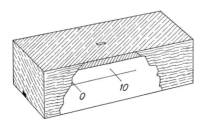

FIG. 21.5 Structure of box used in the study of behavior of insects.

Response to Change in Temperature. Take a heavy piece of glass windowpane and cover it with a sheet of paper that has been soaked in water. Press the wet paper smooth over the glass and drain off excess water. Place the light screen and light upon the glass. Rule two parallel lines on the paper 10 cm. apart (4 in.) and at right angles to the beam of light. Lay a thermometer along one side of the plate and record the temperature. It should be near that of the room. Start a maggot away from the lighted hole and time it from the time it crosses the first line until it crosses the second line. Repeat several times and record the results. Put some cracked ice in a flat cake pan and completely fill the pan with water. Cover the pan with the glass pane and its paper and let stand for 5 min. Record the new temperature. Repeat the preceding tests with the same maggots and record their rates of crawl for the 10 cm. Remove the ice water from the pan replacing it with water at about 45°C. Repeat the tests with the same maggots. Record the higher temperature and the rates of crawl. Make these into a table and prepare a graph to show the results. This experiment offers the student an opportunity to construct simple apparatus, collect data, record it, and then express it in graphic form together with an interpretation. Other temperatures can be introduced and a much more complete graph drawn.

Blowfly Adults. Place the maggots used in the above experiment in a box or jar of sand (they should be full grown) and set them aside for about a week. They will emerge as adult flies.

Response to Light. If a number of the adults are put into a long box or mailing tube with a glass or cellophane covering at one end and turned toward a light, the flies will accumulate at the lighted end in a few seconds. Release one fly into the room. It will fly toward the window or other bright light. The response of the maggot is strongly negative to light, while that of the adult from the same maggot is positive to light.

Meal Worm Beetles (larvae). *Materials.* Culture of beetles (see Chap. 12); large pan; sponge the size of a hen's egg; dried bran; tightly fitting cover for pan.

Response to Humidity. The bran for this experiment must be very dry. It can be dried in a warm (not hot) oven if it is stirred frequently. After cooling the bran, put a dozen meal worms in the pan of bran by burying them around the edges of the pan. Place the sponge, soaked in water, in the center of the bran. Cover the pan closely and wait about 10 min. Lift the sponge. Usually the larvae are under or in the sponge. If they have been desiccated (water starved) they will react quickly and will come to the surface of the bran even in the light and move to the sponge.

Vertebrates

In many respects the vertebrates are not so well suited for a study of simple reactions as are the invertebrates. The higher vertebrates, especially the mammals, have a complicated nervous mechanism that makes much of their behavior too involved for simple analysis. There is no reason, however, for supposing that it is fundamentally different from the behavior of those lower organisms which have a neuromuscular system.

Tadpole. Frog eggs can be collected in early spring and hatched in the laboratory (see Chap. 22), or young tadpoles can be caught with a dip net. Simple observations of their activities at different stages of their development give indication of definite responses to their environment.

Frog. Some of the activities of frogs are so nearly based on simple and compound reflexes that they offer wider use for elementary experimentation than other vertebrates. They are especially well suited for demonstrations in general physiology.

Materials. Living frogs; weak ammonia; small dissecting scissors; dry cells and copper leads; dissecting needle or sharp pointed instrument for pithing frog.

Response to Contact. Try the following contact stimuli on a frog and note the results.

1. The eye. With a pencil or small stick touch the surface of the eye lightly. The lid may close, and if the stimulation is very strong the eye is drawn deeply into its socket. Repeat this several times for each eye to show that the eyes react independently of each other.

2. The nostril and eye. With a sharp pencil or sharpened matchstick tickle the nostril of the frog. Notice that it closes. Repeat and watch the eyes at the same time. The eye on the same side of the head as the stimulated nostril closes and may be withdrawn. There must be an association between the two reflexes.

3. The scratch. With a sharp pointed object scratch the side or back of the frog. If no response is given repeat the stimulation. Usually the frog will strike at the stimulated area with its hind foot. This is called the "scratch reflex" from the well-known reflex in dogs.

4. The croak. Place the thumb on one side of a frog and the forefinger on the other and squeeze repeatedly with a stroking motion. The usual response is a croak with each application of pressure.

Response to Chemicals. Moisten the tip of a matchstick in weak ammonia. Bring the stick slowly toward the frog's eye but do not touch it. The eye will close. It may be drawn into the socket. When the response has ceased, do the same for the nostril. Nostril and eye may close. Now moisten the match again and touch it to the side of the jaw. The front leg on the same side wipes at the stimulated area. Touch a match moistened in ammonia to the frog's back. The scratch reflex is repeated with the hind foot. Wash the frog after each application of chemical to remove the substance and prevent destruction of the skin.

Response to Electric Shock. Bring the two leads from the dry cells to within ¼ in. of each other. Then touch them to the frog's side. The scratch reflex is again initiated. If they are applied to the side of the head, the anterior scratch reflex is initiated.

The Pithed Frog. A very illuminating set of demonstrations can be provided for the student by the use of a pithed frog. Either the entire brain may be destroyed by thrusting a sharp instrument into the cranial cavity from the back (posterior) portion of the head toward the front (anterior), or the brain may be severed from the cord with little damage to either by cutting with a sharp knife or fine scissors. If the brain is not destroyed most of the head reflexes may be demonstrated except the foreleg scratch. Most of the body reflexes may be repeated except the croak (Fig. 18.3).

Hindleg Scratch. For most of the demonstrations, a pithed frog should be suspended by hanging it on a rack by means of a small hook or clamp fastened in the mouth. Apply ammonia to one side of the back and notice the scratch response just as in the normal frog. Apply some ammonia to the ventral wall (abdomen) on the same side of the body. Notice the ability of the frog to "locate" the source. Since the brain has been destroyed or at least severed from the cord, there can be no sense of pain or "thought" involved. This usually interests students immensely. Apply some ammonia to the other side of the back and observe that the other leg is used in the response.

The Eye and Nostril Response. Use a frog that has had the cord carefully severed from the brain and in which the brain has not been injured. The frog should be permitted a 20-min. period of recovery from shock after the operation. Try weak ammonia on the nostril and on the eye. In some cases the response works readily. The operation, however, is sometimes severe enough to prevent them. The foreleg scratch will not work, since the path from the head to the leg has been cut.

The Nerve-Muscle Preparation. Any number of demonstrations may be devised from the well-known nerve-muscle (or femur-gastrocnemius) preparation. Pith the frog. Cut the skin from the leg. Place the frog ventral side down and carefully separate the thigh muscles just above the back of the knee. Look for a shiny white cord. This is the sciatic nerve. It extends forward into the abdomen. Cut it just

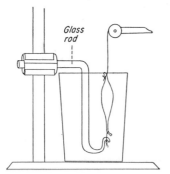

below the hip and lay it out on the muscle without exerting any pull in doing so. Remove most of the muscle tissue from the thigh bone (femur). Detach the calf muscle by removing the tendon at the heel. Make an L-shaped glass rod (see Fig. 21.6) by which the muscle can be suspended and fasten it to a ring stand or other support. The L rod makes it possible to immerse the preparation in liquids.

1. Stimulation of the nerve. With a pair of forceps pinch the end of the nerve and notice the sharp contraction of the muscle. Repeat several times at the same point on the nerve. If the muscle fails to react it is because of the damage done to the nerve by pinching. Pinch again at a point closer to the muscle. The contraction is repeated. Cut away the damaged part of the nerve and stimulate the unremoved portion with the current from a 1½-volt battery or induction coil. Repeat this several times. The contraction always takes place, since

FIG. 21.6 Apparatus used to submerge a muscle in water baths at different temperatures.

the current (if not too strong) does not damage the nerve. Carefully touch the end of the nerve with a matchstick dipped in a chemical such as ammonia, salt solution, or dilute acid. The contraction is violent and continuous (tetanus). Clip off the part of the nerve stimulated and the contraction ceases.

2. Stimulation of muscle directly. Remove the nerve entirely. Place the wires from the battery so that one contacts the upper end of the muscle and the other the lower end. Notice that the muscle contracts just as if the nerve were being stimulated. Press both poles against the ends of the muscle and hold them there. There is a contraction and a relaxation. Break the contact and notice that breaking the current acts as a second stimulus, giving a contraction followed by a relaxation.

3. Effects of temperature. By means of the L rod immerse the preparation in a small vessel of iced water. Allow it to stand 2 min. Stimulate with electric current and measure the height to which it lifts the outer end of the lever. When it has warmed up to room temperature, repeat and measure it again. Immerse in water that feels just warm to the hand (40°C.) and repeat. By including a number of other temperatures and recording the temperatures and height, a rough graph may be constructed showing the relation of height to temperature. The rate (time required per contraction and relaxation) may also be related in this way to temperature.

Make a nerve-muscle preparation with as long a nerve connection as possible. Stimulate the nerve several times to show that it functions. Arrange the apparatus so that the nerve may be laid across a small piece of ice for 2 min. or more. Apply the current and see if it still causes contraction in the muscle. Remove the ice and after several minutes apply the current again. Is there any difference in the result? The lowering of the temperature of the nerve serves as a block to the impulse. It is necessary, however, that the nerve, when tested, should not lie upon the muscles or in a puddle of water since these will conduct the stimulus beyond or around the block. The blocking by means of cold is sometimes employed in desensitizing areas for minor surgical operations.

Man. In connection with the study of the responses of organisms it is desirable to include the human species when possible. The general behavior of man is so complicated that an analysis of it is largely beyond the scope of the more elementary courses; yet many simple demonstrations of response can be devised that may prove quite instructive. Some of those better known in general physiology are given here.

The Iris Response. Have students work in pairs. One student sits so that he faces a window or other light source while the other observes the pupils of his eyes. Shade one eye with the hand or a dark card. Remove the screen and notice the rapid shrinking of the pupil. Repeat, allowing about 5 sec. time for adjustment each time. One individual can perform this experiment upon himself if he uses a mirror near a bright light. While one person observes the pupil of another's eye, let the subject focus upon an object close at hand and then upon an object at considerable distance. The observer will readily see a change in the size of the pupil.

The Inverted Image. That an image of an object is really focused upon the retina in an inverted form but that we learn to transpose it mentally and unawares can be demonstrated by the following test. Make a pinhole in a card and hold it about 1 in. from the eye, looking through the hole. Close the other eye. With the free hand pass a pinhead between the pinhole and eye, causing the pinhead to move from below upward. The head will appear to enter the visual field from above.

Tactile Response. To show that all parts of the body surface are not equally sensitive to contact, try the following. Thrust two ordinary pins through a cork or

376 SOURCES, PREPARATION, AND USES OF MATERIALS

piece of very soft wood. If properly adjusted the points may be placed extremely close together, or by partially withdrawing the pins the points will separate. Using this instrument with the points very close, explore the back of the hand and forearm. If the pins are close enough together they give the sensation of a single contact on the skin. Separate the points a little at a time until just wide enough to give the impression of two contacts. This is the distance apart of the separate sense areas of contact. Repeat these tests for the palm of the hand, fingertips, forehead, or other regions and compare the results. Do not press hard enough to cause pain, as pain and pressure are separate senses.

Temperature Response. The areas of the skin which are sensitive to cold and heat, that is, temperatures considerably below and above body temperature, may be located and marked upon a portion of the body, such as the forearm or back of the hand, by using a metal or glass rod with a tapered blunt point. Cool the rod in ice water or snow and explore the area, making a mark wherever the distinct sensation of cold appears. By heating the rod in water, not hot enough to cause pain, the same tests repeated will locate the warm sensory spots. Place the finger of one hand in a tumbler of water which has been heated until it feels decidedly warm, leaving it there for ½ min. Place the finger of the other hand in water that is decidedly cold, leaving it for the same length of time. Pour the two tumblers of water together quickly and insert the two fingers in the mixture. It feels cold to one finger and hot to the other.

The Knee Jerk. Place the knee in a bent position so that the lower leg hangs limply as when the legs are crossed. Tap sharply upon the tendon just below the kneecap, using the knuckles, the edge of the hand, or a narrow book. The leg straightens or extends without the subject's control.

BEHAVIOR OF PLANTS

Algae

Oscillatoria. *Materials.* Large mat of living *Oscillatoria;* shallow container (dissecting pan, crystallization dish, etc.).

Mat Formation. Carefully pull the large mat apart, forming numerous small clumps. Distribute them evenly over the water surface. Allow it to stand for 24 to 48 hr. in a light, warm situation. Note that the number of mats is smaller and individual mats are larger because of coalescence of the small ones. The oscillating movements shown by *Oscillatoria* are likely responsible for much of this reaction.

Spirogyra. *Materials.* Two fair-sized clumps of living *Spirogyra;* two glass cylinders; battery jars or quart fruit jars; enough pond water to fill the containers approximately three-fourths full.

Buoying Effect of Oxygen Bubbles. Place approximately equal mats in water in each container. Place one in darkness and the other in light at approximately the same temperature. After 24 to 48 hr. examine the two containers for position of the mats. The one in light usually remains floating and shows many bubbles caught in the mesh of filaments. The one in darkness usually sinks and shows comparatively few bubbles. The bubbles contain gas, largely oxygen which escaped in the process of photosynthesis.

Closterium. *Materials.* Culture of *Closterium* (quarter moon-shaped desmid) containing an abundance of organisms; glass cylinder; quart fruit jars or battery jar.

Response to Light. Place the culture in the glass cylinder, filling it nearly full. Set the container so one side is lighted from a window or artificial light and the other shaded. After about 24 hr. note that the organisms have collected mainly at one side because of light intensity.

Any Unicellular or Small Colonial Species. *Materials.* A culture with an abundance of organisms, and a volume of approximately 100 cc.; petri dish or one of about the same diameter and somewhat deeper; 45-volt B battery, or series of smaller dry cells; two pieces of copper wire each about 1 ft. in length and no. 20 gage.

Response to Direct Electric Current. Prepare a coil at one end of each wire shaped like a watch hairspring. Attach each wire to a pole of the battery and submerge the coils in the culture. Suspend them about 1 in. apart. Allow the current to pass through this system for 15 to 30 min. Note that the algal cells collect about the positive electrode, indicating that the cells bear negative charges on their walls.

Precipitation of Suspended Unicellular Algae. Place 10 cc. of a rich culture in a test tube. Best success is obtained when the culture is near the neutral point—if extremely alkaline or acid, results are not so pronounced. Add 5 to 10 drops of saturated solution of copper sulfate or a saturated solution of ammonia alum (ordinary alum) to the culture. Shake the mixture a minute or two and watch for a flocculent precipitate. Often this will occur within 3 to 5 min. or sooner.

Pteridophytes

Equisetum. *Materials.* Small mass of dry spores; glass slide; compound microscope.

Hygroscopic Properties of Elaters of Spores. Collect a fresh cone, lay it on a sheet of paper and allow the spores to shed. Place a few of the spores on a slide with a knife blade. Examine them under medium power. Note the four straplike elaters wrapped about each spore. If they are moist, they will be uncoiled. They will coil about the spore again if placed in a desiccator or in alcohol. After observing in the dry state, carefully blow on the spores, expose them to a moist atmosphere, or mount them in water. Examine them immediately and note the uncoiling and resulting movement of the spores.

Fern Sperms. *Materials.* Fern gametophyte culture (see Chap. 12); sodium malate (0.01 per cent solution—1 drop only is needed); compound microscope; slide and cover glass; fine capillary tube made by heating and drawing out a piece of ordinary glass tubing.

Response of Fern Sperms to Sodium Malate. Place a drop of water containing fern sperms on a clean slide. In this, place the capillary tube after filling with the sodium malate solution. Cover with a cover glass. With the microscope, focus on the mouth of the tube. The fern sperms will concentrate about the opening. Apparently the same sort of reaction occurs about an archegonium when it is mature.

Spermatophytes

Why Do Leaves Fall? In the deciduous forest region, the widespread shedding of leaves, particularly from trees and shrubs in autumn, is a conspicuous event which in a short time drastically changes the appearance of the landscape. However, leaf fall is not limited to the autumn. During the summer in temperate regions and throughout the year in the tropics there is a continuous leaf fall, though not conspicuous. Even in herbaceous annuals a few of the older leaves may abscise during the summer. Leaves are not the only plant organs which may be shed; in addition, flowers, fruits, and even twigs or branches, as in cottonwood (*Populus deltoides*), are shed.

Since the size of trees makes them inconvenient to use, coupled with the fact that most deciduous trees do not grow satisfactorily in a greenhouse, a herbaceous plant such as the common coleus is preferable for many experiments in the laboratory. Numerous varieties of coleus are readily obtainable at greenhouses dealing in ornamentals. They are easily propagated by stem cuttings placed in moist sand at about 70°F. in slightly shaded situations. Rooting should occur within 10 to 14 days, at which time they should be transplanted in good soil in 4-in. clay flower pots. Plants propagated in this way, from a given variety, are genetically identical. Such a group of plants are known as a clone. Another desirable feature of coleus as an experimental plant is the fact that leaves are borne in pairs, with the two leaves borne at a node and opposite each other. Both leaves of a pair are the same age, and their physiology is ordinarily the same. Logically, one leaf of a pair may be used for experimentation and its mate used as a control. The coleus plant, under the proper cultural conditions, maintains a fairly constant number of leaves on a given stem. About every week to 10 days the oldest pair of leaves, toward the base of the stem, loses much of its color and drops off (abscises), with a new pair developing from the stem tip (apex). To obtain a logical answer as to why leaves fall, the following experiments can be easily conducted in any biology laboratory with relatively little expense and effort.

Materials. Six potted coleus plants of the same age and variety, each with about seven pairs of leaves; 2 oz. lanolin (wool fat), obtainable from local druggists; sharp safety razor blade; 1 g. alpha-naphthalene acetic acid crystals (a synthetic auxin or plant hormone); indole butyric acid, another synthetic auxin commonly used in horticulture but more expensive; indole acetic acid, a natural auxin or plant hormone, may be used. However, the latter is unstable in light and a paste made from it is useless within about 3 weeks. Some biological supply houses supply these items; Nutritional Biochemicals Corporation, Cleveland 28, Ohio, is also an excellent source.

Grind the alpha-naphthalene acetic acid crystals to a powder. Add 1 part of this powder to 400 parts of lanolin, thoroughly mixing the naphthalene acetic acid with the lanolin. If your school does not own a chemical balance for weighing such small quantities, a local druggist may be willing to compound it for you. An ounce of this lanolin paste (including the hormone) is sufficient for many demonstrations as proposed here.

See Figs. 21.7 and 21.8 for preparation of the coleus plants. Plant *A* is reserved as a control. Two or three leaves from one side of plants *B, C,* and *D* are debladed (the leaf blade is cut from the petiole, slightly below the point of attachment of the blade, with a sharp razor blade, with the petiole stumps left attached to the stem). The debladed petioles of *B* remain untreated. The cut ends of the debladed

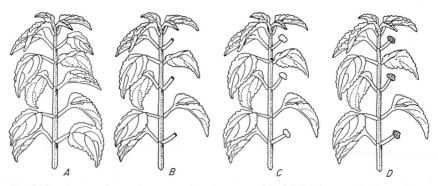

Fig. 21.7   An experiment demonstrating the cause of leaf fall: *A,* control coleus plant; *B,* plant with leaf blade removed from each of three leaves; *C,* plant with three leaves debladed and cut end of petioles covered with pure lanolin; *D,* similar coleus plant with three leaves debladed and cut end of petioles covered with lanolin-hormone mixture. (*Drawn by Elaine Taft.*)

petioles of *C* are covered with pure lanolin. The cut ends of the debladed petioles of *D* are covered with a thick layer of the lanolin paste which contains the naphthalene acetic acid (hormone). After the students have observed the preparation, or even better, if they prepare the setup themselves, as a project, return the plants to a well-lighted situation for 2 or 3 days, keeping the plants watered as previously. After 48 to 72 hr., the debladed petioles of *B* and *C* (Fig. 21.7) will have dropped (abscised), or will do so if slightly pushed. The treated petioles of *D* should still be as tightly attached to the stem as those of *A,* the control.

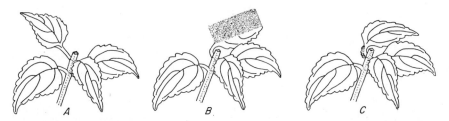

FIG. 21.8 An experiment demonstrating the cause of variation in leaf-blade position by shading: *A,* control coleus plant; *B,* coleus plant with half of one leaf covered with black paper or aluminum foil; *C,* coleus plant with one side of a petiole treated with lanolin-hormone mixture (stippled area on one petiole). (*Drawn by Elaine Taft.*)

With thoughtful questions from the instructor the students will be able to interpret the results obtained in the experiment and come to a definite conclusion as to why leaves fall. Their attention is called to the obvious results that when the leaf blade is removed the petiole abscises, except when the petiole stump is treated with lanolin paste containing the synthetic plant hormone naphthalene acetic acid. Will an application of pure lanolin to the petiole stump prevent abscission? Call attention to plant *C* for the answer. The students come to the conclusion that the hormone prevents abscission. Then they may be asked why the leaves of the control plant (*A*) did not abscise. By inference they may conclude that the presence of the leaf blade prevents abscission and that the leaf blade must synthesize naphthalene acetic acid, or a similar acting substance. The instructor may then provide the information that naphthalene acetic acid is not known to occur normally in plants, but that a similar natural hormone (auxin) indole acetic acid is known to be present and is made in the younger leaves. Depending upon the time that this experiment is performed, the fact that the hormone is made in the young leaves may be a new idea to most students. Aging, drastic changes in the environment, or severe injury to the leaf blade may prevent the manufacture of the hormone. The students soon learn that many other processes occur in the tissues of both plants and animals.

Apple orchardists are often confronted with the problem of leaf drop several weeks before maturity of the fruit, resulting in a low-quality product or total loss. Through experiments, similar to the above, methods have been devised which combine the hormone with a scheduled fungicidal spray. When timed properly, leaf and fruit drop are prevented, resulting in great savings to the producers.

This experiment with the suggested procedure illustrates the application of a scientific method of approach in solving a problem and how it may be applied in the classroom. It involves recognition of a problem, observation and collection of primary facts (by sense perception), and the drawing of best inferences as supported by the data collected. Such logical procedure should be used whenever possible in the biology laboratory.

This experiment may be enhanced and extended by preparing two other coleus plants, as shown by Fig. 21.8. With a piece of black paper or aluminum foil cover both upper and lower surfaces of half a leaf blade, as shown by plant B. Plant A is the control (and may be same as A of Fig. 21.8). Apply a layer of lanolin paste containing naphthalene acetic acid to *one* side of a petiole as shown by C. A third plant (not illustrated) may be included, to which the lanolin-hormone paste is applied to one side of the square stem from near the tip, downward over the length of two internodes.

After 48 to 72 hr. the petiole of the leaf with one-half of the blade covered (plant B, Fig. 21.8) will have curved out of line from its original position, in the direction away from the shaded portion of the leaf blade, as shown in the illustration. Before attempting to draw inferences, consider the results of treating one side of a petiole (plant C) with the lanolin-hormone paste. Within 2 to 3 days the petiole will have turned out of its original position, sometimes almost at a right angle, as shown by C, Fig. 21.8. From this the inference may be drawn that the hormone causes cell walls to stretch and become more permeable to water. Water diffuses into the cells exposed to a greater concentration of the hormone more rapidly than into the cells on the opposite side of the petiole, resulting in greater osmotic pressure in the treated tissues, causing the curvature or bending.

With this information on the bending of petioles caused by an increased supply of hormone on one side, one may consider the bending of the petiole of the partially covered leaf blade of plant B. This petiole reacted in the same way as the leaf of plant C. The obvious inference is that light slowly *destroys* the natural hormone made in the younger leaves and that the auxin *accumulates* in darkness. That is, there is more hormone available in the covered portion of the leaf blade than in the other half which has been exposed to light. This hormone may diffuse through the veins of the covered portion into the same side of the petiole, resulting in greater osmotic pressure and thus causing the petiole to curve away from the darkened half of the leaf blade.

The enlargement of cells is an important phase of growth. This means then that light has a *retarding* effect upon growth. This is a useful concept, enabling one to understand numerous plant reactions.

It was suggested that in addition to plants B and C another coleus plant be included, the stem of which was treated on one side with the same lanolin-hormone paste, extending down two internodes from the stem tip. After 2 or 3 days the stem tip will bend in the direction opposite to the treated side. What obvious inference may be drawn? When potted house plants such as coleus and geranium receive bright light from one side, as is likely in a south window, the tip of the stems and younger leaves turn in the direction of the brightest light. What inference may be drawn?

Why Do Stems of Seedlings in Darkness Grow in Length More Rapidly Than Those in Bright Light? A demonstration of this fact is simple and inexpensive to conduct. Arrival at the proper answer by the students involves some of the principles discovered in the above hormone experiments with coleus and again applies a scientific method of approach to the solution of a problem. This demonstration, if properly conducted, will induce two kinds of answers by the students, those which imply *purpose* on the part of the plants and those based solely upon *cause-and-effect* relations, with consideration as to whether growth is beneficial to the plant or not.

Materials. About 20 seeds of each of any three of the following: beans, peas, soybeans, radish, squash, corn grains, or sunflower achenes. Also, select a good potato tuber which shows slight growth of terminal bud (eye). Potato tubers are dormant when harvested and usually remain so for 2 to 3 months in storage. Eight ordinary clay flower pots, 4 to 6 in. in size, will be needed as containers. Enough reasonably good soil of one kind to fill the pots.

Plant 10 seeds of each species selected in two pots. The seeds of each type should be genetically alike as far as possible, that is, the bean seeds should all be of one variety such as red kidney bean, etc. The seeds should be planted about 2 to 3 weeks before the demonstration is to be used, keeping one pot in as near total *darkness* as possible and the other in full *sunlight*. All should be watered equally. The temperature should be the same (about 70°F.). The potato tuber should be cut, with one eye or bud to each piece, planting one or two pieces in each of two pots of soil, same as for the seeds. The potatoes should be started 4 to 5 weeks before the demonstration is to be used in class.

When the plants are observed after they have grown for the periods indicated, they should be ready for observation by the students. They may be reminded that the only variable in the experiments is that of light. The stems of all plants which grew in darkness may be three to four times as long as those which grew in bright light. The instructor may then ask why are the stems of plants longer when grown in darkness than those which grew in bright light? The obvious answer, if they follow a scientific method of approach, is that the stems *grow faster* in *darkness* than in *light*. However, ordinarily the most common answer is that, "The plants in darkness grow longer stems in order to search for light." Some may notice that the plants which grew in darkness lack the green pigment (chlorophyll), while those exposed to light are green. Leaves of all the plants which grew in darkness, excepting corn, are very small and poorly developed as compared to those which grew in bright light. The stems of all plants which grew in darkness appear to have weaker stems than those which grew in light. Some students may attempt to answer the question first proposed by a combination of one or all of these additional observations. At this point the teacher may point out that it is logical to attempt the solution of one problem at a given time, and not a whole complex of problems. Their attention is then directed to why stems grow faster in darkness than in light.

It must be obvious that both answers cannot be acceptable. By questioning, the students may be led to understand that those who gave the second answer *assumed* that the plants can think and anticipate their needs of the future. In other words, they personified the plants, assuming that they have intelligence and, in some respects, greater abilities than human beings. Also, in arriving at this conclusion, they have ignored the obvious results as demonstrated by the experiment. This is the kind of answer that man has been prone to accept since he began to observe natural phenomena. Unfortunately some scientists, including science textbook writers, will occasionally lapse in this respect. As mentioned previously, the stems grow more rapidly in darkness than in light. Since light is the only variable in this experiment, someone will draw the inference that "light inhibits growth." The same conclusion was arrived at in a somewhat different way in the previous experiment with coleus. Also, in this last demonstration, the inference was drawn that auxins (plant hormones) accumulate more rapidly in darkness than in bright light and that growth in stem length increases as the hormone content increases. This is a useful principle in solving numerous plant problems. It is a cause-and-effect type of answer arrived at by a logical procedure.

It must be realized, however, that these conclusions are true only for plants which have an *adequate food supply,* such as in the seeds still attached to the seedlings and the piece of potato tuber. If these same seedlings and sprouting potato tuber were left in darkness until the stored food supply was exhausted, growth in stem length would stop and eventually the plants die of starvation. The plants in bright light, however, are able to manufacture all the necessary foods. The stems will continue to grow slowly in length and live on indefinitely.

Use of Hormones in Vegetative Multiplication. The vegetative propagation of stems, roots, and leaves of numerous plant species may be accelerated and improved by hormones. These are the safe growth substances as suggested for the demonstrations with coleus, but for this purpose they are generally used in much higher concentrations. However, the lanolin preparation is not satisfactory since this fat would interfere with the movement of water into the cuttings. Aqueous solutions may be used, but for the purposes here perhaps the commercial preparations using talc (hydrous magnesium silicate) as the carrying agent are the most practical. They are available, with directions for use, at horticultural supply stores under the trade names of Hormodin, Auxilin, Quick-Root, Stem-Root, Rootone, and others.

Materials. For an adequate demonstration of the effect of hormones as root-inducing substances, at least six different species should be used with at least twelve cuttings made from each species. Usually it is better to use "softwood" cuttings, that is, a stem which is growing vigorously and before the wood has become hard, and with two or three leaves intact.

Half of the cuttings of each species should be treated with talc only (on the cut end) and the other half with the talc-hormone preparation. Place the cuttings in moist sand, peat, or other desirable rooting medium in a shaded, warm (70°F.) situation. After about 10 days, examine at convenient intervals, for root formation. Holly (*Ilex opaca*), rose, privet, lilac, poinsettia, carnation, and chrysanthemum are examples of desirable species for this demonstration (ref. 1).

Use of Hormones in the Development of Seedless (Parthenocarpic) Fruits. The flowers of most species abscise (drop) if pollination fails to occur. Abscission of the pistil can be prevented by placing a dab of lanolin-hormone paste (same as that used previously on coleus petioles) on the stigma, or cut end of the style. What inference may be drawn as to one function of pollen when germinating on the stigma of a pistil? Also, if pollination does not occur, fertilization fails since the male gametes (sperms) are borne in the pollen tube. If sperms carried by the pollen tubes do not enter the embryo sac of an ovule, the embryo sac containing the egg cell (female gamete) as well as the ovule usually aborts. Since ovules become seeds after fertilization occurs; the fruit in this particular instance will be seedless; the ovulary (ovary) of the pistil continues development as a seedless fruit.

Materials. One or two flowering tomato plants (8 to 9 weeks from planting of seeds) planted in 6 to 8 in. pots filled with soil to within about 1 in. of the top; lanolin-hormone paste (see Fig. 21.7).

Select a flower which is about halfway opened. Carefully remove the sheath of anthers about the pistil. Cut the style about halfway between the stigma and ovulary, discarding the upper half bearing the stigma. Place a small amount of lanolin-hormone paste on the cut end of the style. It is wise to treat several flowers as just described, since one can easily injure the pistil in removing the stamens. To make the demonstration more complete, remove the stamens from at least two other flowers, retaining one without further treatment and the second with *pure lanolin* placed on the cut end of the style. Both these flowers are likely to abscise within a few days. Flowers having received these different treatments may be marked with small perforated price tags, looping the string about the peduncles of each flower. If time and materials are available, the instructor will recognize the possibilities of additional similar experiments.

Gibberellins as New Plant Growth Hormones. In 1926 a Japanese botanist observed that rice plants infected with a fungus *Gibberella fujikuroi* grew much more rapidly than uninfected rice plants. Extracts from the fungus when applied to healthy rice plants gave the same results. In 1938, what proved later to be a complex of growth substances was isolated and identified as gibberellin. Active research in the Western Hemisphere, begun in 1955–1956, initiated research on the physiological action and agricultural potentialities of the gibberellins, resulting now in a bibliography of more than 200 publications. Gibberelic acid is one of the most promising compounds composing the gibberellins. These substances are extracted from cultures of the fungus in much the same way as the antibiotic *penicillin* is obtained from the fungus *Penicillium*. Gibberelic acid is relatively inexpensive and is effective in aqueous solutions in concentrations 1 to 20 parts per million. It is available, under the name of Brellin 10, from the General Biological Supply House, 8200 South Hoyne Ave., Chicago 20, Ill. Directions are included for making dilutions without the aid of an expensive chemical balance. Gibberelic acid is also available from Nutritional Biochemicals Corporation, Cleveland, 28, Ohio.

With some plants, remarkable results have been obtained. Some important applications have been made recently to certain horticultural crops. For biology laboratory demonstrations, genetically dwarf varieties of garden plants such as peas and beans may be converted physiologically into tall plants by treating with gibberelic acid. See Refs. 9 and 11 at end of this chapter.

Sensitive Plant (Mimosa pudica). *Materials.* Potted plants about 3 to 4 months old. These may be grown from seeds which are obtainable from seed dealers.

These plants show very rapid movement of leaflets, leaves, and petioles when stimulated in certain ways. Several other plants, especially of the Leguminosae (pea and bean family) show similar movements, but not nearly so pronounced as mimosa. Do not use the same plant for all the following experiments, unless several hours have elapsed and the plant is again normally expanded and sensitive to touch.

Response to Touch, Pressure, or Slight Blow. Touch, pinch, or strike a terminal leaflet. Note the progressive folding movement of the leaflets and finally a drooping of the whole leaf. Allow the plant to stand without further stimulation for a time. Note that the original position of the leaf parts is regained. Also note that there are special swollen organs at the bases of the leaflets and leaves. These are known as pulvini. This organ is composed chiefly of thin-walled parenchymatous cells. Also large intercellular spaces are present. The permeability of cell membranes of this organ can change rapidly, and the turgidity of cells can change, resulting in the rapid movements observed.

Behavior in Response to Injury. With a hot needle, or match flame, burn the terminal leaflet. Watch the reaction. Prick the main stem with a sharp-pointed needle. Follow this by touching a pulvinus and then a leaflet. Note differences in sensitivity. Also clip off a leaflet with scissors. Pass a direct electric current through the plant. Try different voltages, also alternating current, and note the reactions and time of regaining expanded position.

Behavior in Response to Change in Temperature. Place a plant in a cold (not freezing) situation until it no longer reacts to touch. Keep it there for a while longer, replace in room temperature and note the lapse of time before normal reactions occur. The insensitive condition brought about by low temperature is known as "cold rigor." Plants will regain their normal condition if not allowed to remain in a state of rigor too long. In the same way expose a plant to a temperature of 40°C. until it becomes insensitive, or until heat rigor has set in.

Behavior in Response to Drought. Allow soil about a plant to dry out until the plant is insensitive, or drought rigor has occurred. Then moisten the soil and record the time it takes the plant to become normal again.

Response to Anesthetics. Expose a plant to chloroform under a bell jar for a few minutes, or until it is insensitive. Return to normal conditions and note the time required for return to normality.

Response to Absence of Light. Keep a plant in a dark room or box until it is no longer sensitive to touch. Replace in a light situation and record the time of return of sensitivity.

Sunflower, Coleus, Geranium. *Materials.* Three potted sunflower plants 6 to 10 in. in height. Other plants such as coleus or geranium may be substituted.

Behavior of Stem in Response to Gravity. Place one pot on its side so that the stem is horizontal to the pull of gravity. Suspend another upside down so that the stem tip is pointed in the direction of the gravitational pull. The third plant is kept as a check. Allow the experiment to continue for 2 or 3 days and note the reaction of stems.

Apical Dominance

Apical Growth of Stems and Dormancy of Buds. Growth in length of stems of seed plants occurs at the apex of each stem axis. If terminal buds are present, apical dominance is exerted, inhibiting the growth, ranging from a low rate to complete dormancy of the lateral buds. In many ornamental plants when "bushy" specimens are desired, floriculturists recommend "pinching back" (removal of terminal buds) to increase branching by permitting lateral buds to grow. Those who are most successful with tea roses remove the flowers as rapidly as the buds begin to open. In the laboratory this can be easily and satisfactorily demonstrated by the use of two coleus plants of the same variety and age which have been propagated vegetatively. Use one as the control, and remove the terminal bud from the other, keeping the two plants growing under the same conditions. Within a week or two, appreciable growth of lateral branches from axillary buds will likely be evident. This may also be demonstrated by the use of two plump potato (*Solanum tuberosum*) tubers of the same variety and size which show slight evidence of sprouting. Using one of the tubers as a control, embed the end which was originally attached to the parent plant in moist sand or soil. Cut the remaining tuber into three or more parts, being careful not to injure the "eyes" or buds. Place the tuber pieces, cut surface down, on moist sand or soil as for the control tuber. If the control tuber and tuber pieces are kept under good growing conditions for 4 to 5 weeks, the terminal bud alone will have grown on the control, while the terminal as well as the lateral buds will have developed on the pieces at about the same rate. These experiments also illustrate the usual result of branching or sprout formation after pruning of woody plants.

An examination of the second, youngest growth segment of many angiosperm trees will reveal several *dormant* buds caused by apical dominance exerted by the terminal bud of that season or by nearly terminal lateral buds as in the elms (*Ulmus*). When such trees are cut, sprouts often occur from the stump. These sprouts are from dormant lateral buds which may be many years old. Cutting of the tree removed the inhibiting effect of apical dominance. It seems quite probable that the explanation of apical dominance and polarity exhibited by plant organs may be fully explained in terms of a hormonal mechanism. If suitable tree species are available on the school grounds or near by, a field trip for making observations on trees and shrubs in the winter condition is quite worth while. When a student can make these observations under natural conditions instead of just reading about them or being told about them in a lecture, the educational value accruing is as great as the difference between day and night. This kind of teaching complements and enhances the natural curiosity of the individual for understanding his environment.

Polarity of Vegetative Plant Organs

Stems. Polarity is involved in most growth correlations in seed plants. The two ends of a growing axis may exhibit a remarkable degree of difference in development. A fertilized egg or zygote, by cell division, becomes an undifferentiated embryo. About half the undifferentiated embryo becomes a stem and the other half a root. Horticulturists have long known of the polarity exhibited by stem cuttings, roots developing from the basal end and shoots from the apical end. There are very few known exceptions to this. If the stem cuttings are *inverted* in moist sand, or other "rooting medium," roots fail to develop on the apical end which is embedded in the sand and the cutting usually dies. In some species, when kept in a saturated atmosphere, roots may develop on the inverted stem cutting, but always on the morphologically basal end.

Leaf Cuttings of Sansevieria. The common potted ornamental plant *Sansevieria trifasciata* (bow-string hemp or snake plant, Fig. 23.3) may be propagated vegetatively from leaf pieces. A leaf which is 2 ft. in length may be cut transversely into eight pieces, each of which may be used as a propagule, *if* the morphologically basal end of each piece is placed in moist sand. It may take 5 to 6 weeks for the roots to develop. From one or more of the roots a shoot (rhizome) will likely be differentiated somewhat later. However, if the leaf pieces are *inverted* with the morphologically basal end up and the *apical* end is embedded in the moist sand, no roots will develop from the apical end. If this inverted cutting is retained long enough, root tips may be found developing from the basal end and directed upward, opposite to the pull of gravity.

Roots of Sweet Potato. The common sweet potato varieties and so-called yams (*Ipomoea battatus*) of vegetable markets are anatomically fleshy roots. These have long been used as vegetative propagules. Persons who deal in vegetable plants for the home gardener plant whole sweet potatoes in moist sand, keeping the temperature at about 70°F. In time, numerous shoots appear. When these are 6 to 8 in. in length, they may be pulled, broken loose from the planted sweet potato, and sold as "slips" to the home gardener. The gardener then plants these in his garden where he wishes the crop to grow. Occasionally the sweet potato is used as an ornamental vine in the home. A quart size glass fruit jar or vase filled with water may be used as a container. The basal end (root tip end) of the sweet potato is placed in the container with 2 to 3 in. of the sweet potato submerged in the water and supported in place by the rim of the glass jar (Fig. 21.9). If the diameter of the sweet potato is too small to be supported by the jar rim, insert three pointed match stems in the fleshy root to hold it in the proper position. If kept in a warm (70°F.) room, exposed to sunlight from a window, within 2 to 3 weeks numerous roots will have developed from the basal end in the water. In about the same time a few shoots (stems with leaves) will have developed from near the apical end. If by chance the apical end was placed down in the container and water, it is likely that no roots or shoots will develop, and the sweet potato will decay. When selecting the sweet potatoes from the vegetable market, pick only the ones which show a few buds near one end. The presence of the buds indicates the *apical* end of the sweet potato, or the end where it was attached to the parent plant, and a scar will be found where it was broken. No buds will be found near the basal end, and often the fleshy root tapers to about $1/4$ in. in diameter where the remainder of the root was broken off during harvest. It is obvious from the foregoing that *polarity* is involved in the development of roots and shoots from the sweet potato.

The sweet potato, as previously described, is useful in the biology laboratory in several other ways in addition to the demonstration of polarity. It will be noted, as shown in Fig. 21.9, that the buds or shoots are arranged in parallel rows, running lengthwise of the potato. On a *stem* the lateral buds, each containing a stem tip (apical meristem), are arranged spirally as may be demonstrated on a white potato tuber (*Solanum tuberosum*). Buds which develop from some other organ than a stem, as well as buds on a stem which occasionally develop from tissues of an *internode,* are known as *adventitious* buds. Observations of these parallel rows of adventitious buds on the sweet potato led to an anatomical study which revealed that such buds originate from the stumps of *lateral roots,* usually embedded in the sweet potato tissue. If a young sweet potato is carefully removed from the soil, these lateral roots may still be found intact. It has long been known that lateral roots arise from a main, or primary, root opposite the protoxylem points of the vascular system. This causes the lateral roots to be arranged in parallel rows, running lengthwise of the main or primary root. This can be seen on the roots of many seedlings such as tomatoes, cabbage, and peas, when carefully removed from the soil. The lateral root scars and the buds which develop from remnants of the old lateral roots, as well as the absence of leaf scars on the sweet potato, are evidence that the sweet potato is a fleshy root and not a tuber or stem.

On the stem of the shoots and near the base of the petiole of each leaf of the sweet potato, a pair of prominent root primordia are to be found. Directly below each member of this pair there may be a series of smaller root primordia forming a line on each side of the stem. If the photograph of Fig. 21.9 is carefully observed, these root primordia may be seen. When these shoots ("slips") are removed from the sweet potato and planted in moist soil, these root primordia develop into full-fledged roots usually within 24 hr. or less.

Fig. 21.9   Sweet potato plants propagated from a fleshy sweet potato root are useful in numerous ways in the biology laboratory. (*Photograph by Dr. Alan Heilman.*)

The sweet potato plant is unusual from the standpoint of vegetative multiplication. All three of the vegetative organs, the roots, stems, and leaves, may be used as propagules. The petiole of a leaf, when cut just above where it is attached to the stem and then placed in moist sand to the full length of the petiole, with the leaf blade resting more or less on the sand, will often root within 10 to 14 days. In some varieties, shoot formation will not occur as long as the leaf blade is intact and is in good condition. After the petiole has developed a good root system, if the leaf blade is mutilated or mostly removed, shoot formation will occur. In other varieties shoot formation occurs even though the leaf blade is still attached and in good condition. The sweet potatoes borne from a fleshy root, a stem, and a leaf are ordinarily identical as to variety of the parent type from which the propagules were derived. This means that every cell of a leaf, stem, and fleshy root of a given variety of sweet potato is identical genetically. These observations and facts may be used effectively in introducing a study of mitosis, or ordinary cell division.

A half dozen sweet potatoes cultured in glass jars as described and kept on a windowsill of the biology laboratory will supply an abundance of material for the foregoing observations and for numerous other purposes. The biology laboratory should never be free of some living plant and animal specimens. Leaves of the sweet-potato plants may be used for chlorophyll extractions and the synthesis of starch following photosynthesis. Freehand sections from the fleshy roots are excellent for demonstrating the accumulation of starch as a food. The leaves, stems, and roots may be used in studies on respiration dealing with the release of carbon dioxide. Red-stem varieties may be grafted on to green-stem varieties, or vice versa. Additional uses may be found for such sweet potato cultures after they have been used a few times.

Corn (Zea mays). *Materials.* Wooden box about 4 by 3 in. with bottom removed and replaced with wire screen (hardware cloth) and muslin over the outside of the screen; sawdust or peat to fill the box; 12 to 18 corn grains; means of suspending the box at about a 45° angle either by legs or swinging; large tumbler or glass funnel; filter paper and peat, sand, or sawdust to fill the tumbler or funnel.

Reaction of Corn Roots to Gravity. Line a tumbler or glass funnel with filter paper. Fill the lined container with peat, sand, or sawdust, and thoroughly moisten it. Carefully place several corn grains between the glass and paper, distributing the grains 1 in. or more apart. Place them in a warm situation, keep moist, and wait for germination. If soaked seeds are used, roots will appear within 2 or 3 days. Note that the primary roots grow in the direction of the pull of gravity. After the roots are about 1 in. long carefully remove half of the germinating grains. With a sharp razor blade or other knife cut off about ⅛ in. of the root tips of two or three specimens, leaving the others uninjured. Replace all the specimens in the tumbler or funnel so that the primary roots are pointing upward, or away from the direction of gravitational pull. Keep moist and warm as before. Within 24 to 48 hr. the inverted roots with the tips intact will have curved and turned downward in response to gravity. The decapitated ones remain upright and uncurved, indicating that the tips (meristematic tissues) are necessary in responding to gravitational force. Note the results and compare with the roots which were not removed from the container.

Response to Water against Gravity. Fill a wooden box as described above with sand, peat, or sawdust. Plant about 24 corn grains in it. Suspend at about a 45° angle. Keep very moist and in a warm situation. When the roots come through the muslin bottom, note that they do not grow straight down but turn up against the muslin and wire-screen bottom. This seems to indicate that the reaction to water is stronger than response to gravity.

Wheat. *Materials.* A dozen wheat grains; glass cylinder or fruit jar of about 500 cc. capacity; piece of muslin for covering mouth of cylinder; handful of sand; small amount of erythrosin.

Response of Roots to Light. Make up about 500 cc. of very dilute erythrosin in water (1 part erythrosin to 50,000 parts water). Place this in the cylinder. Tie the muslin over the mouth of the cylinder. The liquid should come almost to the top of the cylinder and just touch the cloth. Place the wheat grains on the muslin, covering them with sand to keep them moist. Set the apparatus in a warm dark place until germination occurs and roots 1 in. or more in length have developed and are growing straight down. Then place the cylinder in a window so that the roots will be brightly illuminated from one side. This exposure should continue for 12 to 24 hr. Usually by this time the root tips will have bent at right angles and toward the bright light. The erythrosin in some way causes the roots to become sensitive to light. This should be checked by a similar setup in which no erythrosin is used.

Opening and Closing of Flowers and Inflorescences. *Darkness.* Dandelion and numerous other composite inflorescences (flower clusters or heads) close during the night and open in bright sunlight. Cut flower stalks placed in water or potted flowering plants may be used for demonstrating these movements. Select two sets of flowers which have opened in sunlight. Place one set in a dark room and leave the other in bright light as a control. Select the dark situation so that the temperature will be as nearly the same as in the light location. After exposure of 2 to 3 hr. in darkness the inflorescences usually close. Compare these with the controls. The closed specimens may be opened again by placing them in bright light. The opening and closing are due to changes in turgor of cells near the inner side of the base of each bract surrounding the head of flowers.

Temperature. Crocus and tulip flowers are very sensitive to changes in temperature. When the flowers are closed and are brought into a room which is 10 to 15°C. warmer than where they were, ordinarily they will open within 5 to 10 min. The flowers are sensitive to changes in temperature as slight as 0.5 to 3°C. If the opened flowers are returned to the colder situation, they will close again within a short time. These movements are due to changes in turgor of tissues at the bases of the sepals and petals.

REFERENCES

1. Avery, G. S., Jr., et al.: *Hormones and Horticulture*, McGraw-Hill Book Company, Inc., New York, 1947.

2. Benton, A. H., and W. E. Werner, Jr.: *Workbook for Field Biology and Ecology*, Burgess Publishing Company, Minneapolis, 1957.

3. Gale, E. F., and R. Davies: *Adaptation in Micro-organisms*, Cambridge University Press, New York, 1953.

4. Gardner, E.: *Fundamentals of Neurology*, 2d ed., W. B. Saunders Company, Philadelphia, 1952.

5. Hoskins, R. G.: *Endocrinology*, W. W. Norton & Company, Inc., New York, 1950.

6. Jacobs, William P.: "What Makes Leaves Fall," *Sci. American*, **193**:82–89, November, 1955.

7. Newman, H. H.: *Evolution, Genetics and Eugenics*, 3d ed., University of Chicago Press, Chicago, 1932.

8. Society for Experimental Biology: *Physiological Mechanisms in Animal Behavior*, Academic Press, Inc., New York, 1950.

9. Strong, C. L.: "On Experiments with Gibberellic Acid, Which Stimulates the

Growth of Plants," *Sci. American,* **199**:134–140, December, 1958. Available in most public libraries, and should be in every school library.

10. Wimmer, E. J., and H. H. Haymaker: *Laboratory Exercises in Biology,* William C. Brown Company, Dubuque, Iowa, 1957.

11. Wittwer, S. H., and M. J. Bukovac: "The Effects of Gibberellin on Economic Crops," *Econ. Botany,* **12**:213–255, 1958. Includes a bibliography of 204 citations.

12. Woodruff, L. L., and G. A. Baitsell: *Foundations of Biology,* The Macmillan Company, New York, 1951. Illustrated.

CHAPTER 22

---⊰{ Reproduction }⊱---

The capacity of self-perpetuation is a fundamental characteristic of protoplasm. This is a phenomenon occurring in all species without which they would become senescent and disappear from the earth. In unicellular organisms cell division and reproduction are synonymous. Also, in many of these organisms, sexual reproduction occurs which involves a union of cells. In multicellular organisms cell division does not lead directly to reproduction, but builds up the organism's complex body which eventually produces specialized reproductive cells, such as spores and gametes, or results in various types of vegetative multiplication. In teaching, it is generally better to start with the lower forms of both plants and animals since they are free from prudish associations and usually less encumbered with secondary sexual structures. Here, too, much terminology may be introduced and the student made familiar with the fundamental steps before application to higher forms. Many of the activities of plants and animals are closely associated with the reproduction of their kind. This is none the less true of man, and the extent to which the subject is taken up in the classroom will depend upon the age of the students, the skill of the teacher, and the intelligence and attitude of the community in which the school is located. In any event the function of reproduction is a perfectly normal, natural one and should be approached as such in the same manner as respiration, digestion, excretion, and the like.

ASEXUAL REPRODUCTION IN PLANTS

Bacteria. Spontaneous Generation. The belief in spontaneous generation reaches far back among the ancients. The Middle Ages was dominated by this conception, backed by Aristotle's authority. As the experimental method of testing observation came into use, these beliefs and superstitions concerning the larger plants and animals were gradually replaced among the educated by facts indicating that all living organisms arise directly from living parents. However, after van Leeuwenhoek discovered bacteria in 1676 a controversy arose concerning the origin of these minute living forms. This argument was not settled among scientists until Pasteur, through a series of experiments made about 1860, showed that even bacteria must have parents. His experiments may be repeated in any laboratory.

Materials. Two test tubes; two small (200-cc.) flasks (if Pasteur's classical experiment is to be tried); two pieces of glass tubing 5 mm. in outside diameter and about 12 in. long; two one-holed rubber stoppers to fit flasks; sufficient cotton for plugging tubes; about 250 cc. of nutrient medium used for culturing bacteria such as grass infusion liquid, beef broth, agar, gelatin, or any other which may be available; steam sterilizer or an autoclave, if available; heat source for sterilizer and the bending of glass tubing.

Fill the test tube half full of the nutrient medium. Push a plug of cotton into the mouth of each tube (see Fig. 12.19) just sufficiently tight to suspend the tube by the cotton. If much tighter than this, the necessary air may not diffuse through the plug. Place one of the plugged test tubes in the sterilizer and heat to the boiling point for about 1 hr. Allow the tube to cool, label, and place along with the unsterilized tube in a dark place at room temperature (70 to 85°F.). Examine the two after 24, 48, 96 hr., or longer. Note the differences that appear to the unaided eye. Examine a drop of each solution under high power (4 mm.) of a microscope. Bacteria are present in the unsterilized cloudy medium. You will not find any living organisms in the sterilized medium. (If they should be present the experiment should be repeated.) Spontaneous generation cannot occur under these conditions. Air can get into each culture, but inoculation does not occur in the sterilized medium, since the cotton plugs act as filters. The presence of vast numbers of bacteria in the unsterilized medium after incubation as compared to the small number at the beginning indicates that rapid reproduction has occurred. Students may be asked to suggest practical applications of the principle of sterilization by high temperature. Commercial and home canning of fruits, vegetables and meats, hospital technics, etc., are the commonest examples.

Pasteur's flask cultures undoubtedly will stimulate interest. Draw one end of each of the two pieces of glass tubing out so that the opening is about ⅟₃₂ in. in diameter.

Bend the tubing as shown in Fig. 22.1, and fit tightly into the stoppers. Fill the flasks about one-third full with the nutrient medium. Fit the stoppers tightly into the flasks. Treat one in the sterilizer for 1 hr. or so at boiling temperature. Allow the flask to cool, label, and set aside with the unsterilized flask. Observe after 24, 48, 96 hr., or longer. Compare appearance of the two cultures. Air can diffuse through the small opening of the glass tubing. The sterilized medium does not become inoculated since gravity causes

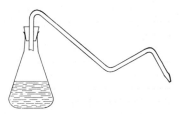

FIG. 22.1   Pasteur's flask.

any bacteria which may be carried in by air to drop out in the bends of the glass tubing.

Grass-infusion Culture. Bacteria are widely known for their rapid rate of reproduction. Milk, meat, and other foods may spoil overnight during hot moist weather. To bring about such rapid spoilage, vast numbers of bacteria must be present. These great numbers may be attained by a process of vegetative reproduction known as "fission." Under favorable conditions this may occur every 15 to 30 min.

Materials. A handful of grass which is starting to decay; source of heat; water; 500-cc. beaker or other container; microscope slide; cover slip; compound microscope.

Place the decaying grass in the beaker with water. Boil the contents for 15 min. or longer. Allow the solution to cool in uncovered vessels and the debris to settle. Examine a drop of the liquid with high power (4 mm.) of the microscope. Very few organisms, if any, will be found. Examine the solution again with a compound microscope after 24, 48, 72, 96, 120, and 144 hr. Look for rod-shaped (bacillus), spherical (coccus), and spiral (spirillum) types. Most of these will be very small, hence requiring careful lighting and focusing. The numbers found from the third to sixth day are usually vastly greater than the number found the first day. Note the scum formation on the surface of the liquid after the culture is several days old. Examine it to see of what it is composed.

Sterile Potato Culture. Pure cultures of bacteria may be obtained, increase in numbers may be observed indirectly, and colony form and pigmentation may be observed on sterile slices of potato from a day to a week after inoculation.

Materials. Slices of potato; petri dish or other container which may be covered and heated to a high temperature; autoclave or ordinary double boiler; water; microscope slides; cover slips; microscope.

Place the potato slices in the petri dish with some water to prevent drying. Cover the dish. Sterilize in the autoclave for ½ hr. at 15 lb. pressure. If the double boiler is used, heat to a high temperature for 1 hr. or more. Allow the dish to cool. Uncover the plate and examine a bit of the potato under the microscope for organisms. After 5 or 10 min. replace the cover and keep in the dark at room temperature. Examine at intervals of 24, 48, and 72 hr. Look for white or pigmented spots on the potato. Examine a bit of these spots in a drop of water under the high power (4 mm.) of the microscope. You will find bacteria. It is quite evident that rapid reproduction has occurred. The class may be induced to draw this inference without being told.

If time and materials are available, have a student cough into a dish containing a sterile piece of potato. Another student may persuade a housefly, with wings removed, to walk across a sterile potato slice. A girl may wish to shake a powder puff over a piece of bacteria-free potato. Others may streak a similar potato slice with a fingernail or lead pencil. Carefully cover all plates and set them away in a warm place for a day or so and note the results.

Algae. Protococcus (Pleurococcus). Unicellular organisms reproduce chiefly by cell division. *Protococcus*, a simple green alga, is obtainable in most regions during any time of year. It may be mounted in a drop of water and observed with a microscope.

Materials. Protococcus from tree bark, stone, or water culture; microscope slide and cover glass; water; compound microscope.

Protococcus ordinarily can be found on moist shaded tree trunks, large rocks, or stone walls throughout the year. It appears as a green granular layer. Other organisms may be mixed with it. Lightly scrape off a bit of the green layer and transfer to a drop of water on the microscope slide. Cover with the cover glass and observe with the microscope. Note that the cells are spherical when they occur singly. Occasionally cells are found showing slight constrictions on opposite sides. This indicates that cell division is occurring. The two new cells may adhere, continuing to divide several times. Eventually the cells break apart (Fig. 22.2). If some of these break loose from the object upon which they are growing, they may be blown about as dust. If these fall in a favorable location, reproduction starts again. This is one of the simplest examples of reproduction in unicellular organisms.

If *Protococcus* is not available *Gloeocapsa*, a blue-green alga, may be substituted. This form can often be collected from wet sandstone cliff surfaces. It appears as a dirty-green gelatinous mass in such habitats. If such material is found at a time when it is not needed immediately, it may be preserved.

Fungi. Yeasts. Budding is a common type of vegetative multiplication among various species of yeasts. By means of a microscope and temporary mounts this activity can be demonstrated from actively growing cultures.

Materials. Scum from sauerkraut juice or dill pickles (if this is not available a culture may be prepared from ordinary baker's yeast in a 5 per cent sugar solution which is allowed to stand overnight in a warm room); microscope slide and cover glass; compound microscope.

Place a drop of the liquid containing the kraut juice, pickle scum, or special culture on the microscope slide and cover with the cover slip. Examine with high power (4 mm.) of the microscope. The light may have to be reduced considerably by means of the iris diaphragm beneath the microscope stage, since the yeast cells are transparent and may not be seen clearly with strong light. The mature yeast cell is oval in outline. When actively growing, a budlike outgrowth may be found near one end of some cells. The bud grows, the nucleus divides, and one nucleus passes into the bud. The constriction deepens and finally separates the bud as a new cell. Sometimes these cells adhere, forming an irregular filament of several cells. Eventually all the cells separate. The diagrams in Fig. 22.2 show the above story in some detail.

Bread Mold. *Rhizopus, or Mucor,* is a common mold often occurring on bread in the household. It grows rapidly and is easily cultured.

Materials. Slice of bread; moist chamber made from any convenient utensil such as a tin can or fruit jar.

Wipe the piece of bread across a table top. Slightly moisten and lay it away in a closed container for 2 to 3 days. It is best to keep it in a dark warm place. A white cottony growth is likely to result. Black dots will be visible scattered throughout the mass. These are sporangia containing many spores. A bit of the cottony material mounted in a drop of water under the microscope will show its general structure, spores, and sporangia. Better mounts will result if 20 to 50 per cent alcohol is used as the mounting medium instead of water (see Fig. 22.2). Bread mold also has a sexual means of reproduction. However, this is not often found. *Plus* and *minus strains* are necessary. When the two strains are placed together on bread or other cultural media, gamete and zygote formation will result. Pure cultures of the plus and minus strains can be obtained from biological supply houses and often from botany departments in colleges. Such material is ideal for showing the essential characteristics of sexual reproduction (Fig. 22.2).

Downy Mildews. The mildewing of clothing and leather goods stored in a damp place is known to nearly everyone. Home-canned fruits and jellies often show a green or black mold growing on the surface. Oranges, apples, and other fruits are often found decaying from a bluish-green mold.

Materials. A decaying orange or other fruit with a coat of bluish-green mold; an orange in good condition; a moist chamber.

With a knife, sharp point of a pencil, or other instrument, streak through the patch of mold on the decaying orange. Transfer this immediately to a good orange, being sure to cut through the skin in a few places. Put the inoculated orange in a moist chamber in the dark. Examine in a week or 10 days for mold. If a bit of the bluish-green material is mounted in water under a microscope, thousands of spores (conidia) will be seen. Fragments of the mycelium also will be found. If the growth is not too old, chains of spores may be observed on branched stalks (conidiophores). Figure 22.2 shows the characteristics of the bluish-green mold (*Penicillium*) and the black mold (*Aspergillus*).

Water Mold (Saprolegnia). The water molds often attack fish, tadpoles, and other water animals. They may become a serious menace in fish hatcheries and aquaria. Reproduction is carried on chiefly by swimming spores.

Materials. A few dead bees, houseflies, grasshoppers, or other insects; pond water.

Fill a gallon container with pond water. In this place half a dozen dead insects. Keep the culture at room temperature or a little lower. If bacterial action becomes too rapid, indicated by cloudiness of the solution, change the water (tap or well water may be used for the change). After 5 to 7 days a cottony growth is likely to appear on the dead insects. If the growth is good, hyphae will radiate in all directions from the dead body. If a mass of this material is examined with the microscope, swimming spores may be found. All swimming objects present are not spores, however. Some may be animal forms. The mold spores are oval in shape and may be found escaping from some of the mold hyphae. Hyphae bearing

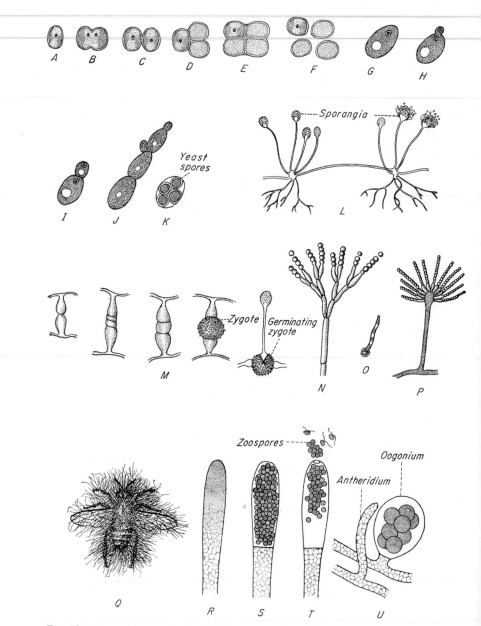

Fig. 22.2 Asexual reproduction in *Protococcus A* to *F;* asexual and sexual reproduction in yeast *G* to *K;* asexual *L* and sexual reproduction in bread mold (*Rhizopus*) *M;* asexual reproduction in the downy mildews, *Penicillium N*, germinating spore *O*, *Aspergillus, P;* reproduction in *Saprolegnia* (water mold) *Q* to *U*.

spores are somewhat club shaped, and the cytoplasm appears denser than in other parts. The sporangia (spore-bearing cells) are terminal. Various stages of the spore development may be observed. In early stages the sporangia appear dense and no divisions of the protoplasm are observable. Later, definite rounded bodies appear. When mature these rounded bodies (swimming spores) will begin to move about within the sporangium. Finally the sporangium breaks open at the tip and the swimming spores swarm out into the surrounding water. These motile spores are attracted by minute amounts of dissolved protein material from the dead insects. They swim in its direction and eventually cause a new infection. The diagrams of Fig. 22.2 give some idea of stages of development. Both sexual and asexual reproduction are illustrated.

Seed Plants. Modified Stems. In numerous instances stems are modified in such a way that they serve as a means of vegetative reproduction. This is of great significance in many plants since such multiplication is the chief method of reproduction. The common white (Irish) potato, gladioli, tulips, irises, and strawberries are good examples. Modified or specialized stems include tubers, corms, bulbs, rhizomes (underground stems), and runners (stolons). Such materials usually can be obtained by the teacher or students without cost. A collection of such examples may be used as a project for an individual or group.

Materials. Potato tubers; cinnamon vine (air potato) tubers; Jerusalem artichoke (a common wild plant, sometimes cultivated) tubers; corms of gladiolus, jack-in-the-pulpit, spring beauty, squirrel corn, or Dutchman's-breeches, *Trillium* (wake-robin), elephant ear plant (*Colocasia*); bulbs of tulip, onion, hyacinth, lily; rhizomes from yarrow, Kentucky bluegrass, iris; runners from strawberry, cinquefoil.

Examine the collection and note the differences between tubers, corms, bulbs, rhizomes, and stolons. If a suitable place is available they may be planted and development watched. A few of these are illustrated in Fig. 22.3.

Grafting. All the better varieties of apples, pears, peaches, plums do not breed true to the parent stock if propagated from seeds. However, the parent stock can be reproduced by means of grafting and budding. The principle is to transplant and grow buds or twigs of a desirable variety on the roots or stems of a less desirable variety. The chief essential of success in grafting depends upon getting the cambium layers of the bud or stem to be grafted (cion) in contact with the cambium of the stem or root (the stock) on which it is to grow.

Materials. Stems (about 1 in. in diameter and 1 ft. long) of apple or pear; several twigs (3 to 4 in. long) with well-developed buds; cherry, plum, or peach stems ($\frac{1}{4}$ to $\frac{1}{2}$ in. in diameter and 8 to 10 in. long); twigs of the same with well-developed buds; growing tomato and potato plants; rubber bands; raffia; grafting wax [1] or paraffin; sharp knife.

Cleft grafting, budding, and in-arching will be described in some detail. The diagrams will illustrate other methods. For cleft grafting (Fig. 22.4*A, B, C, D*) select one of the large pieces of apple or pear stems as the stock. With the sharp knife split one end as indicated in the diagram. Select two twigs with buds as the cions, cut the stems into a wedge shape and insert in the split cleft of the stock so that the cambium layers of the stock and cion are in contact. With rubber bands or raffia (cotton string will do) wrap tightly the cleft end of the stock to hold the cions in place; cover the whole cut end including the cleft portion with grafting wax or paraffin to prevent drying out. The graft is then finished. If this can be

---

[1] Grafting wax is made of 4 parts (by weight) rosin, 2 parts beeswax, and 1 part beef tallow. The whole mixture is melted by heating. Pour the melted mass into cold water. When cool enough to handle it should be kneaded and pulled, as taffy is, or until it becomes a creamy-brown color. To apply to a graft, press it into crevices, covering all cut surface.

done on a living tree and the growth watched, it makes a much finer demonstration. The details for the budding methods are shown in Fig. 22.4E, F, G, H, I.

An in-arch graft may be made between a potato and tomato plant. Start the two in separate flower pots or together in a large pot. When the stems are 8 to 10 in. high, bring the stems together as shown in the diagram. Slice off enough tissue to expose a few vascular bundles of each stem at the point of contact. Carefully tie the stems together. Cover the wounded region with paraffin or grafting wax. Allow growth to continue for 3 to 4 weeks, by which time union between the two stems is likely to have occurred. If so, the tomato stem between the graft union and the root may be severed. The upper part of the potato stem, above the union, may be removed. The tomato stem is now growing on the potato and gets its water and minerals through the potato roots. The lower part of the potato stem and its roots

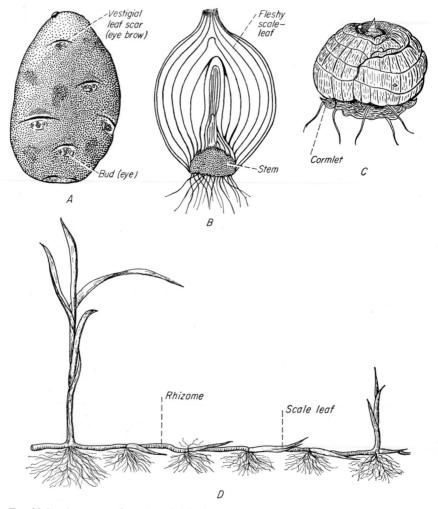

Fig. 22.3   *A*, potato tuber; *B*, onion bulb; *C*, corm of *Gladiolus*; *D*, vegetative reproduction in Kentucky bluegrass.

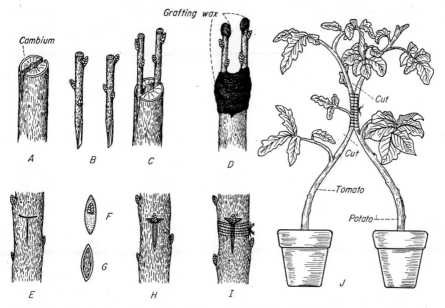

FIG. 22.4   Types of grafting A to D; types of budding E to I; J, an inarched graft between a tomato and a potato.

obtain food from the tomato leaves. It is quite possible to produce tomato fruits on the tomato part of the plant and potato tubers in the soil. The in-arch diagrams of Fig. 22.4J illustrate this type of graft.

Stem, Leaf, and Root Cuttings. Many horticultural and wild plant species may be propagated from cuttings made from stems, roots, or leaves. Such propagation is of vast economic importance in time saved over that required for seedling development, enables the grower to propagate varieties which do not breed true from seed (hybrids), and makes possible the propagation of seedless mutants. With a little planning the teacher can obtain sufficient demonstration material by assigning the work as a project for a group of students. A window box enclosed with glass is ideal for this. If time, space, or material is not available for constructing this window box, a wooden box with sand, covered with a pane of glass, will serve. Also, in many instances, a container for water (fruit jar) is sufficient. Suggestions as to plant forms to use are given below. Others, especially of local interest, likely will occur to the instructor. Many of the plants propagated may be used in other experiments.

Materials. Stems of geranium, coleus, *Tradescantia* (wandering Jew), *Epiphyllum* (Christmas cactus), *Opuntia* (prickly-pear cactus), fuchsia, German ivy (parlor ivy), English ivy, *Iresine* (bloodleaf), lantana, oleander, poinsettia, willow, grape, rose. Roots of sweet potato, horse-radish, *Paeonia*, *Dicentra* (bleeding heart), blackberry, dewberry, sumac, sassafras, wistaria, *Yucca* (Spanish bayonet). Leaves of Rex begonia, *Bryophyllum* (chandelier plant), *Kalanchoe* (air plant), English ivy, *Peperomia*, rose, lemon, red clover, lilac, cabbage, *Hoya* (wax plant), *Echeveria weinbergii* (ghost plant), *Sansevieria*, sweet potato. (Geranium, coleus, *Tradescantia*, German ivy, English ivy, *Iresine,* fuchsia, lantana, oleander, poinsettia, Rex begonia, and *Sansevieria* may be obtained from the florist. *Epiphyllum, Opuntia, Bryophyllum, Kalanchoe, Peperomia, Hoya,* and *Echeveria* can often be obtained from florists or other dealers in succulents.)

The stems of geranium, coleus, *Tradescantia,* German ivy, English ivy, and willow may be rooted in a container of water or in moist sand. Cuttings should not be over 2 to 4 in. long and should contain some of the more mature stem. The other stems mentioned root better in moist sand. If a damping-off fungus gets started it is well to replace the sand and to wet the new sand with a solution of potassium permanganate (2 per cent solution in water). A temperature of about 65 to 70°F. is favorable for most cuttings. The fleshy roots of sweet potato may be sprouted by setting one end of the potato in a tumbler of water or burying in moist sand. From 4 to 6 weeks may be required for stem development. Moist sand is better for the other roots mentioned. The begonia leaves mentioned should have the thinner edges of the leaf removed and cuts made through the larger veins. Where the veins are cut a new plant may arise. The leaf is laid flat on moist sand. The leaves of *Bryophyllum, Hoya, Kalanchoe,* and *Echeveria* are to be laid on the surface of the sand. The leaves of the English ivy, *Peperomia,* rose, lemon, red clover, lilac, cabbage, and sweet potato should have the petioles buried in the sand. *Sansevieria* leaves are cut across the short axis into pieces 3 to 4 in. long. One end should be embedded in the sand.

ASEXUAL REPRODUCTION IN ANIMALS

Protozoa. Simple Division. While asexual reproduction occurs in numerous forms of animals, material from metazoa for illustration is not easy to obtain or to maintain. Microorganisms, however, furnish an abundance of evidence. If the class prepares several hay infusions and examines them at intervals, there is every probability that several (sometimes numerous) instances of cell division may be discovered and used as examples of asexual reproduction. This is the direct method. A second method is to prepare several bottles of culture media and to transplant one protozoan into each bottle and observe the increase in population from day to day. This is the indirect method.

Materials. Dead vegetable remains from fence rows, gutters, ditches (grass leaves and stems are usually best); battery jars or quart and ½-gal. jars; water from tap or well; small bottles or mayonnaise jars or test tubes; piece of glass tubing which can be drawn into a micropipette; cotton.

Let students collect the grass, leaves, and other dead vegetation and bring to class. Place enough of this material in each of several jars to about half fill them. Add enough cold water to nearly fill the jars. These are the stock cultures of microorganisms and may be covered and set aside for use as desired. Allow the class to examine the fluid from each culture as soon as they are prepared. In this they may find few or no microorganisms. At the end of 3 or 4 days, 1 week, and 10 days have the cultures examined. The increase in abundance of life will be very impressive if the cultures have been kept at about 70 to 80°F. At some examinations there may be found protozoa, especially paramecia, in a state of fission, as shown in Fig. 22.5. These will serve as excellent examples of asexual reproduction.

Preparation of a Pure Culture. Boil some dead grass (blades and seeds if available) in water for 20 min. Divide the vegetable matter and the liquor and distribute it in several bottles (glasses or test tubes) and allow these to stand open until contaminated by bacteria. (The appearance of a faint scum on the surface is good evidence.) Draw out a piece of glass tube over a flame until it is of a very fine bore, about 1 mm. in diameter. Using this as a pipette take up a very small amount of the culture medium from a stock jar which has an abundance of paramecia. It is not easy to pick out one paramecium from a mixed culture. This may be accomplished, however, in the following manner. Place a clean slide under the low power of the microscope and upon it place with the micropipette a few very small drops of culture medium. Examination will disclose one or more droplets with a single paramecium in it. Clean the micropipette (Fig. 22.6) by dipping it into very hot water and then into cold water. The capillary point of the micropipette should be touched to a drop containing a single paramecium. Capillary attraction will draw the water and animal into the pipette. Examine under the microscope to be sure one is in the pipette. Transfer the organism to a tube or glass of culture medium by blowing it out of the pipette. Treat each tube in this manner except one. Save this one as a check. Set these inoculated tubes of medium aside for a period of 10 days. During this time have them examined at 1- or 2-day intervals until a culture of paramecia appears. This will be a pure culture descended from *one* ancestor. Students will enjoy making these cultures. Several of them must be started as some may not materialize if the transplanted paramecium is injured or killed by handling. (More than one paramecium might be transplanted if desired.) It is possible to find dividing individuals, but if they are not seen it is obvious that asexual reproduction took place in the early stages of development of the culture since one paramecium was used to start it. The foregoing makes a good group problem for a few students.

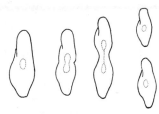

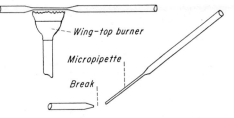

Fig. 22.5 Paramecium reproducing by fission.

Fig. 22.6 Steps in the making of a micropipette.

Hydra. Budding. The fresh-water coelenterate hydra cannot always be obtained out of doors, and it is difficult to rear. If it can be had or purchased at the desired time, it may be used to illustrate a form of asexual reproduction called "budding."

Materials. Hydra in large jars or pans; elodea or some aquatic plants other than algae; daphnia (water fleas).

If placed in water (about 10 hydra per 2 qt. of water) and fed an abundance of small organisms such as daphnia, the hydra will soon begin to reproduce by budding. This is well worth doing if material can be obtained without too much trouble or expense. The hydra, of course, can also be used in other ways.

Regeneration in Animals. Planaria. Under certain conditions some animals go through a process of bodily division so that half or some major portion of their bodies is cut off from the rest. This excised part may regenerate the structures which it lacks and become a new individual, which amounts to reproduction. In a few cases this may be accomplished artificially by cutting an animal into parts and allowing it to regenerate lost parts. Planaria regenerate slowly. The water must be changed frequently to prevent bacteria and fungi developing to the point of killing the worms. See Chap. 12 for collecting and rearing.

Materials. Planaria; safety-razor blade or sharp knife; small dishes about the size of saucers.

Thoroughly wet a sheet of paper and spread it upon a table. With a wide-mouthed pipette transfer a worm to the paper. With the safety-razor blade cut the worm into two or more parts as illustrated in Fig. 22.7. Mark the small dishes and transfer the parts of the animal to them so that each dish contains but one piece. Set these aside, taking care that they do not dry. They will need daily attention.

The process of regeneration will be slow, but it is usually a revelation to students to see how the pieces of these worms continue to live. Worms cut as *A, B, C* regenerate best. Those cut as *D* may survive, but are likely to curl up in such a manner as to make observation difficult. A hand lens or low-power microscope is desirable but not necessary for this experiment. It also is a good individual problem for a student.

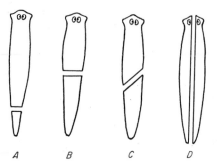

Fig. 22.7   Planaria cut for regeneration.

Earthworms. Earthworms may be had at all times of year. They can be found in cold weather in or under manure piles, under piles of straw, or they may be collected and kept as described in Chap. 12. Their regenerating power is well known.

Materials. Several earthworms in good condition; razor blade or sharp knife; several small boxes or cans half filled with loose moist (not wet) soil.

Place a worm on a board or table. Cut it in two about two-thirds of the distance from the anterior to the posterior end. Cut another worm into halves approximately. Cut a third worm about the clitellum, the place where there seems to be a smooth band around its body (see Fig. 22.8). Examine the cut ends of the worms and notice the constrictions as if a string were tied about it, which prevents it from bleeding to death. Place the anterior ends in one container of soil and the posterior ends in another and label. Set aside and examine daily for several weeks. All parts do not regenerate. The anterior ends seem best able to do this.

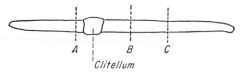

Fig. 22.8   Points of cutting an earthworm experiment in regeneration.

Additional Illustrations. It is not at all uncommon to find several starfish in a single group of specimens which have one or more arms regenerating. These should be preserved for demonstration. Among crawfish it is also common to find one which has lost a pincher or one of its walking legs and has started to replace it. Some small lizards break off their tails if seized by the tail. A new tail is regenerated. They may be kept alive during observation, or several preserved specimens showing different stages of development could be kept for demonstration.

SEXUAL REPRODUCTION IN PLANTS

Algae. Spirogyra or Zygnema. *Spirogyra* is a green alga common in most regions in April and May where there are ponds, pools, and small streams. It is ideal for demonstrating the fundamentals of sexual reproduction. If good material is obtained a single mount under the microscope will show all stages of conjugation (union of cell walls) and gamete and zygote formation. When good material is found it may be preserved and kept until needed.

Materials. Living or preserved *Spirogyra* in the sexual reproductive phase; microscope; slides and cover glasses.

With forceps or needle place a very small mass of filaments in a drop of water (preservative, if preserved material is used) and examine under the medium and high powers of the microscope. Look for filaments which have become arranged parallel with each other. Connections may be seen between two filaments, the walls of opposite cells having conjugated, forming a tubelike connection. If several such connections have been made, a ladderlike arrangement is presented. The cell contents round up, forming gametes. One gamete passes through the conjugation tube and fuses with the other, forming a zygote in the original cell. This zygote will eventually germinate and produce a new *Spirogyra* filament. Various stages of development are shown in Fig. 22.9.

Mosses. Nearly 13,000 species of mosses have been described. These are distributed in nearly all habitats except in marine waters. They are of particular interest because all of them have a definite alternation of generations. In any region there are forms which are available for class study.

Materials. Male gametophytes; female gametophytes with archegonia; female gametophytes with sporophytes attached; protonema; microscope; forceps (tweezers); two dissecting needles; microscope slide and cover glass.

The male gametophytes of *Polytrichum* (pigeon wheat moss). *Catharinea, Mnium* have a cup-shaped tip which distinguishes them from the female plants. Place one of these antheridial cups in a drop of water on a slide. Insert a dissecting needle into the cup and with a stirring motion dissect out the antheridia. These are club shaped or banana shaped. They contain the sperms. The female plants are more or less pointed at the tip. The scales overlap and cover the archegonia. The archegonia are more difficult to dissect out than the antheridia, but with a little patience it can be done. To do this, cut off a tip, tear away the scales, and finely dissect the tip in a drop of water. The fertilized egg cell develops inside the archegonium which is still attached to the female gametophyte. The mature sporophyte also remains attached to the female plant. If the sporangium is crushed in a drop of water,

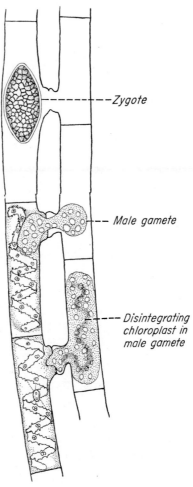

FIG. 22.9 Conjunction, gamete and zygote formation in *Spirozya.*

many spores will be found. The spores germinate, developing into a branched, filamentous green structure known as a "protonema." If the protonema is mature enough green buds will be found on it which develop into the mature gametophytes. The protonema often will form green felts on moist soil, logs, or rocks. Cultures in water may be prepared. Characteristics of various parts of the moss life cycle are shown in Fig. 22.10.

Ferns. The fern life cycle is of particular interest to botany and biology teachers because of the clear-cut case of alternation of generations which it illustrates. With a little effort upon the part of the teacher, living material may be had during any time of the year.

Materials. Fern prothallia culture (see method for preparing in Chap. 12); living fern plant such as *Polypodium*, *Aspidium* (sword or shield fern), *Polystichum* (Christmas fern), all of which are evergreen and may be obtained in fair condition even in midwinter, or they may be grown in a window box. Greenhouse ferns such as *Pteris longifolia*, *Pteris cretica*, and the holly fern (*Cyrtomium*) are ideal for growing in the laboratory. The common Boston fern and its varieties should not be selected since they are sterile in practically all varieties. If living material is not available, dried material may be substituted. A microscope, slides, cover slips, water, and a penknife will be needed.

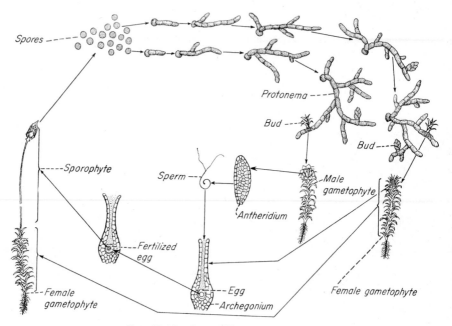

Fɪɢ. 22.10   Sexual life cycle of a moss.

Select fern leaves which show brown dots (sori) beneath or brown lines bordering the leaflet edges on the lower side. If not too old these brown areas will contain sporangia (spore cases) which contain spores (see Fig. 22.11). They will vary with the species. Scrape off a bit of the brown material, mount in water, and examine under the microscope. Various stages of spore germination may be observed by making mounts from the fern prothallia cultures. Antheridia (sperm-containing organs) may appear during early stages of the gametophyte development. Sperms escaping from the antheridia and swimming rapidly through the water will likely be discovered if carefully observed. The chances for obtaining these are increased if the prothallia (gametophyte) culture is allowed to dry slightly before mounts are made. This may be done by removing the glass cover for 10 to 20 min. When the gametophytes have acquired their heart-shape form, they are also likely to have archegonia present which contain the egg cells. These are located on the underside of a gametophyte just below the notch (sinus). The necks protrude from the thallus. Sperms swim down the canals in the archegonial necks and fertilization occurs. The fertilized egg develops into the young sporophyte which will be found developing abundantly in the older cultures. These soon can be detected without aid of the microscope. The diagrams of Fig. 22.11 illustrate the complete life cycle. This shows the striking fact that the gametophyte and sporophyte may live entirely independent of each other. Both of these are definitely fern plants; yet the sporophyte is usually regarded as "the fern plant." Most people have never seen the gametophytes, which are fern plants just as much as are the sporophytes.

Seed Plants. Seed development is not only of importance in the multiplication and distribution of plants in nature, but also in the propagation of many cultivated plants. Such reproductive structures, with their rich stores of carbohydrates, fats, and proteins, become one of man's most valuable food sources. Some understanding of the fundamentals of such development is essential in the education of any individual.

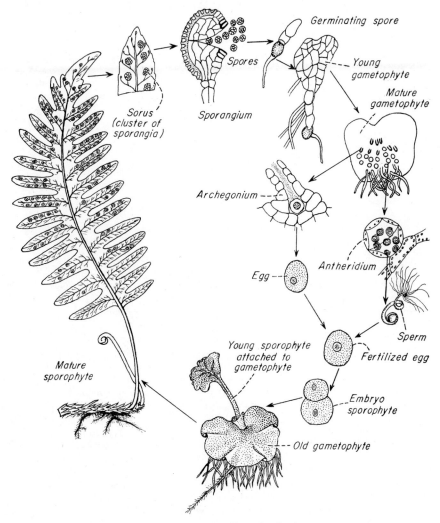

FIG. 22.11   Sexual life cycle of a fern.

Materials. A microscope; slides and cover glasses may be used, but are not absolutely necessary. Simple flowers of some sort which happen to be in season.

In winter, forsythia, Japanese quince, pear, or peach may be forced by bringing the stems into a warm room and placing the cut ends in water for 3 or 4 weeks before needed. Much better results will be obtained if the stems have been exposed to freezing temperatures before attempting to force them. The Duc Van Thal tulip, one of the earliest tulips, will force readily after a low-temperature treatment of 4 to 6 weeks. For this treatment, plant the bulbs in sand at a depth of about 6 in. and expose to winter temperatures. After this treatment they are brought into a warm room and will bloom about 1 month later. This tulip makes ideal material for such study. The breaking of dormancy and forcing development out of season may be capitalized upon by the teacher. Numerous examples for projects will be discovered in the newer horticultural books and publications. The Boyce-Thompson Institute for Botanical Research, Yonkers, N.Y., has carried out many such investigations. Lists of their publications may be obtained by writing. Flowers of lily, yucca, tulip, spring beauty, apple, cherry, pear, wake-robin (*Trillium*), black mustard, make good material when in season.

Familiarity with parts of a flower is essential in the understanding of what happens in the development of fruits and seeds. The diagram in Fig. 22.12 illustrates

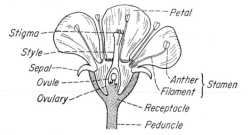

Fig. 22.12   Parts of a generalized flower showing pollen tube growing down the style.

the major structures. In the simpler types, ovularies mature into fruits. In more complex forms, one or more ovularies with parts of the calyx and receptacle may contribute to the make-up of the fruit. Ovules mature, becoming the seeds.

Crush an anther and look for the powdery pollen grains. If a microscope is available, pollen grains of several plants may be observed for their form, color, and size. In some species these pollen grains may be caused to germinate and produce pollen tubes (see Chap. 14). These may be examined with the aid of the microscope. The sperms probably will not be visible. Lily, *amaryllus,* and *petunia* pollen often will germinate by placing it on water or a 2 per cent sugar solution for 2 to 24 hr.

Sultana or touch-me-not (*Impatiens sultanii*), a common ornamental pot plant, usually remains in bloom almost continuously throughout the year. The pollen will usually germinate in a drop of distilled or tap water on a microscope slide within 5 to 10 min. When observed with the high-power objective of the microscope, the growth of the pollen tube can be watched. Within the tube, protoplasmic streaming can be seen.

Ovularies may be cut or broken open and the tiny ovules observed. A simple magnifier or the low-power objective of the microscope will aid in this observation. If living plants are available, pollination (transfer of pollen from the anthers to the stigma) may be demonstrated as carried on by insects, wind, gravity, or artificially by man. Stamens may be removed carefully from an unopened flower, the flower covered with a paper sack to prevent cross pollination, and the results noted. In such experiments the pistil usually abscises within a few days. This sometimes happens in nature. In some species the ovulary matures into a fruit without pollination and fertilization occurring. Seeds are not found in such fruits. The banana, navel orange, pineapple, and seedless grapes are examples. Such *parthenocarpic* fruits may be produced for class use by preventing cross-pollination in the common sunflower. This plant is self-sterile. An inflorescence which is about ready to open is covered with a paper sack, tied, and left for 2 or 3 weeks. When the head of the sunflower fruits (the so-called seeds) are mature they will be found hollow except for a remnant of the aborted ovule. A good sunflower fruit may be dissected to demonstrate the difference.

Seed Types. Generally, seeds may be classed into one of three groups. Such a classification emphasizes the importance of knowing the origin and what becomes of the various parts of a seed. Especially for the laboratory with limited equipment and supplies, such study is worth considering since a minimum of apparatus and material is all that is required.

Materials. Dry and soaked grains of corn, beans, and castor beans; a penknife; dissecting needle.

The corn grain is a fruit, but it is made up of structures belonging to a seed, except for the thin outer coat. A median longitudinal cut is made through the grain at right angles to the broad surface. The corn grain illustrates a seed rather typical of monocotyledonous plants, that is, a single cotyledon and an accompanying endosperm.

Any bean such as the kidney bean, those used as green snap beans, or Lima beans may be used to demonstrate a second seed type. Note the oval scar where it was attached to the ovulary wall (pod). At one end of the scar note a small, pinhole-size opening, the micropyle. Through this the pollen tube entered the young ovule. Carefully remove the leathery coat and observe the parts. This seed is typical of a group of dicotyledonous seeds which have no endosperm when mature. Food is stored chiefly in the cotyledons. Castor-bean seeds may be obtained at seed stores or from persons who grow the plants as ornamentals. Although castor oil is extracted from the seeds, certain parts contain a poison which will cause illness and even death if eaten. Note a wartlike knot (caruncle) at one end. On the more flattened surface and just under this structure is located the hilum (point of attachment to the ovulary). Note the hard, brittle seed coat (testa). Remove the seed coat. With a knife make a median shallow cut about the remaining seed part in a plane parallel with the flat surface. If properly done the body will fall apart and expose the cotyledons, plumule, and hypocotyl. This seed characterizes a dicotyledonous form which has two cotyledons and an endosperm in the mature seed.

Seed Germination. The germination of some common seeds enables the teacher to demonstrate the fate of each part of the seed. Also an opportunity is offered to review and apply a number of physiological processes which have been dealt with during the course.

Materials. Grains of corn, seeds of castor bean, and beans; box with sand, sawdust, or peat.

Plant some of the grains and seeds at intervals of 2 or 3 days. When seedlings from the first planting are 3 to 4 in. high (about 10 days old if kept moist and warm), wash the soil from all seedlings. Soak some seeds of each seed type for 24 hr. to add to the series of seedlings. Soaked and dry seeds may be compared. The swollen condition of the soaked seeds is apparent and was caused by imbibing water. Swelling of the seeds usually results in rupturing the seed coats. Stored food in the endosperm of corn and castor bean and the cotyledons of beans disappear gradually as the embryos and seedlings enlarge. This food is digested and finally is oxidized. An enzyme extract may be made from germinating corn. This extract may be used in digesting starch paste in a test tube. If a microscope is available, starch grains may be scraped from the endosperm of a germinating corn grain and compared to those from a freshly soaked seed. Mount the starch grains in water on a slide and cover with a cover glass. Examine the grains from the germinating material for corroded appearance. Those starch grains from the freshly soaked seeds are regular in outline. The corroded surfaces indicate that the grains are in the process of digestion. Moisture and temperature of about 70°F. are necessary before enzymes (digestive substances) become satisfactorily activated.

Seed Dormancy. Numerous seeds will not germinate immediately even when they have available moisture and a sufficiently high temperature. This is of considerable concern to the horticulturist and other agriculturists. Causes of dormancy may be divided into two groups—external and internal causes.

Materials. Two sheets of sandpaper; file; water; lotus (*Nelumbo*) fruits (so-called seeds); canna seeds; honey locust seeds; cocklebur fruits; sweet clover seeds (unscarified, preferably hand-picked); beans; wide-mouthed bottles or cans.

Place six beans in each of two containers filled with sand, soil, sawdust, or peat. Moisten each with an equal quantity of water. Place one in a refrigerator or out of doors in winter weather. Keep the other at room temperature. See that both remain moist. The one at low temperature does not germinate. This illustrates the effect of one external factor of the environment upon seed germination. In two other similar sets of seeds, moisten one set and keep the other dry. Keep both in a warm situation. Germination does not occur among the dry ones. The lack of moisture as an external factor of the environment often operates in nature. Seeds at the bottom of a pond or buried deep in the soil are in a situation which lacks an abundant supply of oxygen. A lack of oxygen can prevent seed germination.

To demonstrate an internal factor which may prevent seed germination for a long time, use unscarified sweet clover or red clover seeds (use hand-picked seeds rather than threshed ones), lotus fruits, canna seeds, honey locust. The coats of such seeds and fruits are impermeable to water unless broken or treated in some way. If the sweet clover or red clover seeds are used, the seeds may be scarified by gently rubbing them between two sheets of sandpaper. Plant a similar lot which has been unscarified and compare germination results with the treated ones. If the lotus, canna, or honey locust seeds are used, file a notch in the coats of some and place in water with some which were not filed. Compare germination results.

Split open several cocklebur fruits. Carefully remove the seeds. Separate those with unbroken seed coats (a papery tissue) from those with broken coats. Keep all the seeds moist. Note that both swell but only those with the broken coats germinate. It is known that these coats are impermeable to oxygen. Some cocklebur seeds do not germinate the first year in nature because the membranelike seed coats are impermeable to oxygen.

Fruit Types and Their Structure. From the botanical standpoint the term "fruit" is applied correctly to numerous structures not so considered by the layman. The flattened so-called seed of the sunflower, beggars' ticks, buckwheat grains, grains of corn, oats, bean pods, a cucumber, and a pumpkin are as much fruits as are apples or oranges. Botanically, a fruit is a ripened pistil or group of pistils with or without accessory parts (peduncle, receptacle, parts of the calyx or involucre). The classification of a group of common fruits enables students to become more familiar with what happens to various parts of a flower in fruit and seed development. Such a study has decided economic application since these structures making up fruits are often of great value as sources of food.

Materials. A collection of fresh, dried, or preserved fruits of various kinds. It will be necessary for the teacher to supply certain facts about the flower structure in some instances since flowers and fruits are not often available at the same time. Diagrams (Figs. 22.13) of fruits and their parts are given as aids to the teacher, who may also capitalize on the more complicated fruits which are partly composed of peduncle, involucral bracts, receptacle, and calyx, by pointing out the physical and chemical effects of pollination and fertilization upon other parts adjacent to the ovulary. Technically this is known as "ectogeny." The so-called seeds of the dandelion are technically fruits. Also they are of interest since the embryo develops from an unfertilized egg. This phenomenon is known as "parthenogenesis." If time is available the teacher may construct a key to fruits found locally and have the students trace a number through, determining the fruit type.

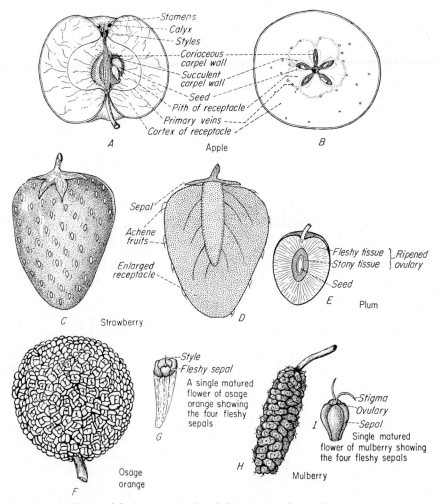

FIG. 22.13   Types of fruit, *A* to *I*: *A* and *B*, a pome; *C* and *D*, an aggregate fruit; *E*, a drupe; *F* to *I*, multiple fruits.

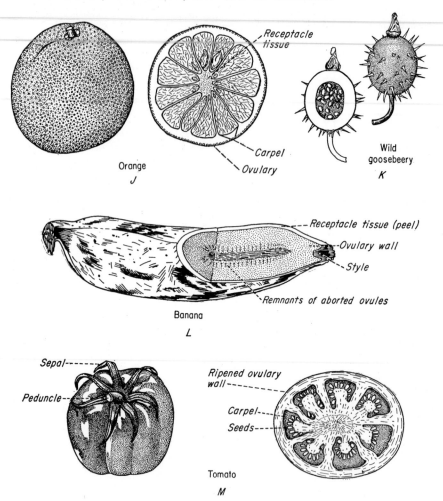

FIG. 22.13 (*cont.*)   *J* to *M,* berry fruit types.

SEXUAL REPRODUCTION IN ANIMALS

The Snail. Most biology classrooms have some sort of aquarium or tank for living plants and animals. One of the animals most commonly found in the aquarium is the snail. It usually thrives well, multiplies rapidly, and requires no attention. Seldom, however, is much use made of it in classroom demonstrations, and yet it presents one of the nicest illustrations of sexual reproduction. Water snails usually lay their eggs upon the sides of the aquarium or upon the plants where they may be found by a little careful searching.

Materials. Some water snails from a pond, brook, or creek; aquarium, or jars of water and aquatic plants; hand lens, or microscope.

Put the snails in your school aquarium. If there is no aquarium, use fruit jars with creek water, sand, and a few water plants. The water may be replaced as it evaporates by using tap water. The snails will lay eggs in small groups or chains. They have transparent jelly capsules and are not readily seen. If careful watch is maintained it will be possible to remove newly laid eggs and keep them in a small dish supplied with some of the aquarium water and a little of its vegetation. These can be examined regularly with a good hand lens or microscope, and the formation and development of the embryos may be followed. Their transparency makes the study easy and instructive. If you find it desirable to slow down the rate of development so as to be able to watch it over a longer period of time, proceed as follows. Use some small jars, pint fruit jars, or mayonnaise jars that may be plugged with cotton or covered with cloth (do not use the screw cap). Set your egg cultures in an icebox or refrigerator where the temperature will be low but not freezing. The cold environment will retard the development of the eggs so that they will develop very slowly or will develop only when they are not in cold storage. Thus the student will be able to see more stages in the embryology than he otherwise could.

The Fruit Fly. The production of gametes (eggs and sperms) is common throughout the animal kingdom and can be shown among insects as illustrations of sexual reproduction. The life history of *Drosophila*, the common fruit fly or vinegar fly (also called "sour gnat"), is one good example which can be demonstrated by students or teacher with little difficulty.

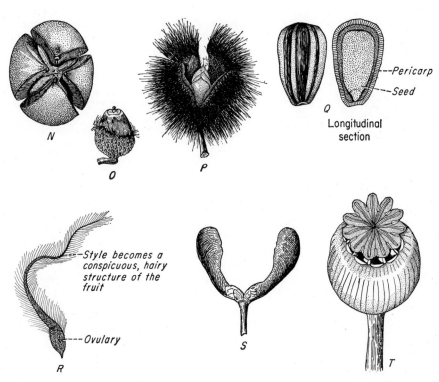

Fɪɢ. 22.13 (*cont.*)   N to P, nut types; Q and R, achenes; S, samara; T, poppy capsule.

Materials. Half-pint milk bottles are ideal but any large-mouthed jar will do; cotton for plugging the bottle mouth or cheesecloth to tie over the opening; whole banana which is not overripe and which has not had the skin broken. See page 422 for method of preparing culture medium as described by J. C. Cross.

Boil the bottles or jars in water for 20 min. to sterilize. Do the same with the cheesecloth. Wash your hands and the outside of a whole banana. Peel part of the banana, being careful not to touch the peeled portion. Use a knife of which the blade has been sterilized with hot water or a flame, and cut small pieces from the banana. Place these in the bottles and plug with a wad of clean cotton or cover the opening with a double thickness of the sterile cheesecloth. The culture jars or bottles are now ready for use. At any fruit store, market, or grocery, you can get the flies in warm weather by setting one such culture jar near the fruit stands or baskets and leaving it open. The small flies will enter and can be trapped. A few (6 to 10) may be removed and placed in another bottle by the method shown in Fig. 22.14. These flies will lay eggs on the banana, and in 1 to 4 days careful examination will show very small maggots in the banana. A few days later these maggots will crawl up the sides of the bottles and pupate. The pupae appear as very small yellowish-brown seed-shaped bodies. Within another week there will appear rather suddenly a very large number of adult flies in the culture jars, because of emergence from the pupae. The whole life cycle is completed in 12 to 16 days at temperatures around 75°F. The culture bottles are small and easily handled and will sometimes run several generations without changing if a little more banana is added at times. The flies do quite as well in winter as in summer if kept in a warm room. All the stages from tiny white eggs to adult may be seen.

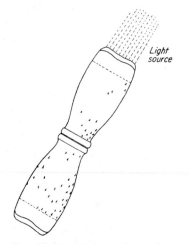

Light source

FIG. 22.14 Method of transferring flies from one culture jar to another.

The Wax Moth. Another insect that can be reared easily at any time of year and will need little care is the wax moth. Its stages are larger and easier to see than the fruit fly, and its cycle is short. The only problem is getting a start for stock, and this can be accomplished by inquiring of beekeepers.

Materials. Beeswax (not purified) or, better, some old honeycomb from which the honey has been lost or extracted; a few 2-qt. jars or small cages; some wax moths (any stage); cloth to cover the mouth of the jar.

Place some of the wax or comb in a jar or cage, add a number of adults, or larvae, close with a cloth tied over the jar, and your culture is ready. In a short time the adults will begin laying eggs on the wax or jar. These are round shotlike structures readily visible. The eggs will hatch into caterpillars (larvae) which feed upon the wax and its contents. When full grown the larvae spin small cocoons on the sides of the jar and pupate. The adults emerge from the cocoons and lay eggs. Then the cycle is repeated. The addition of a little more wax may be necessary in time. The cultures need no other care. The spinning of the cocoons and the emergence can be watched, and the stages are large enough to be seen easily. This is an excellent form and one of the easiest to rear.

The Meal Worm Beetle. A beetle life history is as instructive as that of any insect for an illustration of sexual reproduction. The common meal worm

(*Tenebrio*) is well known, easy to rear, and may be kept throughout the year. It has complete metamorphosis and is of sufficiently large size to be useful.

Materials. Two or three large (½ to 2-gal.) jars, cans, or boxes; about 2 lb. of bran (corn meal or oatmeal will do); cheesecloth or muslin to cover the open end of the jar or can; small stock of meal worm beetles.

Place enough bran in one of the containers to fill it about one-fourth full. If the original stock of beetles is all of one stage, for example, the adult stage, place them in the bran and cover with the cloth. The adults will lay eggs in the bran, and these will hatch into the larvae or "meal worm" stage. When these begin to appear in the bran in numbers, it is well to pick out the adults and place them in the second jar to start another culture. Allow the meal worms to continue their growth and watch for pupae to appear in the bran. The pupae should also be removed if the larvae are numerous since the growing larvae feed upon the bran and may also chew the pupae and any eggs not yet hatched. If the adults are placed in another culture, their newly laid eggs will go unharmed. The pupae will yield more adults and they may be placed in an entirely new culture. The plan is merely to keep the feeding larvae away from the helpless egg and pupal stages. Have some of the students hunt out a number of eggs from the bran or meal. This is not easy but not too difficult. A good hand lens or reading glass will help considerably. Small amounts of material should be examined at a time. These eggs can be used as a demonstration for the class and if placed in a small dish with a very small amount of fine meal or bran dust, their hatching may be observed. The rest of the development may be followed either by the class or by a group assigned to it.

The Cheese Skipper. One of the simplest insects to rear in a classroom or laboratory and one that is both fascinating and instructive is the cheese skipper fly. Its metamorphosis is complete, all stages being easy to see and obtain from cultures. The life cycle is short, about 15 to 20 days, and the amount of care needed is negligible.

Materials. Several quart or ½-gal. jars; cheesecloth to close them; a piece of cheese or cured ham; a small stock of any stage of the fly. A small cage is more convenient than jars but not necessary.

Place the cheese or meat in a jar with the adults and close with cheesecloth. The adults will feed upon the meat and lay eggs upon it. The eggs are large enough to be seen if you look closely. They are oval whitish objects. It is advisable to use several smaller slices of cheese or meat so that some of it can be removed easily to search for eggs. The eggs will hatch in 24 to 48 hr. and the maggots (skippers) feed upon the meat or cheese until full grown, after which they pupate. The pupae are dark brown and elongated, 3 to 5 mm. Adults will emerge after about 5 days at 75°F. The whole reproductive process can be watched and the stages of the life history kept by preserving.

Amphibia. Frog, Toad, and Salamander. In early spring there appears in most of our ponds, streams, and lakes another interesting illustration of reproduction. The amphibia lay their eggs early, varying with the season and latitude. They appear on the surface or submerged in shallow water as masses of jelly-coated beads attached to grass or reeds. They usually are fertilized at the time of laying. They will develop indoors. Their development may be studied and stages preserved for use at other times.

Materials. Collecting apparatus consisting of dipper and bucket, aquarium or large jars or tank; water plants; eggs of an amphibian and the adults.

When the eggs have been located dip up some of the water into your collecting bucket, add a few plants if they are abundant, and then with your dipper lift the eggs, together with some of the water. Transfer them to the bucket carefully and lower the dipper into the bucket until the egg mass floats free from the dipper. Then remove the dipper without disturbing the eggs. Do not transfer by pouring them into the bucket (see Fig. 22.15).

If the eggs were laid recently they will not have developed far. They may be placed in the aquarium or other container. Use about 3 gal. of water (or more) for an egg mass the size of a large hen's egg. If slowly running water can be provided, the chances for success are greater. Do not bring eggs from a cold pond or brook and dash them suddenly into warm aquarium water. Let the collecting pail stand until the temperature of the water is that of the schoolroom before changing the eggs to the tank. Examine some of the eggs immediately with a lens. If development has begun, the eggs will have changed to embryos of several cells (see Fig. 22.16). The development is rapid at higher temperatures but may be slowed down by placing the eggs out of doors if the weather is cool or by keeping them in a refrigerator. Preserve some of each stage in vials of formalin or in alcohol. Whether the eggs are from frogs, toads, or salamanders will be evident at hatching if you do not know before. Such material is excellent since it offers a chance to see development by cell division on a large scale.

FIG. 22.15   Floating an amphibian egg mass out of a dipper into a bucket to avoid the churning effect of pouring.

Fish. Paradise Fish. Several kinds of fish reproduce in aquaria. The paradise fish which makes a bubble nest is very interesting if the temperature of the aquarium can be controlled at 80 to 85°F. The embryological development may be watched since both the eggs and embryos are so transparent that such things as heart beat and circulation are easily seen.

FIG. 22.16   Early cleavage stages in the development of a frog.

Guppies. Guppies are reared easily and make a good example of viviparous reproduction. In spring the eggs of wild fish may be obtained from ponds, lakes, and garden fish pools. They should be collected and handled exactly as are frog eggs.

Birds. A Simple Incubator Box. The biology teacher who has not used living bird embryos in the teaching of reproduction has missed one of the greatest opportunities of creating interest and enthusiasm in his class. Perhaps the use of incubated eggs has occurred to the teacher but has been omitted because of the lack of an incubator. The following substitute for a commercial incubator can be relied upon and is highly recommended.

Materials. A common store box of wood about 1 ft. square by 20 to 25 in. long, two boards or panes of glass to cover box, an electric light, thermometer, two pans or a pan and a tray. If the walls of the box are thin or cracked the box should be lined with corrugated paper or with heavy wallboard. Install the electric light in one end of the box. This is to serve as a heating unit. Place both pans in the box, one under the light. Fill this pan with water. The other pan is for the eggs.

Set the box as shown in Fig. 22.17. If the incubator is placed in a room where the temperature is even and not likely to change, as in a basement room or closet, it will be much easier to regulate. The panes of glass, or boards, covering the top should be pushed close together and the thermometer hung between so that its bulb is near the egg pan. Turn on the light and keep a record of the temperature for

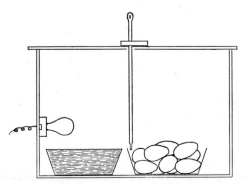

FIG. 22.17   A simple homemade incubator for obtaining the early stages of the chick embryo.

several hours. If it rises above 103°F. it may be corrected by opening the crack in the top a little wider. If the temperature is very high use a weaker light bulb; if it fails to rise to 103°F. use a stronger bulb. It may take 2 days or more to regulate the incubator. Be sure not to place the eggs in it until it reaches a constant temperature. Keep the water pan filled. It serves as a humidifier and, more important, it helps regulate the temperature. Turn the eggs by rotating each egg 180° once or twice a day. Mark each egg with an X on one side so as to be able to tell when it has been turned. Such an incubator will successfully incubate embryos during the first 5 or 6 days when they are of most interest for class use. Complete hatching has been accomplished by careful watching. If the temperature drops 2 or 3° for a short time it is not likely to be serious.

The Embryo. The teacher will find the use of the living chick embryos a most exciting class project. The students will gladly furnish the materials and do the work of assembling the incubator. Be sure to get fertile eggs. Usually they cannot be had at grocery stores.

Remove an egg from the incubator after 4 days and place it upon a warm cloth pad. With a pair of fine-pointed scissors puncture the shell and then cut a hole on top as shown in Fig. 22.18. Examine the embryo with a good hand lens or low-

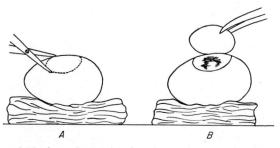

FIG. 22.18   A method of opening an incubated egg to expose the embryo: *A*, inserting scissors; *B*, removing shell and membrane.

power microscope. A good light should be directed upon the embryo. Its heart may be seen beating, and with a microscope the circulation in the yolk vessels can be seen. The formation of the head structures are readily visible at this time, and a beginning of the wings and legs can be made out. A clearer view may be had, especially when a microscope is used, if the egg contents are emptied into a small glass dish and the embryo carefully lifted away from the yolk and placed upon a glass slide or in a petri dish.

Mammals. Mouse, Rat, Guinea Pig, Rabbit, or Pig. The fundamental steps in sexual reproduction have been explained and demonstrated for lower forms in both plants and animals in the earlier parts of this chapter. It will, however, fall short of completeness unless the mammals are included. After all, we ourselves are mammals and we are most interested in our own type of reproduction. If the subject is treated frankly but seriously, students never fail to show keen interest, enthusiasm, and a surprising lack of prudishness.

Materials. Male and female mammal of some small species such as the white rat, guinea pig, or rabbit; dissecting scissors; small jars of formalin.

Inquiry among your students, especially outside of class, will very likely disclose the fact that one of them has a colony of pet mice, rats, guinea pigs, or rabbits. If not, they are almost certain to have a friend or relative who has. Explain your need of having a pregnant female for class use. It may be found necessary to pay something for the specimen, but this amount will be small. They also may be purchased from supply houses or from colleges and universities or commercial laboratories. By all means get it from a source within your class if possible.

Open the pregnant female ventrally to expose the uterus. (This, together with the killing, might be assigned to two dependable and interested boys.) While fresh, display the uterus and its blood vessels to the class. Slit the uterus and expose one of the embryos, being careful not to rupture its membranes. These may be removed later and the embryo exposed. Make clear such facts as the umbilical cord and its connection with the wall of the uterus. Compare this with the vessels seen in a chick embryo. Point out the ovary and oviduct.

A local slaughterhouse, or packing company, can, and usually will, supply a quantity of embryos often with membranes unbroken of such food animals as pigs. This makes excellent material for class study. Visit the packing house personally and explain your needs. Do not send a student or write a note. If time and material are available, the male animal may be dissected to expose a testis and its connection with the urethra. Slit open the skin and squeeze out a testis. Enlarge the slit and continue to dissect, following the tube leading from the testis into the body. Split this tube a short distance from the testis (usually an enlarged portion) and press out its contents. This contains sperms in a mature male. If an adult rat or mouse is used the contents may be smeared thinly on a warm slide and examined under the high power of the microscope. Fertilization or the union of sperm and egg can be recalled and reviewed. Lessons on reproduction will require more careful planning than most topics.

Man. The study of reproduction of organisms in schools should always include a study of human reproduction. There are problems confronting the teacher which are of two kinds. The first of these has to do with the teacher. There is sometimes a lack of proper training and understanding on his part and sometimes a reticence toward approaching the subject openly. The second problem lies in the possibility of objection from prudish school authorities or a misunderstanding public. The teacher can overcome his personal difficulties by acquiring the necessary knowledge and by a little practice in presentation. The attitude of the school authorities and the public may offer insurmountable obstacles especially to the young teacher of little experience. In any event it is always best first to go over the situation with the proper school authorities and let them know the content of the subject matter you intend to present.

When the study of human reproduction is preceded by the study of reproduction in plants and lower animals, the students and teacher will have used and accepted a set of terminology which can be used without further definition, and this makes it easy to continue into reproduction in man by showing the similarities to plants and lower animals. This procedure also removes the feelings of prudery which may have been acquired by some students and permits a normal healthy approach to the subject. Always speak openly and unhesitatingly yourself, and this will soon break down the shell of secrecy which may exist. Treat the subject as calmly and frankly as you have treated their study of digestion, respiration, or any other topic, and the students will be glad to respond accordingly. If there is anything really sinful about a knowledge or mention of sex it is this barrier of prudishness which tends to place sex outside the realm of a natural physiological function and to keep it secretive and unclean. The time when this is most successfully taught is in the first stages of puberty while the child is thoroughly aroused in his curiosity about sex and before he has acquired a degree of sophistication concerning his supposed knowledge of the subject.

Reproduction in man can be illustrated by first going over the matters of germ cells, fertilization, and embryonic origin, the formation of the embryonic membranes, and the placental attachments as found in other mammals. The use of a pregnant rat, guinea pig, or rabbit will be found to furnish powerful motivation and an excellent impersonal means of illustration. It is an easy matter to say that the same structures and relationships exist in man. Such books as Arey (Ref. 13) furnish a source of diagrams of sex structures if these are considered necessary or useful. An understanding of reproduction does not necessarily require a discussion of the social implications of sex. There is a vast amount of literature upon this subject, and the following bibliography will give plenty of reading for the teacher who finds an opportunity for adding a discussion of the so-called social hygiene to the study of human reproduction. If this matter of sex is made a part of the subject, it is best to avoid the all too frequent morbid moral and religious elements to which it is so often attached. Many lecturers upon the subject produce a dreadful fear and depressed outlook upon the immature minds of their audiences by overemphasizing the degradation and pathological consequences of excesses, without giving the pleasant, normal, healthy reaction that should be the goal toward which they direct their efforts.

REFERENCES

General

1. Allen, Edgar: *Sex and Internal Secretions,* The Williams & Wilkins Company, Baltimore, 1932. Animal experiments and their application to man. Excellent illustrations of cellular structures.

2. Blaydes, Glenn W.: "The Romance of Domesticated Plants," *Ohio J. Sci.,* **53**:193–215, 1953. Also reprinted in *Smithsonian Report for 1954,* pp. 317–336, 1955. Deals with the origin of domesticated plants, genetic variation in seeds, vegetative multiplication, hybridization and somatic mutations with 41 photographic illustrations (2 in color).

3. Blaydes, Glenn W., and L. V. Domm: "The Effectiveness of Our Schools in the Teaching of Biological Sciences," *Sci. Teacher,* **15**:57–58, April, 1948.

4. Fuller, Harry J., and Oswald Tippo: *College Botany,* Holt, Rinehart and Winston, Inc., New York, 1955.

5. Robbins, W. W., T. E. Weier, and C. R. Stocking: *Botany, An Introduction to Plant Science,* 2d ed., John Wiley & Sons, Inc., New York, 1957.

6. Rugh, R.: "Ovulation Induced Out of Season," *Science,* **85** (22):588–589, June 18, 1937.

7. Sinnott, E. W., and K. S. Wilson: *Botany: Principles and Problems,* 5th ed., McGraw-Hill Book Company, Inc., New York, 1955.

8. Smith, G. M.: *Fresh-Water Algae of the United States,* 2d ed., McGraw-Hill Book Company, Inc., New York, 1950.

9. Tiffany, L. H.: *Algae, the Grass of Many Waters,* Charles C Thomas Publisher, Springfield, Ill., 1958.

10. Transeau, E. N., H. C. Sampson, and L. H. Tiffany: *Textbook of Botany,* rev. ed., Harper & Brothers, New York, 1953.

11. Weatherwax, Paul: *Botany,* 3d ed., W. B. Saunders Company, Philadelphia, 1956. The discussion on reproduction in all plant groups is recommended particularly for the beginning student.

12. Wilson, Carl L., and Walter E. Loomis: *Botany,* 2d ed., The Dryden Press, Inc. (combined with Holt, Rinehart and Winston, Inc.), New York, 1957.

Sex Education

13. Arey, L. B.: *Developmental Anatomy,* W. B. Saunders Company, Philadelphia, 1954.

14. Berrill, N. J.: *Sex and the Nature of Things,* Dodd, Mead & Company, New York, 1953.

15. Clemensen, J. W., et al.: *Life Goes On,* Harcourt, Brace & Company, New York, 1942.

16. Dickerson, R. E.: *So Youth May Know,* rev. ed., Association Press, New York, 1948.

17. Duvall, E. M.: *Facts of Life and Love,* Association Press, New York, 1950.

18. Ellis, H.: *On Life and Love,* New American Library of World Literature, Inc., New York, 1960.

19. Ellis, H.: *Psychology of Sex,* Emerson Books, Inc., New York, 1944.

20. Faegre, M. L.: *Understanding Ourselves,* University of Minnesota Press, Minneapolis, 1944. Illustrated.

21. Funk, M. S., and Beatty, W. W.: "Relating Sex to Life," *Jr.-Sr. High School Clearing House,* **8**:235–238, 1933.

22. Langdon-Davies, J.: *Seeds of Life,* The Devin-Adair Company, New York, 1955.

23. Lerrigo, M. O., and H. Southard: *Sex Facts and Attitudes,* E. P. Dutton & Co., Inc., New York, 1956. Illustrated.

24. McHose, E.: *Family Life Education in School and Community,* Bureau of Publications, Teachers College, New York, 1952.

25. Mozes, E. B.: *Sex Facts and Fiction for Teen-agers,* Ottenheimer, Publishers, Baltimore.

26. National Education Association, Health, Physical Education and Recreation Department: *Sex, Education Series.* Washington 6, D.C., 1955.

27. O'Brien, J. A.: *Sex Character Education,* The Macmillan Company, New York, 1960.

28. Strain, F. B.: *New Patterns in Sex Teaching,* rev. ed., Appleton-Century-Crofts, Inc., New York, 1951. Illustrated.

29. Strain, F. B.: *Being Born,* rev. ed., Appleton-Century-Crofts, Inc., New York, 1954. Illustrated.

30. Tucker, T. F., and M. Pout: *Answers to Sex Questions of Childhood,* Emerson Books, Inc., New York.

31. Weininger, O.: *Sex and Character,* rev. ed., G. P. Putnam's Sons, New York, 1955.

CHAPTER 23

⚬⚬⚭ Heredity ⚭⚬⚬

Genetics is the newest and in some respects the most accurate of the biological sciences. It has had a phenomenal growth during the past half century and is continuing to grow rapidly. The subject is of widespread importance because of its application to human beings as well as to domesticated animals and plants. Human heredity is of importance and interest to every individual. It is the basis for the improvement of human society in spite of the opposition of sociological theory and religious preachment. Whether any social order will ever be so bold as to attempt to control its own heredity remains to be seen, but genetics and environment have operated together to produce what now exists and to eliminate what has become extinct. As civilization becomes more complex, there is a greater demand for improved plant and animal products as well as increased quantities. By application of the fundamental principles of heredity, a solution of these problems is approached.

There is very definite need for the study of heredity on the more elementary levels since many high school students never enter a college or university. One of the difficulties involved in giving it on this elementary level is the highly technical and symbolic methods which the geneticist employs. Since there is every reason, however, for having more of the general public appreciate the importance of heredity, it seems fitting that some methods be devised for more readily translating its principles into terms that are understandable to those of less mature standing. With this in mind the following suggestions are made to aid teachers in their endeavors to handle the subject in the secondary schools. The use of the problem method of introducing the subject is strongly urged, allowing terminology and technics to appear incidentally wherever needed. Every biology teacher should read "Heredity for High School" by Robert C. McCafferty, published in *School Science and Mathematics,* May, 1952.

PROBLEMS WITH LIVING PLANT MATERIALS

Albinism in Corn (Maize) and Kaffir Corn (Sorghum). *Materials.* About 100 grains of either or each of the maize or kaffir corn, carrying the factor for albinism; two ordinary flats or wooden boxes as used by florists or gardeners; sand or soil to fill each.

The study of heredity may be introduced by the presentation of a problem in the form of living plants showing an approximation of a simple 3:1 ratio. By means of these plants, variation and phenomenon of dominance and recessiveness of

417

certain characters, as well as the segregation of pure lines, are demonstrated. Albino strains of corn (maize) and kaffir corn are almost ideal for this purpose since the seedling stage is used. The material may be assigned as a project for a small group of students or may be prepared by the teacher. Plant about 100 grains of either the maize or kaffir corn in moist soil or sand in a box. Within 8 to 12 days seedlings will develop sufficiently to show green and albino plants (see Fig. 23.1). The two kinds may be counted and the numbers compared. The ratio of green to albino is approximately 3:1. Usually this exact ratio is not obtained, but is approached. The per cent deviation from the exact ratio is less when large numbers of individuals are used than when small numbers are used. It should be emphasized that 75:25 (3:1) is not commonly obtained for 100 seedlings. The numbers are more likely to be somewhat like the following: 65:35, 68:32, 73:27, etc.

FIG. 23.1   A living demonstration of Mendel's law of hybrid segregation, from a self-pollinated hybrid corn plant possessing the recessive trait of albinism.

If students study the corn grains before planting, they learn that there is no essential observable difference in the dry grains, but when the seedlings develop, a decided color difference is apparent. When asked to give a cause for this, the question of environment is likely to arise. This can be settled immediately by calling attention to the fact that all the grains developed under identical environmental conditions. It is apparent that the difference in color must be due to some internal genetic factor. This establishes the fact that there is such a thing as heredity which is independent of the environment. Students may be asked to count the albino plants and compare with the number of green plants. A 3:1 ratio is likely to be discovered. If they are available observe plots of kaffir corn showing albinism, jimson weeds showing green and purple hypocotyls, and a mouse litter showing the offspring from parents that are hybrid for black and albinism. From these observations students conclude that the mathematical ratio is a genetic principle. All the foregoing necessitates an explanation based upon knowledge of the germ cells and behavior of the chromosomes according to some such method as illustrated by Figs. 23.5 and 23.6.

Of the green plants 33⅓ per cent develop as pure line green (albino character is absent), and 66⅔ per cent are green hybrids (albino potentiality is present, but is hidden by the dominant green). Since albinism in maize and kaffir corn is lethal (dies off before maturity) as soon as the reserve food supply in the seed has been exhausted, it is impossible to obtain a pure line of plants lacking chlorophyll in the mature state. One, then, has to depend upon hybrids for seed in each generation in which albinism occurs. It is from the above-mentioned 66⅔ per cent group that the original seeds for the experiment must be obtained, and of course, self-pollinated plants must be used to get the 3 : 1 ratio.

For schools under the Smith-Hughes system and others of rural communities, proper seed may be produced as a project by some interested student. To do this, plant grains from an experimental lot of albino maize in good garden soil and cultivate as for ordinary corn. The albino plants die within 2 or 3 weeks. When tassels and ears on the green plants begin to appear, cover and tie a paper sack (grocery-store type) over the tassel and ears before stamens and silks appear. When the pollen is shedding in the sacks over tassels, vigorously shake each sack-covered tassel to release as much pollen as possible. Remove a sack with pollen and dust it over the silks of an ear or ears of the same plant which have been covered. Replace sacks over the ears to prevent entrance of foreign pollen, leaving them for about 10 days or longer. Be sure to tag each self-pollinated plant so that it may be recognized at harvest time. After the corn is dry, and before using experimentally, a few grains from each ear must be given a germinating test. This is to eliminate the pure line green which is of no value for demonstration purposes. Save only those ears of which some grains produce albino seedlings. As for the albino kaffir corn, the principles of preparing new seed are the same as for the maize, except that the process is somewhat simpler. The flowers are bisporangiate, so it is only necessary to sack the spike of unopened flowers as it is breaking from its sheath. Wind will shake pollen over the stigmas. After the flowers are past their pollinating period the sacks should be removed to prevent molding. Be certain to have each self-pollinated plant marked. As the grains are maturing it may be necessary to cover each spike with muslin to prevent loss due to birds. Each mature head or spike must be given a germination test as for the maize.

The following plant species and varieties are desirable for preparing living demonstrations of Mendel's laws of inheritance, as previously mentioned: Selfed hybrid albino corn grains; Selfed hybrid albino sorghum (kaffir corn) grains; Selfed hybrid sorghum (Feterita-white grain), which segregates seedlings with red and green stems in a 3 : 1 ratio; Selfed hybrid Datura (Jimson weed) seeds, which in the seedling stage segregates purple and green hypocotyls and stems in a 3 : 1 ratio. A dihybrid ratio of 9 : 3 : 3 : 1 may be demonstrated from these same *Datura* seedlings, if they are permitted to mature—purple and green stems, armed (spiny) and unarmed (smooth) capsules (fruits). These items are available from the Ohio Biological Supply Company, 214 Westwood Road, Columbus 14, Ohio.

Heredity and Environment. Which is the more important, environment or heredity? is a question often asked by students. If it does not come from them, the instructor should present it. This problem may be effectively demonstrated by use of the hybrid albino corn.

In each of two flower pots, filled with soil or sand, plant about 25 grains of Selfed hybrid albino corn grains. Keep the soil moist and in a temperature of about 70°F. Place one pot where it will be exposed to bright light during the day, and keep the other in complete darkness. Within about 10 days, the corn grains will have germinated and the seedlings should be 2 to 3 in. in height. The pot of seedlings which grew in complete darkness will be free of chlorophyll and appear to be albinos. In the pot of seedlings which were exposed to light, about three-fourths will be green and one-fourth albino. Since all the grains planted in the two pots were of the same source, theoretically three-fourths of the seedlings which grew in darkness should have genes with the potentiality of chlorophyll synthesis, and only one-fourth should be pure for albinism and not capable of manufacturing green pigment. If time permits, these points may be tested by exposing the pot of chlorophyll-free seedlings to light. With light exposure for 2 to 3 days, about three-fourths of the seedlings will become green and one-fourth will remain as albinos, duplicating results for the pot of seedlings exposed to light at the beginning of the experiment.

The obvious inference is that the pure albinos do not have the genes (heredity) which would enable them to manufacture chlorophyll regardless of light—the environmental factor in this instance. However, the green seedlings did possess the proper genes to synthesize chlorophyll when exposed to the proper environment (light).

From this demonstration it will be obvious that the question, Which is more important, environment or heredity? cannot be answered. However, it does demonstrate the importance of both heredity and environment, since a given hereditary potentiality cannot become expressed unless exposed to the proper environment. This is of importance in both biological and sociological relationships.

PROBLEMS WITH LIVING ANIMALS

While problem crosses suitable for introducing the student to a study of heredity may be drawn from either plant or animal materials, the number of simple crosses that are available for class use is not great. A few examples from animals which may be handled without too much work and which will not involve too long a period of preparation are given here.

Mice. One of the simplest problem crosses that can be made for class use would be with the pure lines of black mice and albino mice which are pure for the factor for black color (homozygous).

Materials. Two or more pairs of tested mice with the formulas of $CCBB$ and $ccBB$ (such tested mice may be obtained from General Biological Supply House, 8200 South Hoyne Ave., Chicago, Ill.); cages to keep the pairs separate; feed.

To Show Dominance. Mate the mice in such a manner that a white mouse and a black mouse always constitute the members of a pair. This cross is $CCBB$ (black) × $ccBB$ (albino). All the offspring from such a cross must of necessity be $CcBB$, which is hybrid black.

To Show Segregation (the 3:1 ratio). By inbreeding the males and females of this F_1 generation the F_2 generation will produce both black and albino mice. If the number of offspring in the F_2 generation is sufficiently large, the ratio will be approximately 3 black to 1 albino. If these crosses are presented to the class in problem form, they may furnish the basis for establishing many of the concepts and principles of heredity essential to an understanding of the subject just as has been suggested above for the green and albino corn.

To Show How a Pure Line Is Selected. By mating any pair of the albinos from the F_2 generation, a pure line of albino mice is established at once. To select a pure black line would take longer than would be useful for classwork but could be undertaken by one or more students as a special project. This selection can be done only by repeated matings of a back-cross type. It should be discussed fully in class even if not actually undertaken. These methods of selecting pure lines are a valuable concept for the student since they represent some of the methods used in producing breeds of domestic stock. Other interesting crosses of mice may be made by introducing the chocolate (dark brown) *CCbb* or *Ccbb*. In all these formulas *C* equals the ability to express color and *c* the lack of that ability. Thus, if two chocolate mice with the composition *Ccbb* are crossed, their offspring may be albino or chocolate.

Poultry. There are some simple crosses among domestic fowls that might be obtained as easily as any other material if a poultry breeder is near who would be willing to furnish the original cross so that eggs of a known mating could be obtained.

Materials. A setting of 50 or more fertile eggs that were obtained by crossing white leghorn with any colored breed of chicken such as black or the Rhode Island Red; an incubator.

The white of the leghorn is dominant over colored plumage. The result is that all the offspring are white in the F_1. This in itself illustrates dominance and recessiveness. If, however, such a cross has already been made previously and eggs from such hybrids are available, then the F_2 generation can be hatched and white and colored may be obtained in the proportion of 3 white to 1 colored. Other crosses may be obtained, depending upon the kinds of poultry bred in the locality. A good breeder can suggest possible different crosses that might be used. White leghorn is such a common breed that it has been chosen here as an example. In any cross between different breeds it is absolutely necessary that the hens have not mated with another cock during the preceding 3 weeks.

Drosophila (common fruit fly or vinegar gnat). Because these tiny insects have a complete life cycle in about 2 weeks, are easily handled, and have very distinct dominant and recessive traits, they make desirable subjects for a schoolroom problem. Special mutant types such as the vestigial winged flies suggested here may be obtained from some of the genetics departments of the larger universities and from the General Biological Supply House, Chicago, Ill. Sometimes prepared crosses of two types may be purchased already made up.

Materials. Cultures of wild type drosophila and a culture of vestigial-wing-type drosophila (or a culture of hybrid drosophila made by crossing the wild type with the vestigial-wing type); several small jars about the size of ½-pt. milk bottles; banana; cotton to plug jars; knife; oven or double boiler for sterilizing culture jars; baker's yeast culture.

The one enemy of successful cultures is mold. Hence it is necessary to sterilize the jars and plugs and keep them that way until the jar has developed a good stock of flies, after which it will take care of itself. Sterilizing is not difficult. A steam-pressure boiler is good but not a necessity. A small oven or a double boiler is sufficient. Make some balls of cotton large enough to fit snugly into the mouths of the culture jars. Plug the jars and heat slowly in the oven for ½ hr. or longer, starting with the jars in the cold oven. Or place the jars in a double boiler and bring the secondary water up to as near boiling as possible. Continue heating for another 20 min. Sterilize the knife at the same time. Remove and cool slowly. Do not remove the plugs from the jars until ready to add the food. Select a ripe banana that has no breaks in the skin. Peel it carefully so as not to allow the fruit to touch anything. Cut about 2 in. in small pieces from the peeled part and drop them into a culture jar. These pieces should be crushed into a pulp in the bottom of the jar using the sterile knife or a flamed glass or metal rod. Drop a few (two or three) drops of yeast culture on the banana and replace the plug. The plug must not be laid on a dirty table while the jar is being prepared or it will carry mold into the culture. The jar is now ready to be stocked.

Another method of preparing the culture medium for drosophila is described as follows by J. C. Cross: [1] "In a pyrex beaker 750 cc. of water and 75 cc. of white Karo syrup are mixed. To this is added 20 grams of shredded agar. The mixture is boiled until the agar is liquefied. In a separate container two medium-sized bananas are crushed and 25 to 30 cc. of 95 per cent alcohol is added. The bananas and alcohol are well stirred and allowed to stand about 20 min. and are then added to the water-syrup-agar mixture after this mixture has quit boiling and has cooled to about 90°C. The food amounts to about one liter in volume and is ready for bottling immediately. It is best to autoclave the bottles and cotton plugs, but this is not absolutely necessary. Since alcohol has been added already it is not necessary to spray the food with yeast as is done in some laboratories, and since no yeast is present carbon dioxide is not formed. The food adheres well to the bottom of the bottle and the flies do not stick to it easily. It has been kept in this laboratory almost two weeks without being covered with mold; however, when the bottles are not autoclaved contamination may appear within four or five days."

To Show Dominance. Remove about 10 flies from a jar of wild-type drosophila (see Fig. 22.14 for method). Anesthetize these and examine them with a hand lens or microscope and select several male flies. They may be distinguished from females

Sex comb

FIG. 23.2   Sex comb of male drosophila.

by the clump or patch of dark bristles on the first (prothoracic) legs (see Fig. 23.2). Place these males in a tiny cone twisted from clean paper and drop the cone and flies into the culture jar. To etherize flies pour a few drops of ether on a piece of cotton and press it over the mouth of the culture bottle. As soon as the flies drop to the bottom and do not move, remove the cotton and dump the flies on a piece of paper or in a dish for examination. If the ether is applied too long, the wings extend above the fly's back and this is an almost sure sign of death. Repeat this procedure using a culture of vestigial-wing drosophila, selecting several females instead of males. Be certain to use a new culture so as to get the flies within a few hours after they emerge from the pupae. The females must be virgin or the experiment is useless. Keep this new stock jar in a place where it will not be disturbed for a week. By this time the pairs will have bred and there may be numerous tiny maggots in the bananas. The best temperature is about 23°C. In another week the maggots will have pupated and emerged; therefore it is important that all the pairs of parent flies be removed from this new culture jar by the time that pupae are first found on the sides of the jar. This new emergence represents the F_1 generation which is all hybrid for the long- and the vestigial-wing character. Since the normal, or long wing, is dominant, all the F_1 generation have long wings. This is contrasted with the yellowish-gray bodies of the wild. The wild type is again dominant so all the F_1 flies have yellowish-gray bodies. This gives two chances for dominance and recessiveness to be illustrated in a single cross. With this hybrid culture the teacher is ready to introduce her class to heredity.

To Show Segregation (or the 3:1 ratio). From the hybrid culture just mentioned above withdraw about 10 adult flies. This must be done while the culture is quite young, that is, during the first week, or before they have had time to produce a second generation. Transfer the 10 flies to a new culture jar, and when larvae or pupae appear on the jar remove the parent flies, allowing the new generation to reach the adult stage. When adults have appeared in rather large numbers, remove most of them from the jar and anesthetize or kill them. Be sure to shake those from the jar which seem more sluggish than the rest since they are vestigial winged and cannot move about so readily as the long-winged ones. The students may count

[1] *Science,* vol. 89, no. 2298.

the number of flies having long wings and compare the number having vestigial wings. The ratio will be close to 3 long to 1 vestigial. For example, the count may run 152 with long wings to 48 with vestigial wings. If the students are given an opportunity to examine the hybrid parents and later count the F_2 generation and find that every fourth fly has crumpled short wings, there is a distinct problem presented as to what causes this new type. It should be handled in the same manner as the albinism in corn discussed above, where the students offer hypotheses that are later checked and discussed. These furnish the basis of further study.

To Show How a Pure Line Is Selected. In the discussions aroused in the preceding problem there should be developed the ideas of pure lines, hybrids, dominance, and recessiveness. Have one or more interested students select male and female flies with the vestigial wings from the above culture and make a new cross in a fresh jar. If allowed to run for several generations it will be seen that all the offspring are vestigial winged. This is a simple way of selecting a pure line from a mixed culture, and the student can make use of the problem later by showing how selective breeding has been employed in producing varieties of domestic stock. If the teacher chooses to show that the problems of selection and pure lines are sometimes more difficult, it may be done by mating pairs of the long-winged flies from the segregated culture above. Some of these matings will produce pure-line long-winged cultures, but most of them remain hybrid, producing vestigials in F_1 or F_2 generations.

ILLUSTRATIONS OF VARIATIONS IN PLANTS

The Origin of New Potentialities. When new seed and nursery catalogues appear each year, many new varieties are described and offered for sale. Many of these new varieties came about by a recombination of potentialities through hybridization of two species or varieties. However, this is a recombination of characteristics which may have existed separately in two species or varieties for a very long period of time. No new potentiality is involved, but it is a new combination.

Another kind of heritable variation is known as a *mutation*. The individual plant or animal in which the mutation occurs is known as a *mutant*. The mutation results in a new characteristic, having been unrecorded previously in the species where found. The frequency of this kind of heritable variation is less than variation due to hybridization, but is probably much more frequent than formerly believed. Most present-day mutations are recessives and may remain hidden indefinitely, because of the influence of dominant genes.

The change which results in a mutation is a change which occurs in a gene. A gene is the hereditary unit of matter (deoxyribonucleic acid or DNA). A single chromosome may be composed of many genes. This kind of change in a gene cannot be distinguished by even the highest magnification available with the electron microscope at the present time.

Polyploidy is another heritable type of genetic change which should be considered here. It is a matter of increase in the number of chromosomes per cell ordinarily found in given species. The increased number of chromosomes can be observed with the high-power objective of a microscope if the cells are properly prepared (see Chap. 14) when they are in the metaphase or anaphase stages of mitosis. The genes composing each chromosome are *not* necessarily changed. The tetraploid state is probably the most common polyploid form. It results from a doubling of the usual diploid number of chromosomes. This occurs when something prevents the formation of a new cell plate (wall) in a dividing cell. This may occur spontaneously. An example is illustrated in Fig. 23.3, plant no. 7. In 1937 it was discovered that if colchicine, an alkaloid extracted from the autumn-blooming crocus (*Colchicum autumnale*), is applied properly to stem tips, flower primordia, root tips, cambium, and germinating seed during mitotic cell division, the tetraploid condition may be established. For details of this technique, see Ref. 21, Chap. 21, and also Ref. 9 of this chapter. A tetraploid *Sansevieria* (plant no. 2, Fig. 23.3), originated from a colchicine-treated stem (rhizome) tip.

Polyploidy occurs in both plants and animals. At present it appears to be of little importance in animals, but is quite significant in many plants. This is particularly true for many domesticated species and varieties. In addition to the increased number of chromosomes, the plants are larger, with leaves about twice the thickness of leaves of a diploid, a darker green color (due to an increased number of chloroplasts), and have more brilliantly colored flowers, fruits, and

FIG. 23.3   A living demonstration showing the origin of new varieties of *Sansevieria trifasciata* (bowstring hemp): (1) by vegetative or somatic mutations and polyploidy; (2) tetraploid derived from 1, by colchicine treatment of rhizome tip; (3) *S. trifasciata* var. *Laurentii*, characterized by a yellow border of the leaves; (4) *S. trifasciata* var. *variegata* from 1; (5) Bantel's variegated variety (Patent No. 796) from 1: (6) dwarf variety *Hahnii* from 1 (Patent No. 470); (7) spontaneous tetraploid of *Hahnii*; (8) variegated, O.S.U. *Hahnii*, from 6; Nos. 3, 4, 5, and 8 are chimaeras, that is, each is composed of two or more genetically different tissues. (*Photograph by Dr. Alan Heilman.*)

seeds. Mutations, polyploidy, and some chromosome aberrations are mechanisms by which new potentialities and the resulting new characteristics come into existence. This is what is meant by evolution (Ref. 21).

Mutations may occur in either haploid or diploid cells, in both plants and animals. However, in all animals, except for some of the lower invertebrates, a mutation which occurs in a somatic cell is lost at death of the animal. At present, there is no known method by which a dog can be regenerated from a dog's leg or other organ. Vegetative (somatic) multiplication or regeneration is common among all the larger plant groups. A few outstanding examples are potatoes, sugar cane, sweet potatoes, apples, peaches, plums, cherries, pears, grapes, apricots, pineapples, oranges, grapefruits, lemons, bananas, and pecans. The "bud sports" of horticultural literature are the result of vegetative or somatic mutations.

Generally, the dome-shaped mass of embryonic cells (apical meristem) of a stem tip is composed of three layers of embryonic cells. The outermost layer contributes the epidermis of both the leaf and stem. It may also contribute, in addition, a few layers of cells inside the epidermis, but near the leaf margin. From the second layer, the remainder of the leaf is differentiated, as are other stem tissues, excepting the pith. Stamens and pistils (carpels) develop from the third layer. It may be obvious then that if a mutation should occur in the second layer of the meristem, which prevents chlorophyll synthesis, both the leaves and stem may show varying degrees of albinism. This is the mechanism by which most variegated plants are initiated. If such a variegated branch is propagated vegetatively, the variegated mutant may be maintained indefinitely. Some common examples of this may emphasize the point: there are several variegated varieties of English ivy (*Hedera helix*), coleus, geranium (*Pelargonium*), Evonymus, bowstring hemp (*Sansevieria*), *Hibiscus sinensis*, Sultana (*Impatiens sultanii*), and many others (see Ref. 4).

Ordinarily, all living cells of a plant are genetically identical, since they are derived through mitotic divisions, starting with the zygote or fertilized egg. However, if a mutation occurs in the meristematic tissue of the stem tip, the plant is no longer genetically uniform, but has two or even more genetically different tissues composing the plant. Plants so constituted are known as *chimaeras,* and the variegated plants listed previously are examples.

For a living demonstration of the origin of new varieties of plants from a single species, the group of *Sansevieria* plants shown in Fig. 23.3 is recommended. *Sansevieria trifasciata* (bowstring hemp, snake plant), native of Africa, was introduced as a house plant more than a century ago. It is a monocotyledonous plant belonging to the lily family. The long fibers obtained from retted leaves were used by natives in making bowstrings, cords, ropes, and some textiles. Perhaps the reason for its popularity is that it will live and thrive under more adverse conditions than most other ornamental potted plants. It is usually propagated vegetatively by pieces of the leaves or rhizomes bearing a stem tip (apical meristem). *Sensevieria* seeds may also be used as propagules; however they are not usually produced in abundance in either home or laboratory conditions.

Colchicine-induced polyploidy, as discussed previously, is of increasing importance. Plant no. 2 (Fig. 23.3) is an example and was obtained by treating a rhizome tip from a leaf cutting of plant no. 1, with 0.1 per cent colchicine.

Plant no. 3 (Fig. 23.3) was discovered in about 1900 by a French botanist Laurent, being cultured by a single tribe in the Belgian Congo. In 1904 this plant was described as a new species *Sansevieria laurentii*, honoring the discoverer. It is still known in the ornamental horticultural trade as *S. laurentii*. Botanists now know that it is a variety of *S. trifasciata* and not a different species. This variegated variety is characterized by a golden-yellow leaf margin, often extending in from the margin for ¼ in. or more. When leaf pieces 3 to 4 in. are used as propagules, the leaves of the new shoots are *without* the yellow leaf margin and are identical with the original species *S. trifasciata* (no. 1, Fig. 23.3). Florists have known this for many years. It is one of the few exceptions to the general rule that in vegetative multiplication, the regenerated plant is *identical* with the parent plant. The variegated condition can be propagated only from the rhizome (stem). Under somewhat special conditions it is possible to obtain chlorophyll-deficient shoots from the yellow strip of the leaf margin (Ref. 2). The entire shoot is yellow-green when young, gradually becoming yellow and free of chlorophyll. It is so chlorophyll deficient that when severed from the leaf cutting it dies within about 2 weeks from starvation. When seeds from *Laurentii* are planted, germination will occur within 3 months, and all the seedlings are green and without the yellow leaf margin or variegation. When these seedlings mature, the plants are identical with *S. trifasciata* (plant no. 1, Fig. 23.3). Results obtained from the leaf cuttings and seedlings of *Laurentii* lead to the inference that the yellow tissue composing the leaf margin is genetically different from the remainder of the leaf. Also, this yellow tissue must have originated by a mutation in the second embryonic layer of the rhizome tip (apical meristem). The *Laurentii* variety of *Sansevieria* is another example of a chimaera. For many years it has been widely used as an ornamental.

Plant no. 4 (Fig. 23.3) is a highly variegated plant which originated by mutation from a leaf cutting of *Sansevieria trifasciata*. Leaf cuttings will usually produce green shoots which are identical with the parent plant (plant no. 1, Fig. 23.3). Occasionally, albino shoots arise from the mutant white tissue. These die of starvation when cut loose from the leaf cutting. The photograph of this variety in Fig. 23.3 shows the plant in flower. Rarely are fruits set which contain viable seeds. All the seedlings are albino, or highly chlorophyll deficient. The plant can be propagated only from rhizomes having a stem tip.

Plant no. 5 (Fig. 23.3) is another variegated plant occasionally found on the floral market under the name of Bantel's Sensation, Patent No. 796. The leaves are more narrow, usually shorter, and the central portion is thicker than plant no. 4. Cuttings from the leaves will usually bear green shoots which appear to be identical with *Sansevieria trifasciata*. Occasionally an albino shoot may appear on leaf cuttings as in plant no. 4.

Plant no. 6, Fig. 23.3, is a dwarf variety, named Hahnii (Plant Patent No. 470). It is occasionally found under the name Birdnest *Sansevieria*. This mutant was discovered in 1923 in a nursery south of New Orleans, La. It was attached to a rhizome of *Sansevieria trifasciata*. It is a popular house plant, being found in stock at nearly all florists. The leaves are conspicuously shorter than those of the parent plant *S. trifasciata* (no. 1, Fig. 23.3). An old plant may have 15 to 25 leaves, differentiating from a single stem tip. In the parent (*S. trifasciata*) the maximum number of leaves from a stem tip is about four, with one to two being the usual number (Fig. 23.3). Apparently there is no record of flowering in the variety *Hahnii*. If this proves to be true, the elimination of flowering by this one mutation is a most unusual occurrence. This dwarf plant may be propagated from either leaf cuttings or rhizomes.

Plant no. 7 (Fig. 23.3) is a spontaneous tetraploid of variety *Hahnii*. The leaves are very dark green and have about twice the thickness of *Hahnii*. At present it is not generally available from dealers in ornamental plants.

Plant no. 8 (Fig. 23.3) is a variegated mutant which occurred from a leaf cutting of *Hahnii* in the botany greenhouses of The Ohio State University in 1942. It can be propagated in the variegated condition only by rhizome tips. Vegetative multiplication will occur from leaf cuttings; however the new shoots will be green and identical with *Hahnii,* or they will be highly chlorophyll deficient with considerable yellow pigment being present. In other words, the plant is not genetically uniform and may be referred to as a chimaera. It is quite desirable as an ornamental plant. A similar mutant, but with somewhat larger leaves, known as Golden Hahnii (Patent No. 1224), is available on the floral market.

The set of *Sansevieria* plants illustrated in Fig. 23.3 can be a valuable adjunct in the teaching of biology, botany, and horticulture. The living plants may be maintained with a minimum of effort on the windowsills of a biology classroom or in the home. Plants nos. 1, 2, 3, 5, 6, and 8 are available from dealers in ornamental plants. Essentially the same set of plants shown are available from the Ohio Biological Supply Company, 214 Westwood Road, Columbus 14, Ohio. It is likely that there will be other varieties of *Sansevieria trifasciata* available as time goes on. This group of varieties composes a living demonstration of mutations and polyploidy which are the basic mechanisms of evolution for all kinds of living organisms.

Hybrids (F_1) with Desirable Characteristics. In some instances, the hybrid or F_1 generation (first generation after crossing) displays characteristics which are desirable. This may be a matter of (1) combining desirable features from two desirable varieties; (2) the F_1 generation may exhibit vigor (*heterosis*), resulting in increased yield of fruit and vigorous vegetative growth; (3) immunity or resistance to disease-causing organisms; (4) hybridization between a diploid and a tetraploid plant, resulting in a parthenocarpic (seedless) triploid.

The following citations are a few of many outstanding examples. There are now available two new apple varieties of known parentage which rank high among the best of all apple varieties. These two superior food plants are a reward to the originator Dr. F. S. Howlett, Department of Horticulture of The Ohio State University, for his knowledge, skill, and patience. One of these varieties is known as Melrose and resulted from a cross between Delicious and Jonathan. The other variety is designated as Franklin and is a hybrid between McIntosh and Delicious.

A third example is presented, not particularly for its unusual value as an ornamental pot plant, but because it resulted from *crossing two genera* of the plant family Araliaceae. Generic crosses are relatively rare. *Hedera helix* (English ivy) crossed with *Fatsia japonica* (Japanese aralia) resulted in a sterile hybrid combining some of the desirable characteristics of both parents. This hybrid now bears a new generic name *Fatshedera lizei.* A mutant of this new genus is variegated. All four plants may be propagated vegetatively. Pot specimens of the two parents, the hybrid and the variegated variety, are available commercially from dealers in ornamental plants. A set of these four plants in the biology classroom can be effective visual aids as well as being ornamental.

Hybrid Vigor. Hybrids from crosses between certain varieties exhibit increased vigor. In 1910 Dr. George Shull, a geneticist for many years at Princeton University, called attention to the vigorous growth and increased yield which resulted in some of the inbred corn varieties he had crossed. He suggested the possibility of use of his discovery to commercial corn production. However, there were many problems which had to be solved before the principle could have widespread acceptance. The agricultural public insisted upon unquestionable evidence that the new system of corn production was superior to that of open-pollinated corn. A hybrid which gave excellent results in one locality did poorly in an area not far away. This meant the development of suitable varieties for each area. This was a tremendous task, worked on by many corn breeders and geneticists. It was discovered that hybrid vigor (heterosis) was due to heterozygosity. Eventually it was discovered that the "double cross" would increase the heterozygous condition. This was accomplished by selecting two pairs of inbred strains, each of which would produce satisfactory increased yields by the hybrid. These two hybrids were then crossed, resulting in increased heterozygosity and yield.

Almost 25 years elapsed from the time of Shull's suggestion before there was widespread acceptance of hybrid corn. Today, over 90 per cent of corn planted each year is hybrid. The increased yield realized is about 25 per cent per acre, with no increase in labor cost. The result is the same as though there had been a 25 per cent increase in land area added to corn production. See Chap. 11 for projects on land conservation.

Hybrid Resistance to Disease. Hybrid sweet corn is produced in the same way as hybrid field corn. The many hybrid sweet-corn varieties produce larger yields, larger ears, and have an increased sugar content. Some open-pollinated sweet-corn varieties such as Golden Bantam were susceptible to Stewart's bacterial disease, a serious disease in many localities. The hybrid Golden-Cross-Bantam is highly resistant to the bacterium causing the disease.

Triploid Hybrids Bearing Seedless Fruits. A triploid (3n) plant may originate from the crossing of a diploid (2n) plant and a tetraploid (4n) plant. Shortly after the discovery (1937) of the colchicine technique, by which tetraploid plants could be synthesized, Prof. H. Kihara of the Biological Research Institute, Kyoto, Japan, applied the new technique to watermelons. Watermelon (*Citrullus vulgaris*) varieties ordinarily have 22 chromosomes per cell. This is the diploid (2n) number. By treating seedlings with colchicine, tetraploids with 44 chromosomes (4n) can be obtained. When a tetraploid is pollinated by a diploid, the embryos in the seeds will be triploid (3n), with 33 chromosomes in each cell. When these triploid seeds are planted, the mature plants derived from the triploid embryos will be sterile. However, excellent fruits develop which are seedless. The triploid hybrid watermelon is a genuine hybrid exhibiting hybrid vigor in yield, vegetative growth, and disease resistance. Varieties of the common commercial banana and pineapple are seedless. They are also triploids and must have arisen spontaneously.

Nonhereditary Variations (Fluctuations). These variations are the expression of a given genotype due to varying environmental factors. In other words, the hereditary make-up does not change, but its range of expression varies with change in the environment. Most of the activities of the gardener, farmer and orchardist are directed toward improvement of plant yields, by providing the proper environment for the best expression of a given hereditary composition. The agriculturist may accomplish this by the proper application of fertilizers, irrigation, cultivation, drainage, pruning, proper seed storage, time of planting, insect pest and disease control, innoculation of leguminous seeds, light and temperature control. The principle applies to farming as a big-scale operation as well as to individual pot culture of ornamental plants in the home.

Fluctuations may be demonstrated in the laboratory, by culturing tomato, pea, or corn plants with a complete nutrient medium and with various elements lacking. A series of plants may be cultured in different lengths of day, as described in Chap. 16.

Beans, Peas, Corn. Divide a group of beans, pea seeds, or corn grains into two equal groups. Plant in similar pots of soil. Keep all conditions the same in the two sets except for varying the amount of water supplied.

Wandering Jew. Root a series of cuttings from a single wandering Jew plant. Place half of them in dense shade and the other group in bright light. Note results in leaf size, leaf thickness, and red or purple pigment (anthocyanin) content of the leaves after a few weeks. Has the wandering Jew's heredity changed? This question may be answered by making cuttings or placing whole plants of the sun form in the shaded situation for a similar length of time. Mark the leaves on the plant in some way so that they will not be considered later. Only the new leaves which will have been produced in the shade are to be used.

Carolina Poplar or Cottonwood Tree. What differences can be noted in sun leaves as compared to shade leaves on the same tree? Usually leaves exposed to bright sunlight throughout their development have a smaller area, are thicker, have a thicker cuticle, fewer epidermal cells per unit area, less intercellular air spaces, and more stomata per unit area than leaves which develop in shade. Similar observations may be made on tulip tree (yellow poplar), ash, etc.

Sassafras. Examine a sassafras tree for three types of leaves—nonlobed, two lobed, and three lobed. Do the same for mulberry. Note that usually the first leaves from a bud are nonlobed and that the lobing increases with growth of the new stem. Some specimens of the cultivated mulberry produce leaves all of which are either lobed or nonlobed.

Honey Locust. Often the first leaves from a honey locust bud are once pinnate. As growth of the stem continues, leaves are produced which show more complex division of the leaflets. In ordinary bean plants the first leaves above the cotyledons are simple; those developing later usually are trifoliately compound.

ILLUSTRATIONS OF VARIATIONS IN ANIMALS

Just as in plants we find that there are various kinds of differences in animals that make it possible to distinguish species from each other, as well as individual differences that make it possible to distinguish between related individuals of the same species. The latter are of several kinds which may be illustrated by the following examples.

Hereditary Variations. These are the variations which are governed by the gene composition of the animal. They may be of a visible character, or they may be carried in the so-called recessive manner and therefore not be expressed. As indicated in the problems suggested above on pages 420–422, such characters as the coat colors of animals and the eye characters and wing characters of the fruit fly are inherited gene-governed variations. Additional examples of such variations are as follows.

Mutations. When, in a stock of animals known to be a pure line by repeated breeding, there suddenly appear one or more individuals that depart from the normal type in some of its characteristics and this change is shown to be inherited in succeeding generations from this variant, the change is called a "mutation." Hundreds of such changes (mutations) are known for drosophila and many other animals. When such mutations appear in a line of animals and are carefully separated, or selected, and inbred, they may be established as a new pure line. This method of selective breeding is responsible for most of the breeds and varieties of our domestic stock. Such common examples as cattle, hogs, horses, sheep, poultry, dogs, cats, rats, mice, guinea pigs, and rabbits have breeds well known to all. The differences between beef and dairy cattle, lard and bacon pigs, draft and racing horses, etc., are genetic variations of which the breeders have taken advantage in producing these breeds. Many of these variations may be seen at stock and pet shows and at local fairs, stock farms, or even pet shops in cities. Students can obtain pictures and descriptions of the better known breeds, and class discussions and display are profitable. In some cases the contrast between the original wild stock and the modern breeds is exceedingly striking. See Refs. 8, 15, 24, 25.

Hybrids and Hybrid Segregates. When two genetically different pure lines of a species are bred together, the resulting offspring (F_1) are said to be "hybrid." The hybrids contain some of the genes for the characteristics of each of the parent lines. If the hybrids are inbred their offspring (F_2) may show some of the characteristics of both pure lines and of the hybrid parents. This is *segregation*. Such a condition often occurs in breeds of stock; for example, when black and splashed-white chickens are bred together, the offspring are blue-gray in color (Blue Andalusian), which is a hybrid showing characteristics of both parents (*blending* or *dilution*). But when the new breed is inbred, it does not produce all blue-gray. Some are blue-gray, some are black, and some are splashed white, in the ratio of 1:2:1, the hybrids being the 2. Some breeds are the result of a combination of a large number of factors bred together to produce a desired type and thus may become hybrid for many characters.

Noninherited Variations (fluctuations). Not all the variations that are noticeable in animals may be passed on from one generation to another. There are those which are the result of environmental conditions producing in the individual differences which are not inherited. These are generally known as "fluctuations." A few examples of this sort of variations are given here. It is difficult sometimes to tell how much of such differences are due to environment and how much to heredity. In many instances the fluctuation can be seen as a modification of a heritable variation.

Mollusk Shells. Examine a collection of snail or other mollusk shells that are all of the same species. Some of the marine species are excellent for this purpose since they are colored in great variety. They can be arranged in a series of shades and colors in the markings. In some instances there will be a definite type of marking such as lines or pattern. These lines may be a definite inherent character. However, the color or extent of the coloration will vary through a wide range, thus showing variation (fluctuation).

Beetles. Collect a quantity of adult beetles such as the Colorado potato beetle or Mexican bean beetle and decide upon some dimension to be measured, for example, length or width. Measure accurately these dimensions for 50 or 100 beetles and record the number of individuals having the various lengths. This will give a set of dimensional data from which a graph may be drawn, showing the extremes, mean, and deviation. Weigh each of 50 beetles and treat in the same manner as the dimensions.

Hair Distribution. Select a place on the back of the wrist just above the joint. Mark off 1 sq. in. and divide it into four approximately equal parts to facilitate counting the hairs which it contains. Have 10 persons count these hairs, each on his own wrist, and note the variation in distribution. Have students make counts with brothers and sisters and with parents and see if there is any inherited similarities or whether the variation is entirely independent of heredity.

Skin and Coat Spots. If a number of leopard frogs are available notice the number and distribution of the skin spots. The spots of guinea pigs, Holstein cattle, dogs, and many other animals show no two individuals exactly the same even when they are in the same litter. When it is impossible to see animals, good pictures of them do very well, though they are never so satisfactory.

Wing Length of Insects. If some insect is numerous, such as houseflies, a hundred or so may be captured and the wing removed from one side of the body. If the lengths are measured, the same variation will be noted as for body length or other dimension.

Rate of Growth and Maturation. Review the vitamin-feeding studies as given in Chap. 16. Notice the difference in the weights due to the presence or absence of a food element such as the vitamins. This is largely environmental. If insect larvae, such as caterpillars, fly maggots, or meal worms (*Tenebrio*), are placed in cultures and divided into three groups one of which is kept at 15°C., one at 20°C., and another at 30°C., a decided difference in the rate of the growth and maturing of the insects will be seen.

PRACTICE PROBLEMS WITH PLANTS

In the teaching of heredity the primary aim is to have the student thoroughly understand the principles and how they apply to himself as well as to plants and animals. Problems such as are given above may serve to introduce the student to the principles, but it is also desirable that the student be given opportunity to solve a sufficient number of such problems so that he will become thoroughly familiar with both the principles and the application. Such problems are almost universally solved with the use of letter symbols and the conventional circles which represent cells. It is a convenient method for the geneticist or the advanced student, but it is much too abstract for the beginner, especially when he is young and accustomed to thinking in terms of the concrete. The following suggestions have been used as a means of simplifying the subject with considerable success because they help him to visualize his problem and they add a great deal of interest for younger students beyond what is obtainable from the use of alphabetical symbols alone (Fig. 23.4).

Garden Pea Seeds. Obtain a quantity of ordinary garden pea seeds. Note that some are smooth and others wrinkled, some are yellow and others are green. These two sets of contrasting characters are hereditary and work out in a simple 3:1 ratio. Seeds may be selected and glued to cards in the form of a diagram to illustrate what happens for three generations after crossing. Match stems may be glued in as connecting lines. The finished chart would appear similar to the diagram shown by Fig. 23.5. The rough seeded plants, represented at extreme right of diagram of the F_2 generation, indicate a pure-line recessive carrying only potentialities for wrinkling of seed coats. The two groups in the center are hybrids, similar to the F_1 generation, as shown by the F_3 generation. The set of smooth seeds to

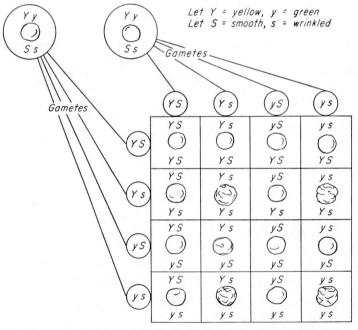

Fig. 23.4 The method of squares as a device for easily determining the seed coat ratios of garden peas.

extreme left of F_2 generation represents a pure line carrying the dominant potentiality for smoothness. This also shows that any wrinkled seed is pure (homozygous) but that only $33\frac{1}{3}$ per cent of the smooth seeds from such a cross may be pure. The chart in addition shows segregation in the F_2 and F_3 generations. The F_1 generation indicates which of a set of characters is dominant and which is recessive. The same sort of chart may be made for yellow and green seeded varieties. The yellow is dominant to green.

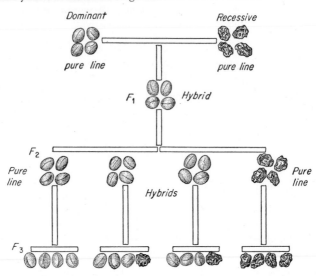

FIG. 23.5   The match-stick chart showing three generations.

Variation in Castor-bean Seeds. If 1 lb. of castor-bean seeds is obtained from a seed store they will be found to show many variations as to size, shape, and color patterns. Many of these variations are known to be heritable. Students may be assigned to select as many types as possible from a given quantity of seeds. It is possible to segregate pure lines of the particular color patterns, sizes, and shapes for most of the conspicuous types by using proper breeding methods.

Inheritance of Flower Color. The literature presents numerous problems in the inheritance of flower color. Many of these work out as simple Mendelian ratios and are desirable for classroom work. However, ordinarily it is not practical, or possible, to grow the plants and have them available when needed. In order to present these problems in a concrete manner, without the actual living specimens, the students may prepare artificial flowers from vegetable fiber strips or other materials for such purposes available at five-and-ten-cent stores, art stores, and stationery concerns. The dominance of blue-flowered peas over white-flowered peas and blending or incomplete dominance which results from crossing red and white four-o'clocks may be illustrated effectively by this method.

PRACTICE PROBLEMS WITH ANIMALS

These illustrations are intended merely as suggestions. The teacher will readily see that the same kind of device may be used for a wide variety of other problems, and other uses than those here included may be made.

Miniature Casts. The teacher obtains a number of small toy cattle, or, better, the students make them as a separate project in fine arts. They may be cast in plaster or metal. For other problems they are colored, if desired. From a mixed group of these casts a pair is selected as the P_1 cross and then the F_1 or F_2 generation is placed on the table. By actual manipulation the student fills in missing individuals to complete the crosses and their offspring. Since the hornless condition is dominant, this is a simple problem. When the miniature cattle have been arranged, the student may select appropriate letter symbols and draw the cells for each type of individual opposite the model in order to explain what takes place among the genes. When completed it appears something like Fig. 23.6. This may be used by the teacher either as a teaching device or as a testing device. By providing a sheet of blank circles and a group of such miniature animals the student may be required to arrange the animals in correct positions and to fill in the gene composition of the cells and gametes. Similar problems may be provided in sheep, poultry, mice, guinea pigs, man, etc.

Cardboard Models. A satisfactory substitute for the toy or model casts of the above problems is a cardboard cut-out model which is made so as to stand on a base. While not so realistic, it is more easily made and can be colored when necessary. Even paper pictures laid flat upon the problem sheet are a relief from the purely formalized letter symbols.

Matchsticks. Another device that gives the student an opportunity to manipulate something with his hands and aids him in visualizing his problem is the use of

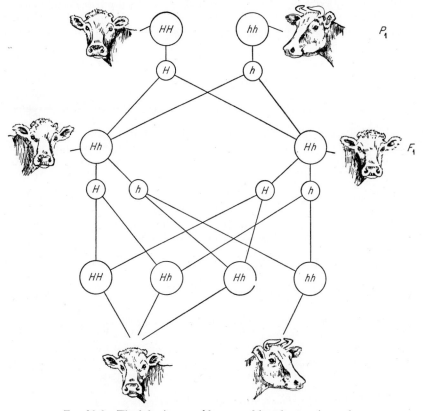

FIG. 23.6   The inheritance of horns and hornlessness in cattle.

colored matches for chromosomes. Wood or paper matches with colored heads or colored sticks are cut and glued into the circles representing the cells of the body or the gametes, and their behavior during crossing and segregation is easily followed.

Use circles mimeographed on sheets of paper. Match sticks of different colors to represent various genes. Each student is given a number of each kind of stick. He makes P_1 generation cells, then separates the chromosomes into germ cells and recombines them into F_1 generation offspring, and so on. This objectifies the problem, gives the student a chance to move the genes from individual to individual, and visualizes both the character and the process.

Modeling Clay. The teacher will find the use of modeling clay convenient especially in showing what happens to chromosomes in mitosis and reduction division. The clays come in a variety of colors and can be used over and over again.

Human Problems. The importance of heredity in man should have a prominent place in the course. The better known traits of color blindness, baldness, feeblemindedness, etc., can be done with illustrations from many sources. Magazines often publish advertisements in colors of family groups showing a parent or both parents and a large family of children. When these are carefully examined there are usually a number of characters that can be observed and short papers written with the picture as an illustration. One of the most illuminating studies for human heredity can be made by the student in his own family by having him investigate with the help of parents or grandparents some family trait or traits that can be traced for several generations. Thus the child can write and report upon an actual case which is very real to him and has a decided effect in producing a proper attitude concerning the significance of heredity in his own life and the lives of other persons.

REFERENCES

1. Adragna, C. M.: "Mendelian Inheritance," *Sci. Teacher,* **17**:179, November, 1950.

2. Blaydes, Glenn W.: "The Romance of Domesticated Plants," *Ohio J. Sci.,* **53**:193–215, 1953; also reprinted in *Smithsonian Report for 1954,* pp. 317–336, 1955. Deals with the origin of domesticated plants, genetic variation in seeds, hybridization and somatic mutations, with 41 photographic illustrations (2 in color).

3. Burdick, A. B.: "Drosophila Experiments for High School Biology," *Am. Biol. Teacher,* **17**:155–159, May, 1955.

4. Camp, W. H., V. R. Boswell, and J. R. Magness: *The World in Your Garden,* National Geographic Society, Washington, D.C., 1957. Deals with the origin of domesticated horticultural plants. Should be in every school library.

5. Daniel, J. C., Jr.: "Generation Mounts for Use in the Study of Heredity," *Am. Biol. Teacher,* **18**:258–259, December, 1956.

6. Darlington, C. D., and A. P. Wylie: *Chromosome Atlas of Flowering Plants,* The Macmillan Company, New York, 1956. A source book for known chromosome numbers in plant species.

7. Dick, William E.: *Atomic Energy in Agriculture,* Philosophical Library, Inc., New York, 1957.

8. Dodson, Edward O.: *A Textbook of Evolution,* W. B. Saunders Company, Philadelphia, 1952.

9. Eigsti, O. J., and Pierre Dustin, Jr.: *Colchicine in Agriculture,* Iowa State College Press, Ames, Iowa, 1955.

10. Elliott, Fred C.: *Plant Breeding and Cytogenetics,* McGraw-Hill Book Company, Inc., New York, 1958.

11. Goldschmidt, R. B.: *Understanding Heredity,* John Wiley & Sons, Inc., New York, 1952. Clear description of linkage mutation, Mendel's laws, etc.

12. Harter, L. L.: "Bud Sports in Sweet Potatoes," *J. Agr. Research,* **33**:523–525, 1926. Illustration in color.

13. Hensill, John S.: *The Biology of Man,* McGraw-Hill Book Company, Inc., New York, 1954.

14. McCafferty, R. C.: "Heredity for High School," *School Sci. and Math.,* **52**:385–403, May, 1952. Problems to be solved; concepts to be understood.

15. Miller, D. F., and J. G. Haub: *General Zoology,* Holt, Rinehart and Winston, Inc., 1955.

16. Riley, Herbert Parkes: *Genetics and Cytogenetics,* John Wiley & Sons, Inc., New York, 1948.

17. Robbins, W. W., T. E. Weier, and C. R. Stocking: *Botany, An Introduction to Plant Science,* 2d ed., John Wiley & Sons, Inc., New York, 1957.

18. Sinnott, E. W., L. C. Dunn, and T. Dobzhansky: *Principles of Genetics,* 5th ed., McGraw-Hill Book Company, Inc., New York, 1958.

19. Sinnott, E. W., and K. S. Wilson: *Botany: Principles and Problems,* 5th ed., McGraw-Hill Book Company, Inc., New York, 1955. Useful for study of all processes and survey of plant kingdom.

20. Snyder, Laurence H., and Paul R. David: *Principles of Heredity,* 5th ed., D. C. Heath and Company, Boston, 1957.

21. Swanson, Carl P.: *Cytology and Cytogenetics,* Prentice-Hall, Inc., Englewood Cliffs, N.J., 1957.

22. Thaw, R. F.: "Heredity in High School Biology," *Am. Biol. Teacher,* **12**:178–179, December, 1950.

23. Transeau, E. N., H. C. Sampson, and L. H. Tiffany: *Textbook of Botany,* rev. ed., Harper & Brothers, New York, 1953. Useful for study of all processes, ecology, and survey of the plant kingdom.

24. U.S. Department of Agriculture Yearbook, 1936. Devoted to the creative development of new forms of life through plant and animal breeding.

25. U.S. Department of Agriculture Yearbook, 1937. History and genetics of cultivated plants and domesticated animals.

26. Vance, B. B., and D. F. Miller: *Biology for You,* J. B. Lippincott Company, Philadelphia, 1958. Illustrations of ways to explain heredity.

27. Weatherwax, Paul: *Botany,* 3d ed., W. B. Saunder's Company, Philadelphia, 1956. Portion dealing with genetics and evolution is recommended for beginning students.

28. Wilson, C. L., and W. E. Loomis: *Botany,* rev. ed., The Dryden Press, Inc. (now combined with Holt, Rinehart and Winston, Inc.), New York, 1957. Useful for study of all plant processes and survey of plant kingdom.

29. Wilson, G. B.: *Outline of Genetics,* Michigan State University Press, East Lansing, Mich., 1952.

--≪ Audiovisual Bibliography ≫--

The motion pictures and filmstrips described below and on the following pages can be used to illustrate and supplement much of the material in this book. For the convenience of users, they are grouped under three broad headings: methods of teaching, laboratory techniques, and biological principles.

The following information is given for each film: title; identification as motion picture (MP) or filmstrip (FS); primary source; year of production; and running time in minutes (min.) or frames (fr.). Abbreviations used for the names of producers and distributors are defined in the list of sources, with addresses, at the end of the bibliography. Unless otherwise indicated, the motion pictures are 16-mm., black-and-white sound films, and the filmstrips are 35-mm., black-and-white, and silent.

In many instances, the films can be borrowed or rented from local or state 16-mm. film libraries. A nationwide list of such sources is given in *A Directory of 3,660 16mm Film Libraries,* available for $1 from the Superintendent of Documents, U.S. Government Printing Office, Washington 25, D.C.

This is necessarily a selective list, and readers should consult *Educational Film Guide* and *Filmstrip Guide,* standard reference catalogs available in most school, college, and public libraries; the film abstracts of the Society of American Bacteriologists; film reviews in the *Journal of the American Medical Association,* collated in annual editions; and film catalogs of pharmaceutical companies and of state universities, such as Iowa, Indiana, and Washington, which have produced a number of biology films.

METHODS OF TEACHING

Chalkboard Utilization (MP, McGraw, 1954, 15 min.) Demonstrates the many ways in which the classroom chalkboard can be effectively used in teaching.

Audiovisual Techniques and Materials (FS series, OSU, 1950–1960, color) Eight filmstrips with supplementary notes, as follows:

> *How to Keep Your Bulletin Board Alive* (33 fr.)
> *A Parade of Bulletin Boards* (46 fr.)
> *How to Make and Use the Felt Board* (54 fr.)
> *Improving the Use of the Chalkboard* (44 fr.)
> *Handmade Lantern Slides* (51 fr.)
> *The Diorama as a Teaching Aid* (59 fr.)
> *The Opaque Projector* (46 fr.)
> *A Simple Exhibit Technique* (40 fr.)

436

Audio-Visual Materials in Teaching (MP, Cor, 1956, 14 min., color or b&w) Shows how audio-visual materials can challenge children's attention and interests in the classroom and demonstrates the integration of such materials into an instructional unit.

Anatomical Models (MP, DG, 1949, 15 min.) Illustrates the production and use of a human torso and head model.

Accent on Learning (MP, OSU, 1949, 30 min.) Shows the various classroom uses of filmstrips, lantern slides, charts, models, motion pictures, and field experiences.

Feltboard in Teaching (MP, Wayne, 1951, 9 min., color) Suggests various uses which the classroom teacher may make of the feltboard.

Demonstration: A Teaching Technique (FS, Wayne, 1952, 38 fr.) Illustrates principles of successful demonstrations through examples in elementary school, high school, and college teaching.

High Contrast Photography for Instruction (MP, Ind U, 1956, 12 min., color or b&w) Shows how materials are prepared for photographic reproduction on high-contrast film. Explains the process of making negatives and positives by this method for use as instructional materials, both transparent and opaque.

How to Make Handmade Lantern Slides (MP, Ind U, 1947, 22 min., color) Demonstrates the basic production techniques for eight types of handmade lantern slides.

Increasing the Effectiveness of Teaching with Tape Recordings (FS, MMM, 1952, with disc recording, 10 min.) Shows various uses of tape recordings by teachers.

Making Field Trips Effective (FS, Wayne, 1952, 46 fr.) Describes techniques for planning field trips and explains their values and purposes. *Motivating the Class* (MP, McGraw, 1950, 19 min.) Portrays a student teacher learning that motivation is basic to good teaching and is obtained by translating the values of the subject matter into terms learners can understand.

New Tools for Learning (MP, EBF, 1952, 19 min.) Shows how teaching films, used with other appropriate materials, can bring richness and greater vitality to teaching.

Projecting Motion Pictures (MP, Calif U, 1951, 10 min.) Shows the relationships between the audience and the various elements in a projecting situation: seating, screen, loudspeaker, and projector.

LABORATORY TECHNIQUES

Animals for Research (MP, USA, 1958, 28 min., color) Describes the procedures and techniques employed in breeding disease-free animals for use in scientific research projects, including the methods and principal factors involved in establishing and maintaining a disease-free colony, the techniques and equipment used in breeding, and the transportation of the animals to research laboratories.

Basic Principles of the Analytical Balance (MP, USPHS, 1951, 19 min.) Explains the uses of the analytical balance and shows how to find the zero point of the balance, find its sensitivity, calibrate the weights, weigh an object, and weigh out a predetermined amount of material.

Care of Laboratory Animals (FS, USPHS, 1953, 80 fr., color, with 33⅓ r.p.m. record, 10 min.) Explains methods for handling, housing, and feeding rabbits, mice, rats, and other laboratory animals.

The Centrifuge (FS, USPHS, 1955, 86 fr., color, with disc recording, 33⅓ r.p.m., 12 min.) Points out some of the hazards of centrifuge operation and suggests safe operating procedures.

The Collection and Shipment of Insects (FS, USPHS, 1957, 70 fr., color, with

33⅓ r.p.m. record, 10 min.) Shows methods of collecting, preserving, and shipping insects and certain other arthropods.

Infectious Hazards of Bacteriological Techniques (MP, USPHS, 1951, 13 min., color) Demonstrates that bacteriological aerosols are produced even in such procedures as shaking liquid cultures, transferring cultures, mixing with a pipette, and blending cultures. Explains ways of lessening such dangers. Five follow-up filmstrips describe specific dangers and protective measures. Titles are:

> *The High Speed Blender* (81 fr., color, 13 min.)
> *The Hypodermic Syringe* (95 fr., color, 12 min.)
> *The Inoculating Needle* (102 fr., color, 9 min.)
> *The Lyophilizer* (76 fr., color, 8 min.)
> *The Pipette* (85 fr., color, 9 min.)

Handling and Use of Glassware (FS, USPHS, 1952, 82 fr., color, with disc recording, 33⅓ r.p.m., 8 min.) Explains methods and precautions to be used in handling glassware in a laboratory.

Laboratory Glassware (FS, NSC, 1948, with 33⅓ r.p.m. disc recording, 10 min.) Illustrates practices of handling glass equipment in the laboratory to avoid accidents.

A Mycological Slide Culture Technique (FS, USPHS, 1951, 36 fr., color, with 33⅓ r.p.m. record, 4 min.) Shows how to grow fungi on glass slides in a moist chamber in order to observe the undisturbed relationship between reproductive structures and mycelium.

Preparation and Staining of Blood Films (MP, USPHS, 1946, 17 min., color) Illustrates smearing and staining procedures for preparing thick and thin blood films. Includes technique for preparing Giemsa and Wright's stains.

Preparing Blood Films for Microscopical Examination (FS, USPHS, 1947, 66 fr., color, with 33⅓ r.p.m. record, 11 min.) Explains how to clean microscope slides and prepare thick and thin blood films.

Using Animals in the Laboratory (FS, USPHS, 1953, 68 fr., color, with 33⅓ r.p.m. record, 10 min.) Shows methods of handling rats, hamsters, guinea pigs, rabbits, and chicks for such purposes as giving injections, making venous punctures, taking temperature, and giving medication.

BIOLOGICAL PRINCIPLES

The Amoeba (MP, UWF, 1948, 10 min.) Shows by microphotography and animated drawings the structure and life functions of a single-celled organism, including production of pseudopodia, amoeba pursuing and capturing prey, process of ingestion, and reproduction by fission.

Asexual Reproduction (MP, Ind U, 1954, 10 min., color or b&w) Illustrates by paintings of prehistoric horses and fossilized imprints of ferns that reproduction is essential to the continuity of life; compares asexual and sexual reproduction and shows reproduction by division, budding, spore formation, runners, cuttings, and rhizomes; and compares offspring produced asexually with those produced sexually. Specimens used in the film are *Chlamydomonas, Planaria, Penicillium, Micrasterias, Rhizopus, Chroococcus, Hydra, Papamedium,* and *Impatiens.*

Basic Nature of Sexual Reproduction (MP, Ind U, 1954, 15 min., color or b&w) Explains that sexual reproduction involves the production and union of gametes, using as illustrations *Chlamydomonas, Zygnema, Allomyees,* and *Vaucheria.* Illustrates by the use of models of cells and chromosomes that sexual reproduction makes provision for great variation because of the random assortment of chromosomes during meiosis and the chance union of sperm and egg during fertilization. Shows the results of different chromosome combinations and pictures man's use of such variation in developing hybrid corn and purebred cattle.

Biography of the Unborn (MP, EBF, 1956, 16 min.) Traces the development of the human fetus from conception to birth. Charts, animated drawings, X rays, and photomicrographs show the process of fertilization, division of the cells, nourishment of the embryo, development of internal organs and the nervous system, and other developments during the gestation period. Approved by the American College of Surgeons.

Budding Yeasts (Monilias) (MP, SAB, 1947, 7 min., silent) Time-lapse microphotography of the process of reproduction of a pair of yeast cells. Recommended by the Society of American Bacteriologists.

Cell Division and Growth (MP, Abbott, 1951, 13 min.) Some aspects of the techniques of time-lapse cinemicrography and its application in tumor cytology, with cinemicrographs of neoplastic cells. Recommended for students of medicine and biology by *Film Reference Guide for Medicine and Allied Sciences.*

Cells and Their Functions (MP, Athena, 1950, 14 min.) Shows by photomicrography and time-lapse photography the activities of a number of kinds of cells, including mitosis, beating cilia, blood cells engulfing bacteria, and proliferation of tissue.

Characteristics of Plants and Animals (MP, Ind U, 1954, 10 min., color or b&w) Explains that all life comes from pre-existing life and that all living things have certain characteristics in common—movement, response to stimuli, reproduction, and growth. Describes the basic details of plant- and animal-cell characteristics and the complex processes performed within these cells. Specimens used include *Vorticella, Hydra, Paramecium, Micrasterias, Volvox, Elodea,* and cat egg, intestine, and nerve cells.

Circulation of the Blood (MP, AHA, 1958, 7 min., color) Shows, by means of diagrammatic drawings, how the heart works and explains the structure of the arteries and how their expansion and contraction controls the flow of blood. Reviewed in *Am. Med. Assoc.* and "highly recommended for college and high school classes in biology, physiology, and health education."

Crustaceans (MP, EBF, 1955, 13 min., color or b&w) Describes the appearance, habitat, and behavior of the fairy shrimp, cypris, crustacean plankton, barnacles, crabs, shrimp lobsters, and crayfish. Explains processes of food gathering, reproduction, autotomy, and molting. Discusses the crustaceans' part in maintaining the balance of nature.

Death of a Cell (MP, Squibb, 1957, 15 min.) Shows, by means of phase-contrast microscopy and time-lapse photography, the death of leucocytes through various processes and etiologies—fragmentation; cellular endema in distilled water; polonium radioactivity; intoxication after ingestion of virulent bacteria; caryolysis, pyknosis, and vacuolization induced by various factors; and cellular aggression (cannibalism) of polymorphs. Reviewed in *J. Am. Med. Assoc.*

Digestion of Foods (MP, EBF, 1938, 11 min.) Explains the digestive process, including the work performed in the mouth, stomach, and small intestines; secretions, enzymes, and systems affected; and the relationship of the circulatory and the nervous systems.

Embryology of Human Behavior (MP, IFB, 1951, 28 min., color) Explains that a child grows in accordance with certain universal laws and at the same time develops as an individual. Traces the patterning processes of behavior. Produced by the American Association of Medical Colleges.

Heredity (MP, EBF, 1939, 11 min.) Explains schematically the transmission of hereditary factors responsible for inherited characters in animals. Describes character dominance by portraying the results of mating guinea pigs of one-unit character and then of two-unit characters.

Heredity in Animals (MP, UWF, 1953, 10 min.) Explains Mendel's laws of heredity and shows how inherited characteristics are handed on from generation to generation. Gives examples of inheritance of physical characteristics, complete and incomplete dominance, and recombination for new types.

Heredity Variations in Coleus (MP, OSU, 1949, 11 min., color) Pictures and explains experiments conducted over a period of time which show the variety of offspring derived from a coleus plant.

Human Reproduction (MP, McGraw, 1947, 20 min.) Portrays by means of animated drawings the process of human reproduction, including the menstrual cycle, male and female reproductive organs, fertilization of the ovum, development of the embryo, and the process of birth.

Improving Strains of Livestock (MP, EBF, 1954, 13 min.) Describes essential procedures in improving strains of livestock, techniques of selecting parent stock, and examples of inbreeding and outbreeding. Identifies the pioneering roles of Robert Bakewell and Gregor Mendel.

In the Beginning (MP, USDA, 1937, 17 min.) Shows by means of time-lapse cinematography the ovulation, fertilization, and early development of the mammalian (rabbit) egg.

Inside the Cell. Part 1: Enzymes of Intracellular Chemistry (MP, USA, 1949, 40 min., color) A study of the theory of enzymes, showing by animated drawings the better-known steps in glucose metabolism and portraying by live-action photography the laboratory techniques practiced by several Nobel prize winners.

Inside the Cell. Part 2: Regulation of Enzymes (MP, USA, 1952, 43 min., color) Explains the factors regulating enzyme action; shows a laboratory demonstration of feeding radioactive acetate to rats; discusses the effects of drugs on enzymes, the action of antimetabolites, glycolysis and Kreb's cycle; and pictures the chemical action inside a cell.

Life in a Drop of Water (MP, Cor, 1946, 11 min., color or b&w) Photomicroscopy of motile and nonmotile, sessile and free-living protozoa, crustacia, rotifers, and hydra in a drop of water.

Life of the Molds (MP, Pfizer, 1958, 27 min., color) Explores, by means of time-lapse photomicrography, the world of the molds, including their implications for modern biology. Traces the life cycle of the fungi and reveals the discovery of sexual reproduction among the molds which, as noted by the Medical Audio-Visual Institute in its April 1958 Newsletter, "is leading to knowledge not merely about the molds but about all living things."

The Living Cell (MP, NET, 1955, 29 min.) Discusses and illustrates the size, shape, composition, and organization of a living cell and shows its parts. Points out some of the differences between a plant and an animal cell.

Living or Nonliving (MP, NET, 1955, 29 min.) Presents the biologist's points of view on the differences between living and nonliving things through the characteristics of a protoplasm. Illustrates differences in responsiveness, nutrition, reproduction, composition, and organization between living and nonliving organisms and points out that these differences are not always obvious and distinct.

Mitosis and Meiosis (MP, Ind U, 1954, 16 min., color or b&w) Uses stained cells, time-lapse cinephotomicrography, and animation to compare and contrast the two processes. Mitosis is illustrated in onion-root tip cells, whitefish embryo cells, and the epidermal cells of a salamander; meiosis in lily anther cells and living grasshopper testis cells.

Mollusks: Snails, Mussels, Oysters, Octopuses, and Their Relatives (MP, EBF, 1955, 14 min., color or b&w) Illustrates the five classes of mollusks and their distinguishing characteristics. Shows the different ways mollusks feed, their protective characteristics, reproduction, and favorable environmental conditions.

The Nature of Life (MP, NET, 1955, 29 min.) Describes life as a process of activity, an energy system of extreme complexity that tends to be self-regulating and self-stabilizing. Answers some of the crucial questions about the nature of life.

Nitrogen Cycle (MP, UWF, 1953, 14 min.) Shows the route followed by nitrogen in its circulation between the atmosphere and the compounds in the protoplasm of living organisms. Photomicrography and cineradiology show the functions of root hairs associated with nodules, fungi, and bacteria.

Osmosis (MP, EBF, 1958, 14 min., color or b&w) Uses photomicrography, time-lapse photography, and animation to show the inner mechanism of plants and explains how water is transported throughout the plant.

Paramecium (MP, UWF, 1948, 10 min.) Shows the features of paramecium—pellicle, cilia, nuclei, contractile vacuoles, gullet and food vacuoles. Demonstrates movement of paramecium and reactions to external stimuli.

The Physiology of Reproduction in the Rat (MP, Wash U, 1954, 20 min., color) Shows complete external and internal changes observed during reproductive cycle in the rat. Approved by American College of Surgeons. Recommended by the American Medical Association for use in college classes in zoology, genetics, and physiology "as a rather complete presentation of the essence of reproductive physiology."

Pin Mold: Life Cycle of a Typical Fungus (MP, IFB, 1950, 11 min.) Uses time-lapse photography and microphotography to show mold growth, mucro, formation of sporangia, single spores, protoplasm, spore germination, plus and minus strains, formation of zygospore, and germination of zygospore with formation of sporangium.

Photosynthesis (MP, UWF, 1950, 14 min.) Shows carbon dioxide entering the plant structure, its conversion in chloroplasts to oxygen, carbon built into glucose, the necessity for chlorophyll, and the process of glucose being changed to starch.

Plant Survival (MP, UWF, 1949, 10 min.) Shows the protective devices used in various stages of plant growth by means of close-ups of roots, seeds, buds, leaves, and flowers.

Protozoa: One-celled Animals (MP, EBF, 1957, 11 min., color) Close-up exploration, by photomicrography, of the world of one-celled animals. Identifies pseudopods, flagelettes, and ciliates and explains how they move, eat, and reproduce. Provides examples of symbiosis, parasitism, and colonial organizations.

Reproduction Among Mammals (MP, EBF, 1937, 11 min.) Describes the reproductive process, using a pig as an example, including fertilization, cleavage, blastulation, gastrulation, formation of neutral folds, development of membranes and embryonic circulation, and parturition.

Reptiles (MP, EBF, 1955, 14 min., color) Describes five orders of reptiles—lizards, turtles, tuataras, crocodilians, and serpents—their physical characteristics, reproduction processes, feeding habits, and special habitats.

Two Cells from One (MP, NET, 1955, 29 min.) Delineates the differences between reproduction and growth. With models, diagrams, and photomicrographs, illustrates the entire process whereby the highly organized cell produces two units, each as complex and organized in the same way as the parent cell.

Work of the Blood (MP, EBF, 1957, 13 min., color) Describes the work of blood in circulating food elements and other materials to all body cells, in removing wastes, and in helping to fight disease and equalize heat distribution. Illustrates the composition of blood, identifies pulmonary and systemic circulation, and describes the four main blood groups. Recommended by the American Medical Association for use in high school or college biology classes.

MAIN SOURCES

Abbott—Abbott Laboratories, North Chicago, Ill.

AHA—American Heart Association, 257 W. 57th St., New York 10, N.Y.

Athena—Athena Films, Inc., 165 W. 46th St., New York 19, N.Y.

Calif U—University of California, Los Angeles 24, Calif.

Cor—Coronet Films, Inc., Coronet Bldg., Chicago 1, Ill.

DG—Denoyer-Geppert Co., 5235 Ravenswood Ave., Chicago 40, Ill.

EBF—Encyclopaedia Britannica Films, Inc., Wilmette, Ill.

IFB—International Film Bureau, Inc., 57 E. Jackson Blvd., Chicago, Ill.

Ind U—Indiana University, Audio-Visual Center, Bloomington, Ind.

McGraw—McGraw-Hill Book Company, Inc., Text-Film Dept., 330 W. 42d St.,
New York 36, N.Y.

MMM—Minnesota Mining and Manufacturing Co., St. Paul 6, Minn.

NET—National Educational Television, Indiana University, Bloomington, Ind.

NSC—National Safety Council, 425 N. Michigan Ave., Chicago 11, Ill.

OSU—Ohio State University, Teaching Aids Laboratory, Columbus, Ohio.

Pfizer—Pfizer Laboratories, Medical Film Library, 267 W. 25th St., New York 1,
N.Y.

SAB—Society of American Bacteriologists, University of Pennsylvania, School of
Medicine, Philadelphia, Pa.

Squibb—E. R. Squibb and Sons, 745 Fifth Ave., New York 22, N.Y.

USA—U.S. Department of the Army, Washington 25, D.C.

USDA—U.S. Department of Agriculture, Motion Picture Service, Washington 25,
D.C.

USPHS—U.S. Public Health Service, Washington 25, D.C.

UWF—United World Films, Inc., 1445 Park Ave., New York 29, N.Y.

Wash U—University of Washington, Seattle, Wash.

Wayne—Wayne State University, Audio-Visual Materials Bureau, Detroit, Mich.

⊶ Index ⊷

Page references in **boldface** type denote illustrations